MINERALOGY

An Introduction to the Study of Minerals and Crystals

BOOKS BY EDWARD H. KRAUS

with Chester B. Slawson

Kraus and Slawson · Gems and Gem Materials (*Fifth Edition*)
332 pages, 6 × 9, 403 illustrations and 4 colored plates

with Walter F. Hunt

Kraus and Hunt · Tables for the Determination of Minerals (*Second Edition*) *266 pages, 6 × 9*

with Walter F. Hunt *and* Lewis S. Ramsdell

Kraus, Hunt, and Ramsdell · Mineralogy (*Fifth Edition*)
686 pages, 6 × 9, 736 illustrations

MINERALOGY

An Introduction to the Study of Minerals and Crystals

EDWARD HENRY KRAUS

Professor Emeritus of Crystallography and Mineralogy, The University of Michigan

WALTER FRED HUNT

Professor Emeritus of Petrology
The University of Michigan

LEWIS STEPHEN RAMSDELL

Professor of Mineralogy
The University of Michigan

FIFTH EDITION

McGRAW-HILL BOOK COMPANY

New York Toronto London

1959

MINERALOGY

 Library of Congress Catalog Card Number 58-11181

8 9 10 11 12 - MAMM - 7 6

35388

Preface to the Fifth Edition

As in previous editions, changes have been made in all chapters and in the Tables for the Determination of Minerals. The more extensive revisions have been made in Chapters 13 and 14, which are now entitled "Chemical Mineralogy and Crystal Chemistry" and "Formation and Occurrence of Rocks and Minerals," respectively. These chapters have been rewritten and materially expanded. Many changes have also been made in Chapters 16 and 18—"Descriptive Mineralogy" and "Classification of Minerals According to Elements"—which involve the revision of the chemical formulas of some of the minerals. These revisions were necessitated by the significant results obtained from extensive X-ray studies and by the modern interpretation of the chemical composition of many minerals. New information concerning the properties, occurrences, production, and uses of the minerals described has also been incorporated. The text has been increased by 22 pages. The continued, rather widespread use of the book since it was first published in 1920 is very gratifying.

We are indebted to users of the book and to our colleagues, Professors Chester B. Slawson, E. Wm. Heinrich, and Reynolds M. Denning, for the constructive suggestions which we have received from them. The very efficient assistance rendered by Mrs. Margaret N. Everett in the preparation of the manuscript is greatly appreciated.

Edward H. Kraus
Walter F. Hunt
Lewis S. Ramsdell

Mineralogical Laboratory
The University of Michigan
January, 1959

Preface to the First Edition

This text is the result of long experience in teaching large classes of beginning students, and the subject is accordingly presented in a direct and simple manner. The essentials of the various phases of the science have been treated so that a single book may serve the needs of the average student. The conventional line drawings of crystals, which students commonly have difficulty in properly visualizing, have been superseded to a very large extent by excellent photographs of crystal models, natural crystals, and minerals, such as are actually handled in the laboratory. These are all original photographs of material contained in the various collections of the University of Michigan.

Furthermore, an attempt has been made to vitalize the subject as much as possible, and accordingly there are chapters on the importance of mineralogy in modern civilization, on gems and precious stones, and on the production and uses of the important economic minerals. Numerous photographs and short sketches of distinguished mineralogists have also been introduced in the hope that they will add a human touch.

The chapters on crystallography are based very largely upon the senior author's "Essentials of Crystallography," while much of the material in the descriptions of the 150 minerals given in this text has been taken from his "Descriptive Mineralogy." The determinative tables are an abridgment of the authors' "Mineral Tables."

We are greatly indebted to Mr. George R. Swain, technical expert in photography in the University of Michigan, whose varied experience and unusual skill made the excellent photographs of models and minerals possible; also to Dr. George F. Kunz for valuable assistance in securing a considerable number of very desirable photographs.

Edward H. Kraus
Walter F. Hunt

Mineralogical Laboratory
The University of Michigan
August, 1920

Contents

1 | Introduction

Mineralogy and Civilization. By the early students of natural history, all substances occurring in nature were commonly referred to three "kingdoms": *animal, vegetable, mineral.* These early scientists placed in the *animal* kingdom all the animal forms observed on the land, in the sea, and in the air. The study of the various forms of animals led to the development of zoology, anatomy, surgery, animal breeding, and related subjects. In the *vegetable* kingdom, the plants and trees were placed; the study of these has given us the science of botany and the closely related subjects of forestry and agriculture. The *mineral* kingdom included the whole inanimate world, that is, the minerals, rocks, soils, and the "waters of the earth." Since bright colors, regularity of form, transparency, and other prominent physical properties have always attracted attention, there is little wonder that minerals, with their great diversity of color and form, should have been among the first objects studied by primitive man.

Although the science of mineralogy was developed in comparatively recent time (much more recently than astronomy), minerals, crystals, and rocks were used very early in the development of civilization. In the earliest stage, called the *stone age,* rocks or stones were hewn into numerous shapes and used for various utensils. They were also made into crude weapons. In the beginning, in fact, the stones were for the most part rough, but subsequently, methods were devised so that they could be made smooth and polished to some extent. This period, therefore, is frequently divided into the rough and smooth *stone ages,* the *Paleolithic* and *Neolithic* ages, respectively.

As his knowledge of rocks and minerals increased, and he was able to recover metals from them, man emerged successively into the *copper, bronze, iron,* and *coal* ages. Because of the enormous progress that has been made in science and technology, and which has resulted in a great increase in the use of minerals, successive periods of advance have been called the *machine, motor, air, atomic,* and *nuclear ages.* It is conservatively estimated that, since 1900, more mineral products have been extracted from the earth than in all previous history. The use of minerals was greatly accelerated by the two world wars.

Moreover, many new industrial uses have been developed for old minerals. Thus, the rock crystal variety of quartz in the form of thin wafers is now used in the frequency control of modern radio and electronic apparatus (page 112). In the rapid and precision machining of metal and other parts, now generally practiced in industry, diamond-set tools (page 273) are used. Large quantities of diamonds are consumed annually in various industrial processes.

Some minerals which were long considered of no commercial value are now used in large quantities, for example, kyanite (page 369) and ilmenite (page 303). Kyanite is now used in the manufacture of spark plugs and chemical porcelains (page 438). Ilmenite has become an important source of titanium. This metal is characterized by its low specific gravity, high melting point, and resistance to corrosion, and is of great importance in the manufacture of jet engines.

In the development of atomic energy, minerals containing uranium and thorium, such as uraninite (pitchblende, page 312), have become extremely important. Reference should also be made to the fact that minerals containing boron, lithium, beryllium, germanium, and the rare earths (yttrium, lanthanum, cerium, praesodymium, neodymium, and samarium) are now required in large quantities to meet the many new technological developments.

In view of the dominant role of minerals in modern industry and commerce, the demand for authoritative information concerning the properties, occurrences, and uses of minerals is insistent and greater than ever. Never before have the peoples of the world been so mineral-conscious.

Sources of Raw Materials. The principal sources of the raw materials used by man are the mines and quarries, the farms, the forests, the sea, and the atmosphere. Of these, the farms, forests, and mines and quarries are the greatest contributors. However, owing to the development of efficient modern chemical processes, the sea has become an important source of bromine and metallic magnesium, and the atmosphere of nitrogen, which is an extremely essential component of fertilizers and explosives.

Divisions of Human Activity. Upon the exploitation of these natural resources rest the greatest and most important divisions of human activity, namely, agriculture, mining, and commerce and industry. As is well known, agriculture furnishes us with many of the products so necessary to our sustenance, that is, with the cereals and other crops. Indirectly, it gives us much of our meat products, wearing apparel, and the like. In order to carry on agriculture with marked success, a knowledge of the composition and nature of soils is absolutely essential. Soils consist to a very large extent of minerals and mineral products. Indeed, all balanced soils suited to general cropping contain a preponderance of mineral matter.

It is obvious that in mining a most comprehensive knowledge of mineralogy is necessary. The discovery and exploitation of new deposits of precious and important industrial metals and of gems have generally led to the development and population of many areas.

Several instances may be cited. Thus, it is well known that the discovery of gold in California in 1849 gave a great stimulus to world-wide migration and trade. About 1850, in further search for gold, Englishmen began to populate antipodal Australia. Moreover, the discovery of diamonds near Kimberley in 1867 and of gold in the Rand district in 1885 led to the subsequent settlement of large sections of Africa. Alaska came into prominence only after the discovery of gold and other valuable minerals toward the close of the last century. The value of the minerals produced in Alaska since those discoveries is nearly a billion dollars. It is of interest to know that this sum is many times larger than the purchase price, $7,200,000, which the United States paid to Russia in 1867 for the entire territory.

Mining has often been the forerunner of agriculture. It is also to a large extent the basis of commerce and industry. In fact, commerce and industry may be said to rest, in general, upon agriculture and mining. In the exploitation of valuable mineral deposits important lines of transportation and communication have invariably been developed. Thus, the principal commerce of the Great Lakes consists of carrying annually enormous quantities of iron ore (about 90,000,000 tons) from the Lake Superior region to various points on the lower lakes and of transporting coal from these ports on the return trip. Likewise, many of the industries in the vicinity of the Great Lakes are directly dependent upon mining in that they utilize the products of the mines and quarries. The construction of the St. Lawrence Seaway makes iron ore from the rich deposits of the Quebec-Labrador region in Canada readily accessible because of cheap water transportation. Conservative estimates show that the carrying of minerals and mineral products constitutes nearly two-thirds of the total traffic of our railroads and about one-fourth of the ocean trade.

The Nation and Its Mineral Resources. Today, as never before, the mineral resources of a nation are recognized as one of its foundations of power. They are also considered among its most valuable assets In this respect the United States has been unusually fortunate, for it possesses very large deposits of the important economic rocks and minerals and vast areas of very fertile soil.

In no small measure the successful exploitation of these natural resources has contributed to the present commanding position of the United States among the nations. This country produces annually about 47 per cent of the world's aluminum, 33 per cent of the copper, 28 per cent of the iron, 22 per cent of the lead, 16 per cent of the silver, 83 per cent of the sulfur, 36 per cent of the zinc, 21 per cent of the coal, 44 per cent of the petroleum, 70 per cent of the corn, 55 per cent of the cotton, and 21 per cent of the wheat. Naturally during periods of depression or emergency, production fluctuates considerably, thus during the Second World War and the Korean War the percentages were in some cases higher than given above.

Relation of Mineralogy to Other Sciences. Mineralogy, then, must be considered as a science which is fundamental in our present civilization. It is a subject of vital importance to many types of students, namely, students of geology, chemistry, physics, forestry, soils, and engineering, as well as those looking forward to mineralogy as a profession.

The geologist whose task it is to observe and interpret the processes which are and have been at work upon the earth should be well grounded in mineralogy, for the earth consists largely of rocks which, in turn, are made up of minerals. Likewise, in the intensive world-wide search for new mineral deposits, a knowledge of minerals is indispensable. Many of the raw materials of chemistry and all of the materials of ceramics, refractories, and metallurgy are minerals. Thus, the well-known Solvay process for the manufacture of the alkalies uses as raw materials—limestone, halite or common salt, and coal—products of the mines or quarries. Moreover, many scientific advances have been made possible by the use, in research and industry, of the optical methods devised by the mineralogist. These methods have many applications in the rapid and accurate determination of substances even when they are available only in very small amounts.

Many of the important laws in physics, especially those relating to the properties of light, have been studied principally on crystallized minerals. The Nobel prizes in physics for 1914 and 1915 were awarded to Laue and the Braggs (father and son) for epoch-making investigations upon the structure of crystallized minerals by means of X rays (pages 149 and 176).

By the use of modern prospecting devices, such as the *mineralight*, to produce ultraviolet light (often called *black light*) which causes some minerals to fluoresce or phosphoresce, and the *Geiger counter* to record radioactivity, valuable deposits of uranium and tungsten minerals have been discovered in the Great Bear Lake and Blind River regions in Canada, in the Colorado Plateau, and elsewhere. Geophysical methods are also being used rather extensively.

The forester and the student of soils are very frequently at work in undeveloped sections. In their field surveys they should be able to recognize at a glance the character of the soil and of the rock exposures. They should also be able to pass fairly accurate judgment upon the possible value of any minerals or ore deposits they may find. In order to do this, some knowledge of mineralogy is required.

In railroad, highway, and waterway construction, the engineer is constantly encountering problems which involve a knowledge of mineralogy. As in the case of the forester and the student of soils, he is frequently working in undeveloped sections of the country. Some of our most valuable ore deposits were discovered as the direct result of railroad building. The great mineral deposits at Sudbury, Ontario, which now furnish such enormous quantities of nickel, and the valuable silver mines at Cobalt, Ontario, to mention only two examples, were discovered in this way.

Fig. 1. Abraham G. Werner (1750–1817). Pioneer mineralogist.

History of Mineralogy. Mineralogy is a comparatively young science, having been developed more recently than astronomy, chemistry, mathematics, or physics. Although minerals and metals were frequently used by the ancients, the first extensive work on mineralogy did not appear until 1546, when Georg Agricola published his *De Natura Fossilium.* It is commonly conceded that Werner (1750–1817), for many years a professor in the famous school of mines at Freiberg, Saxony, was the first to place mineralogy upon a scientific basis. At first, mineralogy and geology were not differentiated, and only in comparatively recent times have they been recognized as distinct sciences.

Minerals and Rocks. The exterior of the earth is made up of solids, liquids, and occluded gases. The solids are commonly called *rocks.* It is with the rocks that we are concerned. Some of the general characteristics of several of the most common rocks may now be discussed. Thus, if a specimen of granite is examined (Fig. 2), it is at once seen that it is heterogeneous in character; that is, it is made up of several components. In general, one can easily recognize in a hand specimen three components: (1) a colorless, granular, and glassy material which is called quartz; (2) a substance with rather even surfaces, known as feldspar; and (3) a dark-colored and scaly material, which is commonly designated as mica. If these three crystalline components are analyzed, it will be noted that characteristic chemical compositions can be assigned to them: thus to quartz, SiO_2, to feldspar, $KAlSi_3O_8$, and to mica, $K(Mg,Fe)_3(OH,F)_2AlSi_3O_{10}$. In examining another common rock, such as syenite (Fig. 3), it will be found that it is quite frequently composed of two components—mica and feldspar. On the other hand, such rocks as sandstone (Fig. 4) and marble (Fig. 5) consist of one component only—quartz and calcite ($CaCO_3$), respectively. The term *mineral* is applied to these rock constituents. Minerals also occur in many other ways in nature and may be well crystallized, that is, possess definite external forms bounded by natural plane surfaces.

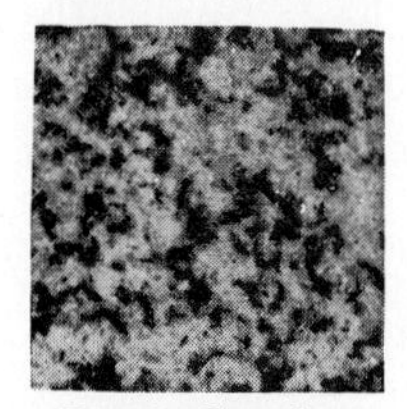

Fig. 2. Granite.

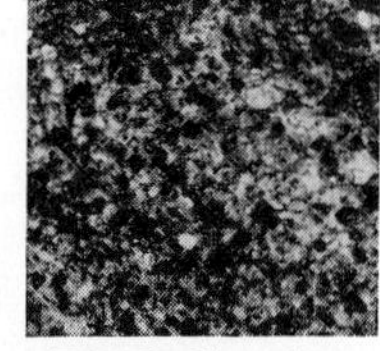

Fig. 3. Syenite.

Fig. 4. Sandstone.

Fig. 5. Marble.

Definition of a Mineral. A mineral may be defined as a *substance occurring in nature with a characteristic chemical composition and usually possessing a definite crystalline structure, which is sometimes expressed in external geometrical forms or outlines.* For example, the chemical substance $CaSO_4$ occurs in nature and is given the mineral name anhydrite (Fig. 6). If it is prepared in the laboratory, it is not interpreted as a mineral and is called calcium sulfate. However, many minerals are being produced in large quantities for commercial uses and may be termed synthetic minerals, for example synthetic rubies and sapphires for gems, and massive synthetic corundum for abrasive and refractory purposes.

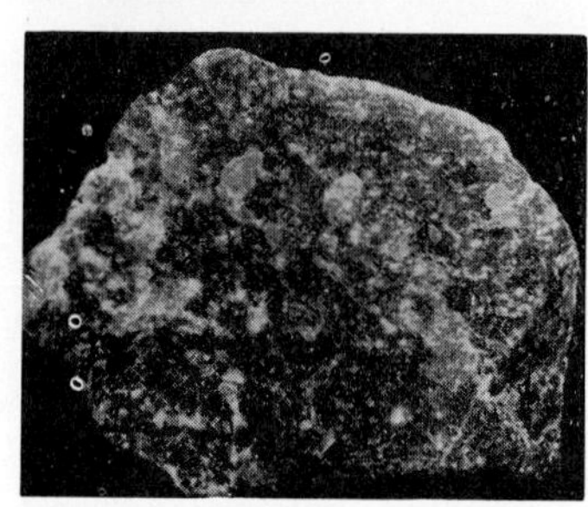

Fig. 6. Anhydrite. Oakwood Salt Shaft, Detroit, Michigan.

Most minerals are inorganic in character and are either elements, such as native sulfur, silver, copper, and gold, or combinations of elements, that is, chemical compounds. Some substances of complex organic nature, for example, coal, petroleum, and asphalt, do not fully qualify as minerals. They are, however, commonly included among our mineral resources.

Crystalline and Amorphous Substances. Most solid substances, whether formed in nature or in the laboratory, have a definite orderly internal arrangement of their constituent atoms and are said to have a *crystalline structure.* Under favorable conditions of formation, crystalline substances may develop as solids bounded by natural plane surfaces and are called *crystals* (Figs. 7 and 8). The natural plane surfaces are termed *crystal faces.*

Crystalline aggregates or masses are composed of irregular grains or particles each of which possesses an orderly internal structure (Fig. 5). When solids are devoid of an orderly internal arrangement of atoms, they are called *noncrystalline* or *amorphous*. Glass and opal are amorphous substances.

Fig. 7. Calcite crystal. Joplin, Missouri.

Fig. 8. Quartz crystals. Dauphiné, France.

In crystalline substances the various properties generally vary with direction, while in amorphous solids the individual properties are the same in all directions. In the study of crystal structure, based upon the internal arrangement of the atoms, X-ray methods are of the utmost importance (see Chap. 12). Many minerals are found as excellent crystals. Accurate and rapid determination of minerals can, in many cases, be most successfully made by recognizing the crystal form. Crystallography is the science which deals with the form and various properties of crystalline substances. A knowledge of the essentials of geometrical crystallography is absolutely indispensable in the rapid determination of minerals.

Divisions of Mineralogy. An elementary course in mineralogy may be conveniently divided into (1) crystallography, (2) physical mineralogy, (3) optical mineralogy, (4) crystal structure and X-ray analysis, (5) chemical mineralogy, (6) descriptive mineralogy, (7) gemology, (8) determinative mineralogy.

Crystallography. This subject aims to make the student familiar with the common crystal forms exhibited by minerals, first by the study of crystal models and later by the recognition of the various forms exhibited by natural crystals.

Physical Mineralogy. This includes the consideration of the various physical properties of solid substances, such as hardness, cleavage, color, luster, streak, specific gravity.

Optical Mineralogy. This phase of mineralogy involves a discussion of the optical properties of solids, as well as a description of the various optical instruments and methods necessary in the determination of minerals and crystals.

Crystal Structure and X-ray Analysis. This section includes a brief survey of the development of the modern theory of crystal structure. X-ray methods are described, and some of the results obtained by X-ray analysis are given.

Chemical Mineralogy. In this portion of the science, the various chemical properties of minerals, and also their origin and formation, are considered. The determination of their chemical constituents, especially by blowpipe methods, is treated in detail.

Descriptive Mineralogy. In Chap. 16, the most common minerals are discussed as to their crystallography, chemical and physical properties, occurrences and associates, and uses. Statistics of mineral production and the application of minerals in industry, as well as the classification of minerals according to their important chemical constituents, are given in Chap. 18.

Gemology. The study of the properties of the minerals used as gems is being emphasized as never before. New instruments and methods for the identification of natural and synthetic gems and gem materials have been developed. Important phases of this new science of gemology are discussed briefly in Chap. 17.

Determinative Mineralogy. For the purpose of acquiring facility in the rapid recognition of minerals by means of their physical properties, pages 493 to 661 contain determinative tables for more than 150 important minerals.

2 | Crystallography

The science of crystallography includes in general the study of (1) the various properties of crystalline solids; (2) the character, arrangement, and classification of the natural plane surfaces observed on crystals, as well as the laws which govern their development; and (3) the determination and interpretation of the orderly internal arrangement of the constituent atoms.

Subdivisions of Crystallography. This branch of mineralogy embraces the study of crystals and crystallized substances. The various branches of the science are (1) *geometrical*, (2) *physical*, (3) *chemical*, (4) *optical*, and (5) *structural crystallography*.

Geometrical crystallography, as the term implies, describes the various forms occurring on crystals. It is sometimes called *morphological crystallography*. The essentials of this branch of the science must be mastered in order to recognize and determine crystals and minerals rapidly. The relationships existing between the crystal form and the physical and chemical properties of crystals are the subjects of discussion of the second and third branches of crystallography (see Chaps. 10 and 13). The fourth and fifth subdivisions deal with the optical properties and the structure of crystals, respectively. The essentials of these branches are given in Chaps. 11 and 12.

Crystallographic Axes. The external crystal form of any substance is dependent upon the arrangement of its atoms. Because of the great number of different chemical substances and structural arrangements, an almost infinite variety of crystal forms is possible. In order to study these forms and define the position of the faces occurring on them, straight lines are assumed to pass through the ideal center of each crystal. These lines are the *crystallographic axes*. Their intersection forms the *axial cross*. Figure 9 shows a common crystal form, called the *octahedron*, referred to its three crystal axes. Since these axes are identical, each is referred to by the same letter *a*. The extremities of the axes are differentiated by the use of the plus and minus signs.

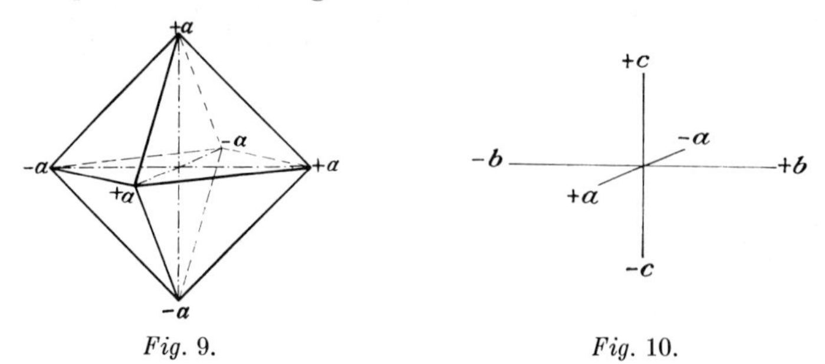

Fig. 9. *Fig.* 10.

If the axes are not alike, the one extending from front to rear is termed the *a* axis, the one from right to left the *b*, while the vertical axis is called the *c* axis. This is illustrated by Fig. 10. The axes are always referred to in the following order, namely, *a*, *b*, *c*.

Crystal Systems. Although a great variety of crystal forms is possible, it has been shown in many ways that all forms may be classified into six large groups, called *crystal systems*. In the grouping of crystal forms into systems, we are aided by the crystallographic axes. The systems may be differentiated by means of the axes as follows:

Cubic System. Three identical axes intersect at right angles. The axes are designated by the letters *a*, *a*, *a*.

Hexagonal System. Four axes, three of which are identical, lie in a horizontal plane, and intersect at angles of 60°. These three axes are often termed the *lateral* axes and are designated by *a*, *a*, *a*. Perpendicular to the plane of the lateral axes is the vertical axis, which may be longer or shorter than the *a* axes. This fourth axis is called the *principal* or *c* axis.

Tetragonal System. Three axes, two of which are identical, horizontal, and perpendicular to each other. The vertical *c* axis is at right angles to and either longer or shorter than the horizontal or *lateral a* axes. The vertical axis is often called the *principal* axis.

Orthorhombic System. Three unequal axes intersect at right angles. These axes are designated by *a*, *b*, *c*, as shown in Fig. 10.

Monoclinic System. Three unequal axes, two of which (*a*, *c*) intersect at an oblique angle, the third axis (*b*) being perpendicular to these two.

Triclinic System. Three axes (*a*, *b*, *c*,) are all unequal and intersect at three different angles.

Axial Ratios. The ratio between the lengths of the axes of crystals of a given substance is constant. This ratio is termed the *axial ratio*. In the cubic system, where the three axes are identical, the ratio is $a : a : a$, or $1 : 1 : 1$, and obviously need not be stated.

In the hexagonal and tetragonal systems the lengths of the vertical c axes differ from those of the lateral a axes, which are equal. In each of these systems the length of the a axis is taken as unity, and the ratio of the length of the c axis to that of the a axis is characteristic for each substance crystallizing in these systems. Thus:

$$\text{Quartz } (SiO_2), \text{ hexagonal, } \quad a : c = 1 : 1.099, \quad \text{or } \frac{c}{a} = 1.099.$$

$$\text{Zircon } (ZrSiO_4), \text{ tetragonal, } a : c = 1 : 0.6404, \quad \text{or } \frac{c}{a} = 0.6404.$$

In the orthorhombic, monoclinic, and triclinic systems there are three axes of unequal lengths, a, b, c. The b axis is taken as unity. Thus for sulfur, which is orthorhombic, the ratio is

$$a : b : c = 0.8131 : 1 : 1.9034.$$

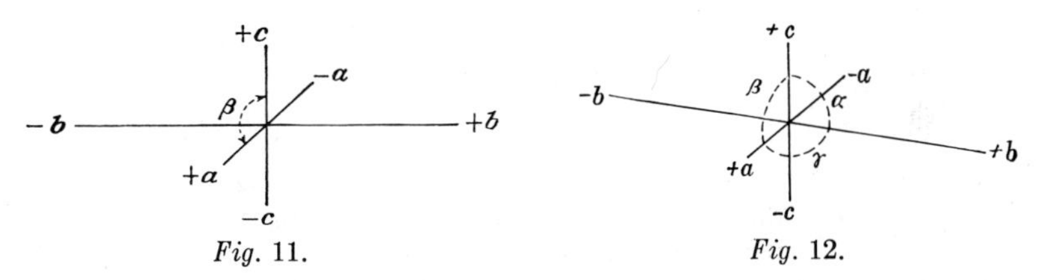

Fig. 11. *Fig.* 12.

In the monoclinic system, in addition to the ratio $a : b : c$, it is necessary to indicate the angle β between the a and c axes (Fig. 11). Thus for gypsum, which is monoclinic, the values are

$$a : b : c = 0.6896 : 1 : 0.4133; \beta = 98°58'.$$

In the triclinic system, since all axes intersect at unequal angles, it is also necessary to know the value of these angles, which are located as shown in Fig. 12, namely, $b \wedge c = \alpha$, $a \wedge c = \beta$, $a \wedge b = \gamma$.

Elements of Crystallization. The axial ratio and the angles showing the inclination of the axes are termed the *elements of crystallization.* Thus, the triclinic mineral albite ($NaAlSi_3O_8$) possesses the following elements of crystallization:

$$\begin{aligned} a : b : c &= 0.6330 : 1 : 0.5573 \\ \alpha &= 94°5' \\ \beta &= 116°27' \\ \gamma &= 88°7'. \end{aligned}$$

If the angles between the crystallographic axes equal 90°, they are not indicated. Therefore, in the tetragonal, hexagonal, and orthorhombic systems, the axial ratios alone constitute the elements of crystallization, while in the cubic system there are no unknown elements.

Parameters and Parametral Ratio. In order to determine the position of a face on a crystal, it must be referred to the crystallographic axes. Figure 13 shows an axial cross of the orthorhombic system. The axes a, b, c are, therefore, unequal and perpendicular to each other. The plane ABC cuts the three axes at the points A, B, and C, hence, at the distance $OA = a$, $OB = b$, $OC = c$, from the center O. These distances OA, OB, and OC are known as the *parameters* and the ratio $OA : OB : OC$ as the *parametral ratio* of the plane ABC. This ratio may be abbreviated to $a : b : c$. It differs from the axial ratio, see above, which gives the numerical lengths of the axes in terms of one of them taken as unity.

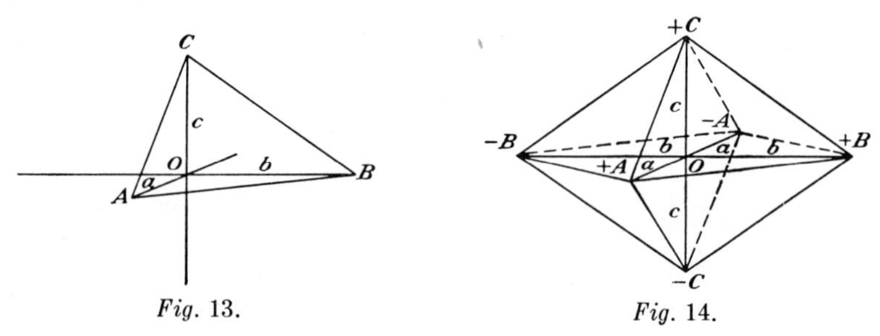

Fig. 13. *Fig.* 14.

There are, however, seven other planes possible about this axial cross which possess parameters of the same lengths as those of the plane ABC (Fig. 14). The simplified ratios of these planes are

$$a : -b : c$$
$$a : b : -c$$
$$a : -b : -c$$
$$-a : b : c$$
$$-a : -b : c$$
$$-a : b : -c$$
$$-a : -b : -c.$$

These eight planes are all similarly located with respect to the crystallographic axes. These planes constitute a *crystal form* and may be called an *orthorhombic unit bipyramid.* It is represented by the general ratio $(a : b : c)$. The number of faces in a crystal form depends, moreover, not only upon the intercepts or parameters, but also upon the elements of symmetry possessed by the crystal (see page 17). Those forms which enclose space are called *closed* forms. Figure 14 is such a form. Those, however, which do not enclose space on all sides, as shown in Fig. 15, are termed *open* forms.

Fundamental and Modified Forms. Figures 16 and 17 show two closed forms of the orthorhombic system. Each of the eight faces in Fig. 16 cuts the a, b, and c axes at unit lengths. The parametral ratio is, hence, $(a : b : c)$, and the form is designated as the *fundamental* or *unit bipyramid.* In Fig. 17 the closed form differs from that in Fig. 16 in that, while each plane cuts the a and b axes at unit lengths, the c axis is intercepted at twice its unit length, that is, at $2c$. This parametral ratio is, therefore, $(a : b : 2c)$, and the form is called a *modified bipyramid.*

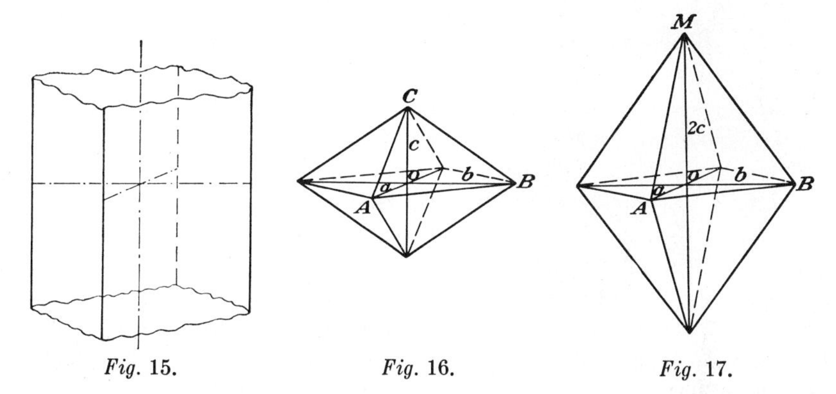

Fig. 15. *Fig.* 16. *Fig.* 17.

Combinations. Several different forms may occur simultaneously upon a crystal, giving rise to a *combination.* Figures 18 and 19 show a combination of two bipyramids observed on sulfur: $p = a : b : c$ (unit)

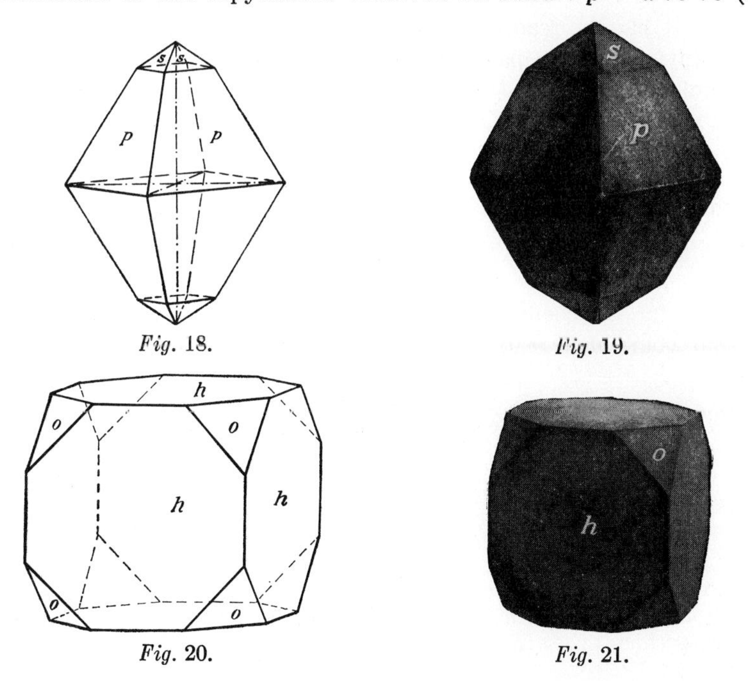

Fig. 18. *Fig.* 19.

Fig. 20. *Fig.* 21.

and $s = a : b : \frac{1}{3}c$ (modified). Figures 20 and 21 show the two forms $o = a : a : a$, and $h = a : \infty a : \infty a$ (see pages 25 and 26).

Rationality of Coefficients. Crystal faces are not accidental surface phenomena. They are directly dependent upon the internal atomic arrangement of the crystal, and their possible positions are definitely limited. The intercepts of any crystal face on the axes are, hence, always expressed as rational multiples of the basic axial units. In the cubic system these units are equal, and the general parametral ratio may be written as $(a : na : ma)$. In the orthorhombic system, the general ratio is $(na : pb : mc)$. The other crystal systems have similar ratios.

Fig. 22. René Haüy (1743–1822). Curator of mineralogy in the Museum of Natural History of Paris (1802–1822). Pioneer crystallographer.

The coefficients n, p, and m always possess rational values, either integers or simple fractions. They can never have irrational values, such as $\sqrt{2}$, 2.6578+, or 3.1416+ (π). This is the *law of rational coefficients*, or *of rational intercepts*. The reason for this limitation is inherent in the structural arrangement of the crystal. It can be readily understood by referring to Fig. 422 and the accompanying text on page 157, in the chapter on crystal structure.

Symbols. The parametral ratio of the plane ABM (Fig. 17) may be written as follows:

$$na : pb : mc.$$

But since, in this case, $n = 1$, $p = 1$, $m = 2$, the ratio becomes

$$a : b : 2c.$$

If, however, the coefficients had the values $\frac{1}{2}$, $\frac{2}{3}$, and $\frac{4}{3}$, respectively, the ratio would then read

$$\tfrac{1}{2}a : \tfrac{2}{3}b : \tfrac{4}{3}c.$$

This, when expressed in terms of b, becomes

$$\tfrac{3}{4}a : b : 2c.$$

Hence, the ratio

$$na : b : mc$$

expresses the most general ratio or symbol for forms belonging to the orthorhombic, monoclinic, and triclinic systems. In the tetragonal system, since the a and b axes are equal, this general symbol becomes

$$a : na : mc.$$

Figure 23 shows a form, the ditetragonal bipyramid, with the symbol $a : 2a : \frac{3}{2}c$. In the hexagonal system there are three equal horizontal axes, and the general ratio is

$$na : pa : a : mc.$$

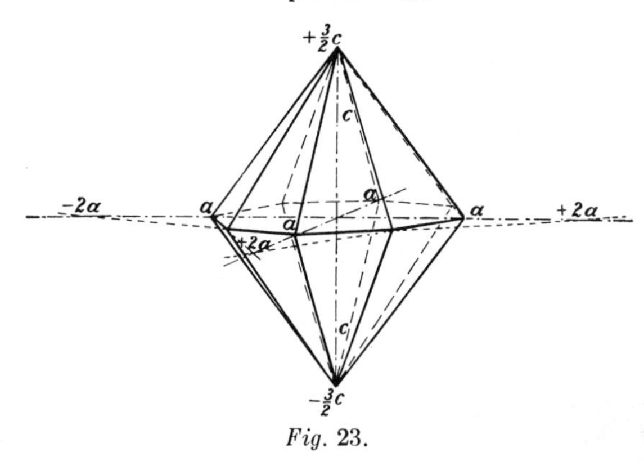

Fig. 23.

In the cubic system, all three axes are equal and the general symbol reads

$$a : na : ma.$$

The ratio $a : \infty a : \infty a$, for example, symbolizes a form in the cubic

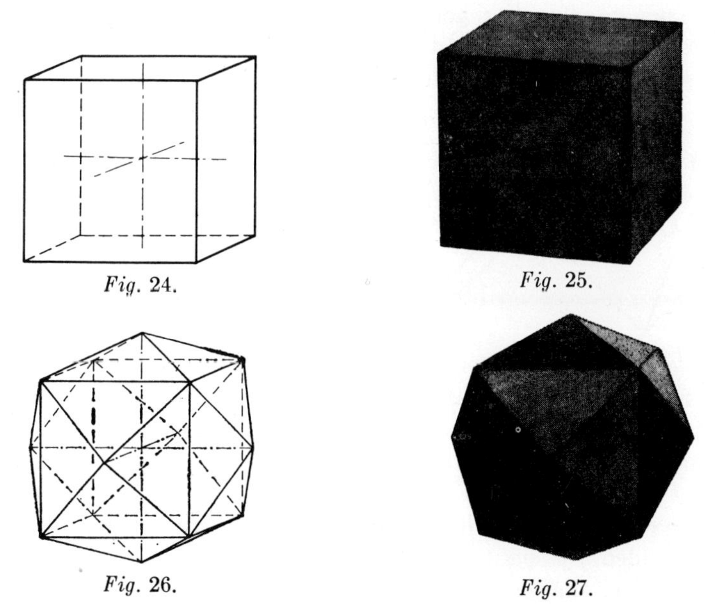

Fig. 24. *Fig.* 25.

Fig. 26. *Fig.* 27.

system consisting of six faces, which cut one axis and extend parallel to the other two. Such a form is the cube (Figs. 24 and 25). The ratio

$a : 2a : \infty a$ represents a form with 24 faces; each face cuts one axis at a unit's distance, the second at twice this distance and extends parallel to the third axis. Figures 26 and 27 show such a form, the tetrahexahedron. This system of crystallographic notation is known as the *Weiss system.* These symbols are very readily understood and well adapted for beginners.

Miller Indices. In this system of notation the letters referring to the various crystallographic axes are not indicated, the values given being understood as referring to the a, b, and c axes, respectively (page 10). The reciprocals of the Weiss parameters are reduced to the lowest common denominator. The numerators then constitute the Miller symbols, called *indices.* For example, the reciprocals of the Weiss parameters $2a : b : 3c$ would be $\frac{1}{2}$, $\frac{1}{1}$, $\frac{1}{3}$. These, reduced to the lowest common denominator, are $\frac{3}{6}$, $\frac{6}{6}$, $\frac{2}{6}$. Hence, 362 constitute the corresponding Miller indices. These are read *three, six, two.*

Fig. 28. William H. Miller (1801–1880). Professor of mineralogy in the University of Cambridge (1832–1880).

A number of examples will make this system of notation clear. Thus, $a : \infty b : \infty c$ becomes 100; $2a : b : 5c$, 5.10.2; $a : a : 3c$, 331; $a : \infty a : 2c$, 201; and so forth. The Miller indices corresponding to the general ratios $a : na : ma$ and $na : b : mc$ are written *hkl.* The Miller indices are important because of their almost universal application in mathematical and structural crystallography.

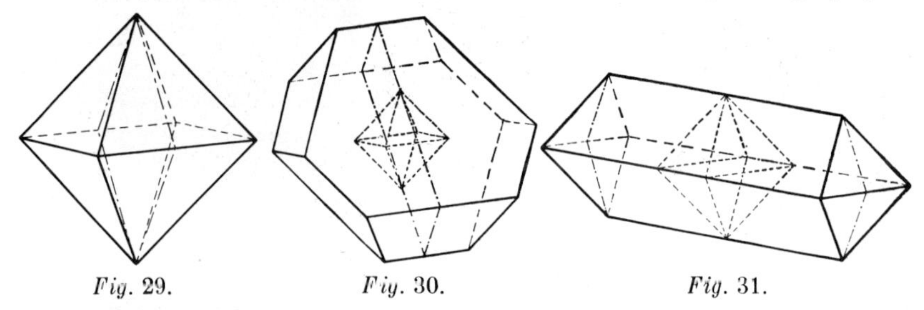

Fig. 29. *Fig.* 30. *Fig.* 31.

Constancy of Interfacial Angles. In general, crystals may result from solidification from a solution, a melt, or from vapor. Let us suppose that some ammonium alum ($NH_4Al(SO_4)_2.12H_2O$) has been dissolved in water and the solution allowed to evaporate slowly. As the alum begins to crystallize, it will be noticed that the crystals are, for the most part, bounded by eight plane surfaces. If these surfaces are all of the same size, that is, equally developed, the crystals will possess an outline as represented by Fig. 29. Such a form is termed an *octahedron.* The octahedron is bounded by eight equilateral triangles.

The angles between any two adjoining surfaces or *faces* is the same, namely, 109°28¼′. On most of the crystals, however, it will be seen that the various faces have been developed unequally, giving rise to forms

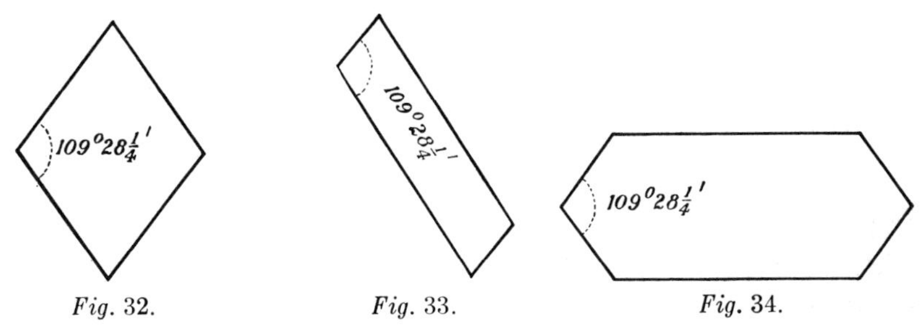

Fig. 32. *Fig.* 33. *Fig.* 34.

as illustrated by Figs. 30 and 31. Similar cross sections through these forms are shown in Figs. 32 to 34, and it is readily seen that, although the size of the faces and hence the resulting shapes have been materially changed, the angle between the adjoining faces has remained the same, namely, 109°28¼′. Such forms of the octahedron are said to be *misshapen* or *distorted. Distortion* is quite common on all crystals regardless of their chemical composition.

Fig. 35. Nicolaus Steno (1638–1687). Discoverer of the law of the constancy of interfacial angles.

It was the Danish physician and natural scientist Nicolaus Steno (Fig. 35) who in 1669 first showed that the angles between similar faces on crystals of quartz remain constant regardless of their development. Figures 36 and 37 represent two crystals of quartz, and Figs. 38 and 39 show similar cross sections through them. This constancy of angles between similar faces applies not only to quartz but to all crystallized substances. This is a fundamental law, and it may be stated as follows: *Measured at the same temperature, similar angles on crystals of the same substance remain constant regardless of the size or shape of the crystal.*

Crystal Habit. During the process of crystallization crystals may assume various shapes. Figures 29 to 31 show some of the shapes observed on alum crystals. These shapes are called their *habits.* Thus, in Fig. 29, the eight faces are about equally developed, and this may be termed the *octahedral* habit. The *tabular* habit (Fig. 30) is due to the predominance of two parallel faces. Figure 31 shows four parallel-edged faces predominating, and the resulting form has a *prismatic* habit.

Elements of Symmetry. The laws of symmetry find expression upon a crystal in the distribution of similar angles and faces. The presence, therefore, of planes, axes, or a center of symmetry—these are the *elements of symmetry*—is of great importance for the correct classification of a

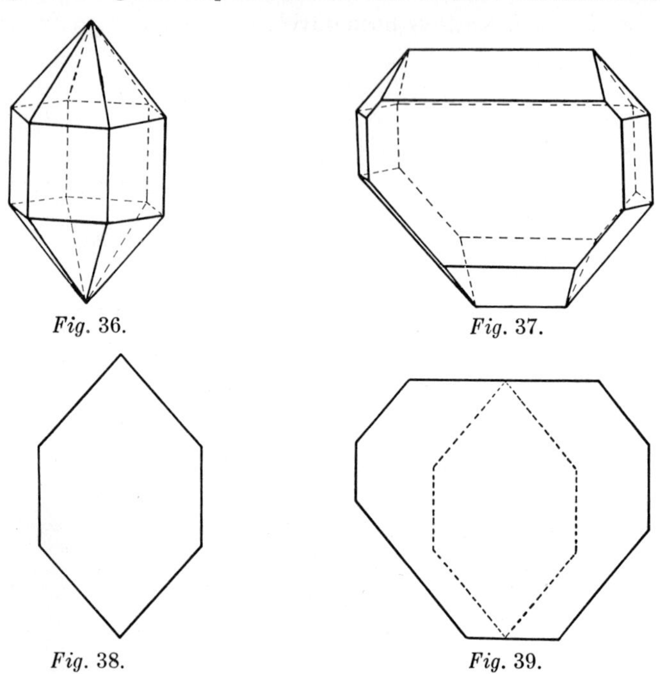

Fig. 36. *Fig.* 37.

Fig. 38. *Fig.* 39.

crystal. Only those elements of symmetry useful in the recognition of the geometrical development of crystals are here considered.

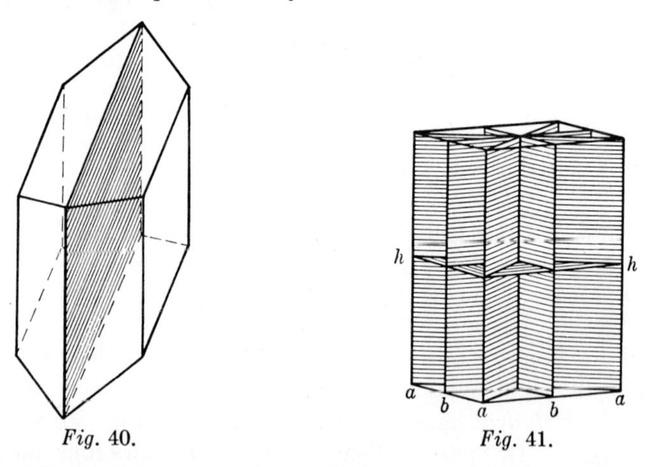

Fig. 40. *Fig.* 41.

Planes of Symmetry. Any plane which passes through the center of a crystal and divides it into two parts, the one being the *mirror image or reflection* of the other, is a *plane of symmetry*. Figure 40 shows a crystal of gypsum ($CaSO_4.2H_2O$) with its one plane of symmetry. Every plane of symmetry is parallel to some face, which is either *present* or *possible* upon the crystal.

It is sometimes convenient to designate planes of symmetry as *axial, diagonal, principal,* or *intermediate* planes. Figure 41 illustrates a crystal of the tetragonal system with five planes of symmetry. Plane *h* is the *horizontal axial* or *principal* plane. The vertical planes are the *vertical axial* (*a*) and *intermediate* (*b*) planes of symmetry.

Fig. 42. Victor Goldschmidt (1853–1933). Eminent mineralogist and crystallographer. For many years professor in the University of Heidelberg, Germany.

Axes of Symmetry. The line about which a crystal may be rotated as an axis so that after a definite angular rotation the crystal assumes a position exactly similar to that which it originally had is termed an *axis of symmetry*. Depending upon the rotation necessary, four types of axes of symmetry are possible from the standpoint of crystallography:

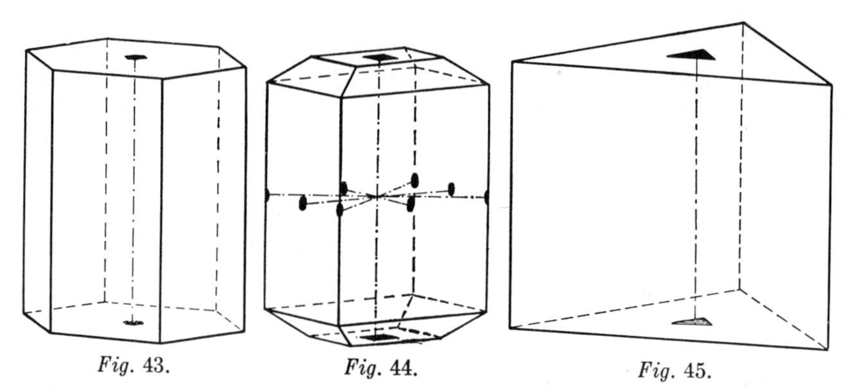

Fig. 43. *Fig.* 44. *Fig.* 45.

1. The axes which involve a rotation of 60° are said to be axes of *sixfold or hexagonal*[1] symmetry. Such axes may be indicated by the symbol ⬢. Figure 43 shows such an axis.

2. If a rotation of 90° is required, the axis possesses *fourfold or tetragonal* symmetry. These axes are represented by ■, as illustrated in Fig. 44.

3. Axes requiring an angular rotation of 120° are *threefold or trigonal* axes of symmetry and may be symbolized by ▲. Figure 45 illustrates this type of axis.

4. An axis of *twofold or binary* symmetry necessitates a rotation through 180°. These are indicated by ⬬ in Fig. 44.

In addition to these four types of axes, there is a type of axis in which

[1] Because in a complete rotation of 360° the position is reassumed six times.

rotation is combined with inversion. Such axes are called *rotary-inversion* axes.

Center of Symmetry. That point within a crystal through which straight lines may be drawn, so that on either side of and at the same distance from it similar portions of the crystal (faces, edges, angles, and so forth) are encountered, is a *center of symmetry*, which involves the *inversion* of opposite parallel faces, Fig. 46. Other elements of symmetry are lacking. The crystal form illustrated by Figs. 87 to 90, page 31, has no center of symmetry, but it possesses six diagonal planes of symmetry and four trigonal and three binary axes of symmetry.

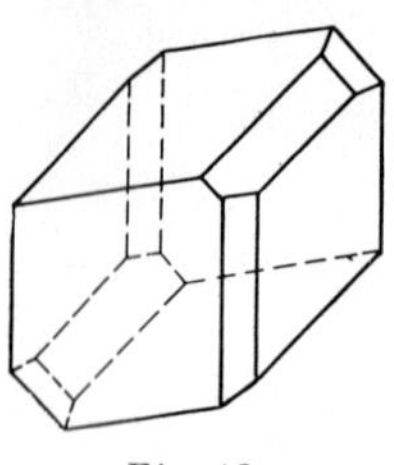

Fig. 46.

Angular Position of Faces. Since crystals are oftentimes *misshapen* or *distorted* (page 17), it follows that the elements of symmetry are not always readily recognized. The *angular position* of the faces in respect to these elements is the essential feature and not their distances from one another or their relative sizes. Figure 47 shows a crystal with a plane of symmetry, a twofold axis, and a center of symmetry. Figure 48 shows a distorted crystal of the same substance, which possesses these elements of symmetry, because the angular position of the faces is the same as in Fig. 47.

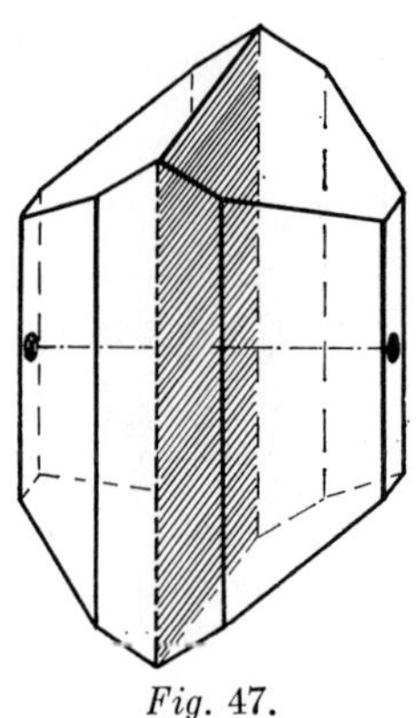

Fig. 47.

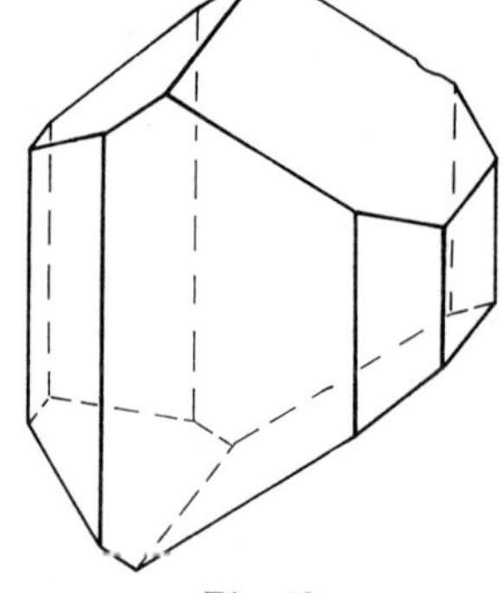

Fig. 48.

Classes of Symmetry. Depending upon the elements of symmetry present, crystals may be divided into 32 distinct groups, called *classes of symmetry*.[1] Only forms which belong to the same class can occur in combination with each other. *A crystal system*, however, includes all those classes of symmetry which can be referred to the same type of crystallographic axes (page 10). The various elements of symmetry

[1] Also termed *classes of crystals*.

and an important representative are given for each of the 32 classes in the tabular classification on page 495. Only 13 classes will be discussed in detail.

Crystallographic Names and Symbols. In geometrical crystallography different names have been applied to certain crystal forms and crystal classes, and even to some of the crystal systems. There is no universal agreement on these names. The nomenclature in this text is in part that established by Groth.

Different systems of nomenclature have likewise been used in structural crystallography. However, by international agreement, the Hermann-Mauguin system of symbols has been adopted to designate the 32 classes of symmetry. These symbols vary from one crystal system to another, being specifically designed to the needs of each particular system. A plane of symmetry is indicated by the letter m, and the various axes of symmetry by the numbers 1, 2, 3, 4, and 6.[1] Axes of rotary inversion are indicated by the same numbers written with a bar, as $\bar{1}$, $\bar{3}$, and $\bar{4}$. The combination of a symmetry plane normal to a symmetry axis is designated by a number and the letter m, as $\frac{2}{m}$, $\frac{3}{m}$. The symbols of the cubic system usually have three parts. The first part refers to the axial directions and indicates the fourfold or twofold character of the a axes, also whether or not the axial planes are present. The second part of the symbol refers to the trigonal axes and is always 3 or $\bar{3}$. The third part, if present, refers to the diagonal planes and the diagonal twofold axes. The hexoctahedral symmetry class has the symbol $\frac{4}{m}\bar{3}\frac{2}{m}$ (abbreviated to $m3m$); the hextetrahedral class, $\bar{4}3m$; and the dyakisdodecahedral class, $\frac{2}{m}\bar{3}$ or $m3$.

In the hexagonal system the first part of the symbol indicates the character of the principal (c) axis and may be 6, $\bar{6}$, 3, or $\bar{3}$ over the letter m if a horizontal plane of symmetry is present, thus, $\frac{6}{m}$. The second part refers to the lateral (a) axes, indicating whether or not these have twofold symmetry and the presence or absence of vertical symmetry planes at right angles to these axes. The third part of the symbol gives the same information concerning the intermediate axial directions. Thus, the symbol for the dihexagonal bipyramidal class is $\frac{6}{m}\frac{2}{m}\frac{2}{m}$ or $\frac{6}{m}mm$; for the ditrigonal scalenohedral class, $\bar{3}m1$.[1]

The symbols of the tetragonal system are like those of the hexagonal system, except that the principal (c) axis is fourfold in character, which requires the symbol to begin with 4 or $\bar{4}$. The ditetragonal bipyramidal

[1] The figure 1 means a onefold axis, which is equivalent to no symmetry at all.

class has the symbol $\frac{4}{m}\frac{2}{m}\frac{2}{m}$ or $\frac{4}{m}mm$; the tetragonal scalenohedral class, $\bar{4}\,2\,m$.

In the orthorhombic system the three parts of the symbol refer to the three axial directions *a*, *b*, and *c*. These may be twofold axes of symmetry, and there may be symmetry planes at right angles to them. There are three symmetry classes in the orthorhombic system which have the symbols $\frac{2}{m}\frac{2}{m}\frac{2}{m}$ or *mmm*, *mm*2, and 222, respectively.

In the monoclinic system the symbol refers to the direction of the *b* axis. This axis may be twofold in character and may have a symmetry plane at right angles to it. The three monoclinic symmetry classes have the symbols $\frac{2}{m}$, *m*, and 2, respectively.

In none of the foregoing symmetry classes is the presence or absence of a center of symmetry directly indicated. It is present or absent, depending upon whether or not the combination of elements indicated by the symbol will produce a center. In the triclinic system, there are two symmetry classes. One class has merely a center of symmetry, the other no symmetry at all. The symbol $\bar{1}$ is used for the class with the center of symmetry, and the symbol 1 for the class with no symmetry.

These Hermann-Mauguin symbols for the 32 crystal symmetry classes are easily extended to cover all the 230 space groups, by adding a letter designating the type of lattice and by the substitution of special symbols for glide planes and screw axes when these replace the normal planes and axes of symmetry (see pages 155 and 485). These symbols are given for some of the minerals described in Chap. 16.

3 | Cubic System[1]

Crystallographic Axes. All crystals which can be referred to three identical and perpendicular axes belong to the cubic system. Figure 49 shows the axial cross. One axis is held vertically, a second extends from front to rear, and a third from right to left. These axes are all interchangeable, each being designated by *a*. Since there are no unknown elements of crystallization in this system (page 11), all substances, regardless of their chemical composition, crystallizing in this system with forms having the same parametral ratios must of necessity possess the same interfacial angles.

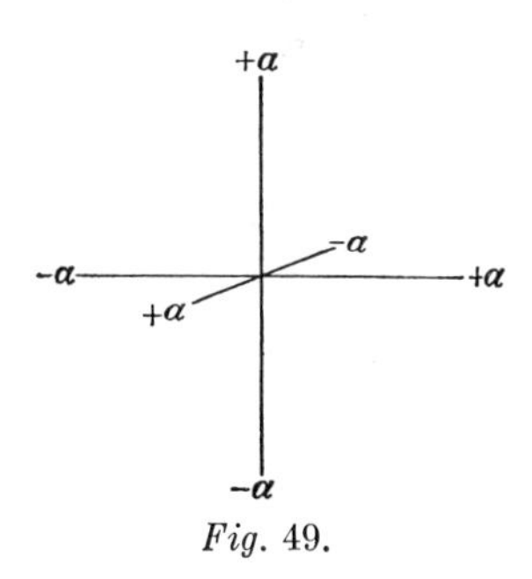

Fig. 49.

Classes of Symmetry. The cubic system includes five groups or classes of symmetry. Beginning with the class of highest symmetry, they are:

1. Hexoctahedral class.
2. Pentagonal icositetrahedral class.
3. Hextetrahedral class.
4. Dyakisdodecahedral class.
5. Tetrahedral pentagonal dodecahedral class.

The first, third, and fourth classes have important mineral representatives. These three classes will be considered in detail.

HEXOCTAHEDRAL CLASS

Elements of Symmetry, $4/m\ \bar{3}\ 2/m$. *Planes.* Forms of this class are characterized by nine planes of symmetry. Three of these are parallel to the planes of the crystallographic axes and, hence, perpendicular to each other. They are the *axial* planes of symmetry. They divide space into

[1] Also termed the *isometric, regular, tesseral,* or *tessular* system.

eight equal parts called *octants*. The six other planes are each parallel to one of the crystallographic axes and bisect the angles between the other two. These are termed the *diagonal* planes of symmetry. By them space is divided into 24 equal parts. The nine planes together divide space into 48 equal sections. Figures 50 and 51 illustrate the location of the axial and diagonal planes, respectively.

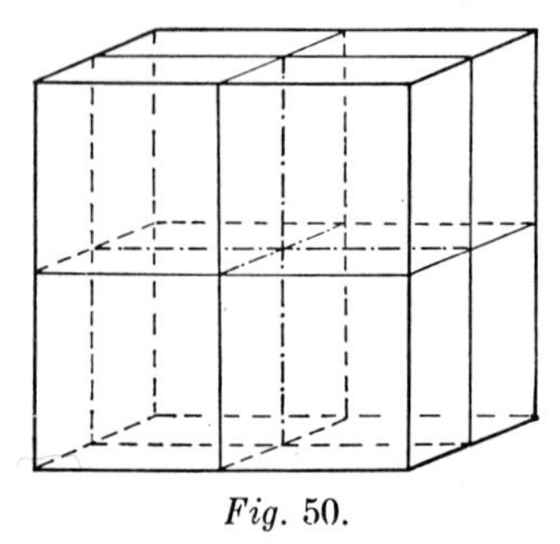

Fig. 50.

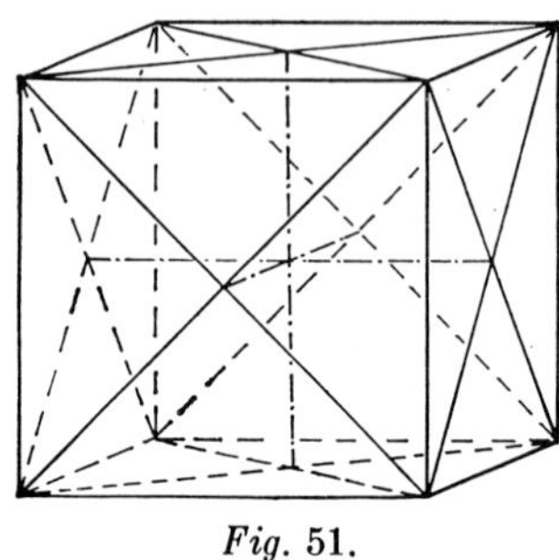

Fig. 51.

Axes. The intersection lines of the three axial planes of symmetry give rise to the three axes of *fourfold* symmetry. These are the

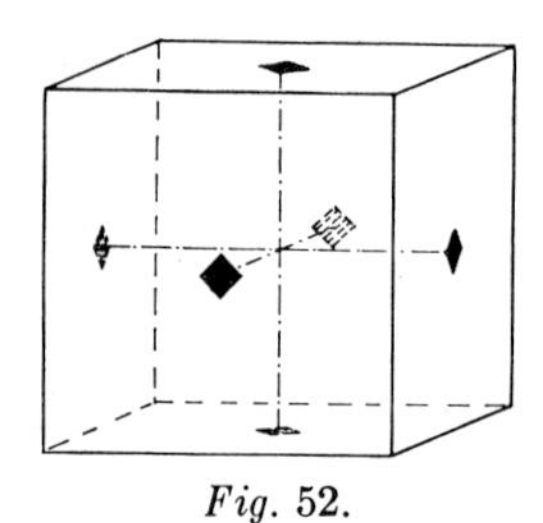

Fig. 52.

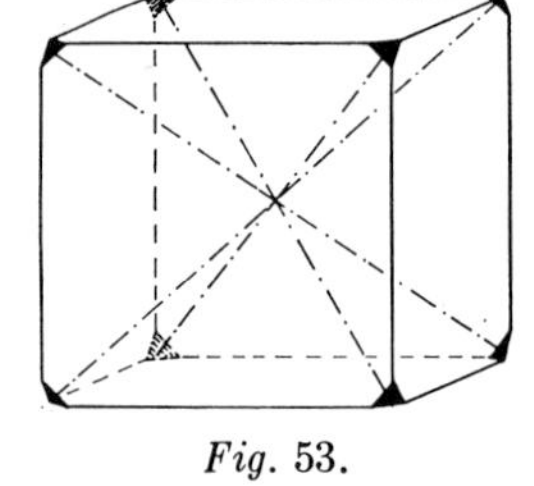

Fig. 53.

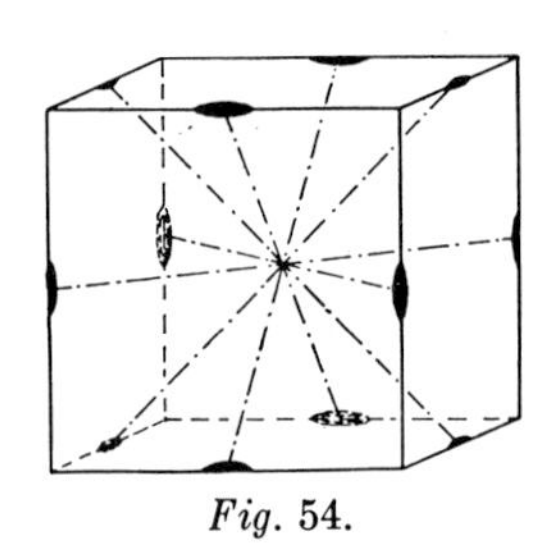

Fig. 54.

crystallographic axes, as illustrated by Fig. 52. The four axes equally inclined to the crystallographic axes are of *threefold* symmetry, as shown by Fig. 53. There are also six axes of *twofold* symmetry. These lie in the axial planes of symmetry and bisect the angles between the crystallographic axes. Their location is indicated in Fig. 54. These 13 axes of symmetry may be indicated as follows:

$$3 \blacksquare + 4 \blacktriangle + 6 \bullet = 13.$$

Center. The forms of this class also possess this element of symmetry. Hence, all planes have parallel counterplanes.

The projection of the most general form of this class upon a plane perpendicular to the vertical axis, that is, in this case an axial plane of symmetry, shows the symmetry relations[1] (Fig. 55).

[1] The heavy lines indicate edges through which axial planes of symmetry pass. The light, full lines show the location of the diagonal planes, while dashed lines indicate the absence of planes (see Fig. 86, p. 31).

Octahedron. As the name implies, this form consists of eight faces. Each face is equally inclined to the crystallographic axes. Hence, the parametral ratio may be written $(a : a : a)$, which according to Miller would be $\{111\}$. The faces intersect at an angle of 109°28′16″ and in the ideal form (Figs. 56 and 57) are equal, equilateral triangles.

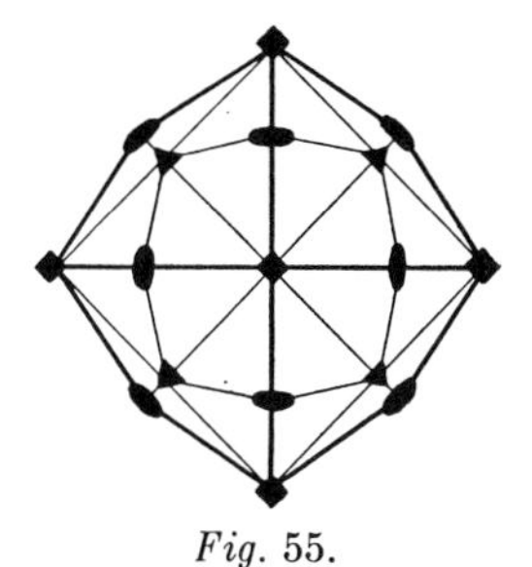

Fig. 55.

The crystallographic axes and, hence, the axes of fourfold symmetry pass through the tetrahedral angles. The four threefold axes join the centers of opposite faces, while the six twofold axes bisect the 12 edges.

Dodecahedron. This form consists of 12 faces, each cutting two of the crystallographic axes at the same distances but extending parallel to the third. The symbols are, therefore, $(a : a : \infty a)$ or $\{110\}$. In the ideal form (Figs. 58 and 59) each face is a rhombus, and, hence, the form is often termed the *rhombic dodecahedron*.

The crystallographic axes pass through the tetrahedral angles, the threefold axes join opposite trihedral angles, and the twofold axes the centers of opposite faces. The faces are parallel to the diagonal planes of symmetry.

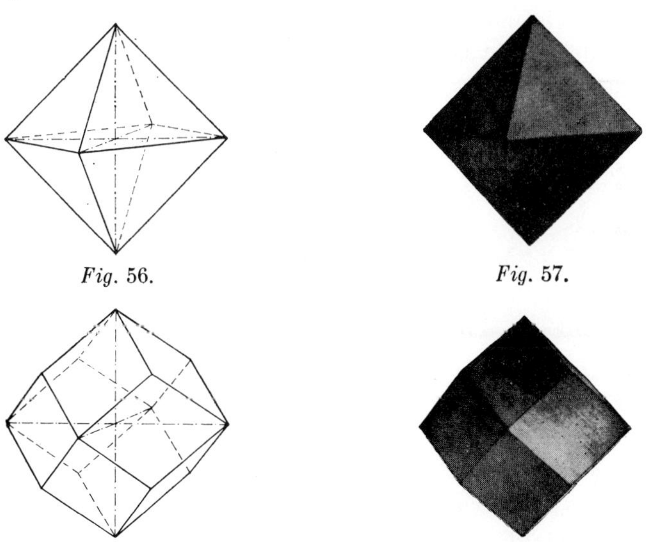

Fig. 56. *Fig.* 57.

Fig. 58. *Fig.* 59.

Hexahedron or Cube. The faces of this form cut one axis and are parallel to the other two. This is expressed by $(a : \infty a : \infty a)$, $\{100\}$. Six such faces are possible, and when the development is ideal (Figs. 60 and 61) each is a square.

The crystallographic axes pass through the centers of the faces. The axes of threefold symmetry join opposite trihedral angles, while the twofold axes bisect the 12 edges (compare Figs. 52, 53, and 54).

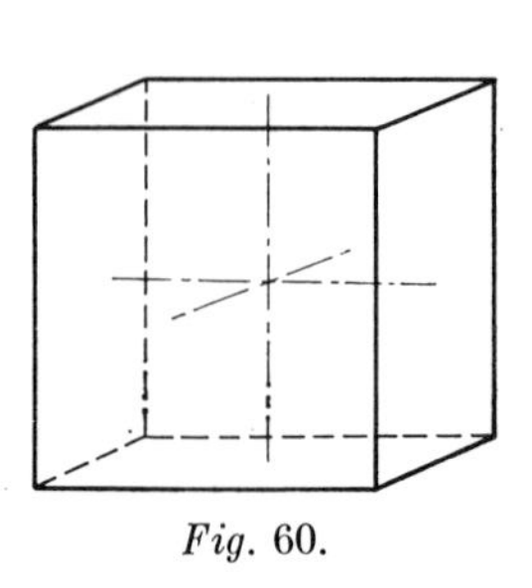

Fig. 60.

Fig. 61.

Trigonal Trisoctahedron.[1] The faces of this form cut two crystallographic axes at equal distances and the third at a greater distance, ma. The coefficient m is some rational value greater than one but less than infinity. The ratio is $(a : a : ma)$, and it requires 24 similar faces to enclose space. The Miller symbols are $\{hhl\}$, where h is greater than l. Because the general outline of this form is similar to that of the octahedron, each face of which in the ideal form is replaced by three equal isosceles triangles, it is termed the *trigonal trisoctahedron*, Figs. 62 and 63, $(a : a : 2a)$, $\{221\}$, and Fig. 64, $(a : a : 3a)$, $\{331\}$.

The crystallographic axes join opposite octahedral angles. The threefold axes pass through the trihedral angles, and the six twofold axes bisect the 12 long edges.

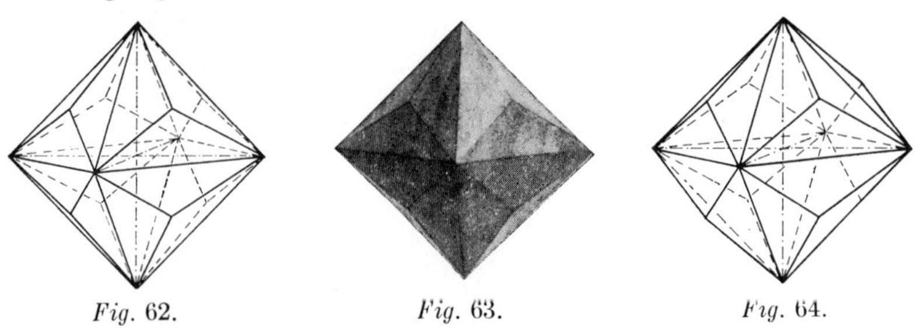

Fig. 62. *Fig.* 63. *Fig.* 64.

Tetragonal Trisoctahedron.[2] This form consists of 24 faces, each cutting one axis at a unit's distance and the other two at greater but equal distances ma. The value of m is, as above, $1 < m < \infty$. The symbols are, therefore, $(a : ma : ma)$, or $\{hll\}$, $h > l$. The ideal forms, Figs. 65 and 66, $(a : 2a : 2a)$, $\{211\}$, and Fig. 67, $(a : 4a : 4a)$, $\{411\}$, bear some resemblance to the octahedron, each face of which has been replaced by three four-sided faces (trapeziums) of equal size. The form is, therefore, termed the *tetragonal trisoctahedron*. The six tetrahedral

[1] Also known as the *trisoctahedron*.

[2] Also termed the *trapezohedron*, *icositetrahedron*, and *leucitohedron*.

angles[1] a indicate the position of the crystallographic axes. The axes of threefold symmetry join opposite trihedral angles, while those of twofold symmetry connect the tetrahedral angles[2] b.

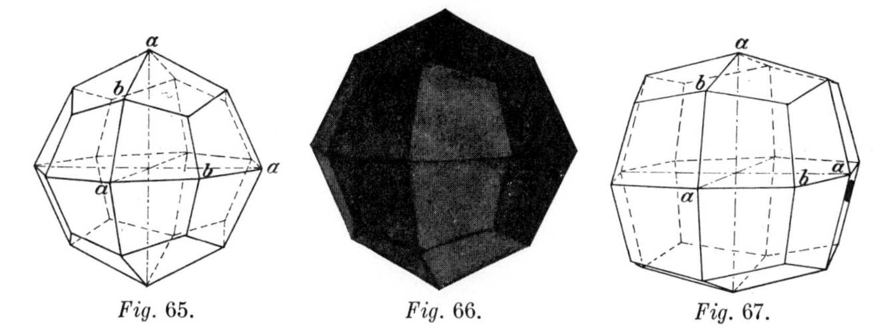

Fig. 65. *Fig.* 66. *Fig.* 67.

Tetrahexahedron. In this form the faces cut one axis at a unit's distance, the second at the distance ma, where $1 < m < \infty$, and extend parallel to the third axis. The symbols are, therefore, $(a : ma : \infty a)$ or $\{hk0\}$. The 24 faces in the ideal forms, Figs. 68 and 69, $(a : 2a : \infty a)$, $\{210\}$, and Fig. 70, $(a : 4a : \infty a)$, $\{410\}$, are equal isosceles triangles. Since this form may be considered as a cube, whose faces have been replaced by tetragonal pyramids, it is called the *tetrahexahedron* or *pyramid cube.*

The crystallographic axes are located by the six tetrahedral angles. The axes of threefold symmetry pass through opposite hexahedral angles, while the twofold axes bisect the long edges.

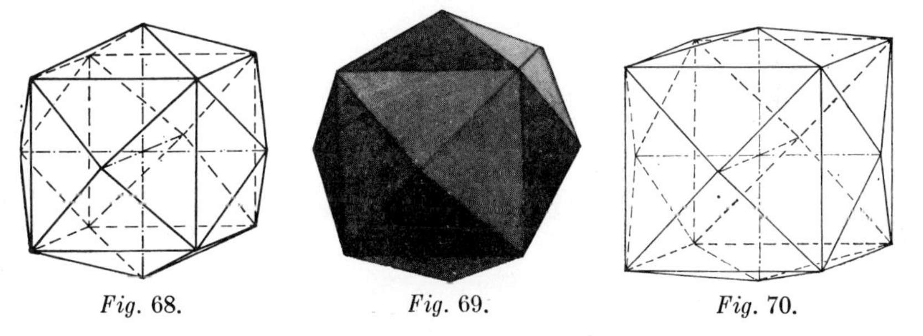

Fig. 68. *Fig.* 69. *Fig.* 70.

Hexoctahedron. As is indicated by the name, this form is bounded by 48 faces. Each cuts one crystallographic axis at a unit's distance, and the other two at greater but unequal distances na and ma, respectively; n is less than m, the value of m being, as heretofore, $1 < m < \infty$. Hence, the symbols may be written $(a : na : ma)$ or $\{hkl\}$. Figures 71 and 72, $(a : 3/2a : 3a)$, $\{321\}$, and Fig. 73, $(a : 5/3a : 5a)$, $\{531\}$, show ideal forms, the faces being scalene triangles of the same size.

[1] With four equal edges.

[2] These have two pairs of equal edges.

The crystallographic axes pass through the octahedral angles, while the hexahedral angles locate those of threefold symmetry. The twofold axes pass through opposite tetrahedral angles.

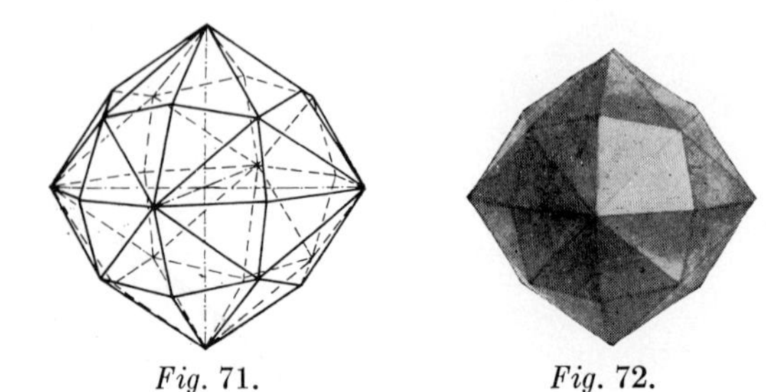

Fig. 71. *Fig.* 72.

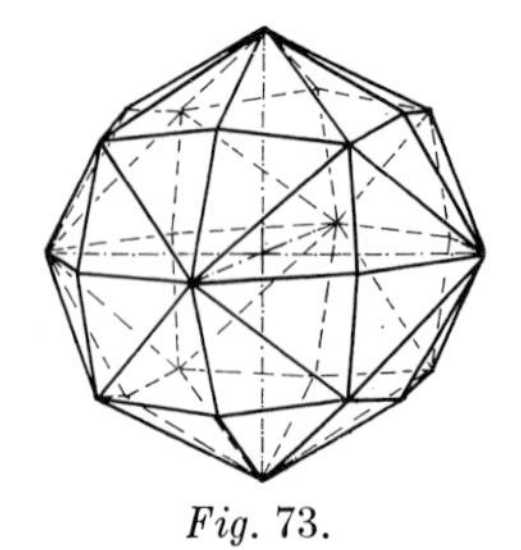

Fig. 73.

The seven forms just described are the only ones possible in this class.

Summary. Table 1 gives a summary of the most important features of the hexoctahedral class.

TABLE 1

Symmetry, $\frac{4}{m}\bar{3}\frac{2}{m}$	Planes		Axes			Center
	Axial	Diagonal	■	▲	●	
	3	6	3	4	6	1

Forms	Symbols: Weiss	Symbols: Miller	Faces	Solid angles: Trihedral	Solid angles: Tetrahedral	Solid angles: Hexahedral	Solid angles: Octahedral
Octahedron	$a:a:a$	{111}	8	—	6	—	—
Dodecahedron	$a:a:\infty a$	{110}	12	8	6	—	—
Hexahedron	$a:\infty a:\infty a$	{100}	6	8	—	—	—
Trigonal trisoctahedron	$a:a:ma$	{hhl}	24	8	—	—	6
Tetragonal trisoctahedron	$a:ma:ma$	{hll}	24	8	6* + 12†	—	—
Tetrahexahedron	$a:ma:\infty a$	{$hk0$}	24	—	6	8	—
Hexoctahedron	$a:na:ma$	{hkl}	48	—	12	8	6

* These have four equal edges.

† Two pairs of two equal edges each.

From this tabulation we see that the ratios of the octahedron, dodecahedron, and hexahedron contain no variables and, hence, each is represented by but one form. These are often called *singular* or *fixed* forms. The other ratios, however, contain either one or two variables and, therefore, each represents a series of forms (compare Figs. 62 to 73).

Relationship of Forms. The relationship existing between the above forms is well expressed by the diagram below.

The three fixed forms are placed at the corners of the triangle and, as is obvious, must be considered as the limiting forms of the others. For example, the value of m in the trigonal trisoctahedron $(a : a : ma)$ varies between unity and infinity (page 26). Hence, it follows that the octahedron and dodecahedron are its limiting forms. The tetragonal trisoctahedron $(a : ma : ma)$ similarly passes over into the octahedron or cube, depending upon the value of m. The limiting forms are, therefore, in every case readily recognized. Faces of those forms, which are on

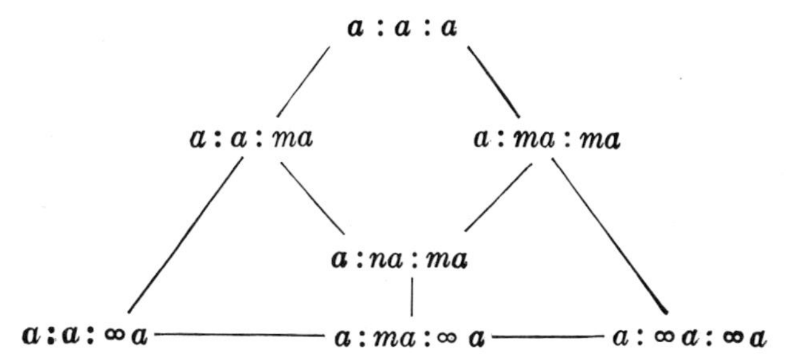

the sides of the triangle,[1] lie in the same zone, that is, their intersection lines are parallel.

Combinations. The following figures illustrate some of the combinations of the forms of this class which are observed most frequently.

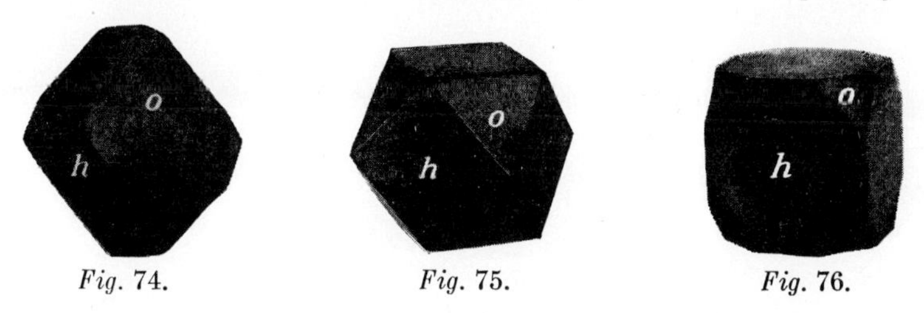

Fig. 74. *Fig.* 75. *Fig.* 76.

Figures 74, 75, and 76, $o = (a : a : a)$, {(111}; $h = (a : \infty a : \infty a)$, {100}. This combination is frequently observed on galena (PbS). In Fig. 74 the octahedron predominates, in Fig. 75 both forms are equally developed, while in Fig. 76 the cube is the predominant form.

Figure 77, $o = (a : a : a)$, {111}; $d = (a : a : \infty a)$, {110}. Observed

[1] For example, the octahedron, trigonal trisoctahedron, and dodecahedron.

on spinel ($MgAl_2O_4$), magnetite ($FeFe_2O_4$), and franklinite (Zn,Mn) (Fe_2O_4).

Figure 78, $h = (a : \infty a : \infty a)$, {100}; $d = (a : a : \infty a)$, {110}. Frequently observed on galena (PbS) and fluorite (CaF_2).

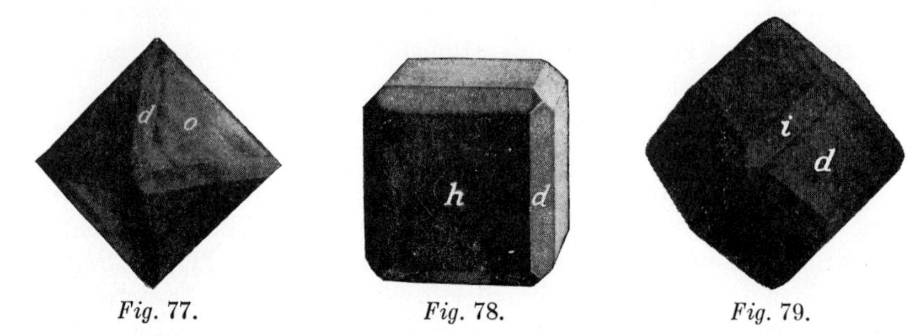

Fig. 77. *Fig.* 78. *Fig.* 79.

Figure 79, $d = (a : a : \infty a)$, {110}; $i = (a : 2a : 2a)$, {211}. This is a frequent combination on garnet ($M_3''M_2'''Si_4O_{12}$).

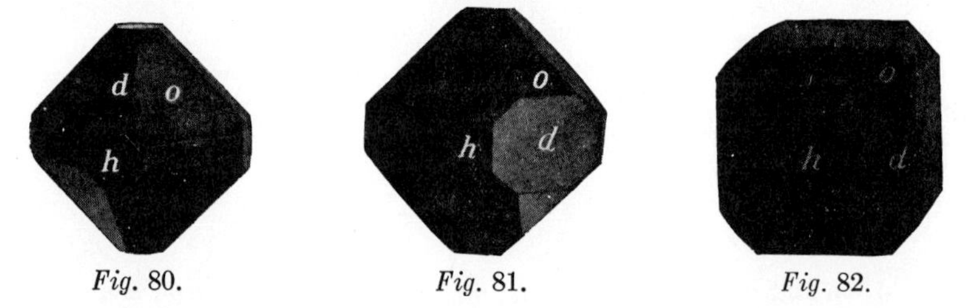

Fig. 80. *Fig.* 81. *Fig.* 82.

Figures 80, 81, and 82, $h = (a : \infty a : \infty a)$, {100}; $o = (a : a : a)$, {111}; $d = (a : a : \infty a)$, {110}. Observed on galena (PbS).

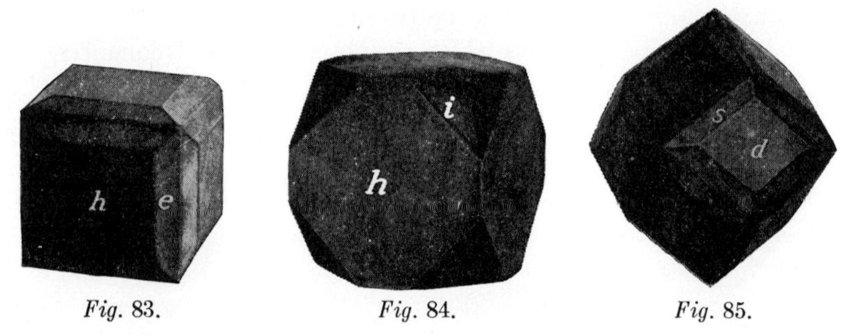

Fig. 83. *Fig.* 84. *Fig.* 85.

Figure 83, $h = (a : \infty a : \infty a)$, {100}; $e = (a : 2a : \infty a)$, {210}. Observed on copper (Cu), fluorite (CaF_2), and halite (NaCl).

Figure 84, $h = (a : \infty a : \infty a)$, {100} $i = (a : 2a : 2a)$, {211}. Observed on analcime ($NaAlSi_2O_6.H_2O$) and argentite (Ag_2S).

Figure 85, $d = (a : a : \infty a)$, {110}; $s = (a : 3/2a : 3a)$, {321}. Observed on garnet ($M_2''M_3'''Si_4O_{12}$).

HEXTETRAHEDRAL CLASS

Elements of Symmetry, $\bar{4}\ 3\ m$. The elements of symmetry of this class consist of six diagonal planes and four trigonal and three binary[1] axes. The trigonal axes are polar in character. The crystallographic axes possess binary symmetry. The diagonal planes of symmetry are easily located since they pass through the edges of the various forms of this class. The symmetry relations are shown in Fig. 86. The absence of the axial planes of symmetry is emphasized by the shading of opposite octants. The faces of the positive forms of this class are located in the unshaded octants, those of the negative forms in the shaded ones. In this class, there are four new forms which differ morphologically from those having the same ratios in the hexoctahedral class, namely, tetrahedrons, tetragonal tristetrahedrons, trigonal tristetrahedrons, and hextetrahedrons. Of these forms the tetrahedrons are the most important.

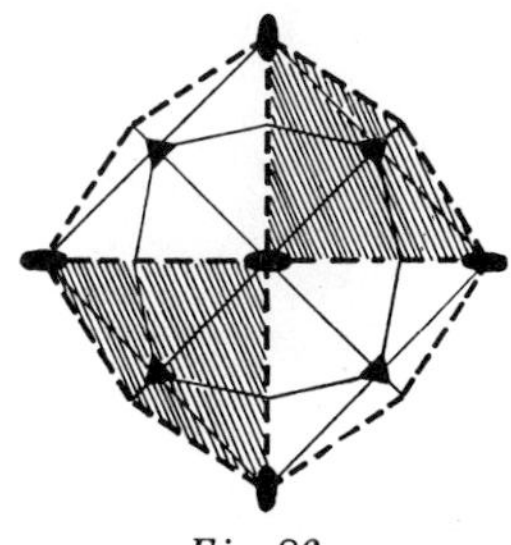

Fig. 86.

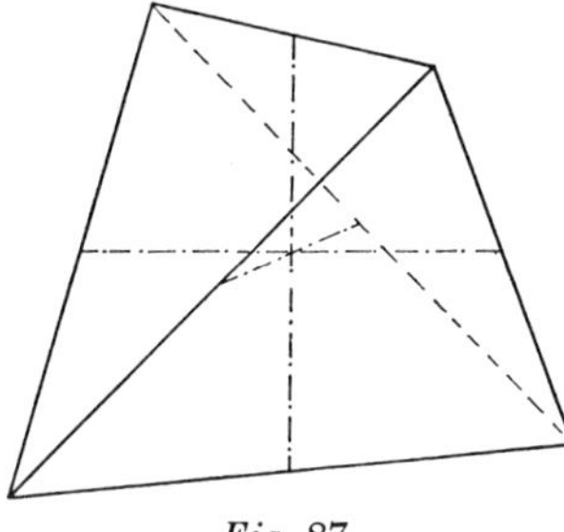

Fig. 87.

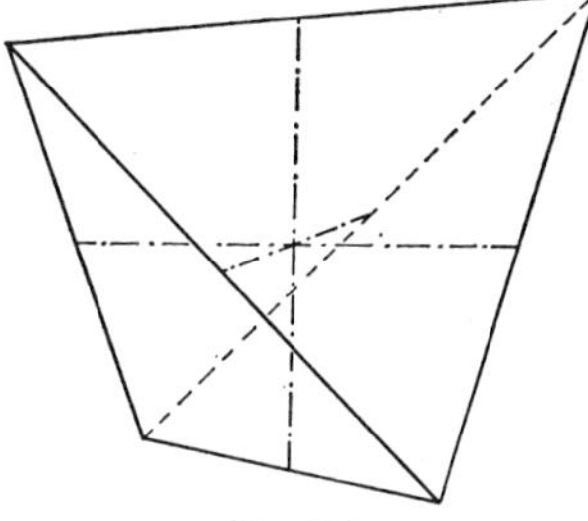

Fig. 88.

Tetrahedrons. These are bounded by four equilateral triangles intersecting at equal angles of 70°32′. Each face is equally inclined to the crystallographic axes, and consequently the symbols are the same as for the octahedron (page 25), namely, $\pm(a : a : a)$ or $\{111\}$ and $\{1\bar{1}1\}$. There are two tetrahedrons possible, which differ only with respect to the positions they occupy in space, as illustrated in Figs. 87 to 90. If the upper face to the front lies in the positive octant, the form is designated as *positive* (Figs. 88 and 90), if not, it is *negative* (Figs. 87 and 89). The forms are said to be *congruent*, for a positive form may be brought into the position of a negative form by rotating through an angle of 90°, and vice versa.

[1] In the morphological descriptions of crystals belonging to this class, these axes are customarily designated as binary or twofold axes although they are in reality fourfold axes of rotary inversion. This is indicated by the use of $\bar{4}$ in the symbol $\bar{4}\ 3\ m$.

The crystallographic axes pass through the centers of the edges and possess twofold symmetry. The threefold axes pass from the trihedral angles to the centers of opposite faces and are *polar* in character.

Fig. 89.

Fig. 90.

Tetragonal Tristetrahedrons. These forms possess a tetrahedral habit and are bounded by 12 faces, which in the ideal development are similar trapeziums. Each face has four angles. Plus and minus forms are possible. The symbols are the same as for the trigonal trisoctahedron (page 26), namely, $\pm(a : a : ma)$ or $\{hhl\}$ and $\{h\bar{h}l\}$. The differentiation between positive and negative forms is analogous to that referred to under

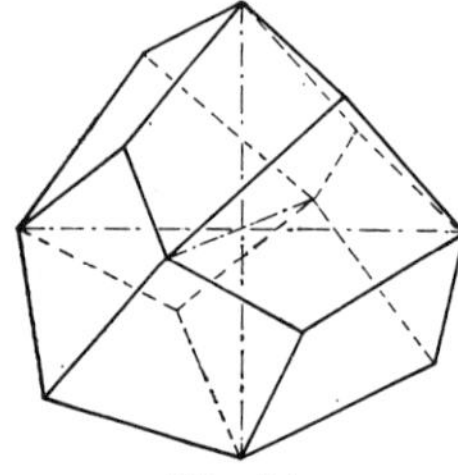

Fig. 91.

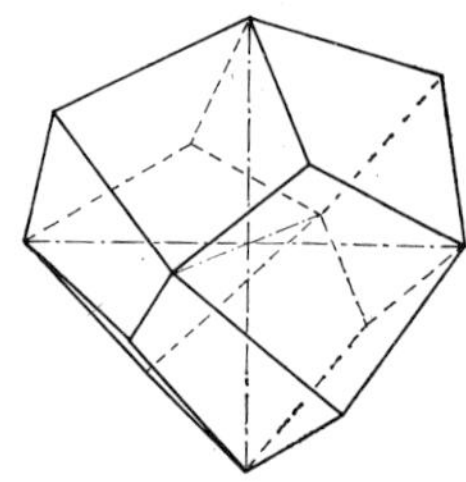

Fig. 92.

tetrahedrons. Figure 92 represents a *positive* and Fig. 91 a *negative* form. The forms are sometimes called *deltoids* or *deltoid dodecahedrons.*

The crystallographic axes pass through opposite tetrahedral angles, while the axes of threefold symmetry join opposite trihedral angles, one of which is acute, the other obtuse.

Trigonal Tristetrahedrons. These are two congruent forms bounded by 12 similar isosceles triangles (Figs. 93 and 94). The habit is tetrahedral, and the forms might be considered as tetrahedrons whose faces have been replaced by trigonal pyramids. They are sometimes called *pyramid tetrahedrons* or *trigonal dodecahedrons.* The symbols are analogous to those of the tetragonal trisoctahedron (page 26), namely, $\pm(a : ma : ma)$ or $\{hll\}$ and $\{h\bar{l}l\}$. Figure 94 illustrates the *positive* and Fig. 93 the *negative* position.

The crystallographic axes bisect the long edges. The threefold axes pass from the trihedral to the opposite hexahedral angles.

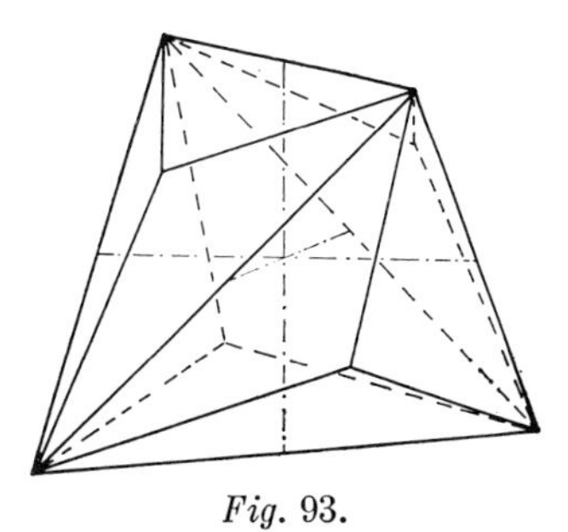

Fig. 93.

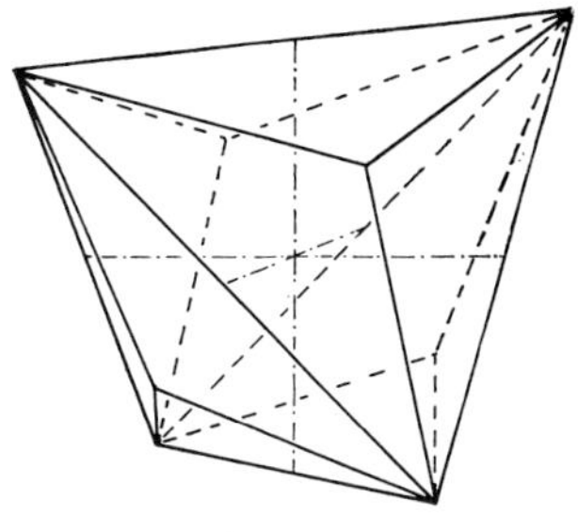

Fig. 94.

Hextetrahedrons. When these forms are ideally developed, they possess a tetrahedral habit and are bounded by 24 similar scalene triangles. They are congruent and hence designated as *positive* (Fig. 96) and *negative* (Fig. 95). The symbols are of the same character as those of the hexoctahedron (page 27), namely, $\pm(a : na : ma)$ or $\{hkl\}$ and $\{h\bar{k}l\}$.

The crystallographic axes connect opposite tetrahedral angles. The axes of threefold symmetry pass through opposite hexahedral angles, one of which is obtuse, the other acute.

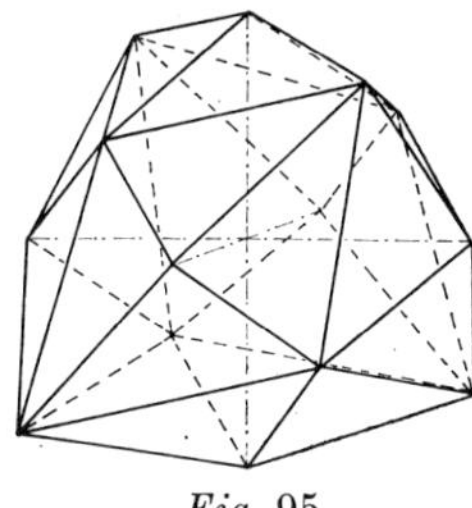

Fig. 95.

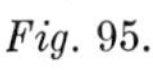

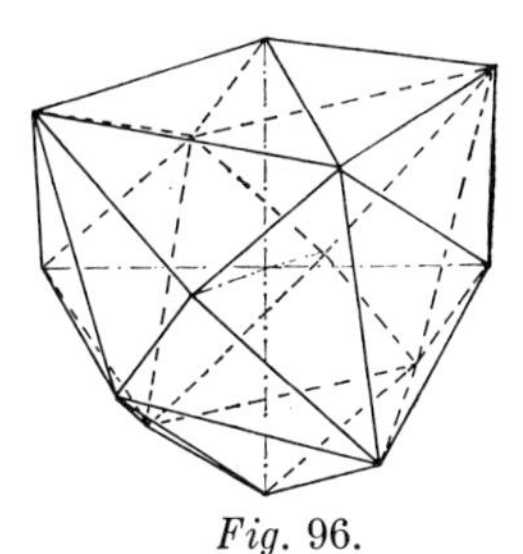

Fig. 96.

Other Forms. The hexahedron, dodecahedron, and tetrahexahedron are morphologically exactly similar to those of the hexoctahedral class. Their symmetry is, however, of a lower grade. This is not recognized on models. On crystals, however, the luster, surface striations, and shape and orientation of *etch figures* will generally reveal the lower grade of symmetry.[1]

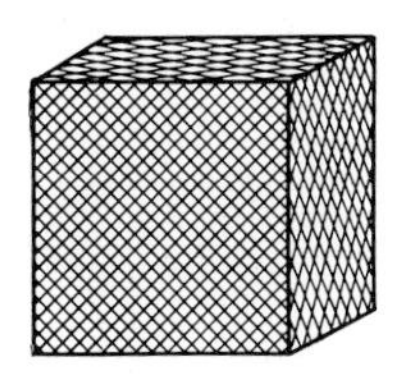

Fig. 97.

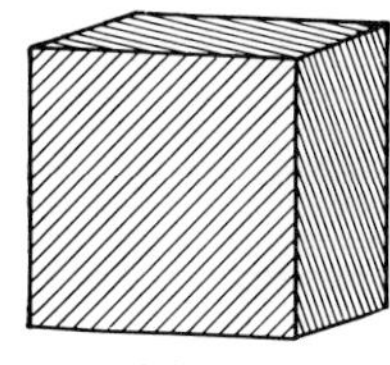

Fig. 98.

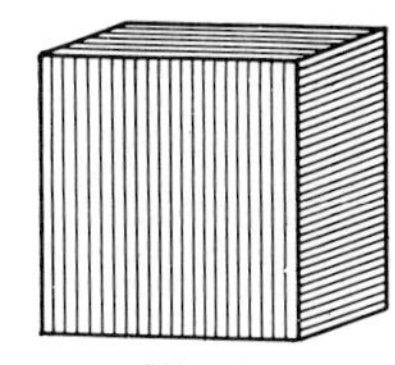

Fig. 99.

[1] Figures 97, 98, and 99 show three cubes representing crystals of fluorite (CaF_2) (Fig. 97), sphalerite (ZnS) (Fig. 98), and pyrite (FeS_2) (Fig. 99). From the character and position of the striations on the faces of these cubes, it is at once recognized

TABLE 2

Symmetry, $\bar{4}3m$	Planes		Axes			Center
	Axial	Diagonal	■	▲	●	
	0	6	0	4 (Polar)	3	0

Forms	Symbols		Faces	Solid angles		
	Weiss	Miller		Trihedral	Tetrahedral	Hexahedral
Tetrahedrons	$\pm a:a:a$	$\{111\}$ $\{1\bar{1}1\}$	4	4	—	—
Tetragonal tristetrahedrons	$\pm a:a:ma$	$\{hhl\}$ $\{h\bar{h}l\}$	12	4 + 4	6	—
Trigonal tristetrahedrons	$\pm a:ma:ma$	$\{hll\}$ $\{h\bar{l}l\}$	12	4	—	4
Hextetrahedrons	$\pm a:na:ma$	$\{hkl\}$ $\{h\bar{k}l\}$	24	—	6	4 + 4
Dodecahedron	$a:a:\infty a$	$\{110\}$	Morphologically the same as in the hexoctahedral class			
Tetrahexahedron	$a:ma:\infty a$	$\{hk0\}$				
Hexahedron	$a:\infty a:\infty a$	$\{100\}$				

that through Fig. 97 nine planes of symmetry may be passed, through Fig. 98 six, and through Fig. 99 only three. That is, the striations indicate clearly that fluorite has the symmetry of the hexoctahedral class, sphalerite of the hextetrahedral class, and pyrite of the dyakidodecahedral class. When crystals are subjected to the action of certain solvents for a short time, small depressions, the so-called *etch figures*, appear.

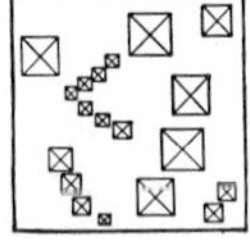

Fig. 100.

Fig. 101.

Being dependent upon the internal structure, their form and position indicate the symmetry of the crystal. For instance, Fig. 100 shows the etch figures on a crystal (cube) of halite (NaCl). Here it is evident that the symmetry of the figures with

Naturally when these forms occur in combination with those which are morphologically new, the lower grade of symmetry of this class is at once apparent.

Summary. Table 2 shows the important features of the forms of this class of symmetry.

Combinations. Some of the more common combinations are illustrated by the following figures:

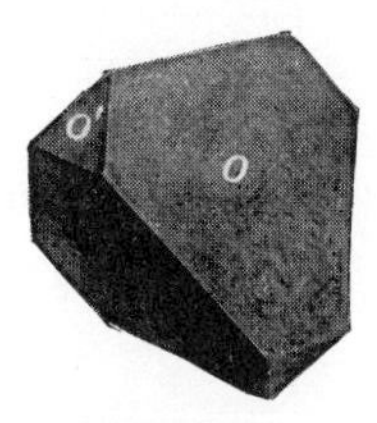

Fig. 102.

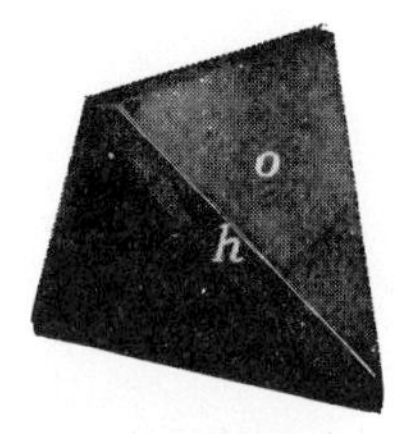

Fig. 103.

Fig. 104.

Figure 102, $o = (a : a : a)$, $\{111\}$; $o' = -(a : a : a)$, $\{1\bar{1}1\}$. This combination is common on sphalerite (ZnS).

Figure 103, $h = (a : \infty a : \infty a)$, $\{100\}$; $o = (a : a : a)$, $\{111\}$. Observed on sphalerite (ZnS) and tetrahedrite ($M_{12}R_4S_{13}$).

Figure 104, $o = (a : a : a)$, $\{111\}$; $h = (a : \infty a : \infty a)$, $\{100\}$. Observed on boracite ($Mg_3ClB_7O_{13}$) and tetrahedrite.

Fig. 105.

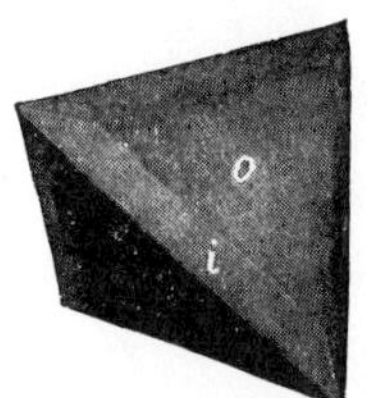

Fig. 106.

Figures 105 and 106, $o = (a : a : a)$, $\{111\}$; $i = (a : 2a : 2a)$, $\{211\}$; $d = (a : a : \infty a)$, $\{110\}$. Frequently on tetrahedrite.

DYAKISDODECAHEDRAL CLASS[1]

Elements of Symmetry, $2/m\,\bar{3}$. The elements of symmetry of this class consist of three axial planes, three twofold and four threefold axes, and the center of symmetry. The crystallographic axes possess twofold sym-

respect to that of the cube is such as to place the crystal in the hexoctahedral class. Figure 101 represents a cube of sodium bromate ($NaBrO_3$), which geometrically does not differ from the crystal of halite. A lower grade of symmetry is, however, revealed by the shape and orientation of the etch figures. This crystal belongs to the tetrahedral pentagonal dodecahedral class (p. 486), for no planes of symmetry can be passed through these figures, which at the same time are planes of symmetry of the cube, as is the case with the crystal of halite. (See also p. 113.)

[1] Also termed the *diploid* class.

metry. Figure 107 shows the symmetry relations. The faces of the *positive* forms of this class are located in the unshaded sections, those of the *negative* forms in the shaded ones.

There are two new forms in this class which differ morphologically from those thus far considered, namely, the pyritohedrons and dyakisdodecahedrons.

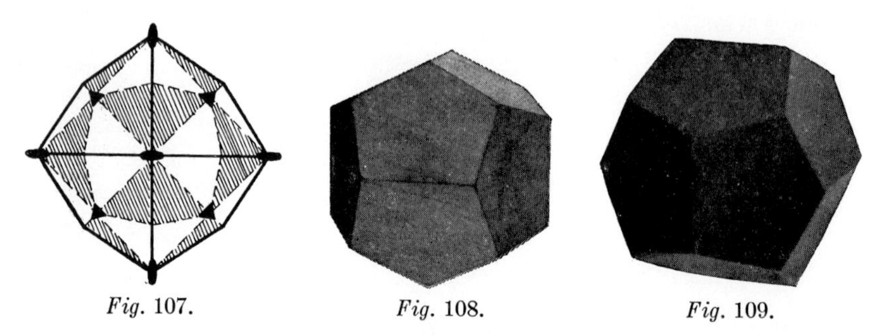

Fig. 107. *Fig.* 108. *Fig.* 109.

Pyritohedrons. The symbols of these forms are analogous to those of the tetrahexahedron (page 27), namely, $\pm(a : ma : \infty a)$, or $\{hk0\}$ and $\{kh0\}$, two axes being cut at unequal distances. There are two congruent forms possible, Fig. 109, *positive*, and Fig. 108, *negative*.

Each form is bounded by 12 similar faces. The faces are unequilateral pentagons, four sides of which are equal. The crystallographic axes possess twofold symmetry and bisect the six long edges. The threefold axes pass through the trihedral angles, the edges of which are of equal lengths. The three planes of symmetry pass through the long edges. These forms are termed *pyritohedrons* because they are very frequently observed upon the very common mineral pyrite (FeS_2). They are also designated as *pentagonal dodecahedrons.*[1]

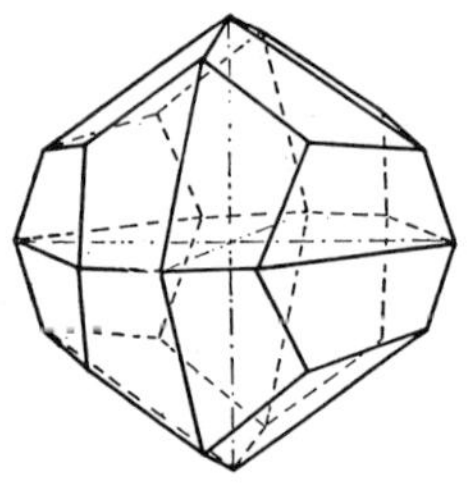

Fig. 110.

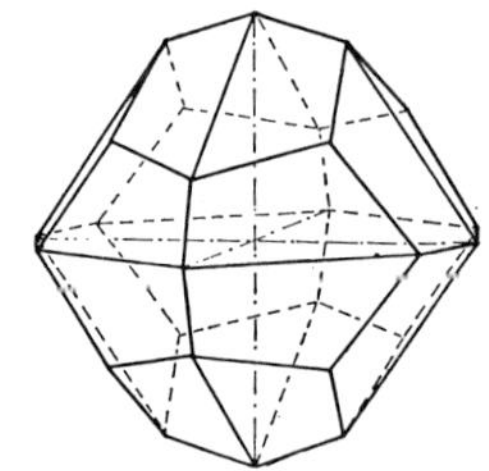

Fig. 111.

Dyakisdodecahedrons. These are congruent forms bounded by 24 similar trapeziums. They possess symbols corresponding to the hexocta-

[1] The regular pentagonal dodecahedron of geometry, bounded by equilateral pentagons intersecting in equal edges and angles, is crystallographically an impossible form, the value of m being $\frac{1 + \sqrt{5}}{2}$, which is irrational.

hedron, namely, $\pm(a : na : ma)$ or $\{hkl\}$ and $\{hlk\}$, and they are sometimes termed *didodecahedrons* or *diploids*. Figure 111 shows a *positive* and Fig. 110 a *negative* form. The crystallographic axes pass through the six tetrahedral angles possessing two pairs of equal edges. The threefold axes join opposite trihedral angles. The three planes of symmetry pass through the continuous edges.

Other Forms. The hexahedron, octahedron, dodecahedron, trigonal trisoctahedron, and tetragonal trisoctahedron occur in this class, each with the same morphological development as in the hexoctahedral class. They, however, possess a lower grade of symmetry. If they occur independently, the lower grade of symmetry may be recognized by etch figures or peculiar physical characteristics of the faces (see page 33).

TABLE 3

Symmetry, $\frac{2}{m}\bar{3}$	Planes		Axes			Center
	Axial	Diagonal	■	▲	●	
	3	0	0	4	3	1

Forms	Symbols		Faces	Solid angles			
				Trihedral		Tetrahedral	
	Weiss	Miller		3 equal edges	2 + 1 edges	2 + 2 edges	2 + 1 + 1 edges
Pyritohedrons	$\pm a : ma : \infty a$	$\{hk0\}$ $\{kh0\}$	12	8	12	—	—
Dyakisdodecahedrons	$\pm a : na : ma$	$\{hkl\}$ $\{hlk\}$	24	8	—	6	12
Octahedron	$a : a : a$	$\{111\}$	Morphologically the same as in the hexoctahedral class				
Dodecahedron	$a : a : \infty a$	$\{110\}$					
Hexahedron	$a : \infty a : \infty a$	$\{100\}$					
Trigonal trisoctahedron	$a : a : ma$	$\{hhl\}$					
Tetragonal trisoctahedron	$a : ma : ma$	$\{hll\}$					

Summary. In Table 3 the important features of the various forms of this class are given, page 37.

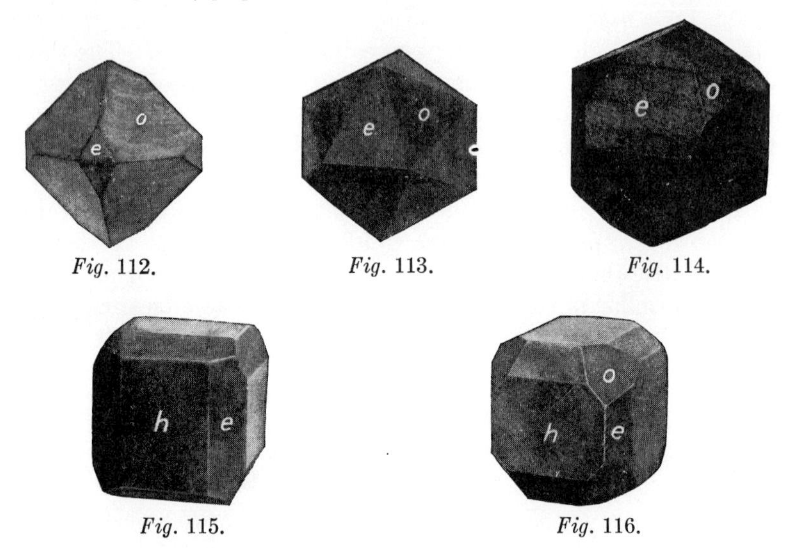

Fig. 112. *Fig.* 113. *Fig.* 114.

Fig. 115. *Fig.* 116.

Combinations. The accompanying figures show some combinations of the forms of this class.

Figures 112 to 116, $o = (a : a : a)$, $\{111\}$; $e = (a : 2a : \infty a)$, $\{210\}$; $h = (a : \infty a : \infty a)$, $\{100\}$. These combinations are frequently observed on pyrite (FeS_2).

4 | Hexagonal System

Crystallographic Axes. This system includes all crystals which can be referred to four axes, three of which are equal and lie in a horizontal plane, and intersect each other at angles of 60°. These are termed the *lateral* axes, being designated by the letter *a*. These axes are interchangeable. The fourth or *principal* axis is perpendicular to the plane of the lateral axes and is called the *c* axis. It may be longer or shorter than the lateral axes. The three equal axes, which bisect the angles between the lateral axes, are the *intermediate* axes. These may be designated by *b*. Figure 117 shows an axial cross of this system.

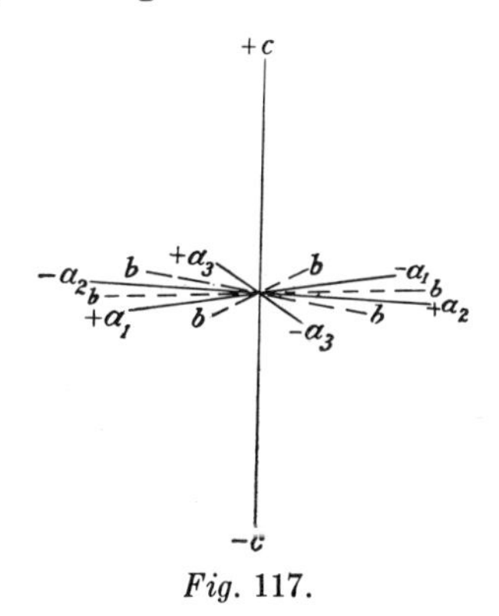

Fig. 117.

In reading crystals of the hexagonal system, it is customary to hold the *c* axis vertically, letting one of the lateral or *a* axes extend from right to left. The extremities of the lateral axes are alternately designated as plus and minus (see Fig. 117). In referring a form to the crystallographic axes, it is common practice to consider them in the following order: a_1 first, then a_2, thirdly a_3, and lastly the *c* axis. The symbols always refer to them in this order. It is also to be noted that in following this order at least one of the lateral axes will always be preceded by a minus sign.

Since the lengths of the *a* and *c* axes differ, it is necessary to assume for each substance crystallizing in this system a fundamental form, whose intercepts are taken as representing the unit lengths of the lateral and principal axes, respectively. The ratio which exists between the lengths of these axes is called the *axial* ratio and is always an irrational value, the *a* axis being assumed as unity (page 10).

Classes of Symmetry. The hexagonal system includes a larger number of classes of symmetry than any other system, namely, 12, as follows:

*1. Dihexagonal bipyramidal class.
2. Hexagonal trapezohedral class.
*3. Dihexagonal pyramidal class.
†4. Ditrigonal bipyramidal class.
*5. Hexagonal bipyramidal class.
6. Hexagonal pyramidal class.
†7. Trigonal bipyramidal class.
†*8. Ditrigonal scalenohedral class.
†*9. Trigonal trapezohedral class.
†*10. Ditrigonal pyramidal class.
†*11. Trigonal rhombohedral class.
†12. Trigonal pyramidal class.

Those classes marked with an * are the most important, for nearly all the crystals of this system belong to some one of them. Those marked † are often grouped together and form the *trigonal* system. Only classes 1, 5, 8, 9, and 10 will be discussed in detail. A fairly comprehensive idea of the hexagonal system, amply sufficient for beginning students, may be obtained from a consideration of classes 1 and 8.

DIHEXAGONAL BIPYRAMIDAL CLASS

Symmetry, $6/m\ 2/m\ 2/m$. This class possesses the highest grade of symmetry of any in the hexagonal system.

Planes. In all there are seven planes of symmetry. One of these, the *horizontal axial* or *principal* (h) plane, is the plane of the horizontal axes. The other planes are vertical and are divided into two series of three each, which are termed the *vertical axial* (a) and the *intermediate* (b), respectively. They intersect at angles of 60°. The intermediate planes bisect the angles between the vertical axial planes.

The four axial planes divide space into 12 equal parts, called *dodecants;* the seven planes, however, into 24 parts (Fig. 118).

These planes are often designated as follows:

1 horizontal axial + 3 vertical axial + 3 vertical intermediate = 7 planes.

Axes. The c axis is an axis of sixfold symmetry, while the lateral and intermediate axes possess twofold symmetry. These axes are often indicated thus:

1 ⬢ + 3 ⬬ + 3 ⬬ = 7 axes.

Center. This element of symmetry is also present, requiring every face to have a parallel counterface. Figure 119, the projection of the most complicated form upon a plane perpendicular to the vertical axis, shows the elements of symmetry of this class.

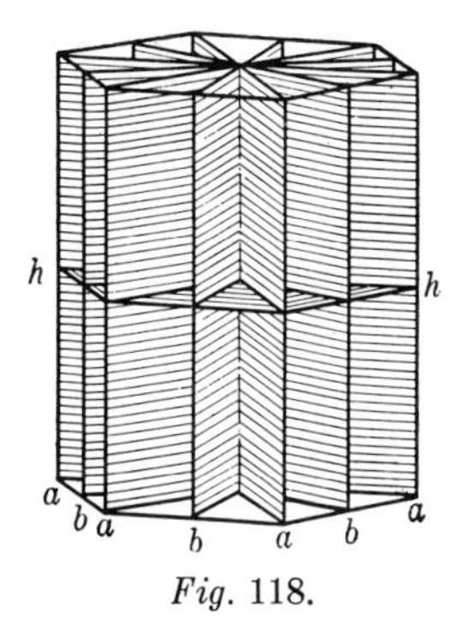

Fig. 118.

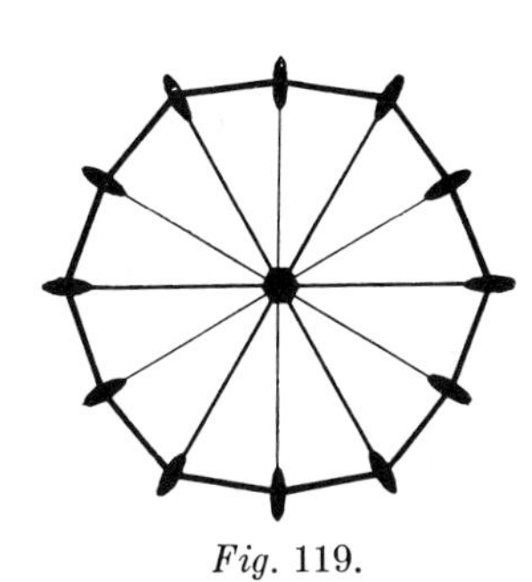

Fig. 119.

Hexagonal Bipyramid of the First Order. From Fig. 120, it is obvious that any plane which cuts any two adjacent lateral axes at the unit distance from the center must extend parallel to the third. If such a plane is assumed to cut the c axis at its unit length from the center, the parametral ratio would then be

$$a_1 : \infty a_2 : a_3 : c.$$

According to the above elements of symmetry, 12 planes possessing this ratio are possible. They enclose space and give rise to the form

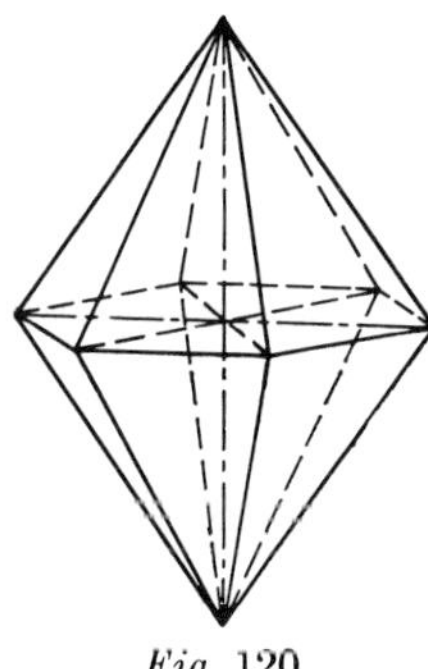

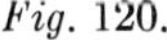

Fig. 120.

Fig. 121.

termed the *hexagonal bipyramid*[1] *of the first order* (Figs. 120 and 121). In the ideal form, the faces are all equal isosceles triangles. The symbols are $(a : \infty a : a : c)$, $\{10\bar{1}1\}$.[2] Because the intercepts along the c and two lateral axes are taken as units, such a form is known as a *fundamental* or *unit* bipyramid.

Planes are possible, however, which cut the two lateral axes at the

[1] Since these are really double pyramids, the term *bipyramid* is employed. Sometimes *dipyramid* is used.

[2] In this system it is advantageous to employ the indices as modified by Bravais $(hk\bar{i}l)$ rather than those of Miller, who uses but three.

unit distances but intercept the c axis at the distance mc, the coefficient m being some rational value smaller or greater than one (page 12). Such bipyramids, according as m is greater or less than unity are more acute or obtuse than the fundamental form. They are termed *modified* hexagonal bipyramids of the first order. Their symbols are

$$(a : \infty a : a : mc) \text{ or } \{h0\bar{h}l\}, \text{ where } m = \frac{h}{l}, \text{ also } 0 < m < \infty.$$

The principal axis passes through the hexahedral angles, the lateral axes join tetrahedral angles, while the intermediate axes bisect the horizontal edges. Hence, when such bipyramids are held correctly, a face is directed toward the observer. The various elements of symmetry are located by means of the axes.

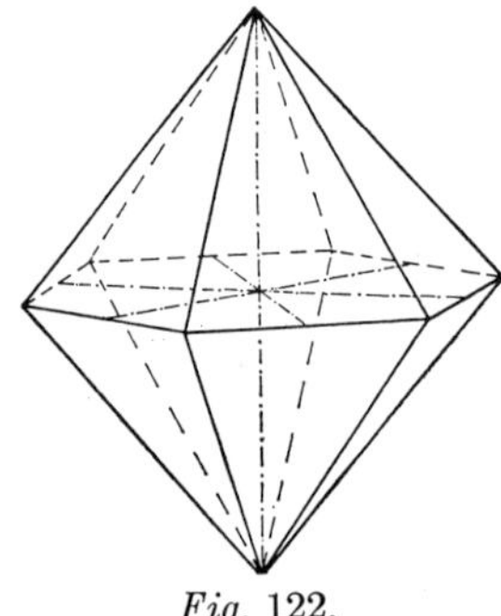
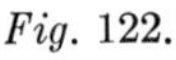
Fig. 122.

Fig. 123.

Hexagonal Bipyramid of the Second Order. In form this bipyramid is similar to the preceding. It is, however, to be distinguished by its position with respect to the lateral axes. The bipyramid of the second order is so held that an edge, and not a face, is directed toward the observer. This means that the lateral axes are perpendicular to and bisect the horizontal edges as shown in Figs. 122 and 123. Figure 124 shows the cross section including the lateral and intermediate axes. From these figures it is obvious that each face cuts one of the lateral axes at a unit distance, the other two at greater but equal distances. For example, AB cuts a_3 at the unit distance OS, and a_1 and a_2 at greater but equal distances, OM and ON, respectively.

The following considerations will determine the length of OM and ON, the intercepts on a_1 and a_2, in terms of $OS = 1$.

As already indicated, the lateral axes are perpendicular to the horizontal edges; hence OS and ON are perpendicular to AB and BC, respectively. Therefore, in the right triangles ORB and NRB, the side RB is common and the angles OBR and NBR are equal.[1]

[1] Since angle ABC equals 120°, angle NBR is 60°, being the supplement of ABC. But the intermediate axis OZ bisects the angle ABC; hence angle OBR is also 60°.

Therefore, $OR = RN$. But $OR = OS = 1$.

Hence, $ON = OR + RN = 2$.

In the same manner it can be shown that the intercept on a_1 is equal to that along a_2, that is, twice the unit length. The parametral ratio of the hexagonal bipyramid of the second order, therefore, is $(2a : 2a : a : mc)$ or $\{hh\overline{2h}l\}$, where $\frac{2h}{l} = m$. Figure 124 shows the positions of the bipyra-

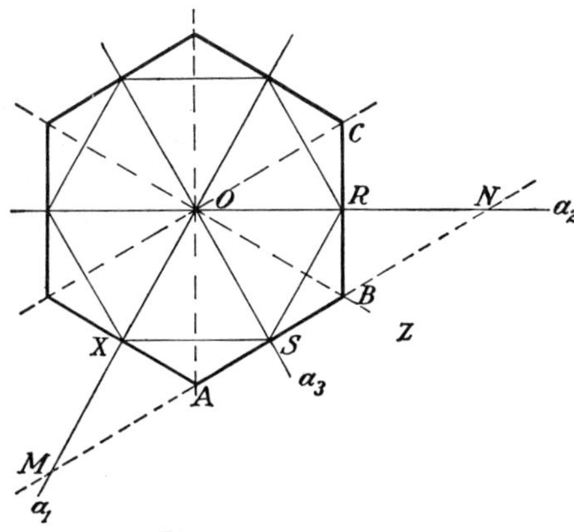

Fig. 124.

mids of both orders with respect to the lateral axes, the inner hexagonal outline representing that of the first, the outer outline the one of the second order.

Dihexagonal Bipyramid. The faces of this form cut the three lateral axes at unequal distances. For example, in Fig. 125 the face represented

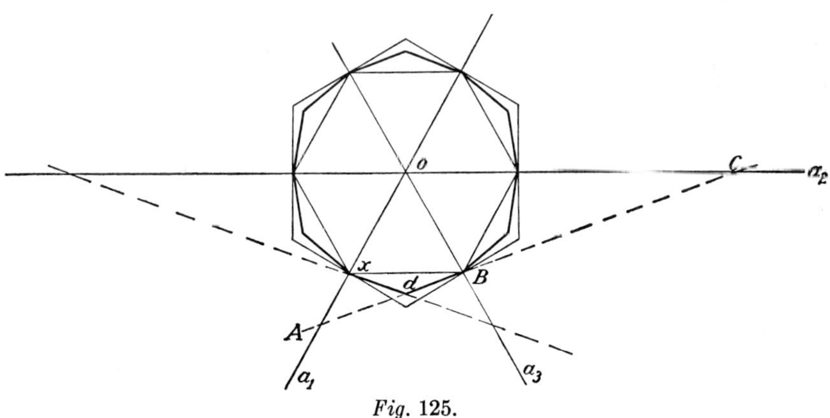

Fig. 125.

by dB cuts the a_1 axis at A, a_2 at C, and a_3 at B. Assuming the shortest of these intercepts as unity, $OB = a = 1$, we at once see that one of these axes is cut at a unit's distance from O, the other two, however, at greater distances. If we let the intercepts OA and OC be represented by $n(OB) = na$ and $p(OB) = pa$, respectively, the ratio will read

$$(na : pa : a : mc),\ \{hk\bar{i}l\}.$$

In this ratio $p = \frac{n}{n-1}$. Twenty-four planes having this ratio are possible and give rise to the form called the *dihexagonal bipyramid* (Figs.

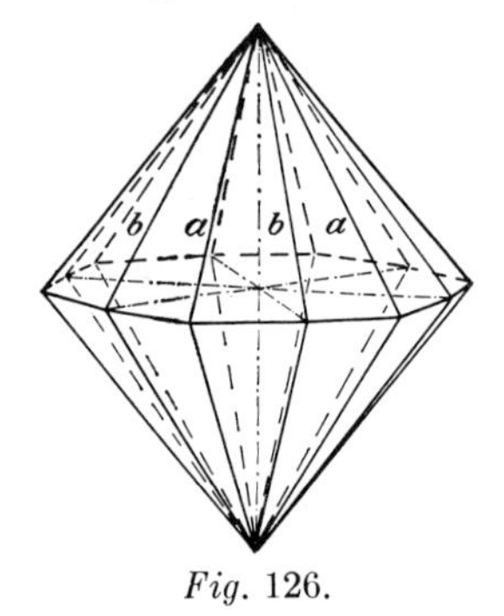

Fig. 126.

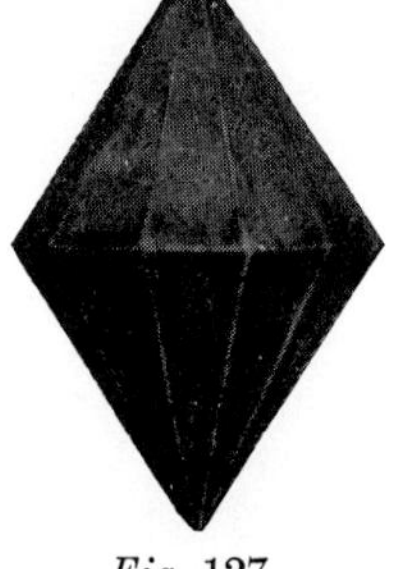

Fig. 127.

126 and 127). In the ideal form the faces are equal scalene triangles cutting in 24 polar edges,[1] a and b, and in 12 equal basal[2] edges. The polar edges and angles are alternately equal. This is shown by Fig. 128, where the heavy inner outline represents the form of the first order, the outer the one of the second, and the intermediate outlines the dihexagonal type, with respect to the lateral axes.

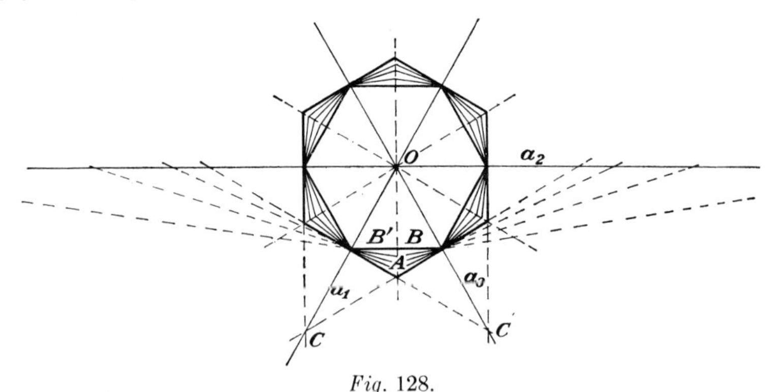

Fig. 128.

These three hexagonal bipyramids are closely related, for, if we suppose the plane represented by AB (Fig. 128) to be rotated about the point B so that the intercept along a_2 increases in length, the one along a_1 decreases until it equals $OB' = OB = 1$. Then the plane is parallel to a_2, and the

[1] Those joining the horizontal and principal axes.

[2] These lie in the horizontal plane of symmetry.

ratio for the bipyramid of the first order results. If, however, AB is rotated so that the intercept along a_2 is decreased in length, the one along a_1 increases until it equals $OC = 2OB' = 2a$. When this is the case, the intercept on a_2 is also equal to $2a$, for then the plane is perpendicular to a_3. This gives rise to the ratio of the bipyramid of the second order.

That the bipyramids of the first and second orders are the limiting forms of the dihexagonal bipyramid is also shown by the fact that $p = \frac{n}{n-1}$. For, if $n = 1$, it follows that $p = \infty$, which gives the ratio of the form of the first order. But, when $n = 2$, $p = 2$ also, therefore the ratio for the second order results. With dihexagonal bipyramids the following holds good:

$$1 < n < 2 \text{ and } 2 < p < \infty.$$

The dihexagonal bipyramid whose polar edges and angles are all equal is crystallographically not a possible form, because the value of n would then be $\frac{1}{2}(1 + \sqrt{3}) = \sqrt{2} \sin 75° = 1.36603+$, which of course is irrational. It also follows that in those dihexagonal bipyramids, where the value of n is less than $1.36603+$, for instance, $\frac{6}{5} = 1.20$, the more acute pole angles indicate the location of the lateral axes, the more obtuse that of the intermediate, and vice versa, when n is greater than $1.36603+$, for example, $\frac{8}{5} = 1.60$. This is clearly shown by Fig. 128.

Hexagonal Prism of the First Order. This form is easily derived from the bipyramid of the same order by allowing the intercepts along the c axis to assume their maximum value, infinity. Then the 12 planes of the bipyramid are reduced to six, each plane cutting two lateral axes at the

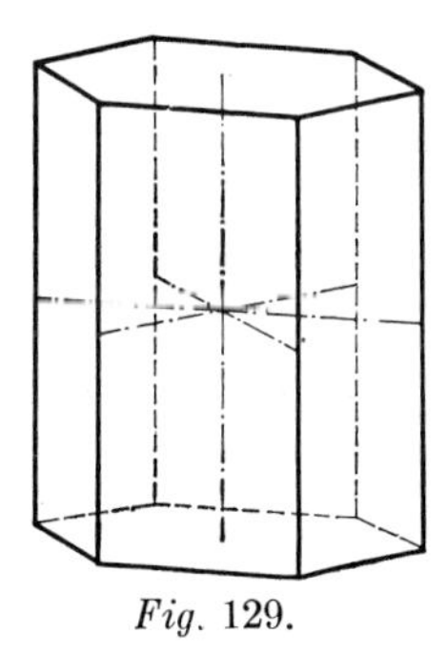

Fig. 129.

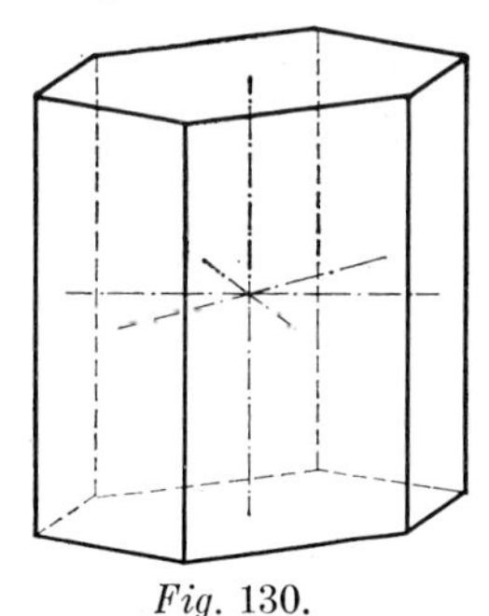

Fig. 130.

unit distance and extending parallel to the c axis. The symbols are $(a : \infty a : a : \infty c)$ or $\{10\bar{1}0\}$. This form cannot enclose space and, hence, may be termed an *open form* (page 12). It cannot occur independently and is always to be observed in combination (Fig. 129). The lateral axes join opposite edges, that is, a face is directed toward the observer when properly held.

Hexagonal Prism of the Second Order. This prism bears the same relation to the preceding form that the bipyramid of the second order does to the one of the first (page 42). The symbols are $(2a : 2a : a : \infty c)$ or $\{11\bar{2}0\}$. It is, hence, an open form consisting of six faces. The lateral axes join the centers of opposite faces; hence an edge is directed toward the observer (Fig. 130).

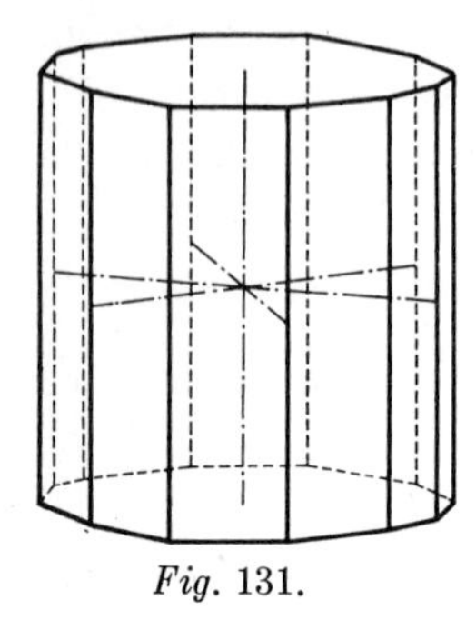

Fig. 131.

Dihexagonal Prism. This form may be obtained from the corresponding bipyramid by increasing the value of m to infinity, which gives $(na : pa : a : \infty c)$ or $\{hk\bar{i}0\}$. This prism consists of 12 faces whose alternate edges and angles are equal. This form (Fig. 131) is closely related to the corresponding bipyramid; hence, all that has been said concerning the dihexagonal bipyramid (page 43) with respect to the location of the lateral axes and its limiting forms might be repeated here, substituting, of course, for the bipyramids of the first and second orders the corresponding prisms.

Hexagonal Basal Pinacoid. The faces of this form, sometimes simply called the *base*, are parallel to the horizontal plane of symmetry and possess the following symbols $(\infty a : \infty a : \infty a : c)$, $\{0001\}$. It is evident from the presence of a center and a horizontal axial plane of symmetry that two such planes are possible. This, like the prisms, is an open form and must always occur in combination. Figure 129 shows this form in combination with the prism of the first order.

Summary. The seven forms of this class and their principal features may be summarized as shown in Table 4.

Relationship of Forms. The following diagram, similar to the one for the cubic system (page 29), expresses very clearly the relationship existing between the various forms:

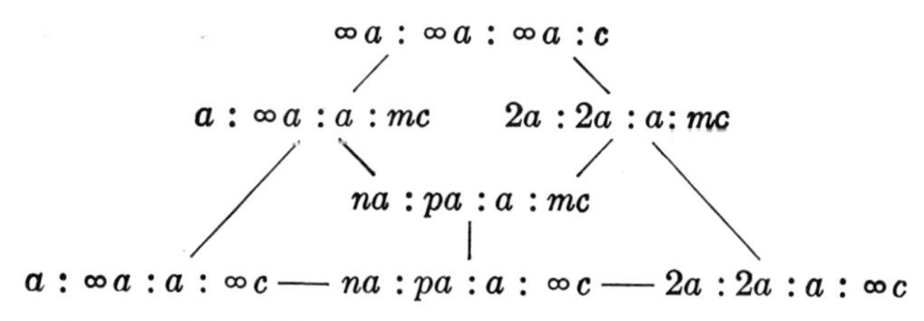

Combinations. The following figures illustrate some of the combinations of forms of this class:

Figure 132, $p = (a : \infty a : a : c)$, $\{10\bar{1}1\}$; $n = (2a : 2a : a : c)$, $\{11\bar{2}2\}$. Figure 133, $m = (a : \infty a : a : \infty c)$, $\{10\bar{1}0\}$; $p = (a : \infty a : a : c)$, $\{10\bar{1}1\}$. Figure 134, $m = (a : \infty a : a : \infty c)$, $\{10\bar{1}0\}$; $a = (2a : 2a : a : \infty c)$, $\{11\bar{2}0\}$; $p = (a : \infty a : a : c)$, $\{10\bar{1}1\}$; $s = (2a : 2a : a : 2c)$, $\{11\bar{2}1\}$;

$c = (\infty a : \infty a : \infty a : c)$, $\{0001\}$. This combination is observed on beryl ($Be_3Al_2Si_6O_{18}$).

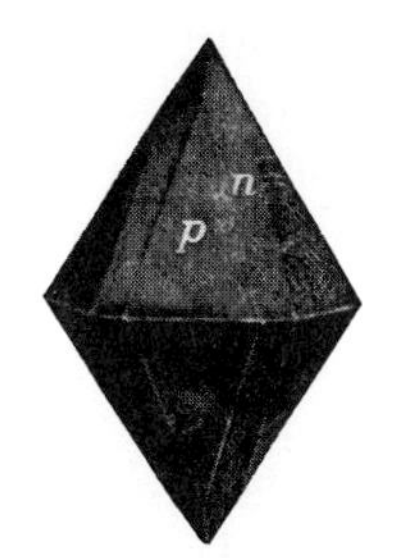

Fig. 132.

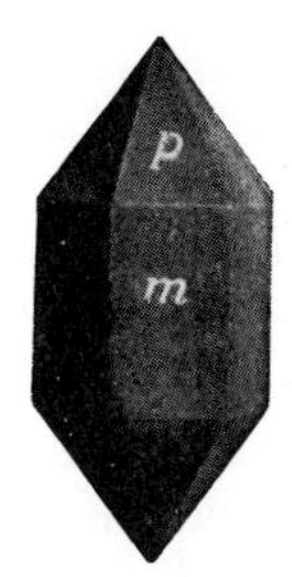

Fig. 133.

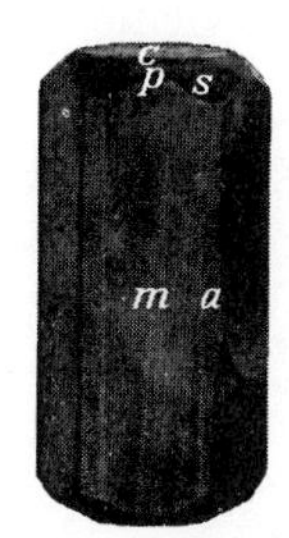

Fig. 134.

TABLE 4

Symmetry, $\frac{6}{m}\frac{2}{m}\frac{2}{m}$	Planes			Axes			Center
	Horizontal	Vertical		Vertical	Horizontal		
	Axial	Axial	Intermediate	⬢ Axial	⬬ Axial	⬬ Intermediate	
	1	3	3	1	3	3	1

Forms	Symbols		Number of faces	Solid angles		
	Weiss	Miller-Bravais		Tetrahedral	Hexahedral	Dodeca-hedral
Unit bipyramid, first order	$a : \infty a : a : c$	$\{10\bar{1}1\}$	12	6	2	—
Modified bipyramids, first order	$a : \infty a : a : mc$	$\{h0\bar{h}l\}$	12	6	2	—
Bipyramids, second order	$2a : 2a : a : mc$	$\{hh\overline{2h}l\}$	12	6	2	—
Dihexagonal bipyramids	$na : pa : a : mc$	$\{hk\bar{i}l\}$	24	6 + 6	—	2
Prism, first order	$a : \infty a : a : \infty c$	$\{10\bar{1}0\}$	6	—	—	—
Prism, second order	$2a : 2a : a : \infty c$	$\{11\bar{2}0\}$	6	—	—	—
Dihexagonal prisms	$na : pa : a : \infty c$	$\{hk\bar{i}0\}$	12	—	—	—
Basal pinacoid	$\infty a : \infty a : \infty a : c$	$\{0001\}$	2	—	—	—

HEXAGONAL BIPYRAMIDAL CLASS

Symmetry, $6/m$. Crystals of this class possess the horizontal axial or principal plane, the sixfold axis, and the center of symmetry. The sixfold axis is obviously the vertical or c axis. Figure 135 shows the relation of these elements of symmetry. The faces of the positive forms of this class are located in the unshaded sections, those of the negative forms in shaded ones. This class contains two forms which are new, namely, the hexagonal bipyramids and prisms of the third order.

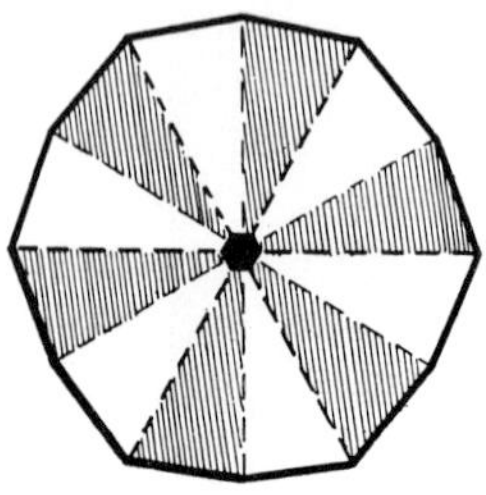

Fig. 135.

Hexagonal Bipyramids of the Third Order. These bipyramids are analogous to those of the first and second orders but differ from them with respect to their orientation. Their symbols correspond to those of the dihexagonal bipyramids (page 43), namely: $\pm(na : pa : a : mc)$ or $\{hk\bar{i}l\}$ and $\{kh\bar{i}l\}$ (Figs. 136 and 137). They are bounded by 12 equal isosceles triangles.

The axis of sixfold symmetry passes through the hexahedral angles. The positions of the lateral crystallographic axes are shown in Figs. 138 and 139. These axes do not pass through the tetrahedral angles or the centers of the basal edges, as is the case with the forms of the first and second orders, respectively, but through some point between them depending upon the value of n (compare Figs. 120 and 122).

Hexagonal Prisms of the Third Order. These forms bear the same relation to those of the first and second orders as do the hexagonal bipyramids of the third order to the bipyramids of the other two orders. These prisms consist of two forms of six planes each, designated as positive (Fig. 141) and negative (Fig. 140). Figures 138 and 139 show the relation of these forms to the other hexagonal prisms. Their symbols correspond to those of the dihexagonal prisms (page 46) and are $\pm(na : pa : a : \infty c)$ or $\{hk\bar{i}0\}$ and $\{kh\bar{i}0\}$.

The axis of sixfold symmetry is parallel to the vertical edges.

Other Forms. The other forms of this class are the hexagonal bipyramids and prisms of the first and second orders and the basal pinacoid. They correspond to the analogous forms of the dihexagonal bipyramidal class.

Combinations. Figures 142 and 143, $m = (a : \infty a : a : \infty c)$, $\{10\bar{1}0\}$; $a = (2a : 2a : a : \infty c)$, $\{11\bar{2}0\}$; $p = (a : \infty a : a : c)$, $\{10\bar{1}1\}$; $y = (a : \infty a : a : 2c)$, $\{20\bar{2}1\}$; $r = (a : \infty a : a : 1/2c)$, $\{10\bar{1}2\}$; $s = (2a : 2a : a : 2c)$, $\{11\bar{2}1\}$; $\mu = (3/2a : 3a : a : 3c)$, $\{21\bar{3}1\}$; $c = (\infty a : \infty a : \infty a : c)$, $\{0001\}$. These combinations have been observed on apatite ($Ca_5F(PO_4)_3$).

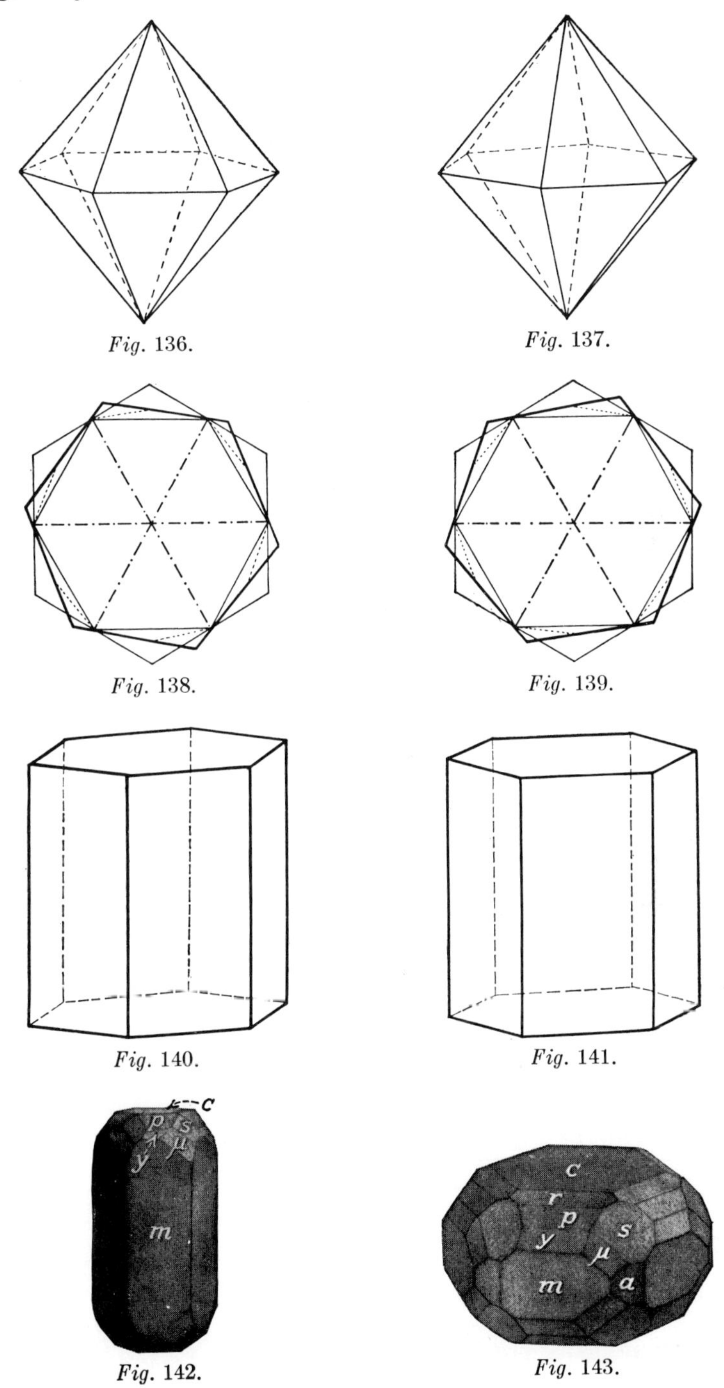

Fig. 136. *Fig.* 137.

Fig. 138. *Fig.* 139.

Fig. 140. *Fig.* 141.

Fig. 142. *Fig.* 143.

Summary. The principal features of this class are summarized in Table 5.

TABLE 5

Symmetry	Planes: Horizontal, Axial	Planes: Vertical, Axial	Planes: Vertical, Intermediate	Axes: Vertical, Axial	Axes: Horizontal, Axial	Axes: Horizontal, Intermediate	Center
$\frac{6}{m}$	1	0	0	1	0	0	1

Forms	Symbols: Weiss	Symbols: Miller-Bravais	Faces	Angles: Tetrahedral	Angles: Hexahedral
Hexagonal bipyramids, first order	$a : \infty a : a : mc$	$\{h0\bar{h}l\}$	Morphologically like in dihexagonal bipyramidal class		
Hexagonal bipyramids, second order	$2a : 2a : a : mc$	$\{hh\bar{2}hl\}$			
Hexagonal bipyramids, third order	$\pm na : pa : a : mc$	$\{hk\bar{i}l\}$ $\{kh\bar{i}l\}$	12	6	2
Hexagonal prism, first order	$a : \infty a : a : \infty c$	$\{10\bar{1}0\}$	Morphologically like in dihexagonal bipyramidal class		
Hexagonal prism, second order	$2a : 2a : a : \infty c$	$\{11\bar{2}0\}$			
Hexagonal prisms, third order	$\pm na : pa : a : \infty c$	$\{hk\bar{i}0\}$ $\{kh\bar{i}0\}$	6	—	—
Basal pinacoid	$\infty a : \infty a : \infty a : c$	$\{0001\}$	Morphologically like in dihexagonal bipyramidal class		

DITRIGONAL SCALENOHEDRAL CLASS[1]

Symmetry, $\bar{3}\ 2/m$. The symmetry consists of three intermediate planes, three axes of twofold and one of threefold symmetry, and the center of symmetry. The twofold axes are the lateral crystallographic axes. The principal crystallographic, or *c*, axis possesses threefold sym-

[1] Also termed the *hexagonal scalenohedral* class.

metry. Figure 144 shows the distribution of these elements of symmetry. This class contains two forms which are morphologically new, rhombohedrons and scalenohedrons. The faces of the positive forms of this class are located in the unshaded sections (Fig. 144), those of the negative forms in the shaded ones.

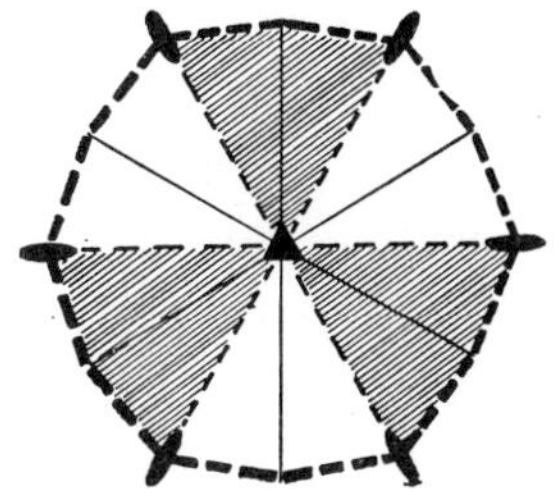

Fig. 144.

Rhombohedrons. These are bounded by six rhombic faces intersecting in eight trihedral angles. The c axis passes through the two equal trihedral angles which may be either larger or smaller than the other six, which among themselves are equal. This is illustrated by Figs. 145 to 147. The size of these angles depends upon the value of the ratio $a : c$.[1] Positive (Figs. 146 and 147)

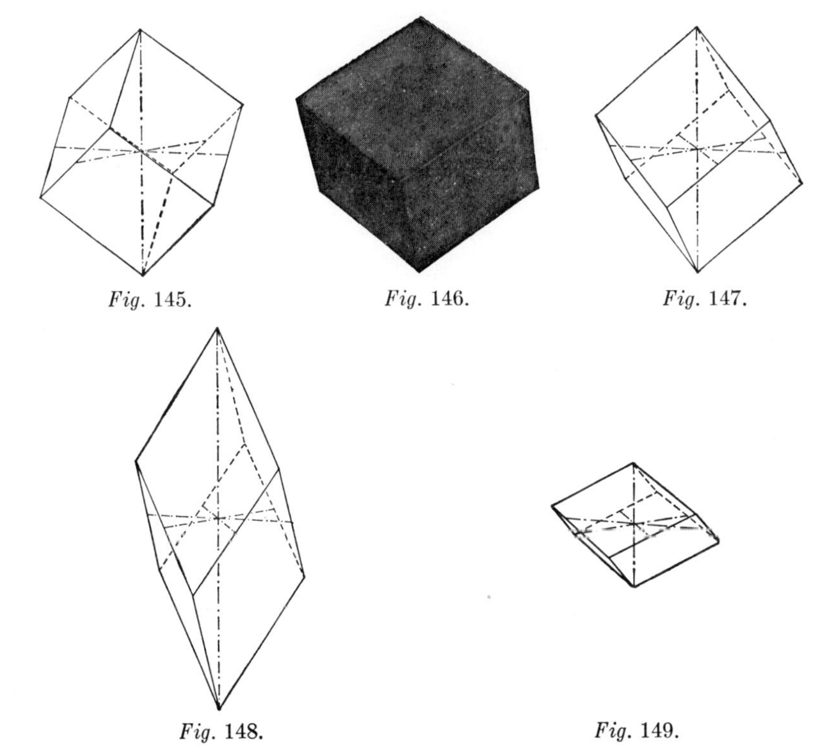

Fig. 145. *Fig.* 146. *Fig.* 147.

Fig. 148. *Fig.* 149.

[1] The cube, when held so that one of its axes of threefold symmetry (p. 26) is vertical, may be considered as a rhombohedron whose edges and angles are equal. The ratio $a : c$ in this case would be $1 : \sqrt{1.5} = 1 : 1.2247 +$. Those rhombohedrons, therefore, whose c axes have a greater value than 1.2247 + have pole angles less than 90°. When, however, the value is less than 1.2247 +, the pole angles are then greater than 90°. Such rhombohedrons may, hence, be spoken of as *acute* and *obtuse*, respectively (Figs. 148 and 149).

and negative (Fig. 145) rhombohedrons are possible. In the positive form, the upper dodecant to the front possesses a face, the negative dodecant an edge. The symbols are $\pm(a : \infty a : a : mc)$, or $\{h0\bar{h}l\}$ and $\{0h\bar{h}l\}$. These ratios correspond to those of the hexagonal bipyramids of the first order (page 41).

The principal crystallographic axis passes through the two equal trihedral angles. The lateral axes bisect opposite lateral edges which form a zigzag line about the form. These axes possess threefold and twofold symmetry, respectively. The intermediate planes of symmetry bisect the various faces vertically.

Scalenohedrons. These forms are bounded by 12 similar scalene triangles intersecting in six obtuse and six more acute polar edges and in six zigzag lateral edges. The forms are congruent and hence may be positive (Figs. 151 and 152) or negative (Fig. 150) in character. As is

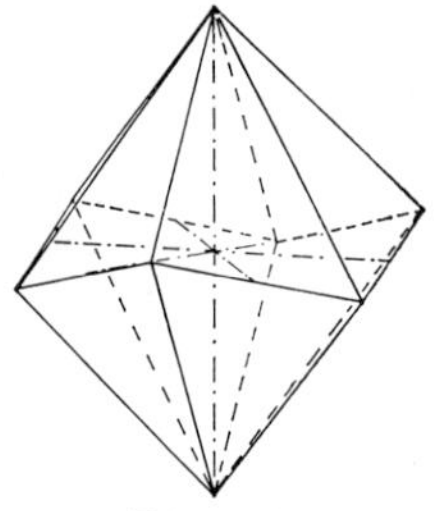

Fig. 150.

Fig. 151.

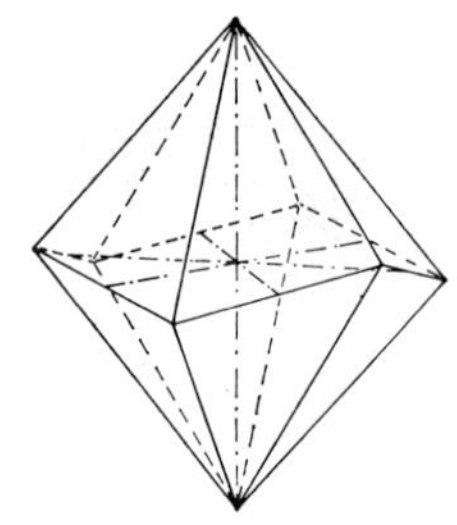

Fig. 152.

the case with the rhombohedrons, obtuse and acute scalenohedrons are also possible, depending upon the value of $a : c$.

The symbols are $\pm(na : pa : a : mc)$, or $\{hk\bar{i}l\}$ and $\{kh\bar{i}l\}$. These symbols correspond to those of the dihexagonal bipyramids (page 43).

The axis of threefold symmetry passes through the two hexahedral angles, while those of twofold symmetry bisect opposite zigzag lateral edges. The intermediate planes of symmetry pass through the polar edges.

Other Forms. The other forms of this class are the hexagonal bipyramids of the second order, the hexagonal prisms of the first and second orders, the dihexagonal prism, and the basal pinacoid, all of which are exactly similar to those of the dihexagonal bipyramidal class.

Combinations. Many important minerals crystallize in this class, for example, calcite, hematite, corundum, and chabazite.

Figures 153 to 156, $m = (a : \infty a : a : \infty c)$, $\{10\bar{1}0\}$; $e = -(a : \infty a : a : \frac{1}{2}c)$, $\{01\bar{1}2\}$; $v = (\frac{3}{2}a : 3a : a : 3c)$, $\{21\bar{3}1\}$; $r = (a : \infty a : a : c)$, $\{10\bar{1}1\}$; $f = -(a : \infty a : a : 2c)$, $\{02\bar{2}1\}$. These combinations are frequently observed on calcite ($CaCO_3$).

TABLE 6

Symmetry, $\bar{3}\,\frac{2}{m}$	Planes			Axes			Center
	Horizontal	Vertical		Vertical	Horizontal		
	Axial	Axial	Intermediate	▲ Axial	● Axial	● Intermediate	
	0	0	3	1	3	0	1

Forms	Symbols		Faces	Solid angles		
	Weiss	Miller-Bravais		Tri-hedral	Tetra-hedral	Hexa-hedral
Rhombohedrons	$\pm a:\infty a:a:mc$	$\{h0\bar{h}l\}$ $\{0h\bar{h}l\}$	6	2 + 6	—	—
Hexagonal bipyramids, second order	$2a:2a:a:mc$	$\{hh\overline{2h}l\}$	Morphologically the same as in the dihexagonal bipyramidal class			
Scalenohedrons	$\pm na:pa:a:mc$	$\{hk\bar{i}l\}$ $\{kh\bar{i}l\}$	12	—	6	2
Hexagonal prism, first order	$a:\infty a:a:\infty c$	$\{10\bar{1}0\}$	Morphologically the same as in the dihexagonal bipyramidal class			
Hexagonal prism, second order	$2a:2a:a:\infty c$	$\{11\bar{2}0\}$				
Dihexagonal prisms	$na:pa:a:\infty c$	$\{hk\bar{i}0\}$				
Basal pinacoid	$\infty a:\infty a:\infty a:c$	$\{0001\}$				

Fig. 153.

Fig. 154.

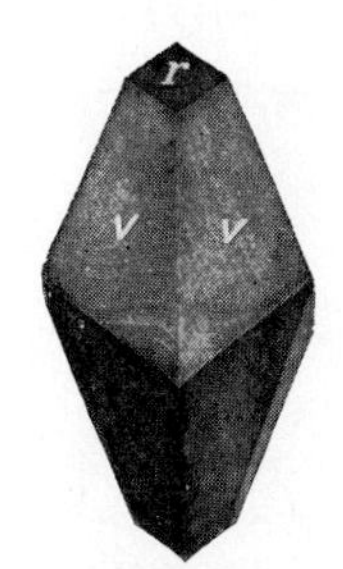

Fig. 155.

Figures 157 and 158, $r = (a : \infty a : a : c)$, $\{10\bar{1}1\}$; $n = (2a : 2a : a : \frac{4}{3}c)$, $\{22\bar{4}3\}$; $u = (a : \infty a : a : \frac{1}{4}c)$, $\{10\bar{1}4\}$; $c = (\infty a : \infty a : \infty a : c)$, $\{0001\}$. Hematite (Fe_2O_3).

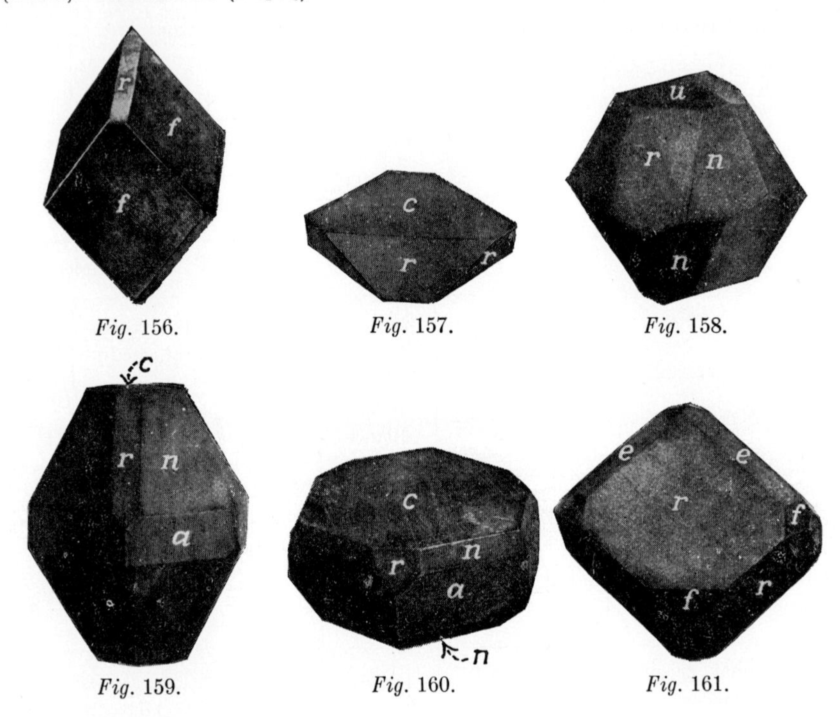

Fig. 156. *Fig.* 157. *Fig.* 158.

Fig. 159. *Fig.* 160. *Fig.* 161.

Figures 159 and 160, $a = (2a : 2a : a : \infty c)$, $\{11\bar{2}0\}$; $n = (2a : 2a : a : \frac{4}{3}c)$, $\{22\bar{4}3\}$; $r = (a : \infty a : a : c)$, $\{10\bar{1}1\}$; $c = (\infty a : \infty a : \infty a : c)$, $\{0001\}$. Corundum (Al_2O_3).

Figure 161, $r = (a : \infty a : a : c)$, $\{10\bar{1}1\}$; $e = -(a : \infty a : a : \frac{1}{2}c)$, $\{01\bar{1}2\}$; $f = -(a : \infty a : a : 2c)$, $\{02\bar{2}1\}$. Chabazite ($CaAl_2Si_4O_{12}.6H_2O$).

TRIGONAL TRAPEZOHEDRAL CLASS

Symmetry, 3 2. The c axis possesses threefold symmetry, while the lateral or a axes have twofold symmetry with a polar development. The symmetry relations are given in Fig. 162.

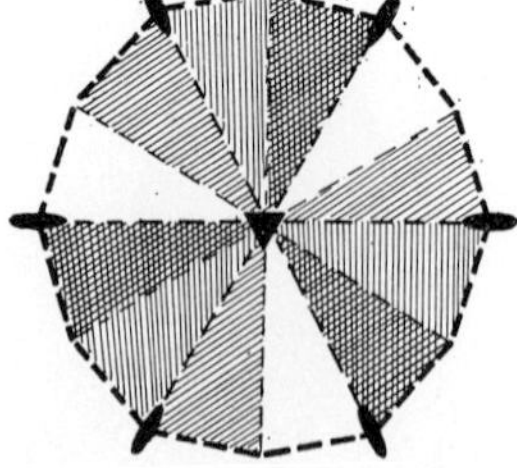

Fig. 162.

The trigonal trapezohedrons are the characterizing forms of this class.

Rhombohedrons of the First Order. These are identical morphologically with those of the ditrigonal scalenohedral class.

Their symbols are

$$\pm(a : \infty a : a : mc), \text{ or } \{h0\bar{h}l\} \text{ and } \{0h\bar{h}l\}.$$

Trigonal Bipyramids of the Second Order. These forms are bounded by six equal isosceles triangles and possess the following symbols:

$$\pm(2a : 2a : a : mc), \text{ or } \{hh\overline{2h}l\} \text{ and } \{2h\bar{h}\bar{h}l\}.$$

The crystallographic a axes pass from a tetrahedral angle to the center of the opposite horizontal edge.

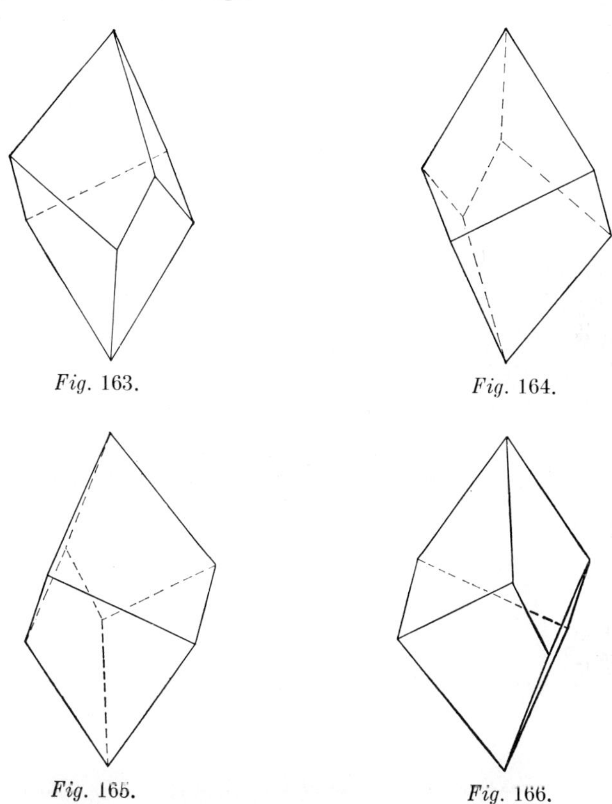

Fig. 163. *Fig.* 164. *Fig.* 165. *Fig.* 166.

Trigonal Trapezohedrons. There are four forms of this type possible. Each is bounded by six faces, which when the development is ideal are equal trapeziums. The symbols are analogous to those of the dihexagonal bipyramids, namely,

1. Positive right, $+r(na : pa : a : mc)$, $\{hk\bar{i}l\}$ (Fig. 164).
2. Positive left, $+l(na : pa : a : mc)$, $\{i\bar{k}\bar{h}l\}$ (Fig. 163).
3. Negative right, $-r(na : pa : a : mc)$, $\{i\bar{h}\bar{k}l\}$ (Fig. 166).
4. Negative left, $-l(na : pa : a : mc)$, $\{kh\bar{i}l\}$ (Fig. 165).

Forms 1 and 2, 3 and 4 are among themselves enantiomorphous, while 1 and 3, 2 and 4 are congruent.

The polar axes of twofold symmetry bisect opposite zigzag edges.

Trigonal Prisms of the Second Order. These possess three vertical planes and have the following symbols:

$$\pm(2a : 2a : a : \infty c), \text{ or } \{hh\overline{2h}0\} \text{ and } \{2h\bar{h}\bar{h}0\}.$$

The axes of twofold symmetry pass through a vertical edge and bisect the opposite face.

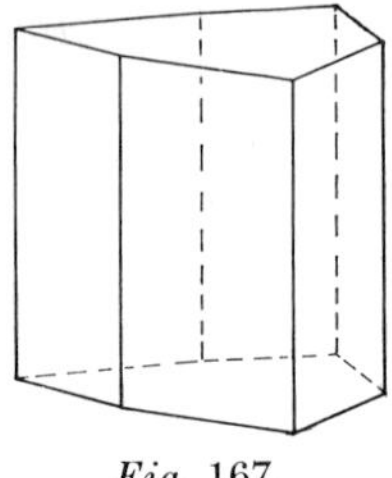

Fig. 167.

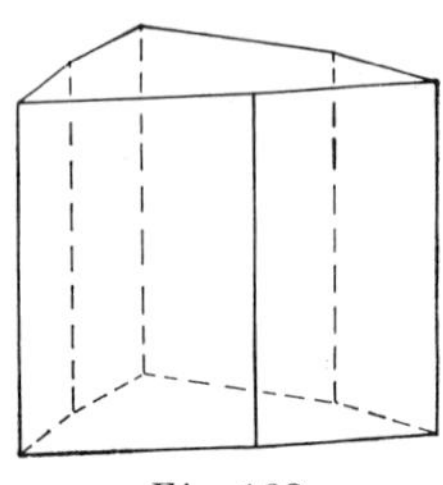

Fig. 168.

Ditrigonal Prisms. Two forms of this type are possible and are designated as positive (Fig. 168) and negative (Fig. 167) ditrigonal prisms. The vertical edges are alternately alike.

The symbols are

$$\pm(na : pa : a : \infty c), \text{ or } \{hk\bar{i}0\} \text{ and } \{i\bar{k}\bar{h}0\}.$$

Other Forms. The hexagonal prism of the first order and the basal pinacoid are analogous to those described on pages 45 and 46.

Summary. The important features of this class are given in Table 7.

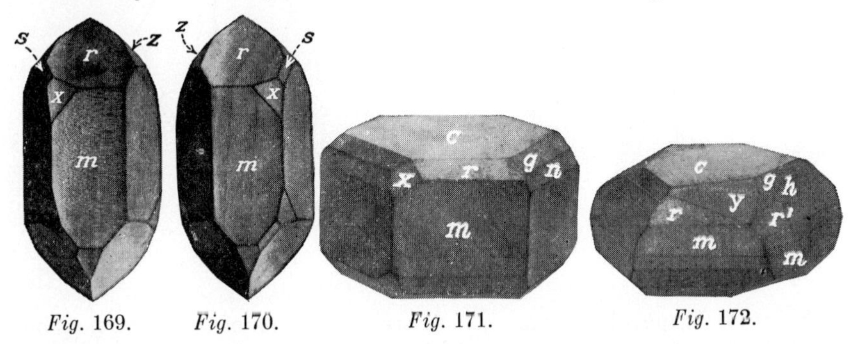

Fig. 169. *Fig.* 170. *Fig.* 171. *Fig.* 172.

Combinations. Quartz (SiO_2) (the *alpha* or *low-temperature* modification, see page 294) and cinnabar (HgS) furnish excellent examples of minerals crystallizing in this class.

Figures 169 and 170, $m = (a : \infty a : a : \infty c)$, $\{10\bar{1}0\}$; $r = +(a : \infty a : a : c)$, $\{10\bar{1}1\}$; $z = -(a : \infty a : a : c)$, $\{01\bar{1}1\}$; s(Fig. 170) $= +(2a : 2a : a : 2c)$, $\{11\bar{2}1\}$; s(Fig. 169) $= -(2a : 2a : a : 2c)$, $\{2\bar{1}\bar{1}1\}$; x(Fig. 170) $= +r(\frac{6}{5}a : 6a : a : 6c)$, $\{51\bar{6}1\}$; x(Fig. 169) $= +l(\frac{6}{5}a : 6a : a : 6c)$, $\{6\bar{1}\bar{5}1\}$. Quartz.

Figures 171 and 172, $c = (\infty a : \infty a : \infty a : c)$, $\{0001\}$; $m = (a : \infty a : a : \infty c)$, $\{10\bar{1}0\}$; $g = -(a : \infty a : a : \frac{1}{2}c)$, $\{01\bar{1}2\}$; $n = -(a : \infty a :$

TABLE 7

Symmetry, 3 2	Planes			Axes			Center
	Horizontal	Vertical		Vertical	Horizontal		
	Axial	Axial	Intermediate	▲ Axial	● Axial	● Intermediate	
	0	0	0	1	3 (Polar)	0	0

Forms	Symbols		Faces	Solid angles	
	Weiss	Miller-Bravais		Tri-hedral	Tetra-hedral
Rhombohedrons, first order	$\pm a:\infty a:a:mc$	$\{h0\bar{h}l\}$ $\{0h\bar{h}l\}$	6	Morphologically like those in the ditrigonal scalenohedral class	
Trigonal bipyramids, second order	$\pm 2a:2a:a:mc$	$\{hh\overline{2h}l\}$ $\{2h\bar{h}\bar{h}l\}$	6	2	3
Trigonal trapezohedrons	$\pm r$, $\pm l$, $na:pa:a:mc$	$\{hk\bar{i}l\}$ $\{i\bar{k}\bar{h}l\}$ $\{i\bar{h}\bar{k}l\}$ $\{kh\bar{i}l\}$	6	2 + 6	
Hexagonal prism, first order	$a:\infty a:a:\infty c$	$\{10\bar{1}0\}$	6	Morphologically like those in the dihexagonal bipyramidal class	
Trigonal prisms, second order	$\pm 2a:2a:a:\infty c$	$\{11\bar{2}0\}$ $\{2\bar{1}\bar{1}0\}$	3		
Ditrigonal prisms	$\pm na:pa:a:\infty c$	$\{hk\bar{i}0\}$ $\{i\bar{k}\bar{h}0\}$	6		
Basal pinacoid	$\infty a:\infty a:\infty a:c$	$\{0001\}$	2	Morphologically like those in the dihexagonal bipyramidal class	

$a : 2c)$, $\{02\bar{2}1\}$; $h = -(a : \infty a : a : \frac{2}{3}c)$, $\{02\bar{2}3\}$; $r = +(a : \infty a : a : c)$, $\{10\bar{1}1\}$; $r' = -(a : \infty a : a : c)$, $\{01\bar{1}1\}$; $y = +r(\frac{3}{2}a : 3a : a : \frac{3}{7}c)$, $\{21\bar{3}7\}$; $x = +l(\frac{8}{5}a : \frac{8}{3}a : a : \frac{8}{5}c)$, $\{53\bar{8}5\}$. Cinnabar.

DITRIGONAL PYRAMIDAL CLASS

Symmetry, 3 *m*. There are three intermediate planes and one axis of threefold symmetry in this class. The axis of symmetry is the *c* axis and has a polar development. The forms of this class, therefore, show a *hemimorphic* development, that is, the upper and lower ends of the *c* axis do not have the same type of faces. The symmetry relations are shown in Fig. 173. The faces of the positive forms of this class are located in the unshaded sections, those of the negative forms in shaded ones. The following forms are morphologically different from those previously described, namely, the trigonal pyramids and prisms of the first order, and the ditrigonal pyramids and prisms.

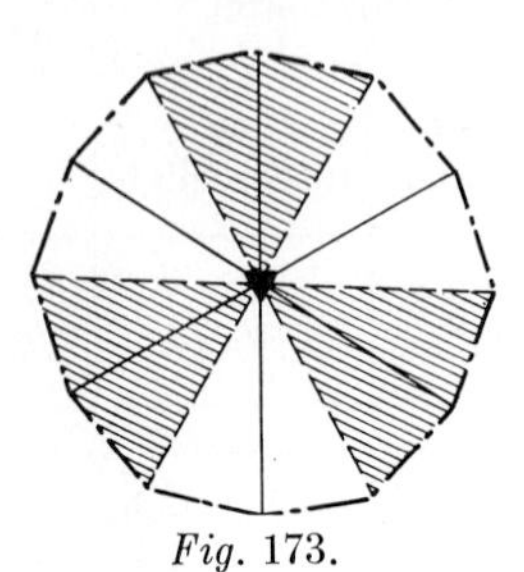

Fig. 173.

Since the *c* axis has a polar development, all forms cutting it will occur as upper and lower forms. Thus, instead of having bipyramids, as discussed thus far, we now have upper and lower pyramids.

Trigonal Pyramids of the First Order. These are bounded by three equal isosceles triangles. They are open forms and may occur in four distinct positions designated as

Positive upper, $+u(a : \infty a : a : mc)$, $\{h0\bar{h}l\}$ (Fig. 176).
Positive lower, $+ l(a : \infty a : a : mc)$, $\{h0\bar{h}\bar{l}\}$ (Fig. 177).
Negative upper, $-u(a : \infty a : a : mc)$, $\{0h\bar{h}l\}$ (Fig. 174).
Negative lower, $- l(a : \infty a : a : mc)$, $\{0h\bar{h}\bar{l}\}$ (Fig. 175).

These symbols correspond to those of the hexagonal bipyramids of the first order (page 41). The axis of threefold symmetry passes through the trihedral angle with equal edges, and the intermediate planes of symmetry bisect the faces.

Trigonal Prisms of the First Order. These prisms possess three faces and occur in positive (Fig. 181) and negative (Fig. 180) forms.

The symbols are

$$\pm(a : \infty a : a : \infty c), \text{ or } \{10\bar{1}0\} \text{ and } \{01\bar{1}0\}.$$

The threefold axis is parallel to the intersection lines of the prism faces, and the intermediate planes of symmetry pass through the vertical edges and bisect the opposite faces. Figures 178 and 179 show the positions of the various trigonal pyramids and prisms with respect to the crystallographic *a* axes.

Ditrigonal Pyramids. These pyramids are also open forms and are bounded by six scalene triangles. Four distinct positions are possible.

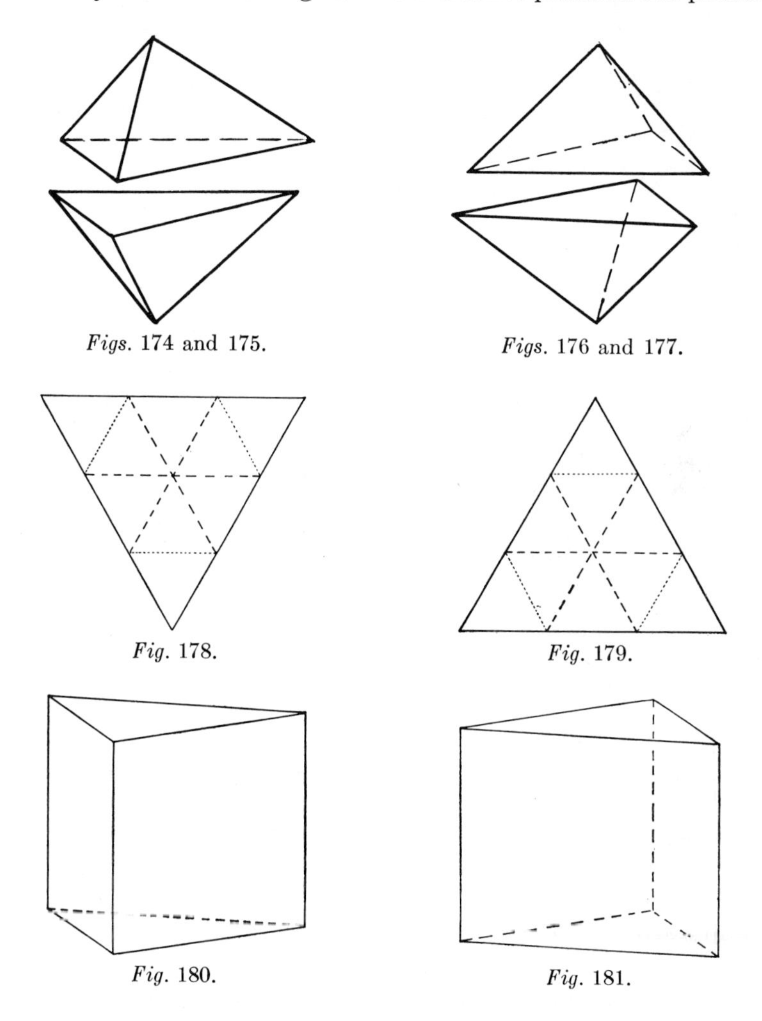

Figs. 174 and 175. *Figs.* 176 and 177.

Fig. 178. *Fig.* 179.

Fig. 180. *Fig.* 181.

Their symbols are

Positive upper, $+u(na : pa : a : mc)$, $\{hk\bar{i}l\}$ (Fig. 184).
Positive lower, $+ l(na : pa : a : mc)$, $\{hk\bar{i}\bar{l}\}$ (Fig. 185).
Negative upper, $-u(na : pa : a : mc)$, $\{kh\bar{i}l\}$ (Fig. 182).
Negative lower, $- l(na : pa : a : mc)$, $\{kh\bar{i}\bar{l}\}$ (Fig. 183).

The threefold axis passes through the hexahedral angles, and the intermediate planes of symmetry include an obtuse and an acute edge.

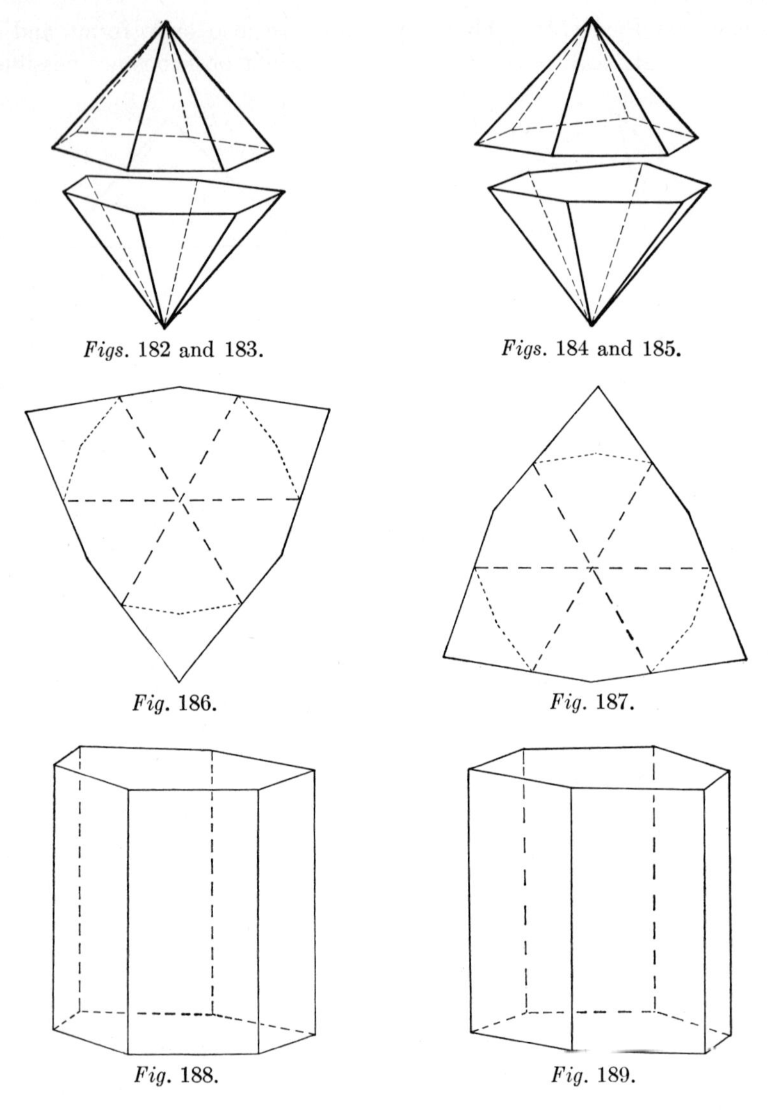

Figs. 182 and 183. *Figs.* 184 and 185.

Fig. 186. *Fig.* 187.

Fig. 188. *Fig.* 189.

Ditrigonal Prisms. These prisms are bounded by six faces intersecting in edges which are alternately alike. Positive (Fig. 189) and negative (Fig. 188) forms are possible.

The symbols are

$$\pm(na : pa : a : \infty c), \text{ or } \{hk\bar{i}0\} \text{ and } \{kh\bar{i}0\}.$$

The threefold axis is parallel to the intersection lines of the prism faces, and the intermediate planes of symmetry join opposite edges of unequal character. Figures 186 and 187 indicate the position of the ditrigonal pyramids and prisms with respect to the a axes.

Basal Pinacoids. On account of the fact that the c axis has a polar development, the basal pinacoids occur with but one face (Figs. 174 to 177). We may therefore speak of an upper and a lower basal pinacoid.

The symbols are

$$u, l\ (\infty a : \infty a : \infty a : c), \text{ or } \{0001\} \text{ and } \{000\bar{1}\}.$$

Hexagonal Pyramids of the Second Order. These forms are the upper and lower portions, respectively, of the hexagonal bipyramid of the second order described on page 42.

The symbols are

$$u, l\ (2a : 2a : a : mc), \text{ or } \{hh\overline{2h}l\} \text{ and } \{hh\overline{2h}\bar{l}\}.$$

Hexagonal Prisms of the Second Order. This form is identical morphologically with that described on page 46.

Summary. Table 8 on page 62 shows the principal features of the forms of this class.

Fig. 190.

Fig. 191.

Combinations. The mineral tourmaline furnishes excellent combinations of the above forms.

In Figs. 190 and 191, $m = +(a : \infty a : a : \infty c)$, $\{10\bar{1}0\}$; $a - (2a : 2a : a : \infty c)$, $\{11\bar{2}0\}$; $u = +u(\frac{5}{3}a : \frac{5}{2}a ; a : 5c)$, $\{32\bar{5}1\}$; $o = -u(a : \infty a : a : 2c)$, $\{02\bar{2}1\}$; $o' = +l(a : \infty a : a : 2c)$, $\{20\overline{21}\}$; $r = -l(a : \infty a : a : c)$, $\{01\overline{11}\}$; $c = l(\infty a : \infty a : \infty a : c)$, $\{000\bar{1}\}$.

TABLE 8

Symmetry, 3 *m*	Planes			Axes			Center
	Horizontal	Vertical		Vertical	Horizontal		
	Axial	Axial	Intermediate	▲ Axial	⬬ Axial	⬬ Intermediate	
	0	0	3	1 (Polar)	0	0	0

Forms	Symbols		Number of faces	Solid angles	
	Weiss	Miller-Bravais		Trihedral	Hexahedral
Trigonal pyramids, first order	$\pm u,\ \pm l,\ a:\infty a:a:mc$	$\{h0\bar{h}l\}$ $\{h0\bar{h}\bar{l}\}$ $\{0h\bar{h}l\}$ $\{0h\bar{h}\bar{l}\}$	3	1	—
Hexagonal pyramids, second order	$u,\ l,\ 2a:2a:a:mc$	$\{hh\overline{2h}l\}$ $\{hh\overline{2h}\bar{l}\}$	6	—	1
Ditrigonal pyramids	$\pm u,\ \pm l,\ na:pa:a:mc$	$\{hk\bar{i}l\}$ $\{hk\bar{i}\bar{l}\}$ $\{kh\bar{i}l\}$ $\{kh\bar{i}\bar{l}\}$	6	—	1
Trigonal prisms, first order	$\pm a:\infty a:a:\infty c$	$\{10\bar{1}0\}$ $\{01\bar{1}0\}$	3	—	—
Ditrigonal prisms	$\pm na:pa:a:\infty c$	$\{hk\bar{i}0\}$ $\{kh\bar{i}0\}$	6	—	—
Hexagonal prism, second order	$2a:2a:a:\infty c$	$\{11\bar{2}0\}$	Morphologically like those in dihexagonal bipyramidal class		
Basal pinacoids	$u,\ l,\ \infty a:\infty a:\infty a:c$	$\{0001\}$ $\{000\bar{1}\}$	1	—	—

5 | Tetragonal System

Crystallographic Axes. The tetragonal system includes all crystals which can be referred to three perpendicular axes, two of which are equal and lie in a horizontal plane. These are termed the *lateral* axes and are designated as the *a* axes. Perpendicular to the plane of the lateral axes is the *principal* or *c* axis, which may be longer or shorter than the *a* axes. The axes which bisect the angles between the *a* axes are the *intermediate* axes. They are designated as the *b* axes in Fig. 192.

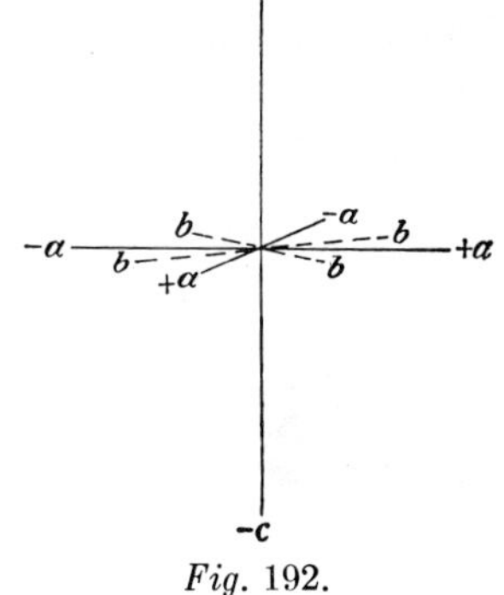

Fig. 192.

Crystals of this system are held so that the *c* axis is vertical, while one of the *a* axes is directed toward the observer.

For crystals of the tetragonal system the unit lengths of the *a* and *c* axes are unequal. The ratio between these unit lengths is the *axial* ratio, $a : c$ (compare pages 10 and 39).

Classes of Symmetry. This system embraces seven classes of symmetry, as follows:

1. Ditetragonal bipyramidal class.
2. Tetragonal trapezohedral class.
3. Ditetragonal pyramidal class.
4. Tetragonal scalenohedral class.
5. Tetragonal bipyramidal class.
6. Tetragonal pyramidal class.
7. Tetragonal bisphenoidal class.

Classes 1 and 4 will be discussed in detail.

[1] Also termed *quadratic* system.

DITETRAGONAL BIPYRAMIDAL CLASS

Symmetry, $4/m\ 2/m\ 2/m$. *Planes.* In this class there are five planes of symmetry. The plane of the lateral and intermediate axes is termed the *horizontal axial* or *principal* (h) plane. The vertical planes including the c axis and one of the a axes are called the *vertical axial* (a) planes, while those which include one of the b axes are termed the *intermediate* (b) planes (Fig. 193).

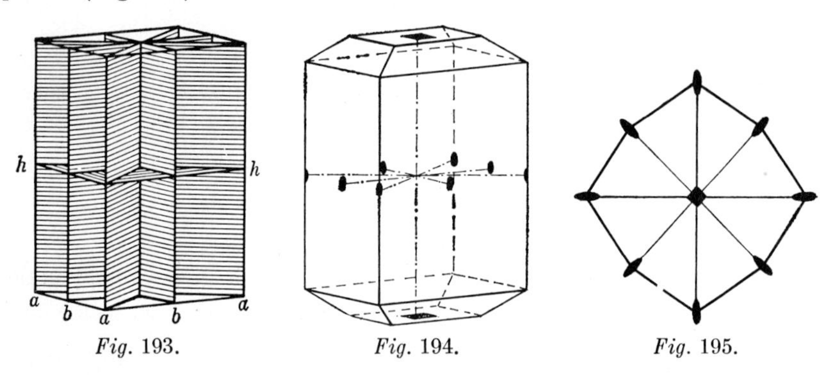

Fig. 193. *Fig.* 194. *Fig.* 195.

The three axial planes divide space into eight equal parts, termed *octants,* while the five planes (Fig. 193) divide it into 16 equal sections. The five planes may be designated as follows:

1 horizontal axial + 2 vertical axial + 2 intermediate = 5 planes.

Axes. The c axis is an axis of *fourfold* symmetry. The lateral and intermediate axes possess *twofold* symmetry (Fig. 194). These may be written: 1 ■ + 2 ● + 2 ● = 5 axes.

Center. A center of symmetry is also present in this class. These elements of symmetry are shown in Fig. 195, which represents the projection of the most complex form upon the principal plane of symmetry.

Tetragonal Bipyramid of the First Order. This form is analogous to the octahedron of the cubic system (page 25). But, since the c axis differs from the lateral axes, the ratio must be written ($a : a : c$), which would indicate the cutting of all three axes at unit distances[1] (Figs. 196 and 197). As the intercept along the c axis may be longer or shorter than the unit length, the general symbols would be ($a : a : mc$) or $\{hhl\}$, where m is some rational value between zero and infinity. Like the octahedron, this form, the *tetragonal bipyramid,*[2] is bounded by eight faces which enclose space. The faces are equal isosceles triangles when the development is ideal.

[1] Indicating a *unit* form (compare p. 13).

[2] The more the ratio $a : c$ approaches 1 : 1, the more does this form simulate the octahedron. This tendency of forms to simulate those of a higher grade of symmetry is spoken of as *pseudosymmetry.*

The principal crystallographic axis passes through the two tetrahedral angles of the same size, the lateral axes through the other four equal tetrahedral angles, while the intermediate axes bisect the horizontal edges.

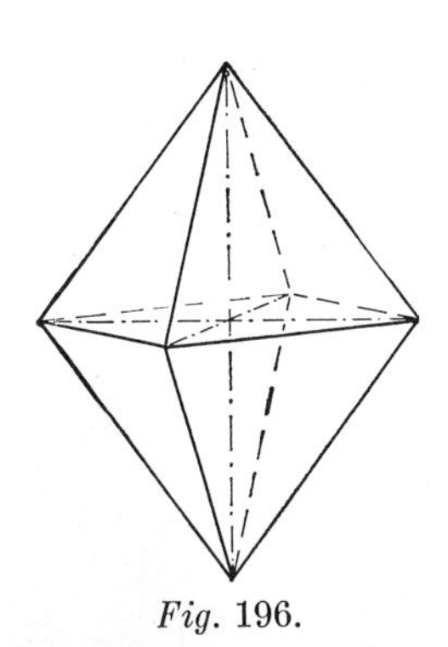

Fig. 196.

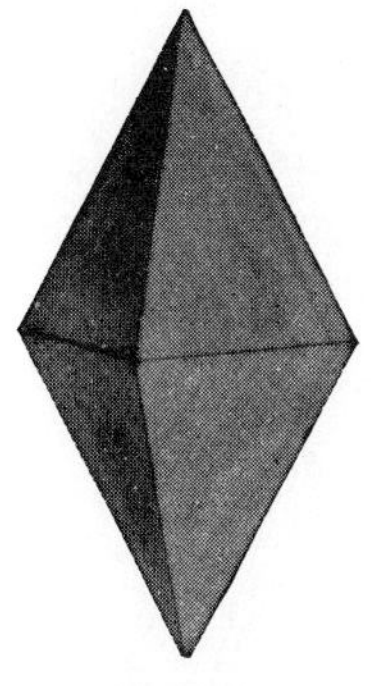

Fig. 197.

Tetragonal Bipyramid of the Second Order. The faces of this form cut the c axis and one of the a axes but extend parallel to the other. The symbols are, therefore, $(a : \infty a : mc)$ or $\{h0l\}$. Eight faces are required to enclose space, and the form is termed the *bipyramid of the second order* (Figs. 198 and 199).

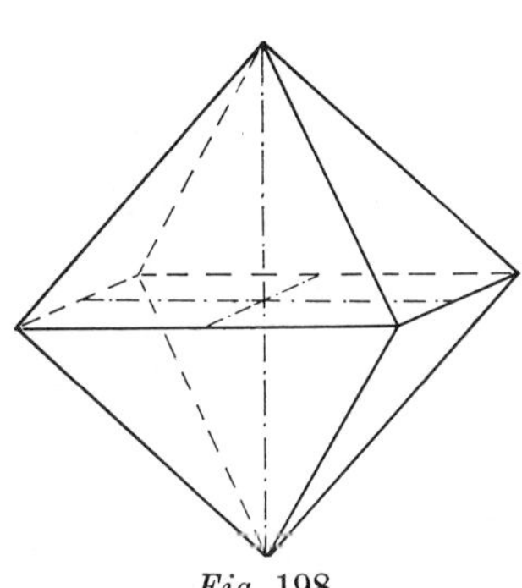

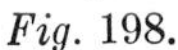

Fig. 198.

Fig. 199.

This bipyramid is very similar to the preceding, but can be readily distinguished from it on account of its position with respect to the lateral axes. In this form, the lateral axes bisect the horizontal edges and the intermediate axes pass through the four equal tetrahedral angles. This is the opposite of what was noted with the bipyramid of the first order (compare Figs. 196 and 197). Hence, the bipyramid of the first order is always held so that an edge is directed toward the observer, whereas the bipyramid of the second order presents a face. In both bipyramids the principal axis passes through the two equal tetrahedral angles.

Ditetragonal Bipyramid. The faces of this bipyramid cut the two lateral axes at different distances, while the intercept along the c axis may be unity or *mc*. Sixteen such faces are possible, and hence the term *ditetragonal bipyramid* is used (Figs. 200 and 202).[1]

The symbols are

$$(a : na : mc) \text{ or } \{hkl\}.$$

Since the polar edges[2] are alternately similar, it follows that the faces are equal, similar scalene triangles. The ditetragonal bipyramid possessing equal polar edges is crystallographically an impossible form, for then the ratio $a : na : mc$ would necessitate a value for n equal to the tangent of 67°30′, namely, the irrational value 2.4142+.[3]

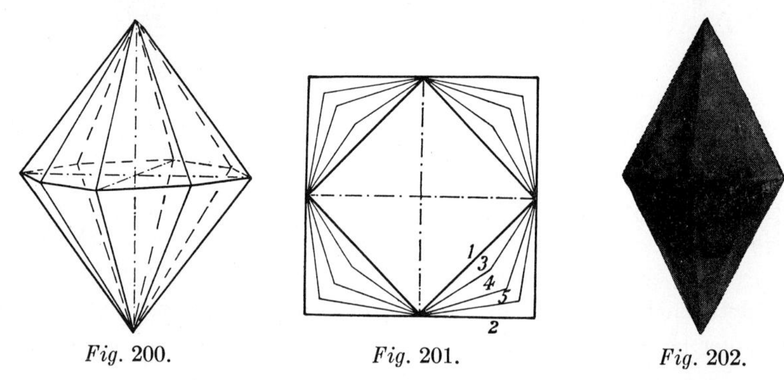

Fig. 200. *Fig.* 201. *Fig.* 202.

From the above it follows that, when n is less than 2.4142+, the ditetragonal bipyramid simulates the tetragonal bipyramid of the first order, and finally, when it equals 1, it passes over into that form. On the other hand, if n is greater than 2.4142+, it approaches more the bipyramid of the second order, and when it is equal to infinity passes over into that form. Hence, $1 < n < \infty$. Figure 201 illustrates this clearly. It is also to be noted that, when n is less than 2.4142+, the lateral axes pass through the more acute angles, whereas, where n is greater than 2.4142+, they join the more obtuse. Outline 1 represents the cross section of the tetragonal bipyramid of the first order, 2 that of the second order, and 3, 4, and 5 the cross sections of ditetragonal bipyramids where n equals $3/2$, 3, and 6, respectively.

Tetragonal Prism of the First Order. If the value of the intercept along the c axis of the tetragonal bipyramid of the first order becomes infinity, the number of the faces of the bipyramid is reduced to four, giving rise to the *tetragonal prism of the first order* (Fig. 203). This is an open form and possesses the following symbols:

$$(a : a : \infty c) \text{ or } \{110\}.$$

[1] Compare Fig. 23 (p. 15).
[2] Compare footnote (p. 44).
[3] See also p. 45.

The lateral axes join opposite edges; hence an edge is directed toward the observer.

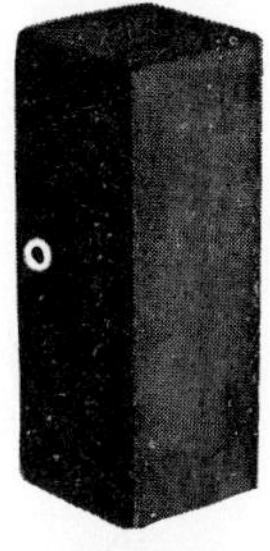

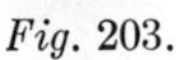

Fig. 203. *Fig.* 204. *Fig.* 205.

Tetragonal Prism of the Second Order. The same relationship exists between this form and its corresponding bipyramid as was observed on the preceding form.

The symbols are

$$(a : \infty a : \infty c) \text{ or } \{100\}.$$

This is also an open form consisting of four faces (Fig. 204). The lateral axes join the centers of opposite faces; hence, a face is directed toward the observer.

Ditetragonal Prism. As is obvious, this form consists of eight faces possessing the following symbols:

$$(a : na : \infty c) \text{ or } \{hk0\}.$$

What was indicated on page 66 concerning the polar angles and the position of the lateral axes applies here also. Figure 205 represents a ditetragonal prism.

Basal Pinacoid. This form is similar to that of the hexagonal system (page 46). It is parallel to the lateral axes but cuts the c axis. The symbols may be written

$$(\infty a : \infty a : c) \text{ or } \{001\}.$$

This form consists of but two faces. They are shown in combination with the three prisms in Figs. 203, 204, and 205.

Combinations. Some of the more common combinations are illustrated by the following figures.

Figures 206 to 209, $m = (a : a : \infty c)$, $\{110\}$; $p = (a : a : c)$, $\{111\}$; $a = (a : \infty a : \infty c)$, $\{100\}$; $x = (a : 3a : 3c)$, $\{311\}$. These combinations have been observed on zircon ($ZrSiO_4$).

Figure 210, $m = (a : a : \infty c)$, $\{110\}$; $p = (a : a : c)$, $\{111\}$; $c = (\infty a : \infty a : c)$, $\{001\}$. Vesuvianite ($Ca_{10}Al_4(Mg,Fe)_2(OH)_4(SiO_4)_5(Si_2O_7)_2$).

Summary. The seven forms in this class and the chief characteristics are given in Table 9.

Relationship of Forms. This is clearly expressed by the following diagram (compare pages 29 and 46):

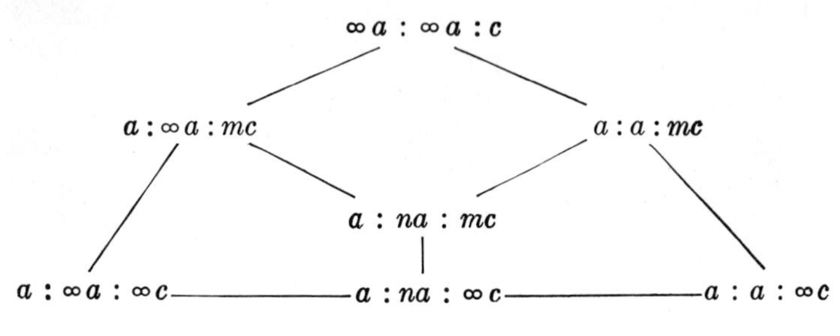

TABLE 9

Symmetry, $\frac{4}{m}\frac{2}{m}\frac{2}{m}$	Planes			Axes			Center
	Horizontal	Vertical		Vertical	Horizontal		
	Axial	Axial	Intermediate	■ Axial	● Axial	● Intermediate	
	1	2	2	1	2	2	1

Forms	Symbols		Faces	Solid angles	
	Weiss	Miller		Tetrahedral	Octahedral
Unit bipyramid, first order	$a{:}a{:}c$	{111}	8	2 + 4	—
Modified bipyramids, first order	$a{:}a{:}mc$	$\{hhl\}$	8	2 + 4	—
Bipyramids, second order	$a{:}\infty a{:}mc$	$\{h0l\}$	8	2 + 4	—
Ditetragonal bipyramids	$a{:}na{:}mc$	$\{hkl\}$	16	4 + 4	2
Prism, first order	$a{:}a{:}\infty c$	{110}	4	—	—
Prism, second order	$a{:}\infty a{:}\infty c$	{100}	4	—	—
Ditetragonal prisms	$a{:}na{:}\infty c$	$\{hk0\}$	8	—	—
Basal pinacoid	$\infty a{:}\infty a{:}c$	{001}	2	—	—

Figure 211, $m = (a : a : \infty c)$, {110}; $a = (a : \infty a : \infty c)$, {100}; $p = (a : a : c)$, {111}; $e = (a : \infty a : c)$, {101}. Observed on rutile (TiO_2).

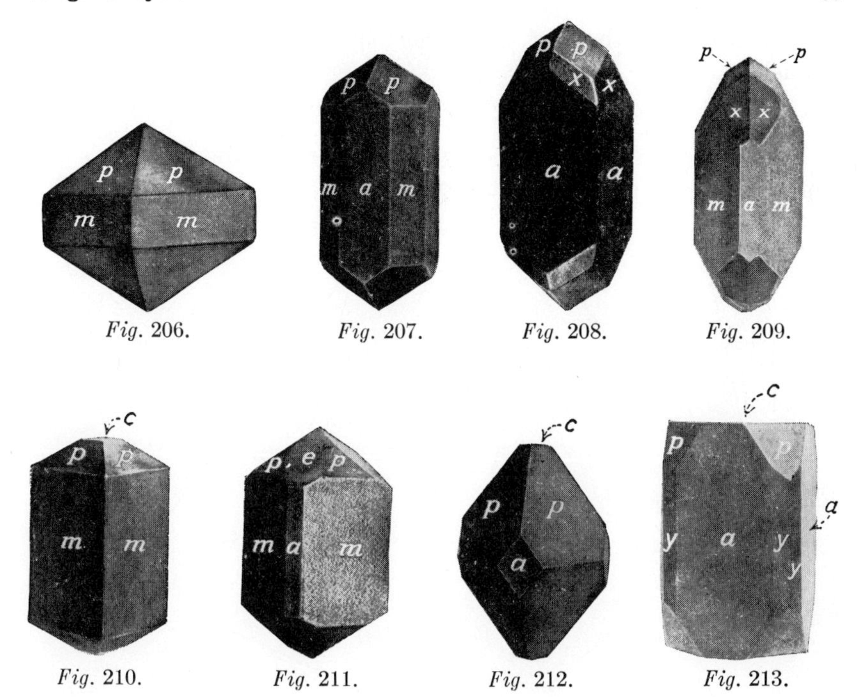

Fig. 206. *Fig.* 207. *Fig.* 208. *Fig.* 209.

Fig. 210. *Fig.* 211. *Fig.* 212. *Fig.* 213.

Figures 212 and 213, $a = (a : \infty a : \infty c)$, {100}; $p = (a : a : c)$, {111}; $c = (\infty a : \infty a : c)$, {001}; $y = (a : 3a : \infty c)$, {310}. Apophyllite ($KFCa_4(Si_4O_{10})_2.8H_2O$).

TETRAGONAL SCALENOHEDRAL CLASS

Symmetry, $\bar{4}$ 2 *m*. This class possesses two intermediate planes and three axes of twofold symmetry.[1] One of the axes of twofold symmetry is the *c* axis, the other two are the *a* axes. This is clearly illustrated in Fig. 214. The faces of the positive forms of this class are located in the unshaded octants, those of the negative forms in the shaded ones. There are two forms in this class which are morphologically new, namely, the tetragonal bisphenoids and scalenohedrons.

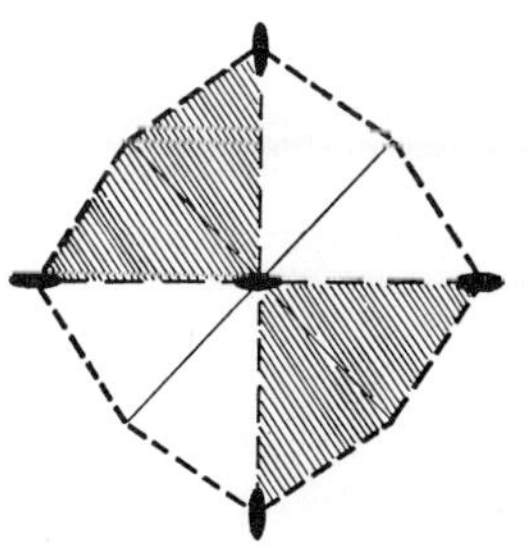

Fig. 214.

Tetragonal Bisphenoids. These forms consist of two types, *positive* (Fig. 216) and *negative* (Fig. 215), each bounded by four equal isosceles triangles. Their symbols

[1] The vertical *c* axis is customarily designated as a binary or twofold axis. It is, however, a fourfold axis of rotary inversion, as indicated by $\bar{4}$ in the symbol $\bar{4}$ 2 *m*; see page 20.

are analogous to those of the tetragonal bipyramids of the first order, namely,

$$\pm(a : a : mc), \text{ or } \{hhl\} \text{ and } \{h\bar{h}l\}.$$

The a axes bisect the four edges of equal length, while the c axis passes through the centers of the other two.

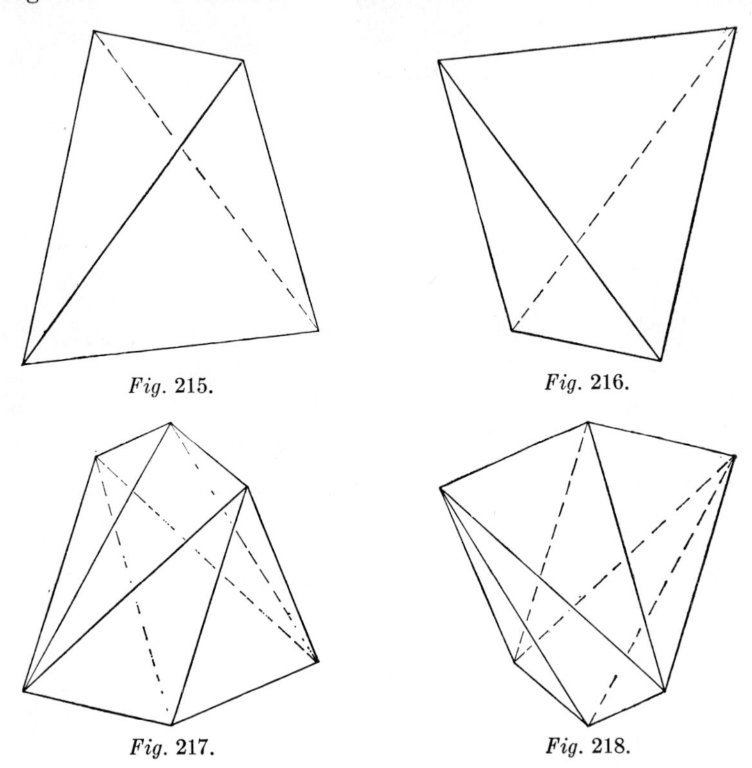

Fig. 215. *Fig.* 216.

Fig. 217. *Fig.* 218.

Tetragonal Scalenohedrons. These consist of eight similar scalene triangles and are termed *positive* (Fig. 218) and *negative* (Fig. 217) forms. Their symbols are

$$\pm(a : na : mc), \text{ or } \{hkl\} \text{ and } \{h\bar{k}l\}.$$

These symbols correspond to those of the ditetragonal bipyramids (page 65). The c axis joins those tetrahedral angles which possess two pairs of equal edges. The a axes bisect the four zigzag edges.

Other Forms. The tetragonal bipyramids of the second order, the tetragonal prisms of the first and second orders, the ditetragonal prisms, and the basal pinacoid are morphologically identical with those of the ditetragonal bipyramidal class (page 64).

Summary. The characteristics of the forms of the tetragonal scalenohedral class are shown in Table 10.

TABLE 10

Symmetry, $\bar{4}\,2\,m$	Planes			Axes			Center
	Horizontal	Vertical		Vertical	Horizontal		
	Axial	Axial	Intermediate	Axial	Axial	Intermediate	
	0	0	2	1	2	0	0

Forms	Symbols		Solid angles		
	Weiss	Miller	Faces	Trihedral	Tetrahedral
Bisphenoids, first order	$\pm a{:}a{:}mc$	$\{hhl\}$ $\{h\bar{h}l\}$	4	4	—
Bipyramid, second order	$a{:}\infty a{:}mc$	$\{h0l\}$	Morphologically like those in ditetragonal bipyramidal class		
Tetragonal scalenohedrons	$\pm a{:}na{:}mc$	$\{hkl\}$ $\{h\bar{k}l\}$	8	—	2 + 4
Prism, first order	$a{:}a{:}\infty c$	$\{110\}$	Morphologically like those in ditetragonal bipyramidal class		
Prism, second order	$a{:}\infty a{:}\infty c$	$\{100\}$			
Ditetragonal prisms	$a{:}na{:}\infty c$	$\{hk0\}$			
Basal pinacoid	$\infty a{:}\infty a{:}c$	$\{001\}$			

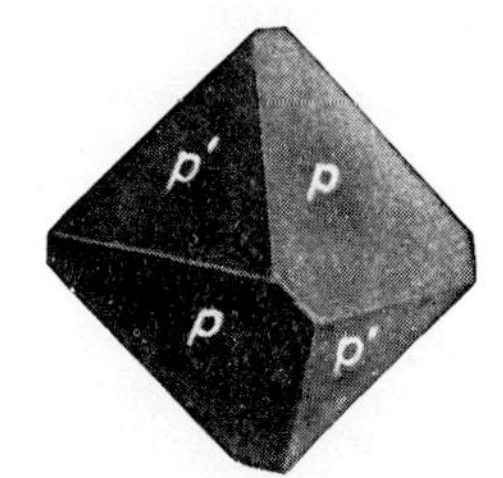

Fig. 219.

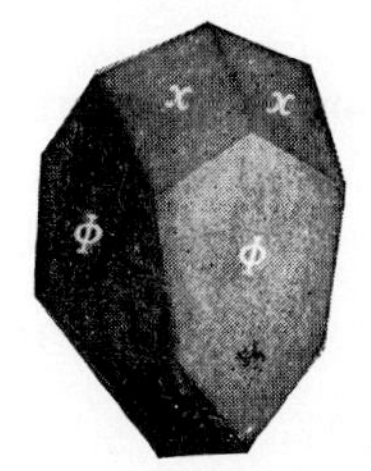

Fig. 220.

Combinations. The following combinations (Figs. 219 and 220) occur on chalcopyrite ($CuFeS_2$): $p = (a : a : c)$, $\{111\}$; $p' = -(a : a : c)$, $\{1\bar{1}1\}$; $\Phi = (a : a : 7/2c)$, $\{772\}$; $x = (a : 2a : c)$, $\{212\}$.

6 | Orthorhombic System

Crystallographic Axes. This system includes all crystals which can be referred to three unequal and perpendicular axes (Fig. 221). One axis is held vertically, which is, as heretofore, the c axis. Another is directed toward the observer and is the a axis, sometimes also called the *brachyaxis*. The third axis extends from right to left and is the b axis or *macroaxis*. There is no principal axis in this system; hence any axis may be chosen as the vertical or c axis. On this account one and the same crystal may be held in different positions by various observers, which has led in some instances to considerable confusion, for, as is obvious, the nomenclature of the various forms cannot then remain constant. In this system the axial ratio consists of three values, for example, for sulfur, $a : b : c = 0.8131 : 1 : 1.9034$ (compare page 11).

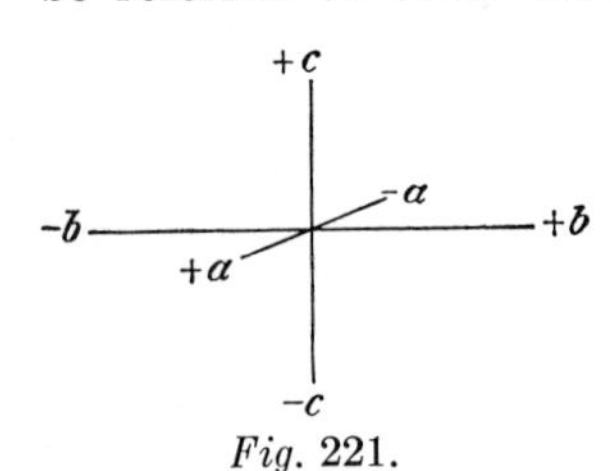

Fig. 221.

Classes of Symmetry. The orthorhombic system comprises three classes of symmetry, as follows:

1. Orthorhombic bipyramidal class.
2. Orthorhombic bisphenoidal class.
3. Orthorhombic pyramidal class.

Numerous representatives of all these classes have been observed among minerals and artificial salts. Only the first class will be considered.

ORTHORHOMBIC BIPYRAMIDAL CLASS

Symmetry, $2/m\ 2/m\ 2/m$. *Planes.* There are three axial planes of symmetry (Fig. 222). Inasmuch as these planes are all dissimilar, they may be written

$$1 + 1 + 1 = 3 \text{ planes.}$$

[1] Sometimes termed the *rhombic, trimetric,* or *prismatic* system.

Axes. Three axes of twofold symmetry are to be observed (Fig. 222). They are the crystallographic axes and are indicated thus:

$$1 \bullet + 1 \bullet + 1 \bullet = 3 \text{ axes.}$$

Center. This element of symmetry is also present and demands parallelism of faces. Figure 223 shows the above elements of symmetry.

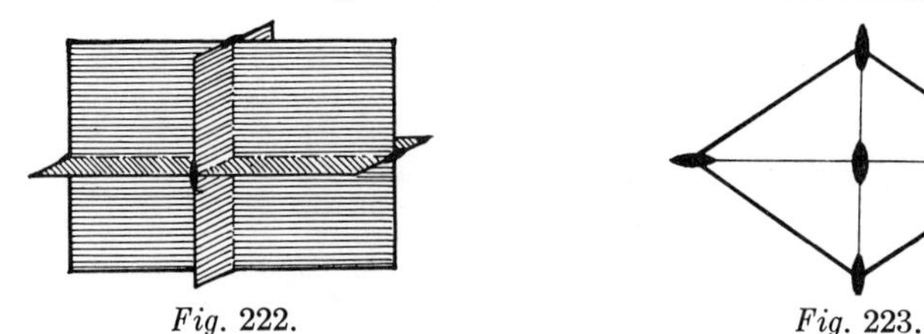

Fig. 222. *Fig.* 223.

Orthorhombic Bipyramids. The form whose faces possess the ratio $(a : b : c)$ or $\{111\}$ is known as the *unit or fundamental orthorhombic bipyramid.* It consists of eight similar scalene triangles (Fig. 224).

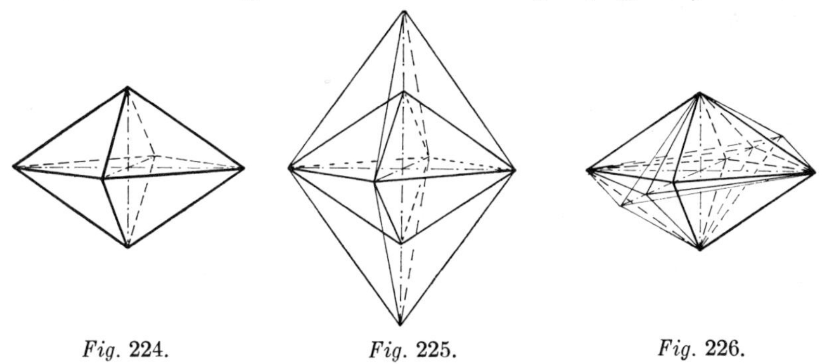

Fig. 224. *Fig.* 225. *Fig.* 226.

The outer form (Fig. 225) possesses the ratio $(a : b : mc)$ or $\{hhl\}$, $(0 < m < \infty)$. In this case $m = 2$. This is a *modified orthorhombic bipyramid.*

In Fig. 226, the heavy inner form is the unit bipyramid. The lighter bipyramids intercept the b and c axes at unit distances but the a axis at distances greater than unity. Their ratios may, however, be indicated in general as

$$(na : b : mc), \ (n > 1; 0 < m < \infty) \text{ or } \{hkl\}, \text{ where } k > h.$$

These are the *brachybipyramids,* because the intercepts along the *brachyaxis* are greater than unity.

Figure 227 shows two bipyramids (outer) which cut the a axis at unity but intercept the b axis at the general distance nb, $(n > 1)$. The ratios would, therefore, be expressed by $(a : nb : mc)$ or $\{khl\}$. Since the intercepts along the *macroaxis* are greater than unity, these are called *macrobipyramids.*

Figure 228 shows the relationship existing between the *unit*, *macro-*, and *brachybipyramids*, while Fig. 229 shows it for the *unit*, *modified*, and *macrobipyramids*.

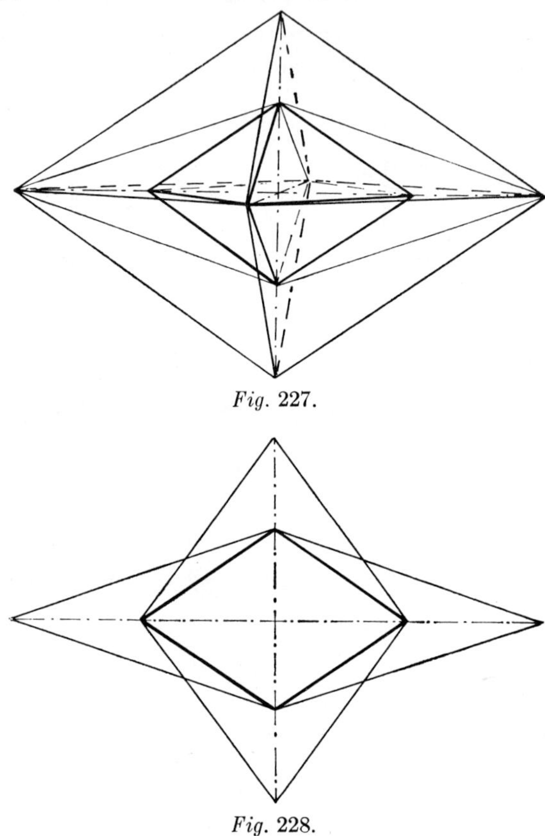

Fig. 227.

Fig. 228.

Prisms. Similarly there are three types of prisms, namely, the *unit*, *macro-*, and *brachyprisms*. Each consists of four faces, cutting the a and b axes but extending parallel to the c axis.

Figures 230 and 231 represent *unit prisms* with the following symbols:

$$(a : b : \infty c) \text{ or } \{110\}.$$

The *brachyprism* (outer form) is shown in Fig. 232. Its symbols are

$$(na : b : \infty c) \text{ or } \{hk0\}.$$

In Fig. 233, there is a unit prism surrounded by a *macroprism*, whose symbols may be written

$$(a : nb : \infty c) \text{ or } \{kh0\}.$$

For the relationship existing among these three prisms, compare Fig. 228.

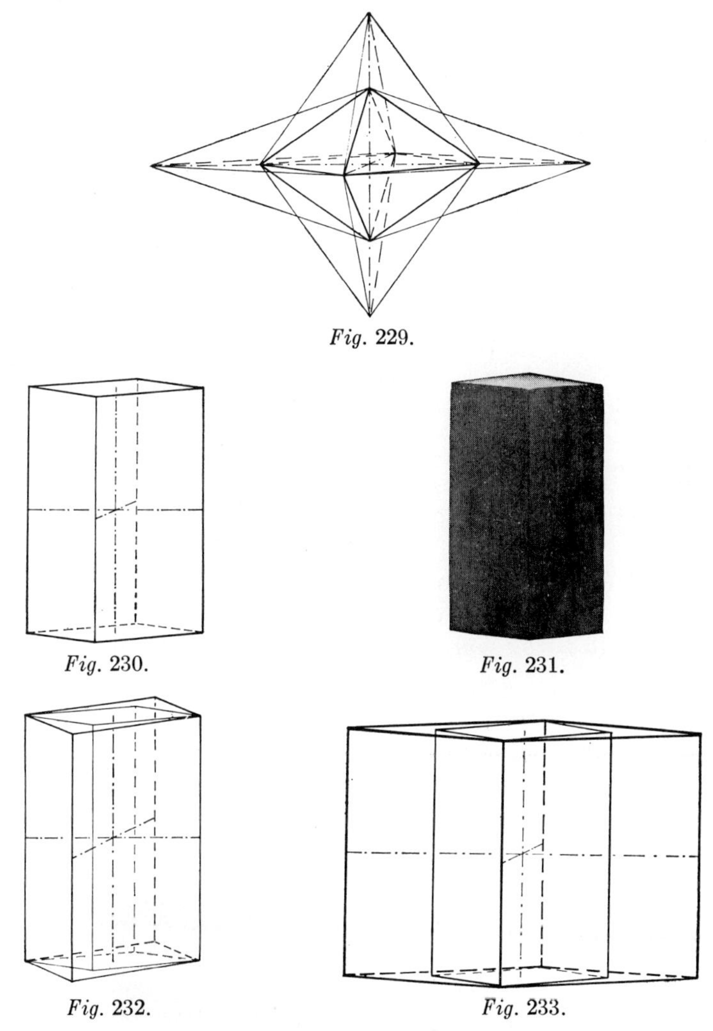

Fig. 229.

Fig. 230.

Fig. 231.

Fig. 232.

Fig. 233.

Domes. These are *horizontal* prisms and, hence, cut the c and one of the horizontal axes. Domes which are parallel to the a or brachyaxis are called *brachy-* or *side domes*. Their general symbols are

$$(\infty a : b : mc) \text{ or } \{0kl\} \text{ (Fig. 234).}$$

Those which extend parallel to the macroaxis are termed *macro-* or *front domes* (Figs. 235 and 236). Their symbols are

$$(a : \infty b : mc) \text{ or } \{h0l\}.$$

As is obvious, prisms and domes are open forms and, hence, can only occur in combination with other forms.

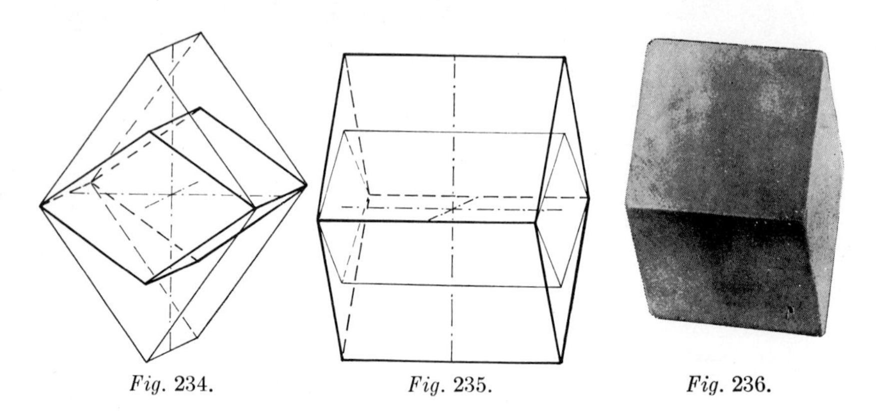

Fig. 234. *Fig.* 235. *Fig.* 236.

Pinacoids. These cut one axis and extend parallel to the other two. There are three types, as follows:

Basal pinacoid, $(\infty a : \infty b : c)$ or $\{001\}$; also called the *base.*
Brachypinacoid, $(\infty a : b : \infty c)$ or $\{010\}$; often termed the *side* pinacoid.
Macropinacoid, $(a : \infty b : \infty c)$ or $\{100\}$; frequently designated as the *front* pinacoid.

These forms consist of two faces. Figures 237 and 238 show a combination of the three types of pinacoids.

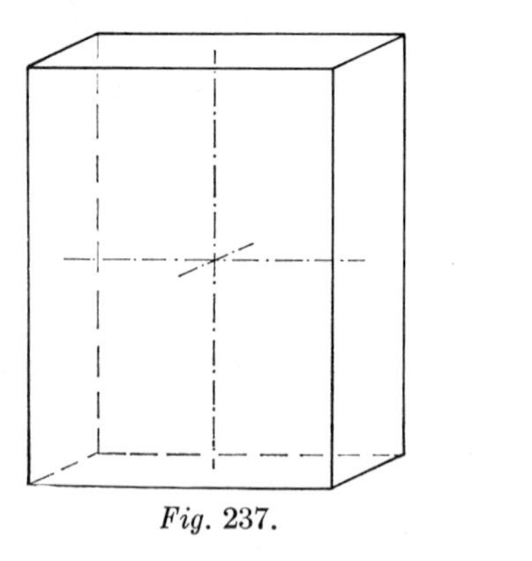

Fig. 237.

Fig. 238.

Summary. The characteristics of the forms of this class are given in Table 11.

TABLE 11

Symmetry, $\frac{2}{m}\frac{2}{m}\frac{2}{m}$	Planes (axial)	Axes	Center
	1 + 1 + 1	1● +1● +1●	1

Forms		Symbols		Faces	Tetrahedral solid angles
		Weiss	Miller		
Orthorhombic bipyramids	Unit	$a:b:c$	$\{111\}$	8	2 + 2 + 2
	Modified	$a:b:mc$	$\{hhl\}$		
	Brachy-	$na:b:mc$	$\{hkl\}$		
	Macro-	$a:nb:mc$	$\{khl\}$		
Orthorhombic prisms	Unit	$a:b:\infty c$	$\{110\}$	4	
	Brachy-	$na:b:\infty c$	$\{hk0\}$		
	Macro-	$a:nb:\infty c$	$\{kh0\}$		
Domes	Brachy-	$\infty a:b:mc$	$\{0kl\}$	4	
	Macro-	$a:\infty b:mc$	$\{h0l\}$		
Pinacoids	Basal	$\infty a:\infty b:c$	$\{001\}$	2	
	Brachy-	$\infty a:b:\infty c$	$\{010\}$		
	Macro-	$a:\infty b:\infty c$	$\{100\}$		

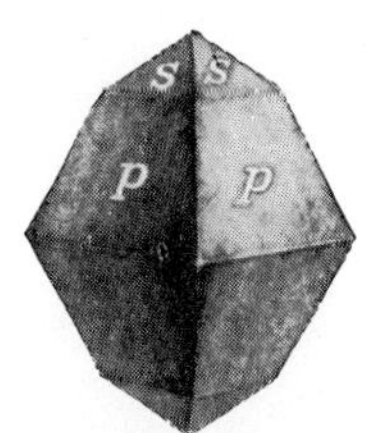

Fig. 239.

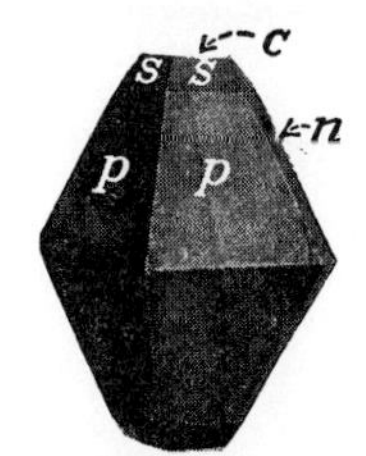

Fig. 240.

Combinations. Figures 239 and 240, $p = (a:b:c)$, $\{111\}$; $s = (a:b:\frac{1}{3}c)$, $\{113\}$; $n = (\infty a:b:c)$, $\{011\}$; $c = (\infty a:\infty b:c)$, $\{001\}$. These combinations occur on native sulfur.

Figure 241, $m = (a : b : \infty c)$, $\{110\}$; $b = (\infty a : b : \infty c)$, $\{010\}$; $k = (\infty a : b : c)$, $\{011\}$. Aragonite ($CaCO_3$).

Figure 242, $m = (a : b : \infty c)$, $\{110\}$; $c = (\infty a : \infty b : c)$, $\{001\}$; $d = (a : \infty b : \frac{1}{2}c)$, $\{102\}$; $o = (\infty a : b : c)$, $\{011\}$. Barite ($BaSO_4$).

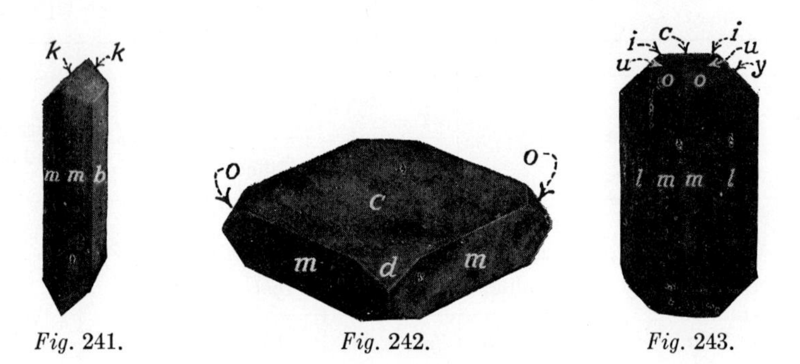

Fig. 241. *Fig.* 242. *Fig.* 243.

Figure 243, $m = (a : b : \infty c)$, $\{110\}$; $l = (2a : b : \infty c)$, $\{120\}$; $u = (a : b : c)$, $\{111\}$; $i = (a : b : \frac{2}{3}c)$, $\{223\}$; $o = (a : b : 2c)$, $\{221\}$; $y = (\infty a : b : 4c)$, $\{041\}$; $c = (\infty a : \infty b : c)$, $\{001\}$. Topaz ($Al_2(F,OH)_2SiO_4$).

7 | Monoclinic System[1]

Crystallographic Axes. To this system belong those crystals which can be referred to three unequal axes, two of which (a and c) intersect at an oblique angle, while the third axis (b) is perpendicular to these two. The oblique angle between the a and c axes is termed β. Figure 244 shows an axial cross of this system.

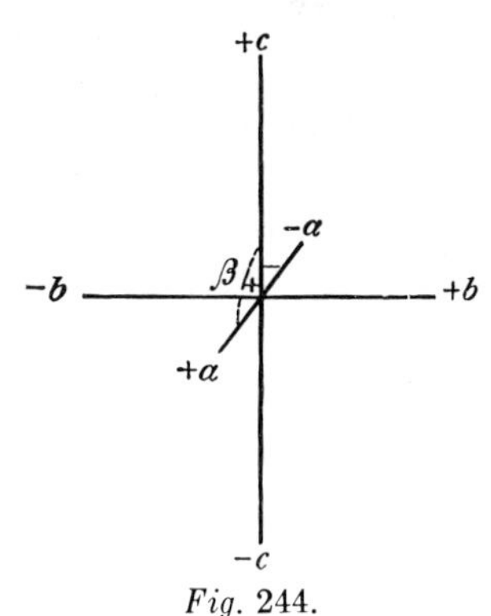

Fig. 244.

It is customary to place the b axis so as to extend from right to left. The c axis is held vertically. The a axis is then directed toward the observer. Since the a axis is inclined, it is called the *clinoaxis*. The b axis is often spoken of as the *orthoaxis*. The obtuse angle between the a and c axes is the *positive* angle β, whereas the acute angle is *negative*. Obviously, they are supplementary angles. The elements of crystallization consist of the axial ratio and the angle β, which may be either the obtuse or the acute angle (compare page 11).

Classes of Symmetry. The monoclinic system includes three classes of symmetry, as follows:

1. Prismatic class.
2. Sphenoidal class.
3. Domatic class.

Only the first class will be considered.

MONOCLINIC PRISMATIC CLASS

Symmetry, $2/m$. This class possesses one axial plane of symmetry (a and c axes). It is directed toward the observer. Perpendicular to

[1] Also termed the *clinorhombic, hemiprismatic, monoclinohedral, monosymmetric,* or *oblique* system.

this plane is an axis of twofold symmetry (b axis). A center of symmetry is also present. In Fig. 245 the presence of these elements is readily recognized. These elements are represented diagrammatically in Fig. 246, which is a projection of a monoclinic form upon the plane of the a and b axes.

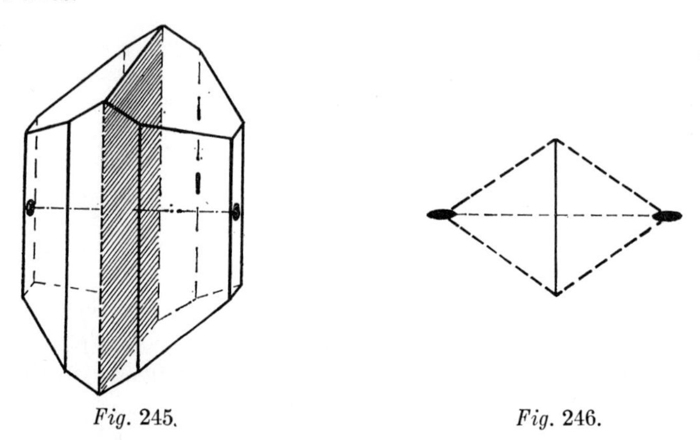

Fig. 245. *Fig.* 246.

Hemibipyramids. On account of the presence in this class of only one plane of symmetry, and an axis of twofold symmetry, a form with unit intercepts, that is, with the parametral ratio $a : b : c$, can possess but four faces. Figure 247 shows four such faces, which enclose the positive angle β and are said to constitute the *positive unit hemibipyramid.* Figure 248 shows four faces with the same ratio enclosing the negative angle β and comprising the *negative unit hemibipyramid.* It is obvious that the

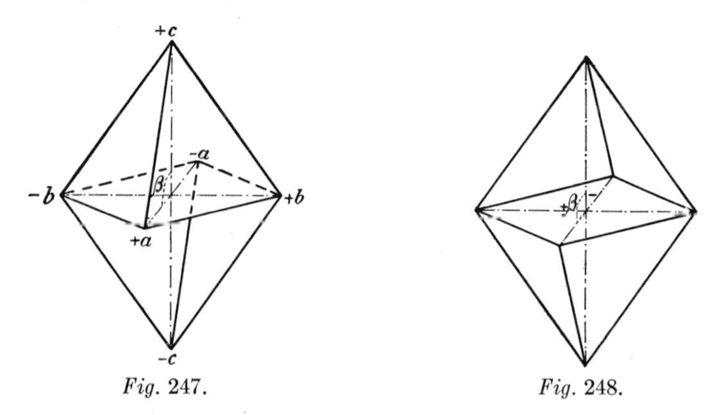

Fig. 247. *Fig.* 248.

faces of these hemibipyramids are dissimilar, those over the positive angle being the larger. The symbols are $\pm(a : b : c)$, or $\{111\}$ and $\{11\bar{1}\}$. Two unit hemibipyramids occurring simultaneously are shown in Figs. 249 and 250.

Since this system differs essentially from the orthorhombic in the obliquity of the a axis, it follows that *modified*, *clino*, and *ortho* hemibipyramids are also possible. They possess the following general symbols:

Modified hemibipyramids,

$$\pm(a : b : mc),\ 0 < m < \infty, \text{ or } \{hhl\} \text{ and } \{hh\bar{l}\}.$$

Clino hemibipyramids,

$$\pm(na : b : mc),\ n > 1; \text{ or } \{hkl\} \text{ and } \{hk\bar{l}\}.$$

Ortho hemibipyramids,

$$\pm(a : nb : mc),\ n > 1; \text{ or } \{khl\} \text{ and } \{kh\bar{l}\}.$$

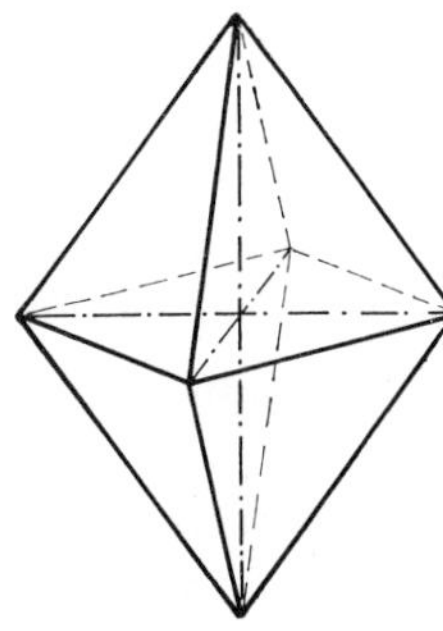

Fig. 249.

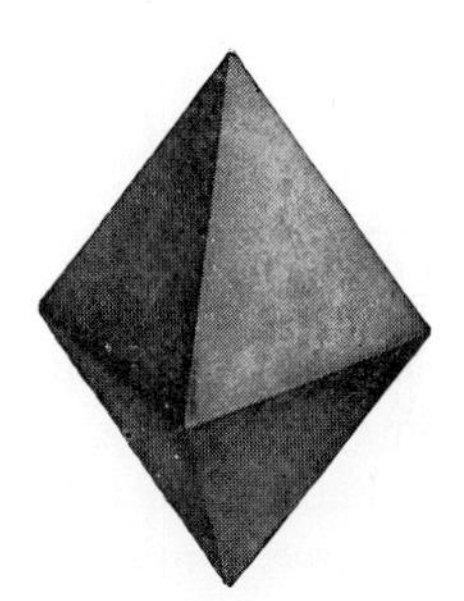

Fig. 250.

Prisms. As was the case in the orthorhombic system (page 74), there are also three types of prisms possible in this system, namely, *unit*, *clino-*, and *orthoprisms.* These forms cut the a and b axes and extend parallel to the vertical axis.

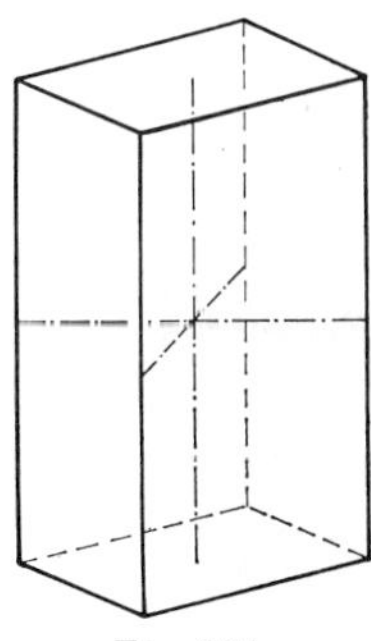

Fig. 251.

Fig. 252.

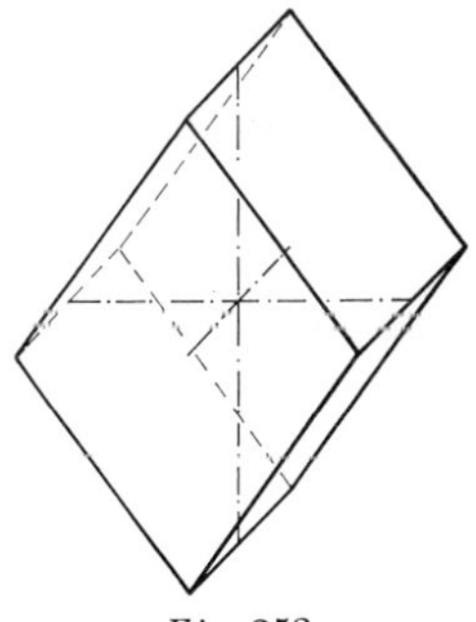

Fig. 253

The general symbols are

Unit prism, $(a : b : \infty c)$, $\{110\}$ (Figs. 251 and 252).
Clinoprism, $(na : b : \infty c)$, $\{hk0\}$; $n > 1$.
Orthoprism, $(a : nb : \infty c)$, $\{kh0\}$; $n > 1$.

Domes. In this system two types of domes are also possible, namely, those which extend parallel to the a and b axes, respectively. Those which are parallel to the a axis are termed *clinodomes* and consist of four faces (Fig. 253). The general symbols are

$$(\infty a : b : mc),\ \{0kl\}.$$

Since the a axis is inclined to the c axis, it follows that the domes which are parallel to the b axis consist of but two faces. Figure 254 shows such

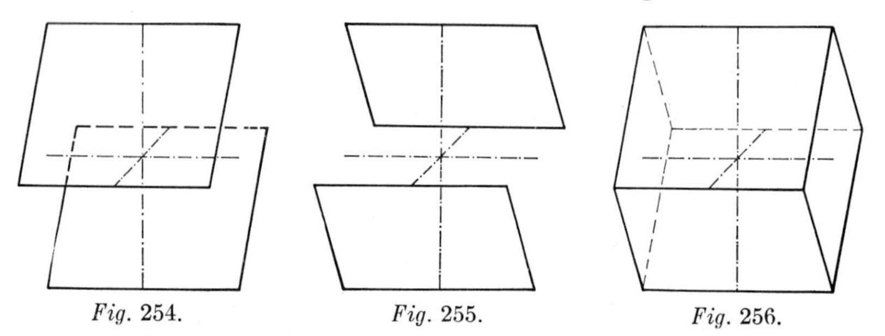

Fig. 254. *Fig.* 255. *Fig.* 256.

faces enclosing the positive angle and termed the *positive hemiorthodome*, whereas in Fig. 255 the *negative hemiorthodome* is represented. It is evident that the faces of the negative form are always the smaller. Figure 256 shows these hemidomes in combination. Their general symbols are

Positive hemiorthodome,

$$(a : \infty b : mc),\ \{h0l\}.$$

Negative hemiorthodome,

$$(a : \infty b : mc),\ \{h0\bar{l}\}.$$

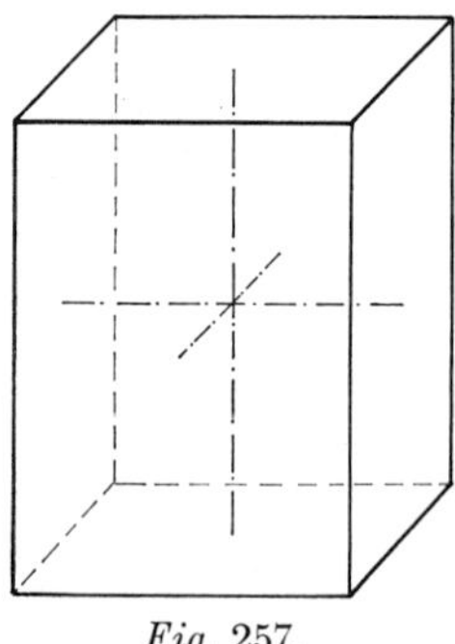

Fig. 257.

Fig. 258.

Pinacoids. There are three types of pinacoids possible in the monoclinic system, namely,

Basal pinacoid, $(\infty a : \infty b : c)$, $\{001\}$.
Clinopinacoid, $(\infty a : b : \infty c)$, $\{010\}$.
Orthopinacoid, $(a : \infty b : \infty c)$, $\{100\}$.

These forms may also be termed the *base* and the *side* and *front* pinacoids, respectively. They consist of but two faces. Figures 257 and 258 show combinations of these pinacoids.

All forms of the monoclinic system are open forms, and, hence, every crystal of this system is a combination.

Summary. The forms of this class are shown in Table 12.

TABLE 12

Symmetry, $\frac{2}{m}$	Plane	Axis	Center
	1 (*a* and *c* axes)	1 (*b* axis)	1

Forms		Symbols		Faces
		Weiss	Miller	
Hemibipyramids	Unit	$\pm(a:b:c)$	$\{111\}$ $\{11\bar{1}\}$	4
	Modified	$\pm(a:b:mc)$	$\{hhl\}$ $\{hh\bar{l}\}$	
	Clino	$\pm(na:b:mc)$	$\{hkl\}$ $\{hk\bar{l}\}$	
	Ortho	$\pm(a:nb:mc)$	$\{khl\}$ $\{kh\bar{l}\}$	
Prisms	Unit	$a:b:\infty c$	$\{110\}$	4
	Clino-	$na:b:\infty c$	$\{hk0\}$	
	Ortho-	$a:nb:\infty c$	$\{kh0\}$	
Clinodomes		$\infty a:b:mc$	$\{0kl\}$	4
Hemiorthodomes	Positive	$a:\infty b:mc$	$\{h0l\}$	2
	Negative	$a:\infty b:mc$	$\{h0\bar{l}\}$	
Pinacoids	Basal	$\infty a:\infty b:c$	$\{001\}$	2
	Clino-	$\infty a:b:\infty c$	$\{010\}$	
	Ortho-	$a:\infty b:\infty c$	$\{100\}$	

Combinations. The following models show some combinations of the forms of this class:

Figure 259, $m = (a : b : \infty c)$, $\{110\}$; $b = (\infty a : b : \infty c)$, $\{010\}$; $p = (a : b : c)$, $\{111\}$. Gypsum ($CaSO_4.2H_2O$).

Figures 260, 261, and 262, $m = (a : b : \infty c)$, $\{110\}$; $b = (\infty a : b : \infty c)$, $\{010\}$; $c = (\infty a : \infty b : c)$, $\{001\}$; $y = (a : \infty b : 2c)$, $\{20\bar{1}\}$; $x = (a : \infty b : c)$, $\{10\bar{1}\}$; $o = (a : b : c)$, $\{11\bar{1}\}$; $z = (3a : b : \infty c)$, $\{130\}$. Orthoclase ($KAlSi_3O_8$).

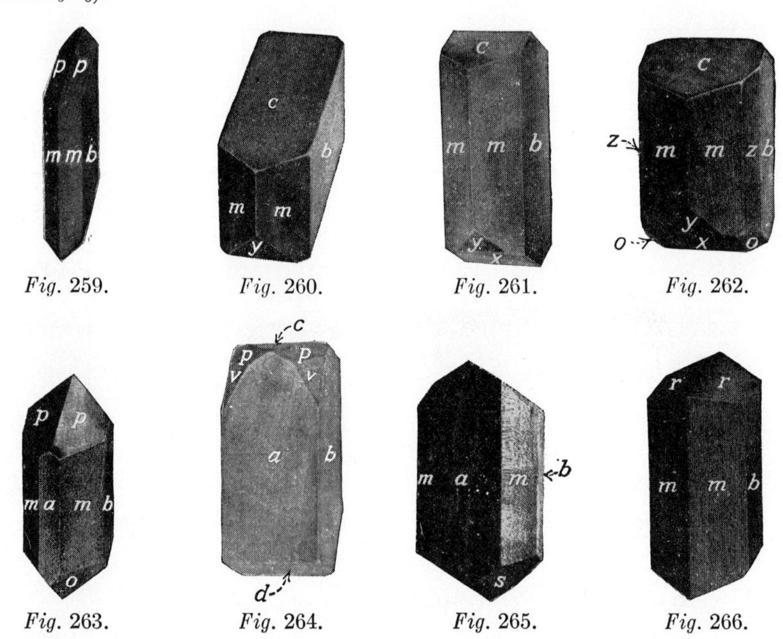

Fig. 259. *Fig.* 260. *Fig.* 261. *Fig.* 262.

Fig. 263. *Fig.* 264. *Fig.* 265. *Fig.* 266.

Figures 263, 264, and 265, $m = (a : b : \infty c)$, $\{110\}$; $a = (a : \infty b : \infty c)$, $\{100\}$; $b = (\infty a : b : \infty c)$, $\{010\}$; $c = (\infty a : \infty b : c)$, $\{001\}$; $p = (a : b : c)$, $\{111\}$; $v = (a : b : 2c)$, $\{221\}$; $o = (a : b : 2c)$, $\{22\bar{1}\}$; $d = (a : \infty b : c)$, $\{10\bar{1}\}$; $s = (a : b : c)$, $\{11\bar{1}\}$. Augite.

Figure 266, $m = (a : b : \infty c)$, $\{110\}$; $b = (\infty a : b : \infty c)$, $\{010\}$; $r = (\infty a : b : c)$, $\{011\}$. Hornblende.

8 | Triclinic System[1]

Crystallographic Axes. This system includes all crystals which can be referred to three unequal axes intersecting each other at unequal angles. The axes are designated as in the orthorhombic system, namely, *a*, *brachyaxis;* *b*, *macroaxis;* and *c*, *vertical axis.* From this it follows that one axis must be held vertically, a second is directed toward the observer, and then the third is inclined from right to left. Usually the brachyaxis is the shorter of the two lateral axes. Figure 267 shows an axial cross of the triclinic system. The three angles between the axes are indicated as follows: $b \wedge c = \alpha, a \wedge c = \beta$, and $a \wedge b = \gamma$. The elements of crystallization consist of the axial ratio and the three angles, α, β, and γ (page 11).

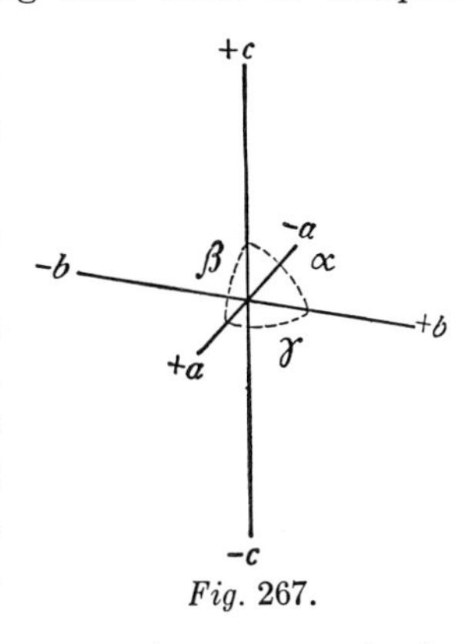

Fig. 267.

Classes of Symmetry. There are but two classes of symmetry in the triclinic system, namely,

1. Pinacoidal class.
2. Asymmetric or pedial class.

The first class will be considered in detail.

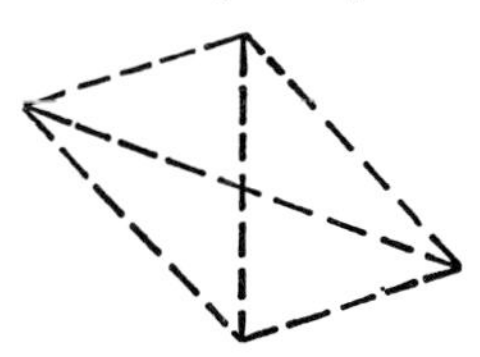
Fig. 268.

PINACOIDAL CLASS

Symmetry, 1. A center of symmetry is the only element present. Hence, forms can consist of but two faces, namely, face and parallel counterface. This is represented diagrammatically by Fig. 268, which shows a triclinic combination projected upon the plane of the *a* and *b* axes.

[1] Also termed the *anorthic, asymmetric,* or *clinorhomboidal* system.

Tetarto-bipyramids. As already shown, triclinic forms consist of but two faces. Therefore, since the planes of the crystallographic axes divide space into four pairs of dissimilar octants, it follows that four types of pyramidal forms must result. These are spoken of as *tetarto-bipyramids.* There are, hence, four tetarto-bipyramids, each cutting the axes at their unit lengths. The same is also true of the modified, brachy-, and macro-bipyramids. That is to say, the various bipyramids of the orthorhombic system, on account of the obliquity of the three axes, now yield four tetarto-bipyramids each. They are designated as *upper right*, *upper left*,

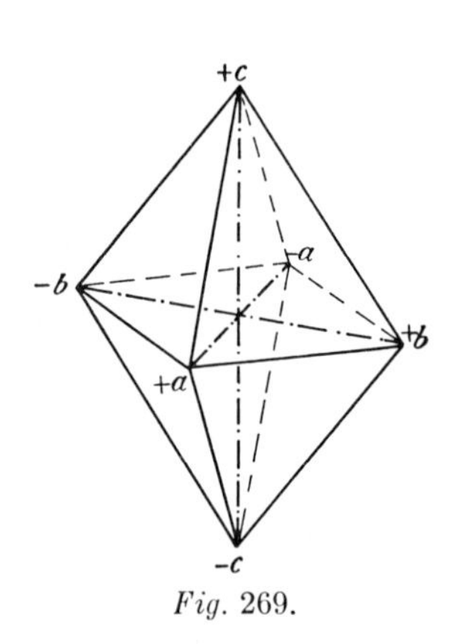

Fig. 269.

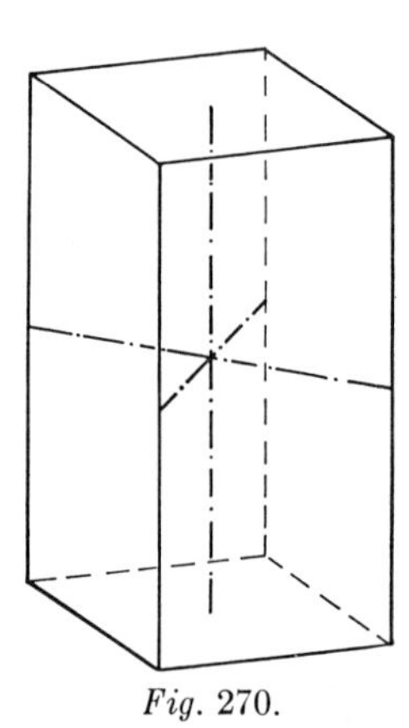

Fig. 270.

lower right, and *lower left* forms, depending upon which of the front octants the form encloses. The general symbols for all types are given in the tabulation on page 88. Figure 269 shows the four unit tetarto-bipyramids in combination.

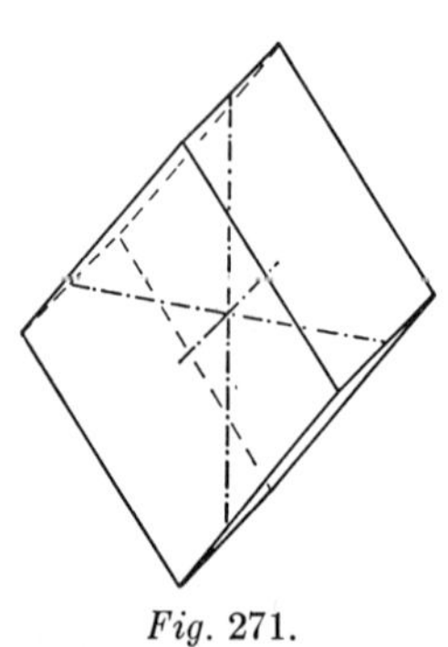

Fig. 271.

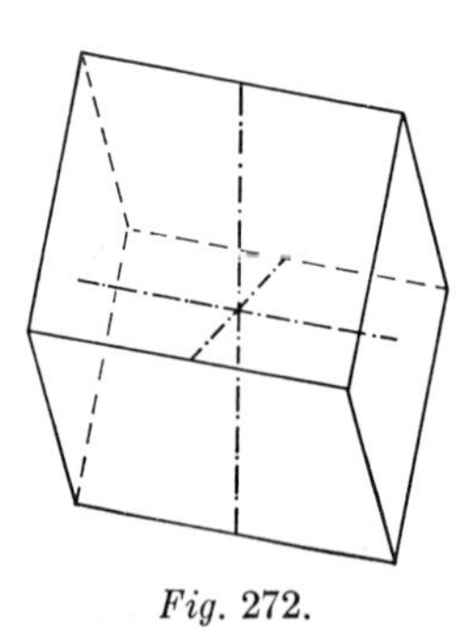

Fig. 272.

Hemiprisms. Obviously the prisms are now to be designated as *right* and *left* forms. These two forms are in combination with the basal pinacoid in Fig. 270.

Hemidomes. All domes now consist of but two faces. Hence, we may speak of *right* and *left hemibrachydomes* and *upper* and *lower hemimacrodomes.* These forms are shown in combination with the macro- and brachypinacoids, respectively, in Figs. 271 and 272.

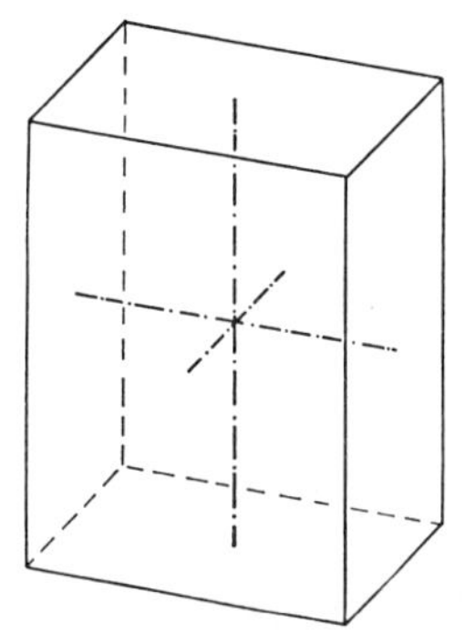

Fig. 273.

Pinacoids. These forms occur with their usual number of faces and are designated, as heretofore, by the terms *basal, brachy-*, and *macropinacoids*, depending upon the fact whether they intersect the c, b, or a axes. They are called the *base* and the *side* and *front* pinacoids, respectively. Figure 273 shows these pinacoids in combination.

Summary. The various forms and symbols are given in Table 13 on page 88.

Combinations. Figure 274, $x = (a : b : c)$, $\{111\}$; $r = (a : -b : c)$, $\{1\bar{1}1\}$; $m = (a : b : \infty c)$, $\{110\}$; $M = (a : -b : \infty c)$, $\{1\bar{1}0\}$; $s = (a : \infty b : 2c)$, $\{201\}$; $a = (a : \infty b : \infty c)$, $\{100\}$. Axinite ($Ca_2(Fe,Mn)Al_2OH$-$BO_3Si_4O_{12}$).

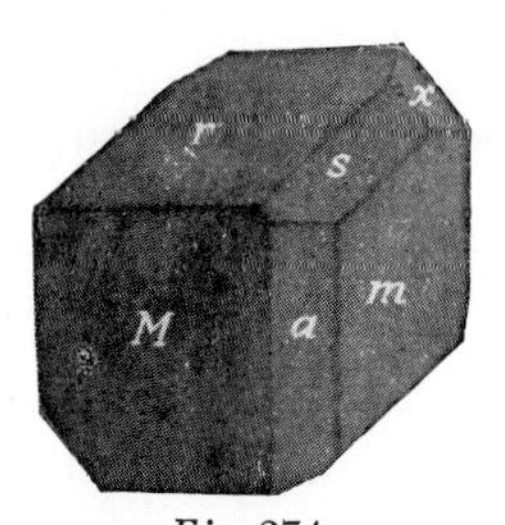

Fig. 274.

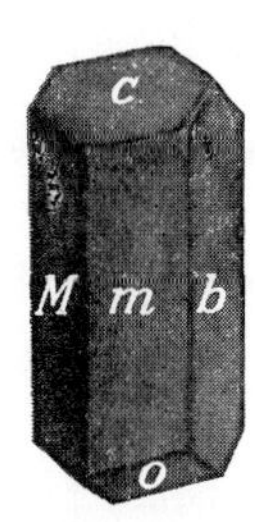

Fig. 275.

Fig. 276.

Figures 275 and 276, $m = (a : b : \infty c)$, $\{110\}$; $M = (a : -b : \infty c)$, $\{1\bar{1}0\}$; $b = (\infty a : b : \infty c)$, $\{010\}$; $c = (\infty a : \infty b : c)$, $\{001\}$; $x = (a : \infty b : -c)$, $\{10\bar{1}\}$; $o = a : b : -c$, $\{11\bar{1}\}$; $y = (a : \infty b : -2c)$, $\{20\bar{1}\}$; $n = (\infty a : -b : 2c)$, $\{0\bar{2}1\}$; $f = (3a : b : \infty c)$, $\{130\}$; $z = (3a : -b : \infty c)$, $\{1\bar{3}0\}$. Albite ($NaAlSi_3O_8$).

TABLE 13

Symmetry, 1		The only element of symmetry in this class is the *center of symmetry*	
Forms		All forms consist of two faces	
		Symbols	
		Weiss	Miller
Tetarto-bipyramids	Unit	$a: b: c$	$\{111\}$
		$a:-b: c$	$\{1\bar{1}1\}$
		$a: b:-c$	$\{11\bar{1}\}$
		$a:-b:-c$	$\{1\bar{1}\bar{1}\}$
	Modified	$a: b: mc$	$\{hhl\}$
		$a:-b: mc$	$\{h\bar{h}l\}$
		$a: b:-mc$	$\{hh\bar{l}\}$
		$a:-b:-mc$	$\{h\bar{h}\bar{l}\}$
	Brachy-	$na: b: mc$	$\{hkl\}$
		$na:-b: mc$	$\{h\bar{k}l\}$
		$na: b:-mc$	$\{hk\bar{l}\}$
		$na:-b:-mc$	$\{h\bar{k}\bar{l}\}$
	Macro-	$a: nb: mc$	$\{khl\}$
		$a:-nb: mc$	$\{k\bar{h}l\}$
		$a: nb:-mc$	$\{kh\bar{l}\}$
		$a:-nb:-mc$	$\{k\bar{h}\bar{l}\}$
Hemiprisms	Unit	$a: b: \infty c$	$\{110\}$
		$a:-b: \infty c$	$\{1\bar{1}0\}$
	Brachy-	$na: b: \infty c$	$\{hk0\}$
		$na:-b: \infty c$	$\{h\bar{k}0\}$
	Macro-	$a: nb: \infty c$	$\{kh0\}$
		$a:-nb: \infty c$	$\{k\bar{h}0\}$
Hemidomes	Brachy-	$\infty a: b: mc$	$\{0kl\}$
		$\infty a:-b: mc$	$\{0\bar{k}l\}$
	Macro-	$a: \infty b: mc$	$\{h0l\}$
		$a: \infty b:-mc$	$\{h0\bar{l}\}$
Pinacoids	Basal	$\infty a: \infty b: c$	$\{001\}$
	Brachy-	$\infty a: b: \infty c$	$\{010\}$
	Macro-	$a: \infty b: \infty c$	$\{100\}$

9 | Compound Crystals

General Statement. The crystals considered thus far have been bounded by either a single form as in the case of an octahedron (Fig. 57, page 25) or by a combination of forms (Fig. 78, page 30). They have, however, in all cases been single individuals. In many instances, crystals occur in groups and may be designated as *crystal aggregates* or *parallel groups.* A single crystal is sometimes made up of two or more individuals arranged according to some definite law. These crystals are designated as *twin crystals* or, simply, *twins.*

Fig. 277. Aggregate of calcite crystals. Cumberland, England.

Crystal Aggregates. These are groups of crystals arranged in no definite manner. They are usually singly terminated (Fig. 277).

Parallel Groups. Often two or more crystals of the same substance are observed to have so intergrown that the crystallographic axes of the one individual are parallel to those of the others. Such an arrangement of crystals is termed a *parallel group.* Figures 278, 279, and 280 show such groups of quartz and calcite, respectively. Occasionally, crystals of different substances are grouped in this way.

Twin Crystals. Two crystals may also intergrow so that, even though parallelism of the crystals is wanting, the growth has, nevertheless, taken place in some definite manner. Such crystals are spoken of as *twin crystals* or, in short, *twins*. Figure 281 illustrates a twin crystal commonly observed on staurolite. In twin crystals both individuals have at least one crystal plane or a direction in common. Figure 282 shows a twinned octahedron. The plane common to both parts is termed the *composition plane*. In general, the plane to which the twin crystal is symmetrical is the *twinning plane*. In some instances, *composition* and *twinning planes* coincide. Both, however, are parallel to some possible face of the crystal, which is not parallel to a plane of symmetry in the untwinned crystal. The line or direction perpendicular to the twinning plane is the *twinning axis*. A *twinning law* is expressed by indicating the *twinning plane* or *twinning axis*.

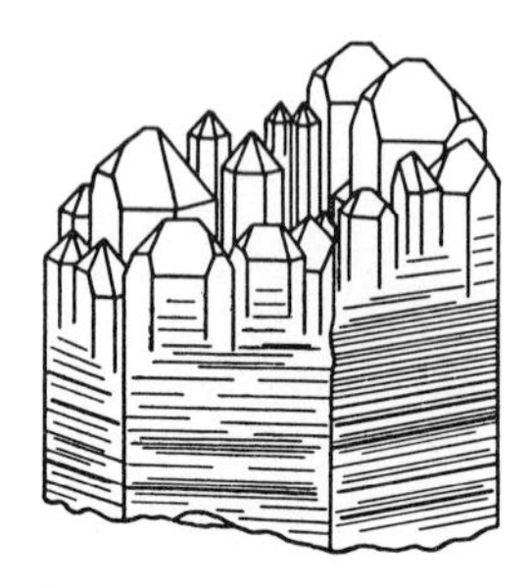

Fig. 278. Parallel group of quartz crystals.

Fig. 279. Parallel group of quartz crystals. Quindel, Switzerland.

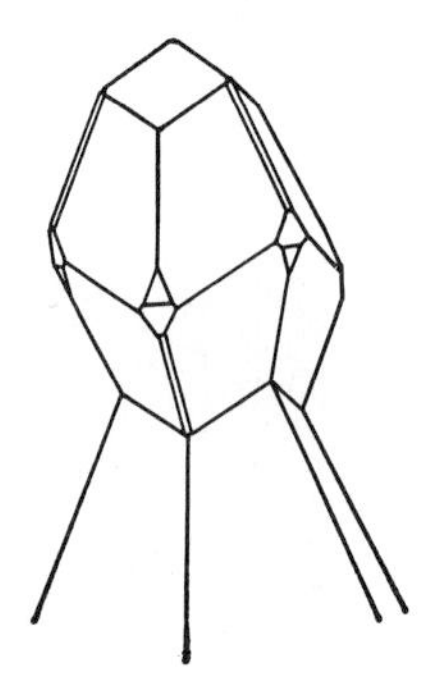

Fig. 280. Parallel group of calcite crystals.

Twin crystals are commonly divided into two classes: (1) *contact* or *juxtaposition* twins, and (2) *penetration* twins.[1] These are illustrated by Figs. 282 and 281, respectively. Contact twins consist of two individuals so placed that if one could be rotated through 180° about the twinning axis the simple crystal would result.[2] In penetration twins two individuals appear to have interpenetrated one another. If one of the individuals could be rotated through 180° about the twinning axis, both individuals would occupy the same position.

[1] Also designated as *reflection* and *rotation* twins, because they are symmetrical to a plane or an axis, respectively.

[2] This can be done with wooden models (Figs. 285, 286, and 287).

Contact and penetration twins are comparatively common in all systems. In studying twins, it must be borne in mind, as pointed out on page 20, that owing to distortion the two individuals may not be morphologically symmetrical. Re-entrant angles are commonly indicative of twinning.

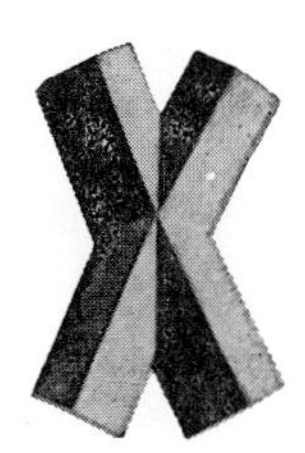

Fig. 281.

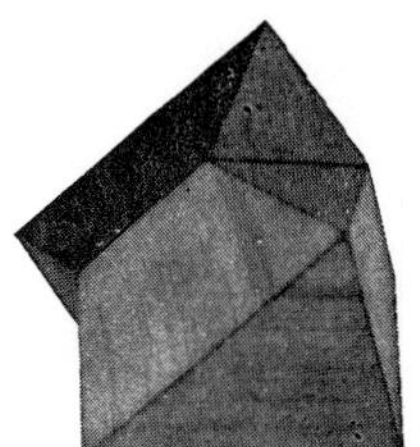

Fig. 282.

Common Twinning Laws. Only those twinning laws which are most frequently observed on the minerals described in this text will be considered.

Cubic System. The most common law in the cubic system is known as the *spinel law,* the twinning plane being parallel to a face of an octahedron, $(a : a : a)$, $\{111\}$. Figure 282 shows such a twin crystal of the mineral spinel. A penetration twin of fluorite is shown in Fig. 283. Here, two cubes have intergrown according to this law.

Fig. 283.

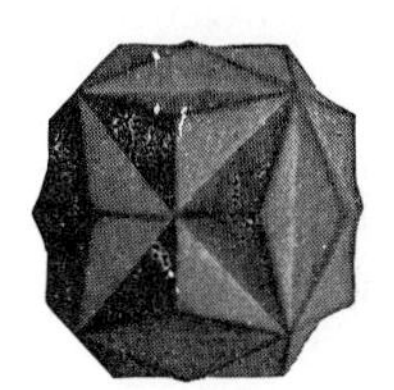

Fig. 284.

Figure 284 shows a penetration twin of two pyritohedrons of the mineral pyrite. These twins are often known as crystals of the *iron cross.* A plane parallel to a face of the rhombic dodecahedron, $(a : a : \infty a)$, $\{110\}$, is the twinning plane.

Hexagonal System. Calcite and quartz are the only common minerals belonging to this system which furnish good examples of twinning.

Upon calcite the basal pinacoid, $(\infty a : \infty a : \infty a : c)$, $\{0001\}$, is commonly a twinning plane. Figures 285 and 286 illustrate this law.[1] A plane parallel to a face of the negative rhombohedron, $-(\infty a : 2a : 2a : c)$, $\{01\bar{1}2\}$, may also be a twinning plane as illustrated by Fig. 287. These are the most common laws on calcite.

[1] Compare with Figs. 146 and 151.

The common or Dauphiné twinning law on quartz is shown in Fig. 288. Here either two right- or two left-hand crystals have intergrown

Fig. 285.

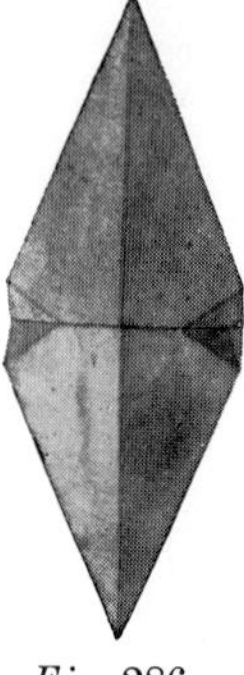

Fig. 286.

Fig. 287.

in such a way that one appears to have been revolved 180° about the c axis as the twinning axis.

The so-called *Brazilian law* is also common on twins of quartz (Fig.

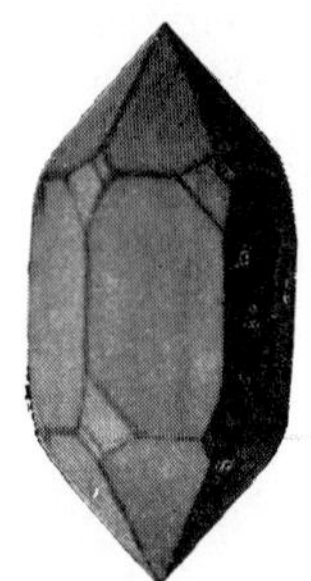

Fig. 288.

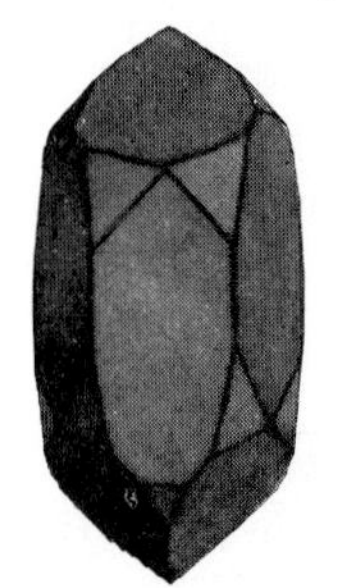

Fig. 289.

289). Here, right and left crystals have intergrown so that the twin is now symmetrical to a plane parallel to a face of the prism of the second order, $(2a : 2a : a : \infty c)$, $\{11\bar{2}0\}$ (see also Figs. 530 and 531, page 294).

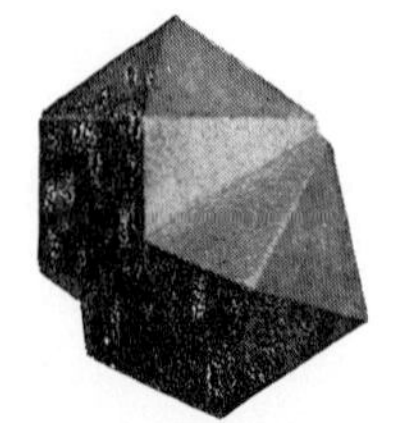

Fig. 290.

Tetragonal System. Most of the twin crystals of this system are to be observed on substances crystallizing in the ditetragonal bipyramidal class. A plane parallel to a face of the unit bipyramid of the second order, $(\infty a : a : c)$, $\{011\}$, commonly acts as the twinning plane. Figure 290 represents a crystal of cassiterite twinned according to this law, which is also frequently observed on zircon and rutile.

Orthorhombic System. The most common twins of this system belong to the bipyramidal class in which any face aside from the pinacoids may act as the twinning plane. Figure 291 shows a penetration twin of staurolite, where the brachydome, $(\infty a : b : \frac{3}{2}c)$, $\{032\}$, acts as the twinning plane. Figure 292 shows the same mineral with the bipyramid, $(\frac{3}{2}a : b : \frac{3}{2}c)$, $\{232\}$, as the twinning plane. Figure 293

Fig. 291.

Fig. 292.

Fig. 293.

represents a contact twin of aragonite. Here the unit prism, $(a : b : \infty c)$, $\{110\}$, is the twinning plane.

Monoclinic System. In this system, gypsum and orthoclase furnish some of the best examples. Figure 294 shows a contact twin of gypsum in which the orthopinacoid, $(a : \infty b : \infty c)$, $\{100\}$, is the twinning plane.

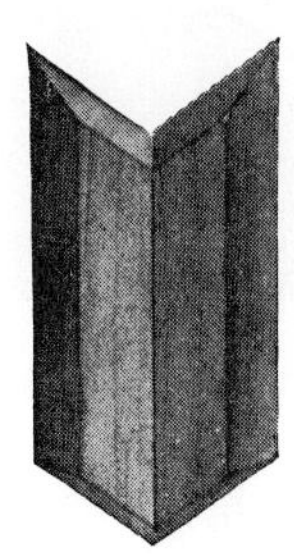
Fig. 294.

Fig. 295.

Fig. 296.

Penetration twins of orthoclase are shown in Figs. 295 (left) and 296 (right). Here, the c axis acts as twinning axis. This is known as the

Fig. 297.

Fig. 298.

Carlsbad law on orthoclase. Two other twinning laws are also frequently observed on orthoclase, namely, the *Baveno* and *Manebach laws*, where the clinodome, $(\infty a : b : 2c)$, $\{021\}$ (Fig. 297), and the basal pinacoid, $(\infty a : \infty b : c)$, $\{001\}$ (Fig. 298), respectively, act as the twinning planes.

Triclinic System. Since there are no planes of symmetry in this system, any plane may act as the twinning plane. The mineral albite furnishes good examples. In Fig. 299, the brachypinacoid, $(\infty a : b : \infty c)$, $\{010\}$, is the twinning plane. This is the *albite law*. Another common

Fig. 299.

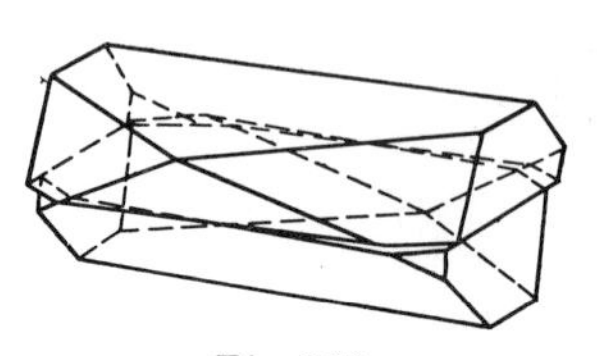

Fig. 300.

law is shown by Fig. 300. Here, the basal pinacoids of both individuals are parallel, the crystallographic b axis acting as the twinning axis. This is known as the *pericline law*.

Fig. 301.

Fig. 302.

Fig. 303.

Summary of the Common Twinning Laws. Table 14 gives the important twinning laws in the different systems and the names of the minerals on which they may be observed.

Repeated Twinning. In the foregoing, crystals consisting of but two individuals have been discussed. Intergrowths of three, four, five, or

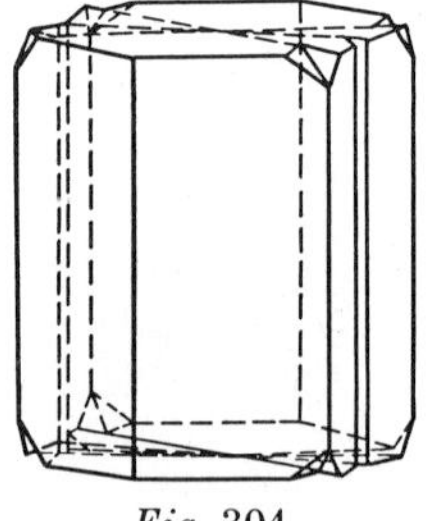

Fig. 304.

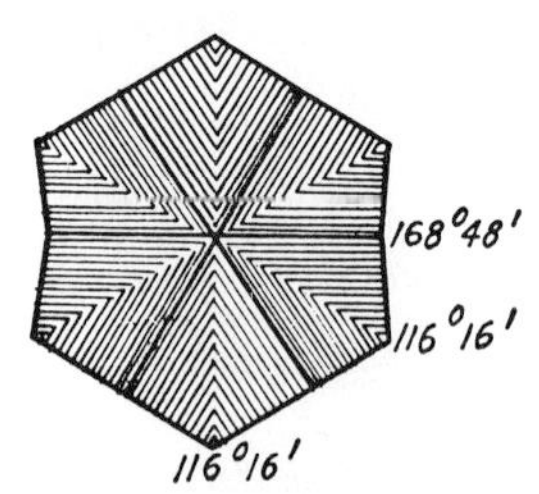

Fig. 305.

more individuals are termed *threelings*, *fourlings*, *fivelings*, and so on. *Polysynthetic* and *cyclic* twins are the result of repeated twinning. In the polysynthetic twins, the twinning planes between adjacent individuals are parallel. This is illustrated by Figs. 301 and 302 showing

TABLE 14

System	Twinning plane or axis, and type of twin	Mineral
Cubic	1. Octahedron, contact and penetration $(a:a:a)$ *Spinel law*	Spinel, fluorite
	2. Rhombic dodecahedron, penetration $(a:a:\infty a)$ *Iron cross law*	Pyrite
Hexagonal	1. Basal pinacoid, contact $(\infty a:\infty a:\infty a:c)$	Calcite
	2. Rhombohedral, contact $-(\infty a:2a:2a:c)$, $-\frac{1}{2}R$	Calcite
	3. c is twinning axis, penetration *Dauphiné law*	Quartz (Two right or two left individuals)
	4. Prism of the second order, penetration $(2a:2a:a:\infty c)$ *Brazilian law*	Quartz (Right and left individuals)
Tetragonal	Bipyramid of the second order, contact $(a:\infty a:c)$	Cassiterite, rutile, zircon
Orthorhombic	1. Prism, contact and penetration $(a:b:\infty c)$	Aragonite, cerussite, marcasite,
	2. Brachydome, penetration $(\infty a:b:\frac{3}{2}c)$	Staurolite (*cross* or *plus* (+) shape)
	3. Brachybipyramid, penetration $(\frac{3}{2}a:b:\frac{3}{2}c)$	Staurolite (x shape)
Monoclinic	1. Orthopinacoid, contact and penetration $(a:\infty b:\infty c)$	Gypsum, pyroxenes, amphiboles
	2. c is twinning axis, penetration *Karlsbad law*	Orthoclase
	3. Clinodome, contact $(\infty a:b:2c)$ *Baveno law*	Orthoclase
	4. Basal pinacoid, contact $(\infty a:\infty b:c)$ *Manebach law*	Orthoclase
Triclinic	1. Brachypinacoid, contact $(\infty a:b:\infty c)$ *Albite law*	Microcline and plagioclase feldspars
	2. b is twinning axis, contact *Pericline law*	Microcline and plagioclase feldspars

polysynthetic twins of albite and aragonite, respectively.[1] If the individuals are very thin, the re-entrant angles are usually indicated by striations. Cyclic twins result when the twinning planes do not remain parallel, as, for example, when adjacent or opposite faces of a form act as twinning planes. This is shown by the cyclic twins of rutile (Fig. 303) in which adjacent faces of the unit bipyramid of the second order, $(\infty a : a : c)$, $\{011\}$, act as twinning planes.

Mimicry. As a result of repeated twinning, forms of an apparently higher grade of symmetry often result. This is especially true of those substances possessing pseudosymmetry (footnote 2, page 64). Figure 304 shows a *trilling* or *threeling* of the orthorhombic mineral aragonite, which is apparently hexagonal in its outline. In Fig. 305 the cross section is shown. This phenomenon is called *mimicry.*

[1] Compare with Figs. 299 and 293.

10 | Physical Properties

Those physical properties which are easily recognized or determined and are important in the rapid determination of minerals will be discussed in this chapter. The optical properties involving the use of the microscope will be treated later.

Luster. The luster of a mineral is the appearance of its surface in reflected light and is a property of fundamental importance in the recognition of minerals. Luster is a function of the transparency, refractivity, and structure of a mineral. It is in no way related to hardness. There are two principal types of luster, *metallic* and *nonmetallic.*

Metallic luster is exhibited by metals and by minerals of a metallic appearance. Substances with a metallic luster are opaque or nearly so and quite heavy. The common minerals pyrite and galena possess metallic luster.

All other kinds of luster are referred to as being nonmetallic. Some of the more important nonmetallic lusters are the following:

Vitreous. The luster of glass or quartz.

Adamantine. The exceedingly brilliant luster of minerals with high indices of refraction, as the diamond and pyromorphite.

Resinous. The luster or appearance of resin. This is well shown by sphalerite.

Greasy. The appearance of an oiled surface. Example, nepheline.

Pearly. This is similar to the luster of mother-of-pearl. It is commonly shown by minerals with a lamellar or platy structure and by those with pronounced cleavages. Example, talc.

Silky. This luster is the result of a fibrous structure and is well shown by fibrous gypsum (satin spar) and asbestos.

Dull. Not bright or shiny, good examples being chalk and kaolin. Sometimes called *earthy* luster.

The terms *splendent, shining, glistening,* and *glimmering* are sometimes used. They have reference to the intensity or quantity of light reflected. In some instances the luster is not the same on all faces of a crystal. Thus, on apophyllite it is pearly on the basal pinacoid and vitreous elsewhere. When a luster is intermediate between metallic and nonmetallic, it is frequently called *metalloidal* or *submetallic.*

Fig. 306. Albin Weisbach (1833–1901). Professor of mineralogy in the Saxon School of Mines, Freiberg, Germany. Pioneer in the use of physical properties for the determination of minerals.

Color. The color of a mineral is one of the first physical properties to be observed. Some minerals have a fairly constant color and are called *idiochromatic.* Other minerals have colors that vary greatly. This variation in color may be due to the presence of pigments, inclusions, or other impurities. Such minerals are termed *allochromatic.*

In idiochromatic minerals the color is an inherent property, for some essential constituent of the mineral is the pigmenting agent. Common examples of idiochromatic minerals are sulfur, yellow; malachite, green; azurite, blue; pyrite, yellow; magnetite, black. In these minerals the color is constant and, therefore, may be of material assistance in their identification.

Fig. 307. Tourmaline showing zonal distribution of color and spherical triangular outline. San Diego County, California.

Fig. 308. Agate. Brazil.

In allochromatic minerals the color may vary greatly. These minerals are colorless or white, when pure. The variation in color is due to pigmenting impurities that may be present in submicroscopic particles or as inclusions of other colored minerals. For example, quartz is entirely colorless when pure, but it is more often colored and among its varieties practically every hue is represented. Some of the colored varieties are the purple amethyst, the brown to black smoky quartz, the pink rose quartz, and the golden yellow citrine.

The pigment of allochromatic minerals is often irregularly distributed. The color may, hence, occur in patches or blotches, as in amethyst or sapphire. On the other hand, the color may be distributed in regular and sharply bounded zones or bands, as, for example, in tourmaline. The zonal distribution of color in tourmaline may be such that it occurs in horizontal bands across the length of the crystal, or in concentric zones parallel to the spherical triangular outline (Fig. 307). Agate, a variety of quartz, is commonly banded with colors (Fig. 308). Moreover, the coloring may be so distributed as to produce interesting and attractive markings, as in moss agate (Fig. 309) and in chiastolite (Fig. 310).

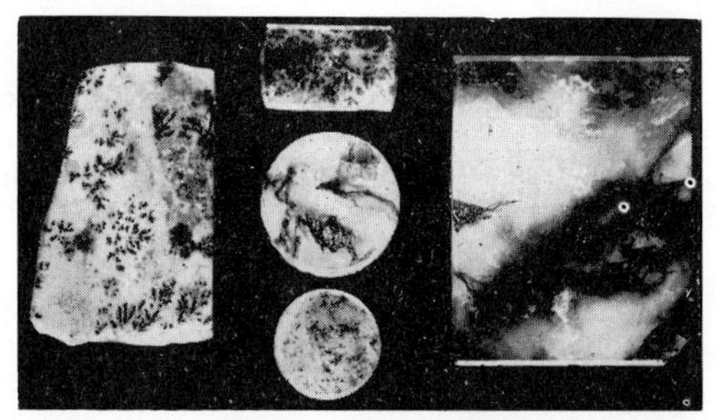

Fig. 309. Moss agate.

Fig. 310. Andalusite: variety, chiastolite. Lancaster, Massachusetts.

Play or Change of Colors. Some minerals exhibit different colors as the specimen is slowly turned, or as the direction of observation is changed. This is well illustrated by labradorite and precious opal.

Opalescence. This consists of milky or pearly reflections from the interior of the specimen, as is seen in some opals and in moonstone. Opalescence is usually observed to best advantage on specimens with rounded and polished surfaces.

Chatoyancy. The changeable, wavy, silky sheen shown by some minerals with a fibrous structure is known as *chatoyancy.* The satin spar variety of gypsum (Fig. 311) and tiger's-eye, a variety of quartz (Fig. 312), are excellent examples of minerals showing chatoyancy. Minerals with this property, cut with a convex surface, called the *cabochon* cut, are frequently used as gems.

Iridescence. Some minerals show a play of bright colors due to a thin coating or film on the surface of the specimen, as is often the case with limonite. In some cases it is due to cleavage cracks.

Tarnish. After certain minerals have been exposed to air, the color of the exposed portions differs distinctly from that of the freshly fractured surfaces. Bornite and copper are good examples.

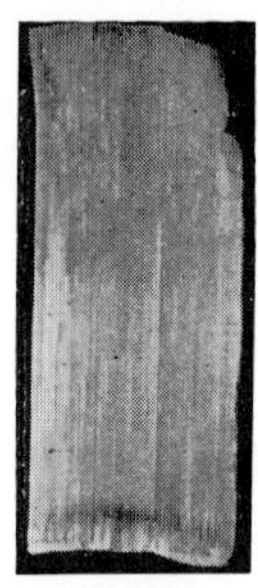

Fig. 311. Gypsum: variety, satin spar. Montmartre, Paris, France.

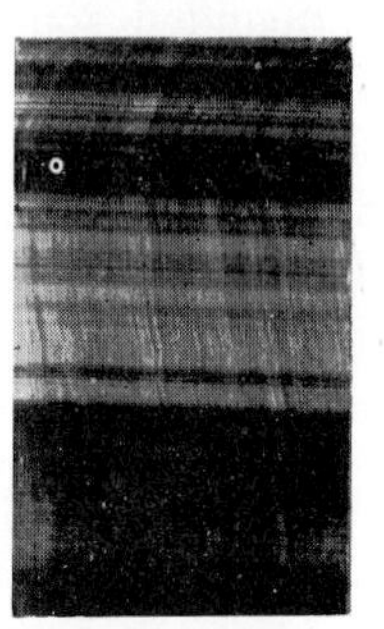

Fig. 312. Tiger's-eye. Griqualand West, Union of South Africa.

Asterism. Some minerals, like certain natural and synthetic sapphires and rubies, exhibit a star-like light effect when viewed in reflected light. Other minerals show a similar effect in transmitted light, that is, when an intense source of light is viewed by holding the specimen close to the eye, for example, phlogopite (Fig. 313).

Fig. 313. Asterism shown by phlogopite from South Burgess, Canada.

Transparency or Diaphaneity. This is the ability of a mineral to transmit light. This property, along with color and luster, can usually be recognized upon first sight. Substances through which objects can be easily and distinctly seen are said to be *transparent.* Rock crystal or colorless quartz (Fig. 314) is an excellent example of a transparent mineral. When some light passes through the substance and objects are seen only indistinctly, the mineral is *translucent.* Relatively thin slabs of Mexican onyx and jade are translucent. Substances are *opaque* when no light is transmitted

Fig. 314. Rock crystal. Dauphiné, France.

even through thin edges or layers, for example, graphite. The terms *subtransparent* and *subtranslucent* indicate intermediate stages.

Streak. This is the color of the fine powder of a mineral and is frequently made use of in the determination of minerals. Although the color of minerals may vary greatly, the streak is often fairly constant. The color of the streak may be determined by crushing, filing, or scratching. The usual and most satisfactory method, however, is to rub the mineral on a piece of white unglazed porcelain, called the *streak plate.* A streak of ¼ inch in length is generally sufficient to determine its color. The ease or difficulty with which the streak can be obtained with the plate is to some extent indicative of the hardness of the mineral. The streak plate cannot be used with minerals with a hardness of 7 or more, for these minerals are harder than the plate. The streak-plate method is the one commonly used in the laboratory.

Fig. 315. Edward S. Dana (1849–1935). Noted American mineralogist. For many years professor in Yale University and editor of the *American Journal of Science.*

When a streak plate is not available, the streak can be determined by crushing a small fragment to a fine powder and examining it for color, either unaided or with a hand lens, on a light background, such as a piece of paper, or on a fingernail. Obviously, when a mineral is filed or scratched as in determining the hardness, a fine powder is produced, which may be examined for color as just indicated.

Some minerals having the same color possess streaks which differ materially. Thus, the following three iron minerals may all be black, but they can be readily distinguished by their streaks: hematite (Fe_2O_3), red brown; goethite ($HFeO_2$),yellow brown; magnetite ($FeFe_2O_4$), black.

The *rubbed streak* is produced when some soft minerals are rubbed on glazed porcelain. The rubbed streak is useful in distinguishing graphite (C) with a black shiny streak from molybdenite (MoS_2) with a greenish streak.

Hardness. The resistance offered by a mineral to abrasion or scratching is termed *hardness.* It is of great importance in the rapid recognition of minerals, for the approximate hardness of a specimen can be very easily determined. Hardness is indicated relatively in terms of Mohs scale, which consists of 10 minerals arranged in order of increasing hardness, as follows:

1. Talc.
2. Gypsum.
3. Calcite.
4. Fluorite.
5. Apatite.
6. Feldspar.
7. Quartz.
8. Topaz.
9. Corundum.
10. Diamond.

Beryl, 7.5 to 8 in hardness, is often substituted for topaz in the above scale. The values assigned to the members of this scale indicate simply the *relative* hardness.

The hardness of a mineral is determined by ascertaining its relative position in the Mohs scale of hardness. The mineral with the greater hardness will scratch the softer mineral, and a softer mineral will be scratched by a harder one. Two minerals with the same hardness will either not scratch each other at all, or they may scratch one another slightly. If quartz (7) scratches a mineral but the mineral in turn distinctly scratches feldspar (6), the hardness of 6½ is assigned to it. In determining the hardness of a mineral the scratch made should be as short as possible, not over ¼ inch, and care exercised to distinguish between a scratch and a chalk mark. The latter is easily removed by rubbing.

The determination of the approximate hardness is greatly simplified by using a fingernail, copper coin, knife blade, a piece of window glass, streak plate, or a steel file, which possess the following values:

Fingernail, up to 2.5.
Copper coin, up to 3.
Knife blade, up to 5.5.
Window glass, 5.5.
Streak plate, 6.5.
Steel file, 6 to 7.

Since the majority of the minerals are less than 6 in hardness, this simplified scale is of great convenience in determining the approximate hardness in the laboratory and field.

Fig. 316. Hardness pencils.

The hardness of crystals and of small specimens, as well as of rough and uncut gems, is best determined by using *hardness pencils*. These are holders with conical-shaped fragments of the test minerals mounted on the ends (Fig. 316). A set of four pencils in a leather case contains the following seven test minerals: feldspar, 6; quartz, 7; zircon, 7½; topaz, 8; chrysoberyl, 8½; corundum, 9; diamond, 10. The *hardness wheel* is a very convenient arrangement of the hardness pencils. The wheel shown in Fig. 317 contains the following six test minerals: olivine, 6¾; quartz, 7; zircon, 7½; topaz, 8; chrysoberyl, 8½; corundum, 9. The pencils and the wheel obviously permit a very easy manipulation.

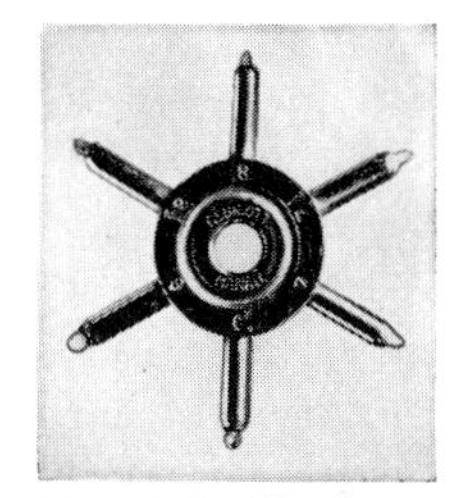

Fig. 317. Hardness wheel.

In testing gems many jewelers first use the steel file. If the file "bites" the tested material, the latter's hardness is below 7. The file will not bite stones harder than 7 but will slide over the edge being tested, often leaving a steel streak. Since many imitation gems, especially those of glass, have a hardness less than 7, while most of the gemstones are harder, this simple test with the steel file is helpful in distinguishing between them.

Since hardness is expressed in terms of a numerical scale, it might well be inferred that the hardness of a mineral is a constant quantity. This is, however, not correct, for the hardness of a mineral varies with the crystallographic direction. Ordinarily the variation is so slight as not to be detected by the usual methods; but in some minerals it is quite marked. Thus, kyanite, which occurs in elongated crystals, has a hardness of 4 to 5 parallel to the length of the crystals, while at right angles to the elongation it is much higher, 6 to 7. That the hardness of the diamond varies with direction has long been known to diamond cutters. Moreover, the apparent hardness of minerals is influenced by their brittleness and by the presence or absence of fractures or cleavages, which must be taken into consideration.

TABLE 15. COMPARATIVE HARDNESS VALUES

Mineral	Mohs*	Pfaff†	Jaggar‡	Rosiwal§	Knoop,¶ Peters, Emerson
Corundum	9	1,000	1,000	1,000	1,000‖
Topaz	8	459	152	139	764.5
Quartz	7	254	40	117	486.2
Orthoclase	6	191	25	32	342.4
Apatite	5	53.5	1.23	7.15	269
Fluorite	4	37.3	0.75	4.66	100
Calcite	3	15.3	0.26	4.49	82.6
Gypsum	2	12.03	0.04	2.42**	19.6
Talc	1	—	—	1.1††	—

*†‡§¶ Scratching, abrasion, boring, grinding, indenting method, respectively.
‖ Alundum, synthetic corundum.
** Halite, rock salt.
†† Steatite.

The hardness of metals and alloys is generally related to their resistance to deformation and is determined by various indenting methods. These indenting methods are usually difficult to use with minerals, since they are not easily deformed under pressure without rupturing.

Many attempts have been made to determine the hardness of minerals on a quantitative basis, using scratching, abrasion, grinding, and indenting methods. Because of the many factors involved, such as (1) brittleness; (2) presence or absence of cleavages, fractures, or twinning; (3) variation of hardness with direction, which in most instances has been neglected; (4) differences in crystal structure; and (5) the use of noncomparable material by the various investigators, the results vary greatly. Table 15 clearly shows this lack of concordant results.

The marked differences in results are further shown by the divergent determinations obtained by Rosiwal (grinding) and by Knoop, Peters, and Emerson (indenting) for the average hardness of the diamond as compared with that of corundum. According to Rosiwal the diamond is ninety times, while according to Knoop *et al.* it is five times, harder than corundum.

In the tables for the determination of minerals on pages 493 to 661, minerals have been divided into three groups based upon the hardness of calcite and feldspar, thus: (1) 1 to 3, softer than or as hard as calcite; (2) 3 to 6, harder than calcite but not harder than feldspar; (3) over 6, harder than feldspar.

Cleavage. Many minerals split or separate readily along definite planes. This property is called *cleavage*. It is frequently very conspicuous and highly characteristic. A mineral can be cleaved either by striking it a properly directed blow with a hammer or by pressing upon it in a definite direction with the sharp edge of a knife blade. Cleavage takes place between those planes in which the atoms are most closely bonded. These planes are called *cleavage planes* and are parallel to possible crystal faces and are so designated. Thus, cubical cleavage,

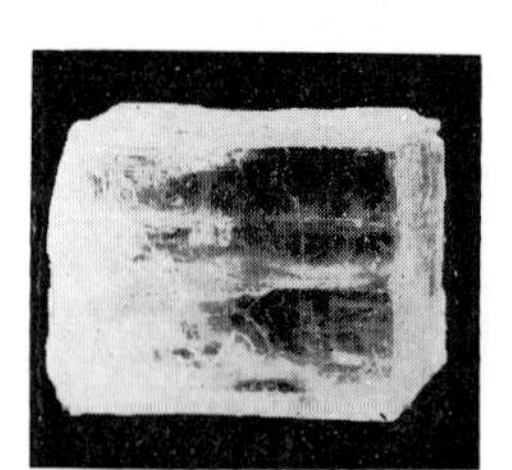

Fig. 318. Cubical cleavage, halite. Stassfurt, Germany.

Fig. 319. Octahedral cleavage, fluorite. Near Rosiclare, Illinois.

that is, parallel to the faces of the cube, is shown by galena and halite (Fig. 318); octahedral cleavage, by fluorite (Fig. 319) and the diamond (Fig. 320); rhombic dodecahedral cleavage, by sphalerite; rhombohedral cleavage, by calcite; prismatic cleavage, by hornblende; basal cleavage, by topaz and mica; clinopinacoidal cleavage, by gypsum. The ease and perfection with which cleavages are obtained are indicated by such terms as *perfect*, *imperfect*, *distinct*, *easy*, and so forth. Thus, calcite is said to have a perfect rhombohedral cleavage.

Fig. 320. Famous Cullinan diamond after being cleaved parallel to face of octahedron.

The cleavage of minerals, and especially of crystals, can often be recognized by the presence and direction of cleavage cracks. Cleavage may also be frequently determined by carefully studying the outline and character of the surfaces of the specimen. In such cases, it is not necessary to resort to striking the specimen a blow and, hence, shattering it somewhat, or to the use of a knife-edge. Moreover, when the shape and character of the small particles resulting from the crushing of fragments or from scratching the specimen are examined with a hand lens, the cleavage of the mineral may often be recognized. As cleavage is dependent upon regularity of structure, it is observed only on crystallized substances. Amorphous substances do not possess cleavage.

The important cleavages in the various systems and the common minerals upon which they may be observed are given in Table 16.

Parting. This is a separation somewhat similar to cleavage and is sometimes called *false cleavage.* It is frequently the result of polysynthetic twinning. It may also be due to pressure applied in definite directions. Corundum has basal, rhombohedral, and prismatic partings.

Fracture. The fracture of a mineral refers to the character of the surface obtained when crystalline substances are broken in directions other than those along which cleavage or parting may take place. Minerals with no cleavage or with only a poor cleavage yield fracture surfaces very easily. As amorphous substances are devoid of cleavage, they always show fracture surfaces when shattered by a blow. The following types of fracture may be distinguished:

TABLE 16

Cleavage	Mineral
Cubic System	
Cubical	Galena, halite
Rhombic dodecahedral	Sphalerite, sodalite
Octahedral	Fluorite, diamond, cuprite
Hexagonal System	
Rhombohedral	Calcite, dolomite, siderite
Basal	Beryl, apatite, nepheline
Prismatic	Apatite, nepheline
Tetragonal System	
Basal	Apophyllite
Prismatic, first order	Rutile, zircon, scapolite
Prismatic, second order	Rutile, scapolite
Pyramidal, first order	Scheelite, wulfenite
Pyramidal, second order	Scheelite
Orthorhombic System	
Basal	Anhydrite (pearly), barite, celestite, topaz
Brachypinacoidal	Anhydrite (vitreous), stibnite, orthorhombic pyroxenes
Macropinacoidal	Anhydrite (greasy to dull)
Prismatic	Barite, celestite, orthorhombic pyroxenes
Monoclinic System	
Basal	Orthoclase, micas, chlorites, epidote
Clinopinacoidal	Orthoclase, gypsum, stilbite
Orthopinacoidal	Epidote
Prismatic	Amphiboles, pyroxenes
Triclinic System	
Basal	Plagioclases, microcline
Brachypinacoidal	Plagioclases, kyanite
Macropinacoidal	Kyanite

Conchoidal. The surfaces are curved and shell-like in character. Example, quartz.

Even. The fracture surfaces are flat or nearly so; that is, they are approximately even planes. Example, lithographic limestone.

Uneven. The surfaces are more uneven. Example, rhodonite.

Hackly. The fracture surfaces have many sharp points and are rough and irregular. Example, copper.

Splintery. The mineral breaks into splinters or fibers. Example, pectolite.

Earthy. The irregular fracture characteristic of earthy substances like chalk, kaolin, and bauxite.

Fracture is best determined by examining carefully the character of the surfaces of the mineral. By using a hand lens, as indicated under cleavage, the fracture may be observed even when the specimen is in small fragments.

Tenacity. Under this heading is included the behavior of minerals when an attempt is made to break, cut, hammer, crush, bend, or tear them. The most important kinds of tenacity are the following:

Brittle. Easily broken or powdered and cannot be cut into slices. Example, quartz.

Sectile. Can be cut and yields shavings, which crumble when struck with a hammer. Example, gypsum.

Malleable. Can be hammered out into thin sheets. Examples, gold and copper.

Ductile. Can be easily drawn into wire. Examples, copper and silver.

Flexible. Thin layers of the mineral can be bent without breaking, and they remain bent after the pressure has been removed. Example, foliated talc.

Elastic. Thin layers of the mineral may be bent without breaking, but they resume their positions when the pressure is removed. Example, mica.

Taste. Minerals soluble in water or the saliva generally possess a characteristic taste, which may be designated as follows:

Acid. The sour taste of sulfuric acid.

Alkaline. The taste of soda or potash.

Astringent. This causes a contraction or puckering. Example, alum.

Bitter. The taste of Epsom or bitter salts.

Cooling. The taste of potassium or sodium nitrate.

Metallic. A very disagreeable, brassy, metallic taste. Example, decomposed pyrite.

Pungent. A sharp and biting taste. Example, ammonium chloride.

Saline. The salty taste of halite or sodium chloride.

Although the taste of a mineral is not a property of great importance, it is sometimes very useful in the rapid determination of minerals.

Odor. Some minerals give off characteristic odors when breathed upon, rubbed, scratched, pounded, or heated, which are designated as follows:

Argillaceous. The clay-like odor obtained by breathing upon kaolin.

Bituminous. The odor produced by minerals containing bituminous or organic matter. Usually it is easily obtained by striking the specimen with a hammer. Example, asphalt.

Fetid. The odor of rotten eggs, due to the liberation of hydrogen sulfide. Example, bituminous limestone.

Garlic. The odor of the vapors evolved when arsenical minerals are heated. Also called *alliaceous* or *arsenical* odor. Example, arsenopyrite

Horse-radish. The very disagreeable odor of decaying horse-radish, obtained by heating compounds of selenium.

Sulfurous. The odor of sulfur dioxide, which is liberated when sulfur or sulfides are heated or roasted. Example, pyrite.

Feel or Touch. The impression one receives by handling or touching a mineral is designated as its *feel* or *touch.* The following terms are in common use:

Cold. The feel of good conductors of heat. Examples, metallic minerals like copper and silver, and some gemstones.

Greasy or Soapy. The slippery feel of talc.

Harsh or Meager. Rough to the touch. Example, chalk.

Smooth. Without projections or irregularities. Example, sepiolite.

Some porous minerals like chalk, kaolin, and diatomaceous earth adhere readily to the tongue.

Specific Gravity. The specific gravity of a solid substance is its weight in air compared with the weight of an equal volume of water. The specific gravity of a mineral is constant, provided its composition does not vary. Many minerals with strikingly similar physical properties often possess specific gravities which differ materially. Thus, celestite ($SrSO_4$) with a specific gravity of 3.95 can be easily distinguished from barite ($BaSO_4$) having a specific gravity of 4.5.

Fig. 321. Philipp von Jolly (1809–1884). Professor of physics in the University of Munich (1854–1884). Inventor of the spiral spring balance, often called the *Jolly balance,* for the determination of specific gravity.

The specific gravity of minerals can be determined most conveniently by means of the spiral spring balance, often known as the *Jolly balance.* An improved, recording model of this balance is illustrated in Fig. 322.[1] This balance consists of an upright tube to which the inner fixed vernier and the movable doubly graduated scale are attached. Within this large tube there is a second, smaller tube which can be moved by the large milled head. To this second tube the outer movable vernier is fastened. A movement of the inner tube upward carries the second vernier and the graduated scale with it. Within the second tube there is a rod of adjustable length, which carries the spiral spring, index, and scale pans. With this form of balance, only two readings and a simple division are necessary to determine the specific gravity.

[1] This balance is known as the Kraus improved Jolly balance. It is manufactured by Eberbach and Son Company, Ann Arbor, Michigan.

In using the balance it is necessary that the graduated scale, the two verniers, and the index, which is attached to the spiral spring, all be at zero, the lower scale pan being immersed in water. This is accomplished by adjusting approximately, by hand, the length of the rod carrying the spring and then introducing the necessary correction by means of the micrometer screw shown directly below the spring in the illustration (Fig. 322). A fragment is then placed on the upper scale pan, and by turning the large milled head, the inner tube, graduated scale, and outer vernier are all driven upward until the index on the spring is again at zero. The fixed inner vernier W now records the elongation of the spring due to the weight of the fragment in air. The scale is then clamped by means of the screw at the lower end of it. The fragment is now transferred to the lower scale pan, immersed in water, and the round tube lowered by the large milled head until the index again reads at zero. During this operation, the outer vernier moves downward on the graduated scale, and its position may now be indicated by L. This is obviously the decrease in the elongation of the spring due to the immersion of the fragment in water. The readings at W and L are all the data necessary for the calculation of the specific gravity. For

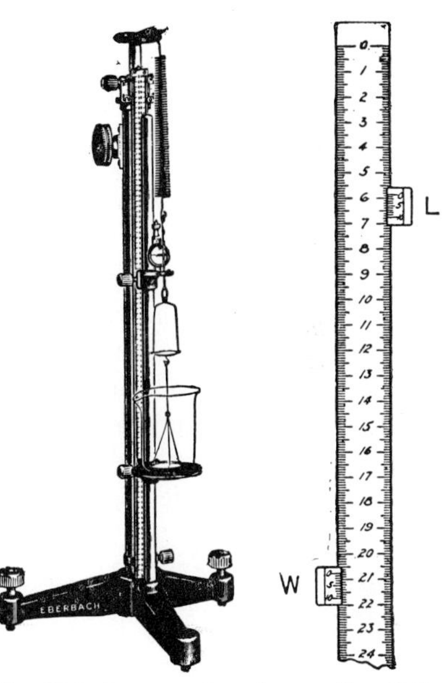

Fig. 322. Improved and recording Jolly balance.

$$\text{Specific gravity} = \frac{\text{weight in air}}{\text{loss of weight in water}} = \frac{W}{L}.$$

It is also obvious that these readings are recorded so that they may be checked, if necessary, after the operations and calculation are completed.

By means of this balance, specific-gravity determinations can be readily made in about two minutes, using for the purpose a crystal or larger mineral fragment as free from impurities as possible. In order to determine the specific gravity of minerals in smaller fragments or grains, it is desirable to make use of either (1) the *pycnometer* or *specific-gravity flask*, (2) the *Berman density balance*, (3) the *Westphal balance*, or (4) the *chemical balance*.

The pycnometer in its simplest form consists of a small glass flask (Fig. 323) fitted with a ground-glass stopper, which is pierced lengthwise by a capillary opening. The pycnometer is first weighed empty (A) and again when filled with distilled water (B). The pycnometer is then emptied and, after being thoroughly dried, the mineral powder, fragments, or grains are introduced and the whole is weighed (C). The pycnometer is again filled with water and a fourth weighing made (D). The specific gravity can then be determined as follows:

Fig. 323. Pycnometer or specific-gravity flask.

$$\text{Specific gravity} = \frac{C - A}{B + C - A - D}.$$

Care must be exercised to remove all the air bubbles, which can usually be done by boiling the water and then allowing it to cool. When this method is carefully carried out, very accurate results may be obtained. When substances are soluble in water, the determination may be made by using some liquid in which they are insoluble, for example, alcohol, and then multiplying the result by the specific gravity of the liquid employed.

Fig. 324. Berman density balance. (*Courtesy of Baird-Atomic, Inc.*)

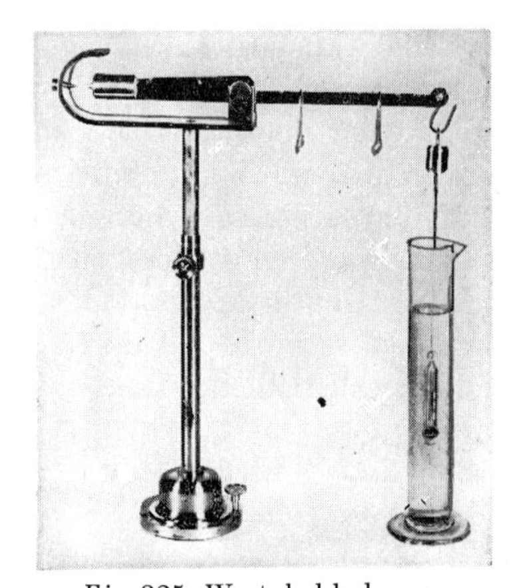

Fig. 325. Westphal balance.

The Berman density (Fig. 324),[1] the Westphal (Fig. 325), and the chemical balances are also well adapted for the determination of the specific gravity of small crystals and fragments. These methods are very accurate and are generally employed in mineralogical research.

[1] Harry Berman, "A Torsion Microbalance for the Determination of Specific Gravity of Minerals," *American Mineralogist*, vol. 24, pp. 434–440, 1939.

Magnetism. Comparatively strong magnetism is shown by a few iron-bearing minerals, their powders or small fragments being readily attracted by a magnet. A convenient method to test the presence or absence of magnetism in a mineral, without crushing it, is to suspend a small horse-shoe magnet from the finger, so that it may swing freely, and then bring the specimen under consideration close to the magnet. If the specimen is magnetic, the magnet will be deviated from its vertical position, the amount of the deviation indicating roughly the relative strength of the magnetism; examples, magnetite and pyrrhotite. Some minerals even act as natural magnets or lodestones and will attract considerable quantities of iron filings, tacks, and nails; examples, certain varieties of magnetite (see Fig. 548, page 306).

Magnetism is of importance in the identification of only a few minerals. However, it may be useful in the separation and concentration of many minerals, both commercially and in the laboratory. When finely ground samples are allowed to fall between the poles of a powerful electromagnet, various fractions can be separated, depending upon the magnetic susceptibility of the different minerals present.

Luminescence. When heated or exposed, in the dark, to the influence of ultraviolet rays, as produced by the iron arc, some minerals glow or become luminescent. Such luminescence may also be produced by exposure to X rays, cathode rays, radiations from radium preparations, and sunlight. Even the mere scratching or pounding of some substances may cause them to show luminescence. The luminescent colors are frequently markedly different from those of the unexcited minerals. The display of these colors is not only interesting but may be even quite spectacular.

Fig. 326. Leonard J. Spencer (1870–). Long associated with the British Museum. Distinguished for his many contributions to mineralogy and as editor for 55 years of the *Mineralogical Magazine.*

A substance is said to *fluoresce* if it is luminescent during the period of excitation, and to *phosphoresce* if the luminescence continues after the cause of excitation has been removed. Fluorescence or phosphorescence, or both, are exhibited by fluorite, calcite, scheelite, sphalerite, willemite, diamond, and other substances.

The luminescence caused by scratching, rubbing, or pounding is called *triboluminescence.* This is often well shown by some varieties of sphalerite. When the luminescence is the result of the application of heat, as is often observed on fluorite, it is termed *thermoluminescence.*

Fluorescence and phosphorescence can be readily induced by the use of mercury-vapor and argon lamps or by an iron-arc apparatus, all of which are available in convenient forms. Portable ultraviolet lamps, sold under trade names, such as *Mineralight* and *Radarlite*, are used in prospecting.

Electrical Properties. Some minerals possess interesting electrical properties. These properties are frequently classified as (1) *frictional electricity*, (2) *pyroelectricity*, (3) *piezoelectricity*, (4) *electrical conductivity*, and (5) *thermoelectricity*. The first three types will be discussed briefly.

Fig. 327.

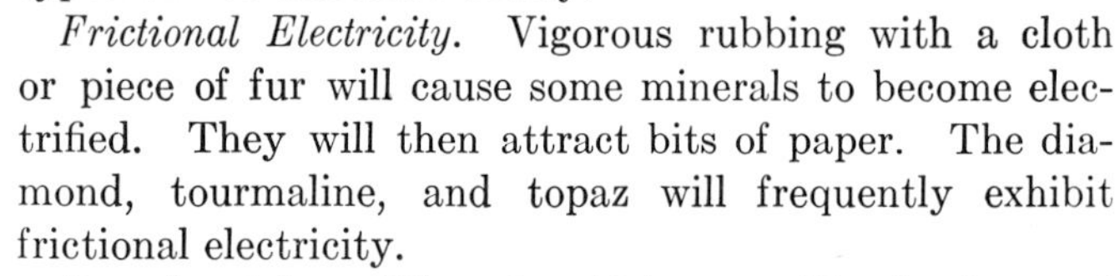

Frictional Electricity. Vigorous rubbing with a cloth or piece of fur will cause some minerals to become electrified. They will then attract bits of paper. The diamond, tourmaline, and topaz will frequently exhibit frictional electricity.

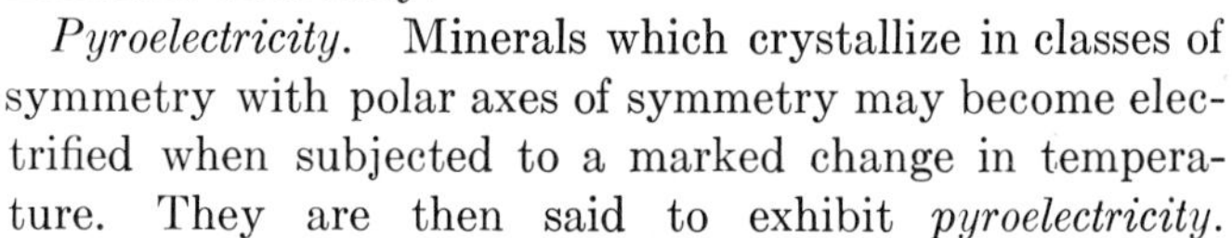

Pyroelectricity. Minerals which crystallize in classes of symmetry with polar axes of symmetry may become electrified when subjected to a marked change in temperature. They are then said to exhibit *pyroelectricity*. Tourmaline is an excellent example of a pyroelectric mineral, for, if a light-colored crystal is heated, positive and negative charges develop on the opposite ends. As can be seen from Fig. 327, crystals of tourmaline are usually elongated along the *c* axis, which is polar in character.

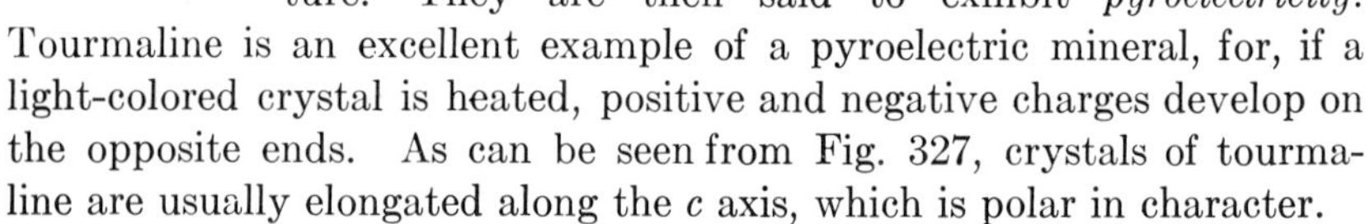

Pyroelectricity can be easily detected by *Kundt's* method. The crystal to be tested is gently heated and allowed to cool on an insulated support. It is then dusted with a finely powdered mixture of red lead and sulfur, the particles of which are electrified by friction in their passage through a fine sieve in the nozzle of the bellows containing the mixed powders. The red lead, having been positively electrified, collects at the negative end of the crystal; the negatively charged sulfur is attracted to the positive end. That is, the negative end of the crystal becomes, on cooling, reddish in color, the positive end yellowish.

Piezoelectricity. By means of pressure, electrical charges may be developed in some minerals. This electrification, called *piezoelectricity*, is most marked along the axes of symmetry that have a polar development. Quartz is an important piezoelectric mineral. Properly oriented thin sections or plates of quartz (Figs. 328 and 329), often called wafers, are used for frequency and wave-length control in electronic and radio apparatus. These plates are cut through a crystal of quartz parallel to the crystallographic *c* axis, so that the length of the plate is also parallel to one of the horizontal axes, *a* or *b*. Figure 328 shows the Y cut. It is parallel to an *a* axis, and hence is perpendicular to an intermediate *b* axis, which is called a Y or *mechanical* axis. The X cut is shown in Fig. 329. This cut is parallel to one of the *b* axes, and hence is perpendicular to an *a* axis, which is termed an X or *electric* axis.

During the Second World War there was an enormous demand for these oscillating quartz plates for use in all manner of war equipment, and many different cuts were developed for special purposes. A number of minerals and chemical compounds possess piezoelectric properties, for example, tourmaline and synthetic ammonium dihydrogen phosphate.

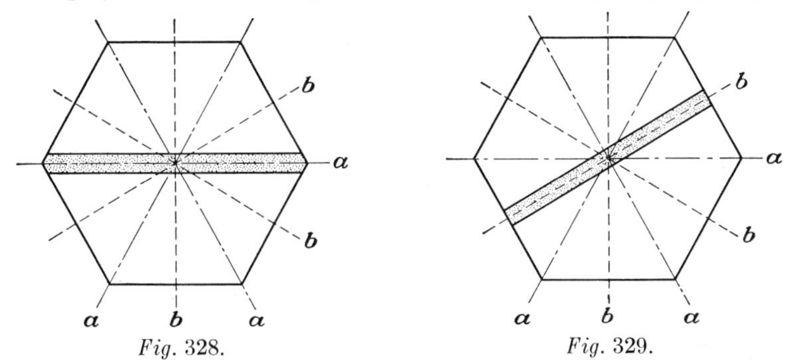

Fig. 328. *Fig.* 329.

Radioactivity. In 1896 Henri Becquerel observed that a photographic plate carefully protected by black paper becomes fogged when a phosphorescent salt containing uranium is placed on or near the plate. He also showed that all uranium compounds give off penetrating rays which darken photographic plates, the same as X rays do. This radiation is of three kinds: (1) *alpha rays,* which consist of helium atoms each with two units of positive electricity; (2) *beta rays,* which are streams of negative electrons; and (3) *gamma rays,* which are very penetrating and of extremely short wave length. This radiation can be detected by (1) the electroscope, to best advantage in the laboratory, (2) the Geiger-Mueller counter, or (3) the scintillation counter. The Geiger counter is available in a very handy portable form and is well adapted for field use. The scintillation counter is also available for field work; although more expensive, it is more sensitive to gamma rays.

Etch Figures. When crystals of either minerals or chemical substances are subjected to the solvent action of certain liquids or gases, small geometrical depressions appear on their surfaces. The shape of these figures, called *etch* or *etching figures,* is intimately associated with the internal structure of the crystal. A study of the shape and position of these figures in relation to the faces on which they occur, and to the geometrical development of the crystal as a whole, is of assistance in determining the symmetry of the crystal. Thus, calcite ($CaCO_3$) and dolomite ($CaMg(CO_3)_2$), both, crystallize in rhombohedrons. The symmetry of calcite is, however, higher than that of dolomite, as revealed by the etch figures. On calcite (Fig. 330) the shape and position of the figures are such that a plane symmetry may be passed through the figures, from top to bottom, which corresponds in direction to a plane of symmetry through the crystal face, that is, to the short diagonal. On dolomite (Fig. 331), on the other hand, the shape and position of the figures reveal that no such plane of symmetry is possible. Not infrequently crystals of minerals show natural etch figures. For an accurate determination of crystal symmetry, etch figures should be studied in conjunction with the findings of X-ray analysis (see page 149).

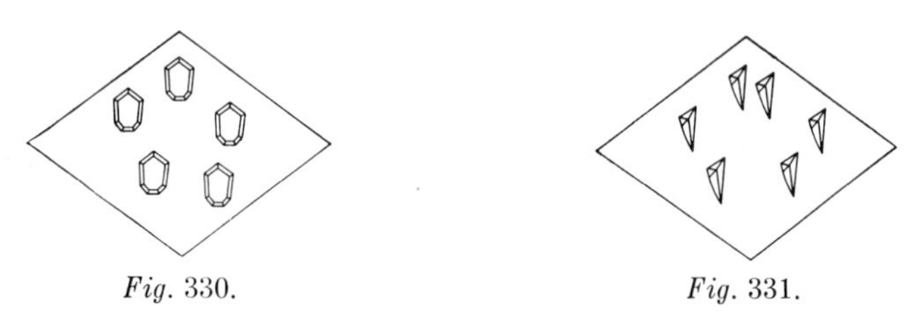

Fig. 330. *Fig.* 331.

In the production of etch figures in the laboratory, care must be exercised in the selection of the solvents and in the time they are permitted to act. Considerable skill in manipulation is also necessary.[1] See also page 33.

Structure. Many minerals occur frequently in good crystals, as is the case with calcite and quartz. But for the most part minerals are found in masses of various types which may be either crystalline or amorphous in character. In fact, the general structure of minerals may be classified as follows:

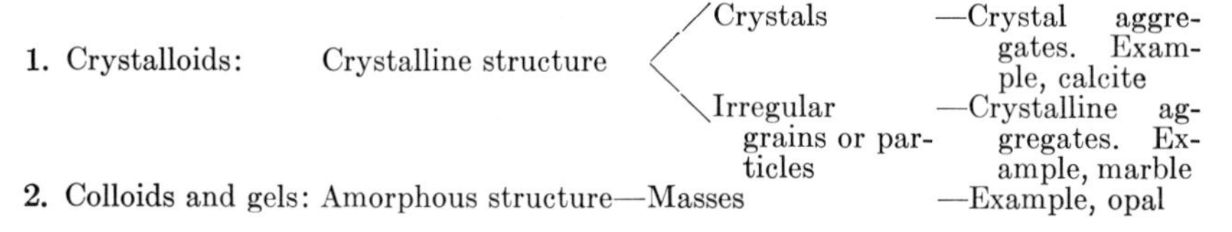

The term *crystalloid* refers to well-developed isolated crystals or to groups or *aggregates of crystals* (Fig. 277, page 89) and also to grains or particles possessing crystal structure but devoid of natural plane surfaces, which are one of the outward expressions of crystallinity. Masses of grains or particles are called *crystalline aggregates* (Fig. 5, page 6). Colloids or gels do not crystallize and therefore yield only *amorphous masses,* which are without definite form and internal structure. Those masses which appear to the unaided eye to be amorphous but are, in reality, crystalline, as revealed by the microscope, are called *cryptocrystalline.*

As was shown in Chaps. 3 to 9, crystals occur in a great diversity of forms. These forms are very useful in the determination of minerals.

[1] For further information, consult A. P. Honess, "The Nature, Origin, and Interpretation of the Etch Figures on Crystals," John Wiley & Sons, Inc., New York, 1927.

There are also many types of crystalline aggregates and amorphous masses, of which the following are the most important:

Acicular. Composed of delicate and slender needle-like crystals (natrolite, Fig. 697, page 419).

Amygdaloidal. Almond-shaped mineral masses occurring in small cavities in lavas (copper, Fig. 484, page 261).

Arborescent. Branching or tree-like aggregates of crystals (copper, Fig. 332).

Fig. 332.

Fig. 333.

Bladed. A tabular or platy structure, the individuals resembling grass or knife blades. The blades may be parallel or divergent (kyanite, Fig. 619, page 369).

Botryoidal. Closely united spherical masses, resembling a bunch of grapes (psilomelane, Fig. 561, page 319).

Capillary. Composed of exceedingly slender or hair-like crystals.

Cellular. Porous like a sponge.

Clastic. Made up of fragments.

Columnar. Composed of thick fibers or columns, often in parallel groups (gypsum, Fig. 591, page 345).

Concentric. Spherical layers about a common center, similar to the layers of an onion (agate, Fig. 537, page 297).

Concretionary. Rounded or nodular masses (flint, Fig. 540, page 297).

Dendritic. Branching or fern like structure (manganite, Fig. 333).

Drusy. A rough surface due to a large number of small closely crowded crystals (scheelite, Fig. 596, page 349).

Fibrous. Consisting of slender fibers or filaments (wavellite, Fig. 601, page 355).

Filiform. Composed of thin wires, often twisted or bent (silver, Fig. 478, page 259).

Foliated. Made up of plates or leaves which are easily separated.

Globular. Spherical, or nearly so.

Granular. Composed of closely packed grains, which may be either coarse or fine (Fig. 4, page 6).

Lamellar. Made of thin plates or layers.

Lenticular. Lens shaped.

Mammillary. Large and rounded masses, larger than grapes.

Micaceous. Composed of very thin plates or scales, like those of mica.

Nodular. Rounded masses of irregular shape (flint, Fig. 540, page 297).

Oölitic. Composed of small rounded particles the size of fish eggs (limestone, Fig. 334).

Phanerocrystalline. Crystals or coarsely crystalline (orthoclase, Fig. 681, page 407).

Fig. 334.

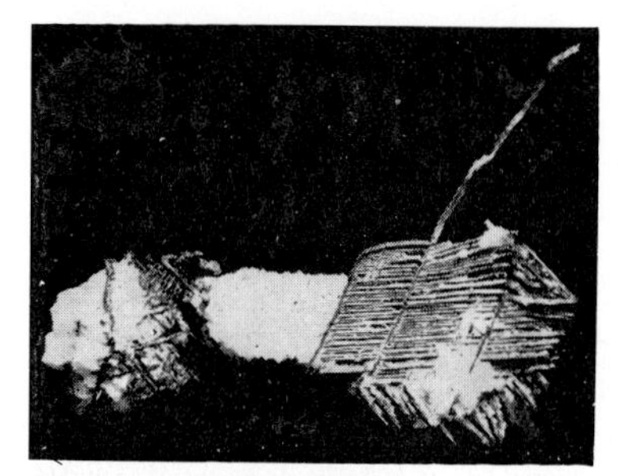

Fig. 335.

Pisolitic. Composed of rounded particles, the size of peas or buckshot (bauxite, Fig. 560, page 317).

Plumose. Feathery structure, sometimes observed on mica.

Reniform. Composed of large rounded masses resembling a kidney in shape (hematite, Fig. 546, page 302).

Reticulated. Composed of fibers crossing in meshes as in a net (silver, Fig. 535).

Scaly. Composed of small thin scales or plates.

Sheaf-like. Aggregates resembling a sheaf of wheat in outline (stilbite, Fig. 700, page 420).

Stalactitic. Cylindrical or conical masses resembling icicles (chalcedony, Fig. 536, page 296).

Stellate. Radiating crystals or fibers producing star-like forms.

Tabular. Composed of broad, flat surfaces, tablet-like (celestite, Fig. 582, page 340).

Less frequently used terms are listed in the glossary (page 479). These are employed only when finer distinctions in structure are made.

11 | Optical Mineralogy

Optical Methods. Relatively simple methods have been devised for the easy and rapid determination of some of the more important optical constants of solids. These methods are especially adapted to the determination of the optical properties of substances that are available as crystals, in thin sections, or in limited quantities as small fragments or powders. Many of these methods involve the use of the mineralogical or polarizing microscope, which differs materially from the microscope ordinarily used by biologists, pathologists, and other scientists in that it is equipped with a rotating stage and various devices permitting the study of objects in polarized light. In fact, in determining solids by optical methods, polarized light is indispensable. It will, therefore, be necessary to review briefly some of the essential properties of light.

Reflection of Light. It is well known that when a ray of light falls upon a polished surface, such as a mirror, it is reflected according to the law of reflection, which states that *the angle of reflection is equal to the angle of incidence, and the reflected and incident rays lie in the same plane.* That is, in Fig. 336, the ray of light EX, from the candle at E, impinges upon the polished surface AB at X with the angle of incidence EXO or i and is reflected to the eye at D, the angle of reflection being DXO or r. The angles i and r are equal. To the eye the object appears at E'. The line EE' is perpendicular to AB, and the distances EP and PE' are equal.

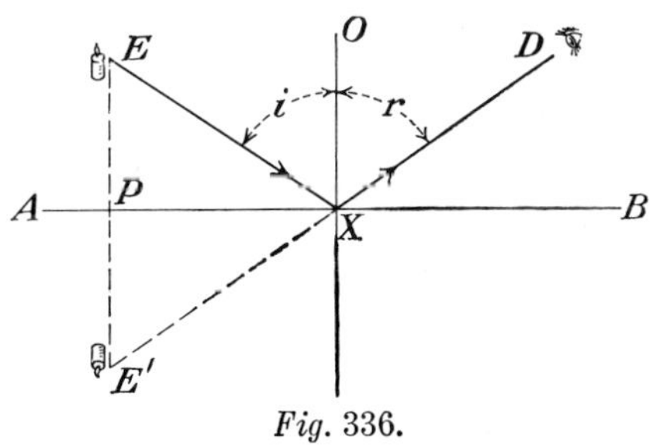

Fig. 336.

Refraction of Light—Single Refraction. When light passes obliquely from one medium into another, for example, from air into water, the path of the ray is not straight but bent. That is, the ray is refracted. We know this from the appearance of a rod or pencil placed in an inclined position in a glass or beaker of water. The phenomenon of refraction is clearly shown by Fig. 337. The ray Dx in air impinges at x upon the surface AB and in passing into the water does not continue in the direction xE' but is bent or refracted toward the normal OM, because the velocity of light is less in water than in air. If the angle of incidence DxO is represented by i and the angle of refraction MxE by r, then the law of refraction may be stated as follows: *the ratios between the velocities of light V and V' in the two media, and between the sines of the angles of incidence and refraction, are equal and constant for the media concerned:* thus, in the case of air and water,

$$n \text{ (index of refraction)} = \frac{V(\text{air})}{V'(\text{water})} = \frac{\sin i}{\sin r} = 1.333.$$

The constant n is called the index of refraction, the velocity of light in air being taken as unity. Thus, the index of refraction of water in terms of air is 1.333; of the garnet 1.75, and of the diamond 2.42. It is evident that the velocity of light in a given substance is proportional to the reciprocal of its index of refraction. Hence, the larger the index, the slower the velocity, and vice versa.

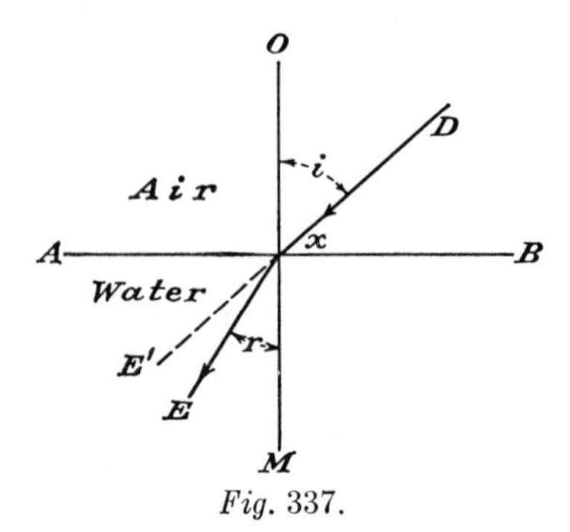

Fig. 337.

In determining these values, white light should not be used, for, when white light passes through a prism, it is resolved into its component colors—a spectrum is produced. Of these component colors, red light is refracted least and violet most. That is, the velocity of light from the red end of the spectrum is greatest and least from the violet end. Indices of refraction must therefore be determined for a definite type of monochromatic light, commonly expressed in wave lengths, mμ (see page 158). Thus, the indices of the diamond may be given as follows:

$$\begin{array}{lll} n_{\text{red}} & 687 \text{ m}\mu & = 2.407 \\ n_{\text{yellow}} & 589 & = 2.417 \\ n_{\text{green}} & 527 & = 2.427 \\ n_{\text{violet}} & 397 & = 2.465 \end{array}$$

The indices of refraction for a certain variety of glass are $n_{\text{red}} = 1.524$ and $n_{\text{violet}} = 1.545$.

As sources of monochromatic light, nonluminous gas flames colored by some volatile salt of the following elements may be used:

Lithium, red,	670 mμ
Sodium, yellow,	589
Thallium, green,	535

Efficient sodium-vapor lamps are now available.[1] Color filters may also be employed to furnish monochromatic light. In the identification of substances by means of the indices of refraction, sufficiently accurate results may be obtained by using ordinary light.

Dispersion. The above examples are sufficient to show that the indices of refraction for a given substance vary considerably for the two extremes of the spectrum. This difference in velocity is called *dispersion*, and in the case of the diamond it is unusually high ($2.465 - 2.407 = 0.058$). The difference in the indices between opposite ends of the spectrum indicates the strength of the dispersion. The dispersion of glass is much lower ($1.545 - 1.524 = 0.021$); see page 118.

Total Reflection and Critical Angle. When light passes from a denser into a rarer medium, for example, from water into air, the refracted ray is bent away from the normal (Fig. 338). That is, the angle of incidence I is now smaller than the angle of refraction R. It is therefore obvious that for a definite angle of incidence i the angle of refraction r may equal 90°. This angle i is called the *critical* angle, for when the angle of incidence exceeds i in value, as for example, I', the ray is totally reflected; that is, it does not enter the second medium but is reflected back into the first, so that angle R' equals angle I'. The value of the critical angle may be expressed as

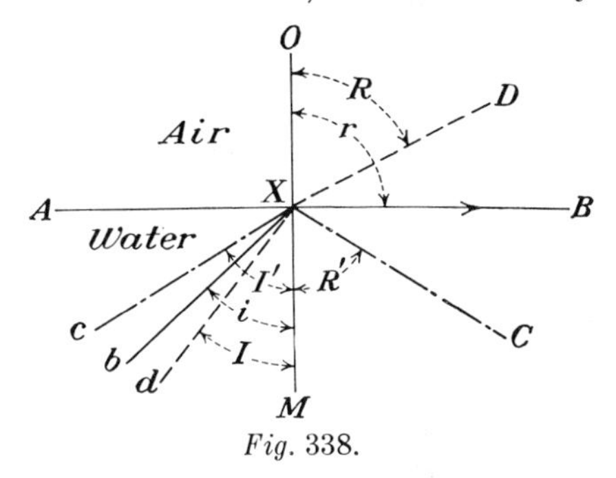

Fig. 338.

$$\sin i = \frac{1}{n}$$

where n is the usual index of refraction and i the angle of the incident ray in the denser medium. Hence, it follows that substances with high indices of refraction have smaller critical angles than those with low indices. The critical angle of the diamond ($n = 2.42$) in terms of air is only 24°26′, while that of water ($n = 1.333$) is 48°36′. The phenomenon of total reflection is of great importance in crystal optics.

Double Refraction. When a ray of light passes through many solids, it is generally not only refracted but is also resolved into two rays,

[1] Manufactured by the General Electric Company.

which travel with different velocities. This phenomenon is designated as double refraction and is characteristic of all crystallized substances other than those of the cubic system. Single refraction has been discussed on page 117.

Double refraction is illustrated in Fig. 339. The ray DX is represented as impinging upon a section of the mineral calcite ($CaCO_3$). DX is resolved into two rays, o and e, of which o is the slower ray and is refracted more than the faster ray e. The velocity of the o ray is the same for all directions in the crystal and is called the *ordinary* ray. The other ray, e, is termed the *extraordinary* ray. Its velocity varies with direction. In the case of calcite, illustrated in Fig. 339, the ordinary ray is slower than the extraordinary ray, but in other substances the conditions may be reversed, for example, zircon.

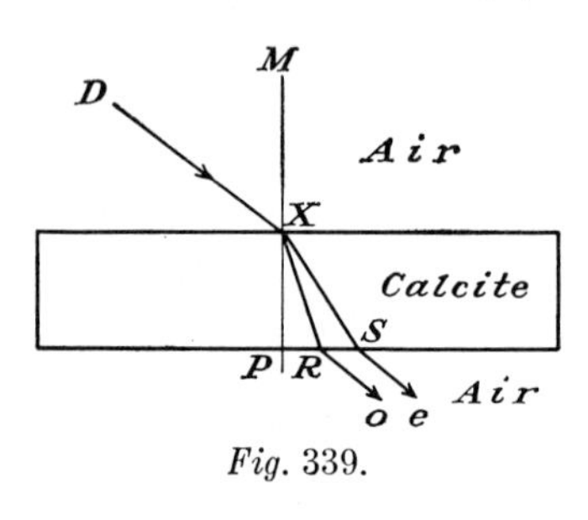

Fig. 339.

Optical Groups. Substances showing single refraction are called *singly refractive* or *isotropic*, while those with double refraction are designated as *doubly refractive* or *anisotropic*. In isotropic substances the velocity of light of a given wave length does not vary with direction. There is, hence, but one index of refraction for such substances. Unstrained amorphous substances and unstrained crystals of the cubic system are isotropic. Examples: diamond (cubic), $n_{Na} = 2.42$; almandite garnet (cubic), $n_{Na} = 1.75$; opal (amorphous), $n_{Na} = 1.45$.

Anisotropic substances are subdivided into two groups, depending upon whether they possess one or two isotropic directions. These isotropic directions are called *optic axes*. Those with one isotropic direction possess two principal indices of refraction, ω and ϵ, and include crystals of the hexagonal and tetragonal systems.[1] Examples: calcite (hexagonal), $\omega = 1.65$, $\epsilon = 1.48$; zircon (tetragonal), $\omega = 1.924$, $\epsilon = 1.968$. These substances have one optic axis and are called *uniaxial*. The direction of the optic axis is that of the c crystallographic axis. If the index ω is greater than ϵ, the crystal is said to be optically *negative*, and optically *positive* when ϵ has the larger value. Compare the values above for calcite and zircon. The difference between the indices of the ordinary and extraordinary rays gives the strength of *double refraction* or *birefringence*. Thus for calcite it is (ω) $1.65 - (\epsilon)\ 1.48 = 0.17$; for quartz it is ($\epsilon$) $1.553 - (\omega)\ 1.544 = 0.009$. The birefringence is characterized as *strong* or *weak*, depending upon the values obtained.

Those anisotropic crystals which possess two isotropic directions, or

[1] For the indices of the ordinary and extraordinary rays, not only ω and ϵ but also O and E, respectively, are used.

optic axes, are called *biaxial*. They include all crystals belonging to the orthorhombic, monoclinic, and triclinic systems. In these crystals there are three principal optical directions at right angles to each other, parallel to which light is propagated with velocities indicated by the three indices, α, β, γ. Examples: topaz (orthorhombic),

$$\alpha = 1.607$$
$$\beta = 1.610$$
$$\gamma = 1.618$$

epidote (monoclinic),

$$\alpha = 1.730$$
$$\beta = 1.754$$
$$\gamma = 1.768$$

axinite (triclinic), $\alpha = 1.672$, $\beta = 1.678$, $\gamma = 1.681$. When β approaches in value α more than it does γ, the substance is, in general, optically *positive*. If the value of β is closer to γ, the crystal is, in general, optically *negative*, for example, epidote and axinite. The *double refraction* or *birefringence* of biaxial crystals is indicated by $\gamma - \alpha$; thus, for topaz it is $1.618 - 1.607 = 0.011$.

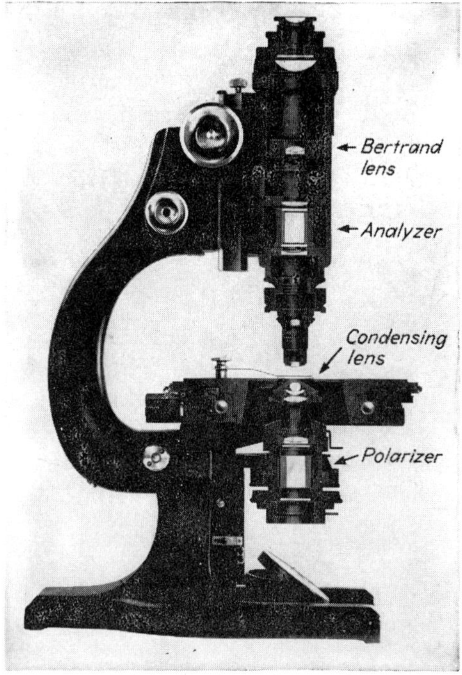

Fig. 340. Sectional view of polarizing microscope. (*Courtesy of American Optical Company.*)

These optical properties may be summarized as follows:

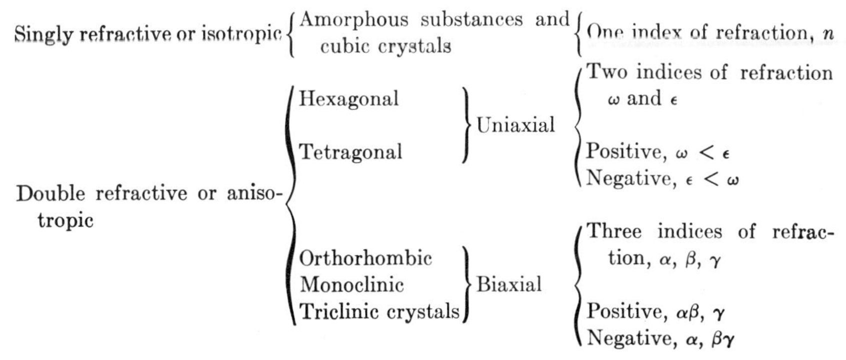

Singly refractive or isotropic	Amorphous substances and cubic crystals		One index of refraction, n
Double refractive or anisotropic	Hexagonal Tetragonal	Uniaxial	Two indices of refraction ω and ϵ Positive, $\omega < \epsilon$ Negative, $\epsilon < \omega$
	Orthorhombic Monoclinic Triclinic crystals	Biaxial	Three indices of refraction, α, β, γ Positive, $\alpha\beta$, γ Negative, α, $\beta\gamma$

Polarizing Microscope. As indicated on page 117, the microscope used by mineralogists (Fig. 340) differs materially from that commonly used by biologists and other scientists in that the stage rotates in the horizontal plane. It is also equipped with devices, called *Nicol prisms*, which permit objects to be studied in polarized light. One Nicol prism is placed below the rotating stage and is called the *polarizer*. The other prism, the *analyzer*, is above the stage, and is mounted upon a slide so that it may be easily removed from the tube. Usually both Nicols can be rotated.

There are several classes of observations which can be made with a mineralogical microscope, namely:

1. General observations in ordinary light.
2. Observations in polarized light.
   a. Parallel polarized light.
   b. Convergent polarized light.

By inserting or removing the condensing lens placed below the microscope stage, the change from parallel to convergent light, and vice versa, is easily made.

GENERAL OBSERVATIONS IN ORDINARY LIGHT

Centering. In order to use the rotating stage to advantage, its center must obviously lie on the vertical axis passing through the tube when the stage is rotated. To permit of centering, the tube is provided with two screws placed at right angles to each other directly above the objective. These screws displace the objective laterally.

Fig. 341. Frederick E. Wright (1877–1953). For many years associated with the Geophysical Laboratory, Washington, D.C. American authority on the polarizing microscope and its applications.

Centering is most readily accomplished by placing on the stage an object glass with a dark speck or small spot of ink and noting the position of the speck with respect to the dark lines crossing the field. These are called *cross hairs*, and their intersection indicates the center of the field of vision. The object glass should then be carefully moved until the speck is at the intersection of the cross hairs. If the stage is centered, the speck will remain at the intersection when the stage is rotated. If it is not centered, the speck will move in a circular path, the center of which, *o*, lies to one side of the center of the field of vision *I* (Fig. 342). The stage should then be rotated until the speck appears to lie upon one of the cross hairs, *AA′*, and the screw parallel to it, *C*, should then be turned until the speck has moved from *X* to *Y*, that is, one-half the distance to the intersection of the cross hairs. The object glass is now moved so that the speck is again at the center of the field, and the stage is rotated. The speck will describe the path indicated by the smaller circle. When it apparently lies on the second cross hair PP', the screw D should be turned until it has moved from X' to Y', again one-half the distance to the center of the field. Upon bringing the speck to the center of the field and rotating the stage, it will be found that it has been centered; that is, the spot will

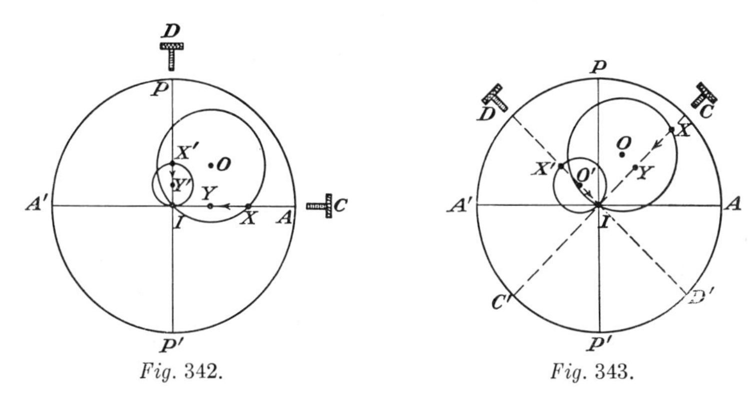

Fig. 342. *Fig.* 343.

remain stationary. Ordinarily, it is necessary to repeat this process several times before the stage is perfectly centered.

On most microscopes, the centering screws are not parallel to the cross hairs, as in Fig. 342, but are placed diagonally, as shown in Fig. 343. When this is the case, the speck should be brought into the diagonal positions indicated by X and X' and the adjustments made by the screws C and D, as described above.

Measurement of Angles. In measuring plane angles between crystal edges or between cleavage directions, the intersection of the edges is brought to the center of the cross hairs and the microscope centered, as described above. The stage is now rotated until one edge is parallel to one cross hair AA' and a reading made on the graduated scale of the stage (see Fig. 344). The stage is then rotated until the other edge is parallel with the same cross hair AA'. The difference between the two readings, angle m, is the supplement of the plane angle under consideration drawn in heavy lines.

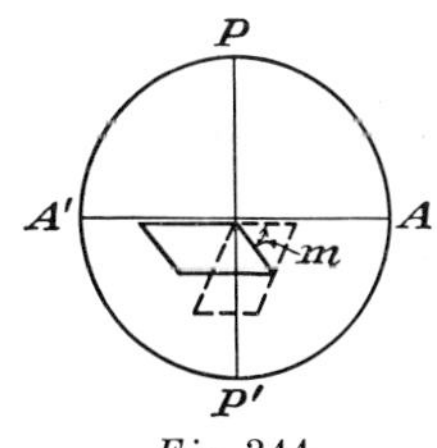

Fig. 344.

Determination of Indices of Refraction. The determination of the index of refraction is one of the most accurate and readily applied means of identifying substances. Three methods are commonly used:

1. Approximate immersion method.
2. Becke method.
3. Refractometer method.

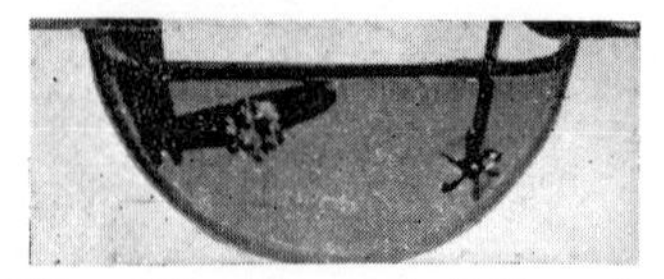

Fig. 345. Diamond (*left*) and glass (*right*) immersed in cinnamon oil.

As indicated previously, monochromatic light should be used for the accurate determination of the index of refraction (see page 118).

Approximate Immersion Method. This method depends upon the fact that a transparent solid becomes practically invisible when placed in a liquid with the same color and the same index of refraction. The solid and the liquid form a continuous medium for the passage of light so that the boundaries of the solid tend to disappear. By using a series of liquids with different indices of refraction, the approximate index of most minerals may be found. The substance is immersed in one liquid after another, until that liquid is found in which it most completely disappears. The specimen then has approximately the index of that liquid. The greater the difference in refractivity between the liquid and the solid, the greater will be the *relief* of the solid, that is, the more plainly will it be visible. Figure 345 shows a cut diamond (n 2.42) and a glass imitation immersed in cinnamon oil (n 1.60). It is quite obvious that the index of refraction of the glass imitation, as indicated by the low relief, is approximately the same as that of the cinnamon oil.

Fig. 346. Friederich J. Becke (1855–1931). For many years professor of mineralogy and petrography in the University of Vienna.

The liquids listed on pages 125 and 126 may profitably be used in the approximate immersion method.

Becke Method. The indices of refraction of solids, in the form of either rock or mineral sections or fragments, may be easily determined by using the method devised by Becke (Fig. 346). This method, often called the *central illumination method*, depends upon the refraction and total reflection of light, as illustrated in Fig. 347. Let A and B be two solids in contact, B having a higher index of refraction than A. If the microscope is focused upon the contact, a band or line of light will be observed at SO, which will move toward B when the tube is raised. On lowering the tube, it moves toward A. This band or zone is caused by the concentration of light on one side of the contact, for all rays of light in A, which impinge upon the contact, will pass into B, irrespective of the angle of incidence i. Thus, the ray X will emerge as OM. But when light passing through B impinges

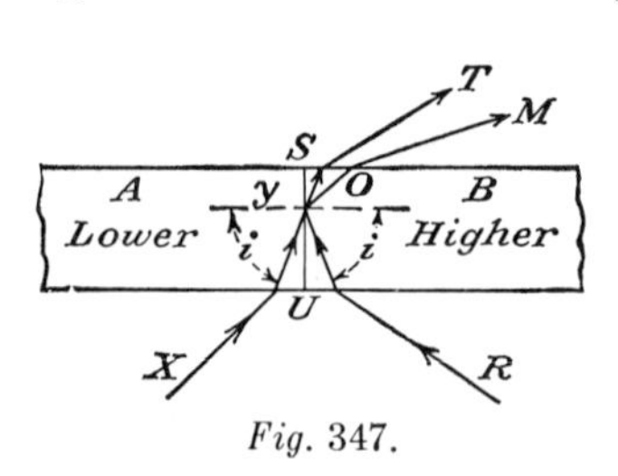

Fig. 347.

upon the contact, the size of the angle of incidence is of great importance, for here the passage is from a denser to a rarer medium. In all such cases, total reflection will take place if the angle of incidence i is larger than the critical angle. That is, the ray R will emerge as ST. As indicated, the raising of the microscope tube will displace the band of light, due to this concentration of rays, toward the substance with the higher index. The intensity of this line of light is often accentuated by lowering the substage or by partly closing the substage diaphragm. Whether or not the index of the substance under investigation is higher or lower than that of a known substance can thus be easily determined (Figs. 348 and 349).

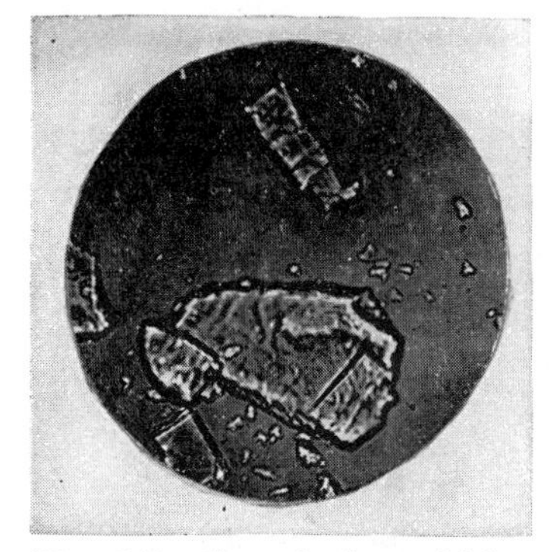

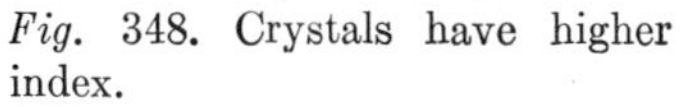

Fig. 348. Crystals have higher index.

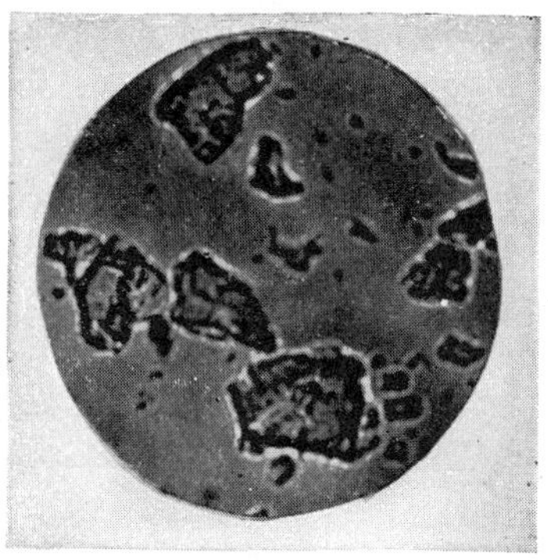

Fig. 349. Crystals have lower index.

The indices of refraction of fragments can be determined by immersing them in liquids of known indices and the movement of the band of light noted. The operation is repeated with different liquids, until one is found with an index equal to that of the fragment. In this case, the fragment is invisible, or only slightly visible. When the difference between the indices of the fragment and the liquid is small, the fragment appears smooth and thin and is said to have *low relief*. If this difference is quite large, then the fragment has a dark border and appears rough and thick and is said to have *high relief*. To determine the indices of refraction by this method, the following liquids are serviceable:

Liquid	
Water	1.33
Ethyl alcohol	1.36
Glycerin	1.47
Petroleum oil (mineral oil)	1.48
Cinnamon oil	1.60
α-monochlornaphthalene	1.63
α-monobromnaphthalene	1.66
Methylene iodide	1.74
Sulfur in methylene iodide	1.79

A set of standardized index liquids[1] with fixed intervals is practically indispensable in determining the indices of refraction of small fragments. Wright (Fig. 341, page 122) suggests the use of the following, mixed in proper proportions:

Mixture of	Index
Kerosene and turpentine	1.450–1.475
Turpentine and clove oil	1.480–1.535
Clove oil and α-monobromnaphthalene	1.540–1.635
α-monobromnaphthalene and α-monochlornaphthalene	1.640–1.655
Monochlornaphthalene and methylene iodide	1.660–1.740
Sulfur dissolved in methylene iodide	1.740–1.790
Methylene iodide, antimony iodide, arsenic sulfide, antimony sulfide, and sulfur	1.790–1.960

Fig. 350. Set of standardized refractive index liquids.

Refractometer Method. For this method four hand-sized instruments are at present available which may be used for the rapid and accurate determination of the indices of refraction.

These are known as the *Tully*, *Smith*, *Rayner*, and *Erb and Gray refractometers.* They make use of the principle of total reflection.

Figure 351 illustrates the Tully refractometer. The most essential part of the instrument is a polished hemisphere of glass B with a very high index of refraction. The exposed portion of the hemisphere is a flat polished surface. The specimen with a smooth plane surface, for example, a cut gem, C, to be tested is placed upon the glass hemisphere. However, a drop of liquid of high index, such as methylene iodide, must be first placed upon the hemisphere in order to displace the film of air which would otherwise be present between the stone and the hemisphere. A broad beam of light from the reflector A enters the instrument through the opening at the left and passes up to the lower surface of the specimen. The instrument is so designed that the hemisphere of glass and the

[1] Sold by J. T. Rooney, P. O. Box 358, Buffalo, N.Y., or R. P. Cargille, 117 Liberty Street, New York 6, N.Y.

mounted stone may be rotated in the horizontal plane. Such rotation is desirable with substances having strong double refraction.

The light thus passes from a denser to a rarer medium, that is, from the hemisphere to the specimen. Part of this light impinges upon the specimen at an angle less than the critical angle and continues through the stone and into the air. But some of the light impinges upon the specimen at an angle which exceeds the critical angle. This light is therefore totally reflected back into the hemisphere and, after passing through it and several prisms and lenses, falls upon a graduated scale *K*,

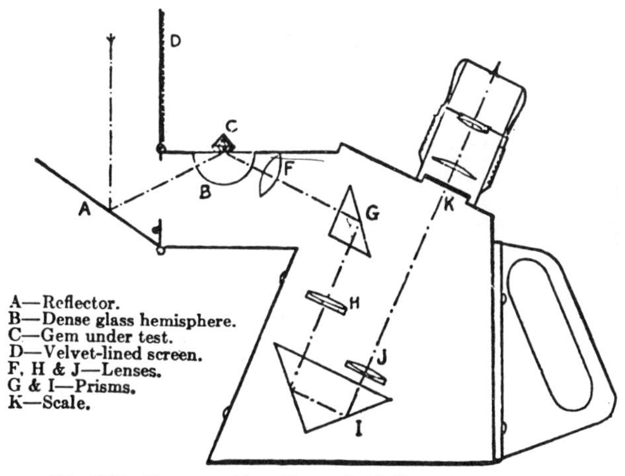

Fig. 351. Cross section through Tully refractometer.

which is viewed through the eyepiece at the right. It is obvious that this light, which has been totally reflected from the specimen *C*, will illuminate part of the graduated scale, while the rest of the scale will be somewhat darker. The position of the boundary between the lighter and darker portions of the scale is a function of the critical angle of the stone with reference to the glass hemisphere. This angle, of course, depends upon the relative indices of refraction of the gem and the glass. Since the index for the glass is known, the scale may be so graduated that the position of the boundary of the illuminated area will indicate the index of refraction of the specimen. Thus, the index of the gem may be read directly from the scale. The divisions of the scale correspond to 0.01, but the index may be estimated to 0.001. The range of the instrument is limited by the index of refraction of the glass used, which may be as high as 1.88.

In using the refractometer the liquid for the film between the specimen and the hemisphere must have an index of refraction higher than that of the stone to be tested. Thus, methylene iodide can be used for substances with indices up to 1.74, whereas a solution of sulfur in methylene iodide permits indices up to 1.79 to be determined. It should be pointed out that, because light is reflected from both the liquid film and the specimen, ordinarily two readings may be made on the scale, one caused by the liquid film, the other by the specimen. The band caused by the liquid film is easily recognized, since the index of the liquid is known. If the specimen has a strong double refraction two index readings may be made.

Fig. 352. The Rayner refractometer. (*Courtesy of Ward's Natural Science Establishment.*)

In case the substance has indices higher than that of the liquid, only one reading, namely, that of the liquid, is possible.

The refractometer method is rapid, and determinations which are usually sufficiently accurate can be made with ordinary light, that is, white light or sunlight. When greater accuracy is desired, monochromatic light should be used (page 118). It is common practice to make determinations with ordinary light, in which case one observes a fringe of

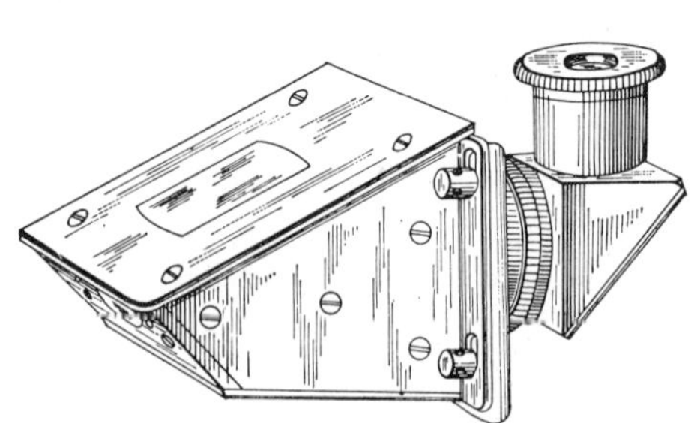

Fig. 353. The Smith refractometer.

Fig. 354. The Erb and Gray refractometer. (*Courtesy of Gemological Institute of America.*)

colors, instead of a sharp boundary to the illuminated area. Readings should then be made in terms of the middle of the colored band. If the substance has more than one index of refraction (page 120), two boundaries may be observed, each for a different index.

The Rayner (Fig. 352), Smith (Fig. 353), and the Erb and Gray (Fig.

354) refractometers are simpler but very useful instruments; the latter is so constructed that the position of the eyepiece can be adjusted and the glass hemisphere rotated.

OBSERVATIONS IN POLARIZED LIGHT

Polarized Light. Light may be considered as consisting of transverse electromagnetic waves (page 158). The direction of vibration is at right angles to the direction of propagation. The velocity of light has been determined to be approximately 186,000 miles, or 300,000 kilometers, per second.

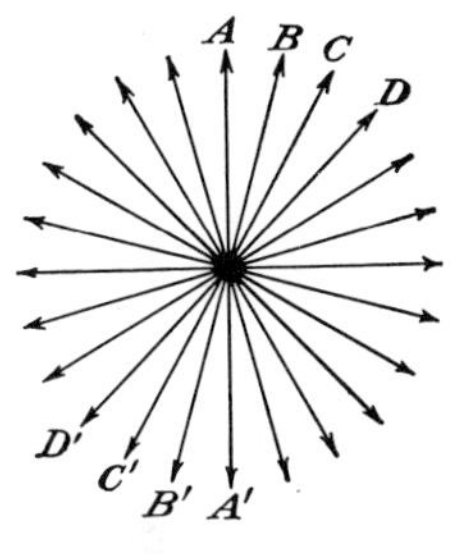

Fig. 355.

In the case of ordinary light these transverse vibrations occur in all azimuths about the line of propagation. Thus, in Fig. 355, if the beam of light is considered to be traveling perpendicular to the plane of the page, the vibrations are in all possible directions such as AA', BB', CC', and so forth.

In *plane polarized* light, which is ordinarily designated simply as *polarized* light, the vibrations are still in a plane at right angles to the direction in which the light is propagated, but they take place in only one definite direction in that plane. This type of light may be produced (1) by *reflection* from glass plates or other smooth surfaces; (2) by the partial *absorption* of ordinary light in passing through certain substances, such as tourmaline or polaroid; and (3) by means of *refraction*, as is the case with Nicol and Ahrens prisms. The third method is the most efficient and is usually employed in the polarizing microscope and other optical instruments. Since the development of polaroid, the second method is sometimes used for the production of polarized light in these instruments.

Polarized Light by Reflection. When ordinary light is reflected from a smooth surface, it is found to be partially plane polarized, the vibration directions being at right angles to the direction of propagation. In Fig. 356, the plane $ABCD$ contains the incident and reflected rays ax and xy. The plane $MPON$, in which the polarized ray xy vibrates, is called the plane of *vibration*. These planes are perpendicular to each other. This method of producing polarized light was formerly used much more extensively than at present.

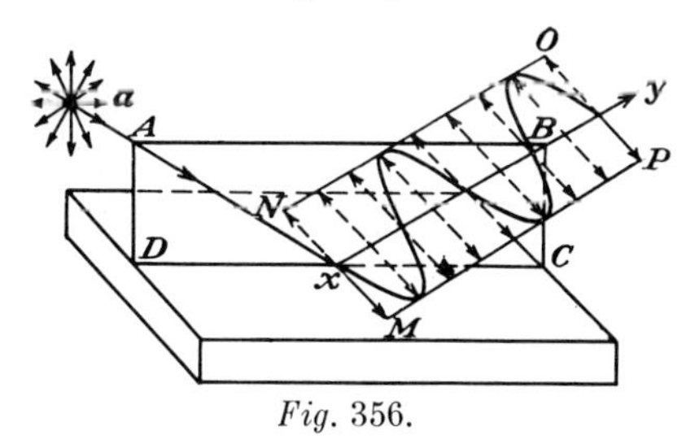

Fig. 356.

Polarized Light by Absorption. When ordinary light passes through substances with highly selective absorption, the light which emerges is plane polarized. This is because such substances permit light to pass through readily when the light vibrates in a given direction xy (Fig. 357). Light vibrating in other directions is absorbed. This can be demonstrated by placing a second plate of the substance in the path of the polarized ray, so that the favorable direction for passage $x'y'$ is at right angles to the vibration direction of the ray. When this is done, no light will emerge from the second plate. Plates of the mineral tourmaline or of the commercial product polaroid can be used for the production of plane polarized light in this manner, although the light which emerges is not completely polarized. Plates of polaroid have been substituted for the Nicol and Ahrens prisms in many optical instruments, with satisfactory results.

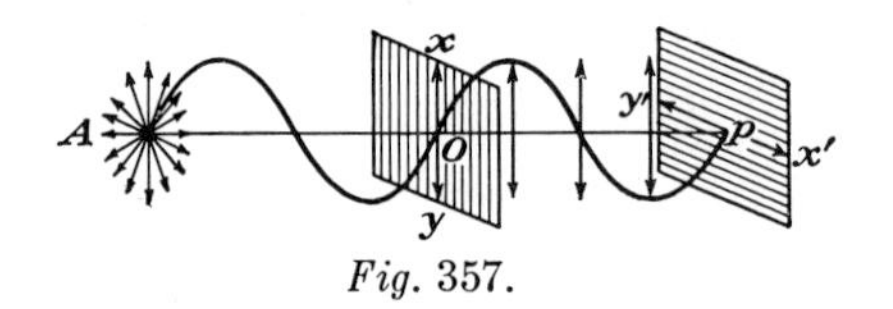

Fig. 357.

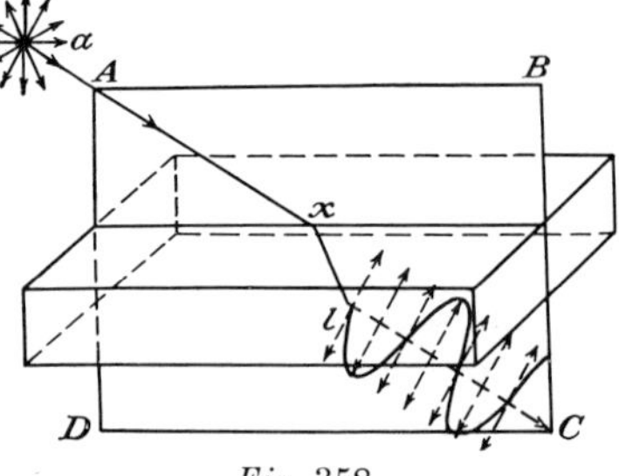

Fig. 358.

Polarized Light by Refraction. A portion of the ray ax in Fig. 358 may enter the plate at x and be refracted. Upon emerging as the ray lC, it is partially plane polarized. The vibrations are now executed in the plane of polarization and are perpendicular to the vibration directions characteristic of polarization by reflection. The polarized light used in the mineralogical microscope is commonly produced by double refraction and total reflection. For this purpose, the Nicol prism has long been employed, but in recent years it has been largely replaced by the Ahrens prism (see page 131).

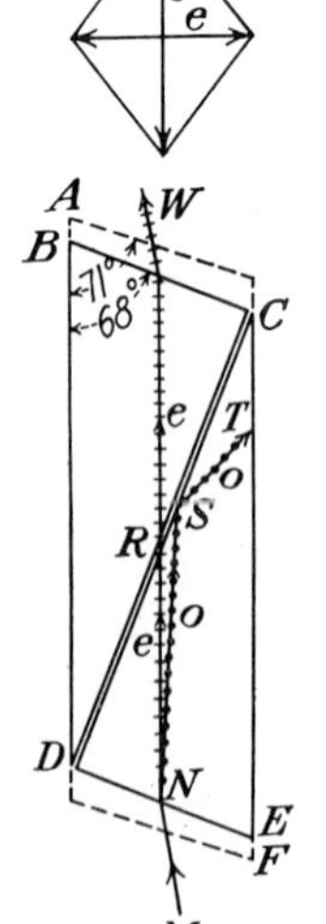

Fig. 359.

Nicol Prism. This consists of a cleavage piece of clear, transparent calcite, commonly called Iceland or double spar. It is usually somewhat elongated, as shown in Fig. 359. The natural angles of 71° at A and F are reduced by grinding to 68°. The prism is then cut in two along the plane CD, which is at right angles to the new end faces BC and DE. After the two parts have been polished, they are cemented together, DC, with canada balsam or thickened linseed oil, which have indices of refraction of about 1.545.

If ordinary light is allowed to fall upon DE in the direction of MN, it will be resolved into two rays, since calcite is a doubly refractive substance. Each of these rays is plane polarized.

One of the rays is called the ordinary ray *o*. It has a constant index of refraction of 1.658. The other ray is termed the extraordinary ray *e*, and its index of refraction varies from 1.486, when propagated at right angles to the *c* axis, to 1.658, when parallel to the *c* axis. In the direction *NR*, its index of refraction approximates that of the canada balsam.

The ordinary ray *o* with an index of refraction 1.658 impinges upon the film of canada balsam at *S* with an angle of incidence which is greater than the critical angle. It is, hence, totally reflected in the direction of *ST*. It, therefore, does not emerge at the upper end of the Nicol prism but is absorbed by the side of the case in which the Nicol is mounted.

The extraordinary ray *e*, however, pursues a path in the Nicol indicated by *NR*. For this direction, the index of refraction of the extraordinary ray is approximately the same as that of the canada balsam, and the ray, therefore, passes through the balsam with little, if any, deviation. It emerges from the prism at *W* and is plane polarized with vibrations parallel to the short diagonal of the end rhombohedral face of the Nicol. This simple device is very efficient for producing plane polarized light by refraction.

Nicol prisms have been used very extensively in polarizing microscopes and other crystallographic optical instruments. In microscopes, a Nicol prism, called the *polarizer*, is placed below the stage, while a second, the *analyzer*, is mounted in the tube above the objective (see page 121). The Nicols can be rotated in the horizontal plane. Observations may be made with the vibration directions of both Nicols either parallel or at right angles to each other. When the directions are perpendicular to each other, the Nicols are said to be *crossed*. Observations with crossed Nicols are much more important than those made with *parallel* Nicols.

Ahrens Prism. The prism devised by C. D. Ahrens permits of a more economical use of calcite than is possible in making the Nicol prism. Accordingly manufacturers of mineralogical microscopes quite generally use the Ahrens instead of the Nicol prism.

The Ahrens prism consists of a rectangular piece of calcite with square ends. The ratio between the lengths of the end and the side edges varies but is often about 1:1.8 (Fig. 360). In general the crystallographic *c* axis of the crystal is perpendicular to the front and rear sides. This square prism is cut as shown, *aaáá*, and cemented together with canada balsam or thickened linseed oil. A section through the prism parallel to the *c* axis is shown in Fig. 361. Rays of ordinary light *m* entering the prism from below are resolved into ordinary *o* and extraordinary *e* rays. The ordinary rays are totally reflected by the cementing films *aá*, as in the case of the Nicol prism, while the extraordinary *e* rays pass through. In describing the construction and use of the polarizing microscope the devices employed for the production of polarized light, whether they be Nicol or Ahrens prisms, are generally referred to as Nicols.

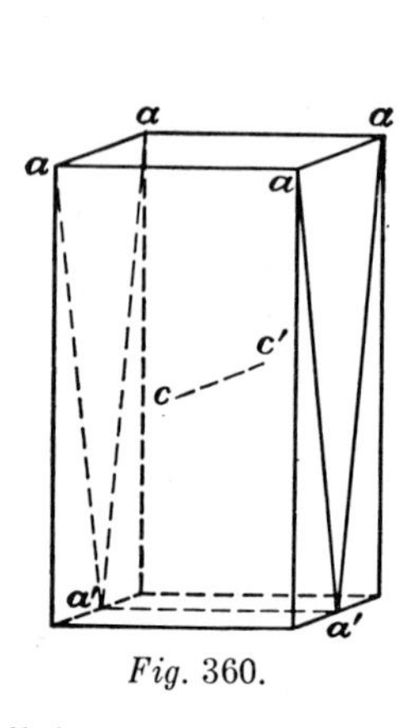

Fig. 360.

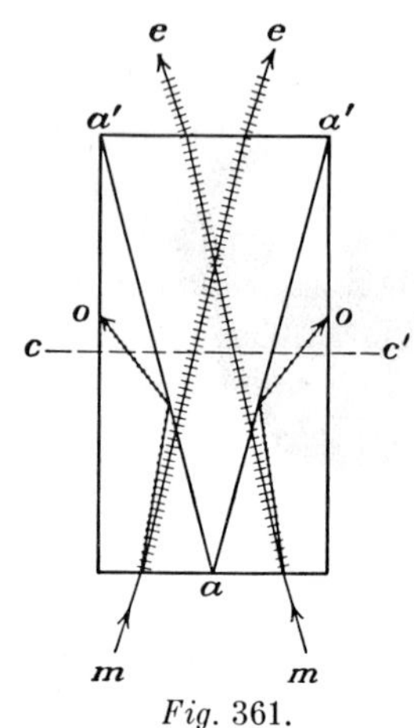

Fig. 361.

Parallel and Convergent Polarized Light. Observations may be carried out with the rays of polarized light passing through the substances parallel to the axis of the microscope tube, or the rays may be made to converge in the substance by means of suitable condensing lenses. We may, hence, speak of observations in *parallel polarized light* and in *convergent polarized light.*

Since solids may be classified optically as isotropic and anisotropic, the effects of parallel and convergent polarized light upon each of these groups will be considered. It must be remembered that anisotropic substances can be subdivided into uniaxial and biaxial groups.

Behavior of Isotropic Substances. *In Parallel Polarized Light with Crossed Nicols.* If the analyzer is removed from the microscope tube and an isotropic substance, either an amorphous substance or a crystal of the cubic system, is viewed on the microscope stage, it will be noted that the field of vision is illuminated. It remains illuminated for all positions of the stage, for the polarized light emerging from the polarizer passes through an isotropic substance and to the eye without change. But when the analyzer is replaced with its vibration direction perpendicular to that of the polarizer, the field of vision is dark and remains so upon rotating the stage. This is due to the fact that the light emerging from the object on the stage vibrates parallel to the vibration direction of the polarizer. This direction, however, is at right angles to that of the analyzer, the Nicols being crossed, and, hence, no light passes through the upper Nicol. All unstrained isotropic substances, therefore, appear dark between crossed Nicols. This observation is very easily made and serves to distinguish isotropic substances from those which are optically anisotropic or doubly refractive which as a rule do not remain dark between crossed Nicols upon rotation of the stage.

In Convergent Polarized Light with Crossed Nicols. When substances are studied in convergent polarized light, the rays of light pass through the substance inclined to the axis of the microscope; that is, they tend to converge. Convergent light is easily obtained by using an objective of high magnification and inserting a condensing lens C below the microscope stage (see Fig. 340, page 121).

Isotropic substances appear dark in convergent light between crossed Nicols for the same reasons as given above. That is, between crossed Nicols they are always dark in both parallel and convergent light.

Behavior of Uniaxial Substances in Parallel Polarized Light with Crossed Nicols. *Sections Perpendicular to the c Axis.* When the analyzer is removed, these sections of uniaxial crystals, that is, crystals of either the hexagonal or the tetragonal system, will appear light and remain so for all positions of the stage. When the analyzer is replaced with its vibration direction perpendicular to that of the polarizer, the field is dark and remains so when the stage is rotated. This behavior of hexagonal and tetragonal crystals is the same as for isotropic substances, as discussed above. This is due to the fact that the light is passing through the crystal or the section parallel to the c axis, which is an isotropic direction. For this particular direction, uniaxial substances behave in parallel polarized light as though they were isotropic.

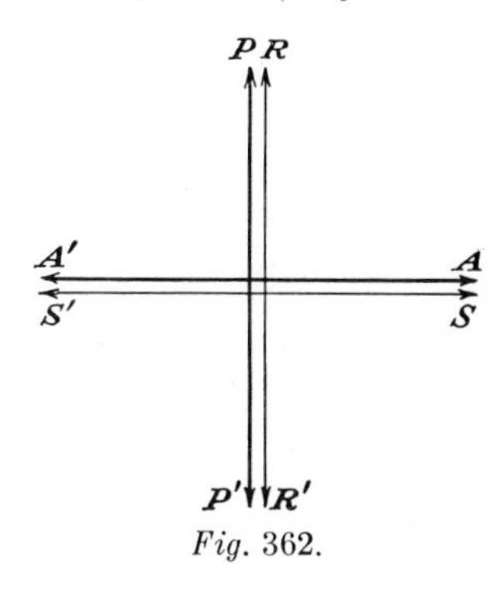

Fig. 362.

Sections Parallel or Inclined to the c Axis. When these sections are viewed with the analyzer removed, the field of vision is illuminated. When the analyzer is replaced and the stage rotated, the field is four times light and four times dark during a complete rotation, provided the Nicols are crossed. That is, when viewed in daylight or white artificial light, interference colors are seen four times during a complete rotation. The positions of greatest darkness or extinction indicate the vibration directions of the rays passing through the section or crystal. When the vibration directions of the crystal are parallel to those of the Nicols, the field of vision is dark. This is illustrated in Fig. 362, where PP' and AA' are the vibration directions of the polarizer and analyzer, respectively, and RR' and SS' those of the crystal. PP' and RR' being parallel, light from the polarizer passes through the crystal without change in vibration direction and enters the analyzer but does not emerge, the favorable direction for passage through the upper Nicol being AA'.

The cross hairs of the microscope are parallel to the vibration directions of the Nicols and are used for the determination of the extinction or vibration directions in the crystal or section. Extinction may take place when the cross hairs are parallel or perpendicular to the edges of the specimen, as in Fig. 363. When this is the case, the crystal is said to have *parallel extinction*. Uniaxial substances may also possess *symmetrical extinction*, as illustrated in Fig. 364.

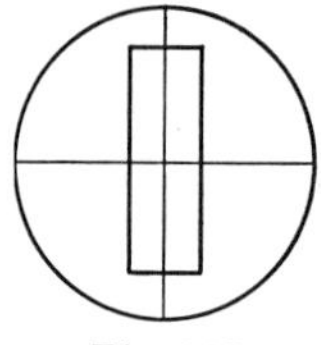

Fig. 363.

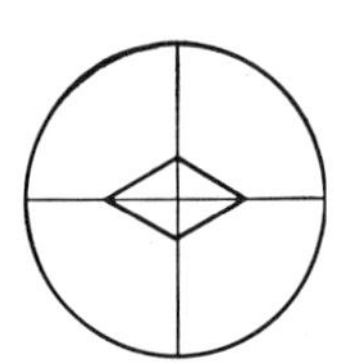

Fig. 364.

Determination of Indices of Refraction. The position of extinction is found as indicated above. The analyzer is then removed, and the Becke test applied (see page 124). In this way, the index of refraction of the ray vibrating parallel to the vibration direction of the polarizer is determined. On rotating the stage through 90°, the index of refraction for the second vibration direction can be determined. The ray vibrating parallel to the c axis is termed the *extraordinary* ray e; the one vibrating at right angles to it, the *ordinary* ray o. With sections (1) *perpendicular to the c axis* (basal sections), only the index of refraction ω for the ordinary ray can be determined; (2) *parallel to the c axis*, the indices ω and ϵ for the ordinary and extraordinary rays, respectively; and (3) *inclined to the c axis*, the index ω for the ordinary and an intermediate value ϵ for the extraordinary ray can be obtained. When the index of refraction ω is larger than ϵ, the crystal is said to be optically negative; when smaller, optically positive (see page 120).

Fig. 365. Reinhard Brauns (1861–1937). Professor of Mineralogy in the University of Bonn (1907–1932). Eminent investigator, author, and editor.

Interference Colors. When the vibration directions in the crystal are not parallel to those of the Nicols, the field shows, in general, an interference color, provided the crystal is viewed in either daylight or artifical white light. The color is due to the fact that the light from the polarizer PP' is resolved into two rays vibrating parallel to xx' and yy', the vibration directions of the crystal (Figs. 366 and 367). The two rays in the crystal travel with different velocities, and when they emerge, the slow ray naturally lags behind the faster. On entering the upper Nicol, each of these rays is further resolved into two rays vibrating parallel to the vibration directions of the *o* and *e* rays of the analyzer. As indicated on page 131, only the latter of these, namely, the two vibrating parallel to the *e* ray, emerge from the analyzer. But these two emergent rays *OS* and *OR*, vibrating in the same plane, travel with different velocities.

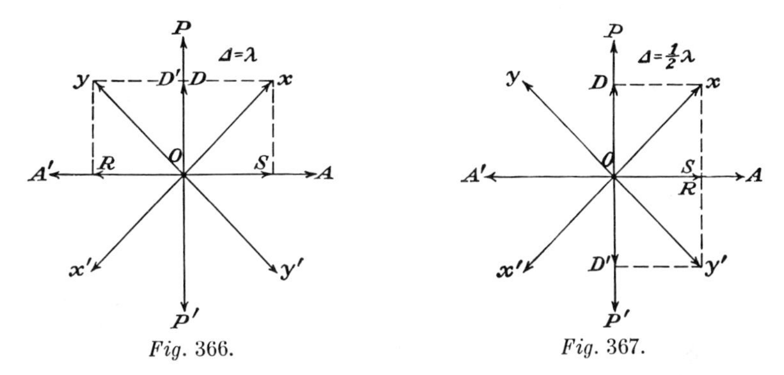

Fig. 366. *Fig.* 367.

Interference of light is thus brought about, and with crossed Nicols, when the phasal difference of the two rays is equal to a whole wave length λ, or some whole multiple thereof, destructive interference results (Fig. 366). When the phasal difference is a half wave length ½λ, or some odd multiple thereof, the rays reinforce each other (Fig. 367).

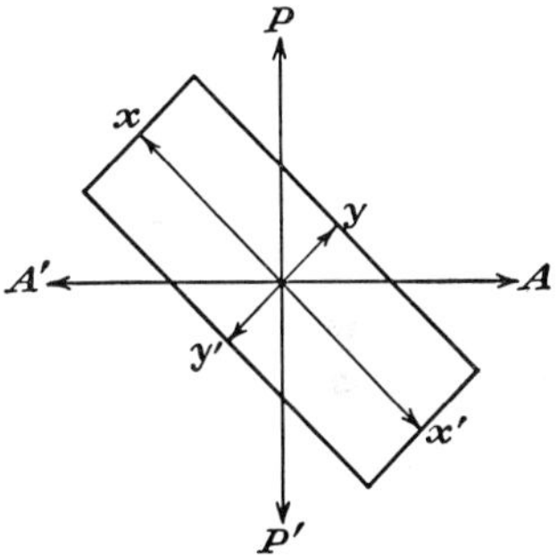

As the phasal differences for the component colors of white light will be of both these types, certain portions of the white light passing through the crystal are destroyed, while other portions are intensified, causing the light which emerges to be colored. The field of vision shows, therefore, what is commonly designated as an interference color. The character of the color depends upon (1) *the strength of double refraction of the substance,* (2) *the position of the plate with regard to the c axis, and* (3) *the thickness of the plate.* Maximum interference colors are observed in sections of uniform thickness of uniaxial substances when cut parallel to the *c* axis, and in biaxial crystals when cut parallel to the optic plane (page 140). When monochromatic light instead of daylight is used, the field will be dark, as before, if the vibration directions in the substance and Nicols correspond. In intermediate positions, the field will be illuminated by light of the particular color employed.

Fig. 368.

Determination of the Fast and Slow Rays. The position of extinction is first determined, and the stage then rotated so that the extinction directions cross the field diagonally; that is, they make angles of 45° with the cross hairs (Fig. 368). This is the position of most intense illumination and color. Into the slot of the microscope tube, which is directly above the objective, a gypsum or selenite test plate (page 139) is now inserted. When viewed alone between crossed Nicols, the test plate yields an interference color which is usually designated as the *sensitive red tint.* By the action of the crystal on the stage, the red tint is changed to either a bluish or yellowish color, if the double refraction of the substance is low. If the tint is changed to a bluish color, it means that the vibration directions of the test plate and those of the crystal correspond; that is, the slow ray in the test plate is over the slow ray in the crystal and the fast over the fast. Now note the direction of the marked ray on the test plate, which is usually given as X or $\mathfrak{a}$. This is the fast ray, and the vibration direction at right angles to it is obviously that of the slow ray, which is commonly designated as Z or $\mathfrak{c}$. In this way, the directions of the corresponding rays are easily recognized in the crystal. If, however, the sensitive red tint is changed to a yellowish color, instead of a bluish, it means that the fast ray of the test plate is over the slow ray of the crystal, and vice versa.

If the mineral has high double refraction, the directions of the fast and slow rays can be more conveniently determined by the use of the quartz wedge. If the wedge is inserted so that the vibration directions of the wedge and of the mineral are of unlike character, the interference colors of the mineral are reduced, that is, they pass to those of a lower order; but if the vibration directions are the same, the interference colors are increased, that is, they pass to those of a higher order.

The expression *character of the principal zone* refers to the character of the ray (fast or slow) that vibrates parallel to the elongation of prismatic crystals.

Order of Interference Colors. The interference colors may be bright and vivid and are said to be of a *low* or *medium order,* or they may be hazy and dull and are then of the *higher orders.* It is well in determining the order of interference colors to study an interference color chart. When the color approximates white, it is characterized as being *white of the higher order.* When sections of different substances have the same thickness and orientation, some indication of the strength of double refraction, or birefringence, can be obtained from the character of the interference colors, for the stronger the double refraction the higher the resultant order of colors. When dealing with one and the same substance, the thicker sections or crystals will show colors of higher order.

The Behavior of Uniaxial Crystals in Convergent Polarized Light with Crossed Nicols. *Sections Perpendicular to the c Axis.* In uniaxial substances, all rays of light inclined to the *c* axis are resolved into two rays, *o* and *e,* which travel with unequal velocities. The phasal difference between these rays increases with the inclination of the incident rays to the c axis. Parallel to the c axis, the phasal difference is zero. Accordingly, the phasal difference increases with the inclination of the rays to the c axis. The increase is the same for all directions around the c axis. Wherever the phasal difference $\Delta = \frac{n}{2}\lambda$, where n is odd, reinforcement of light takes place. Where $\Delta = n\lambda$, n being any whole number, destructive interference results (Fig. 369). Along any diameter through the field of vision, therefore, we shall observe darkness at the center, and at equal distances on either side of the center the same interference colors will appear when daylight or artificial white light is used. In uniaxial crystals, all directions equally inclined to the c axis are optically the same. Hence, the interference colors appear as a series of concentric rings. The colors are brighter and more vivid near the center of the field and gradually fade as the distance from the center increases. These isochromatic circles are farther apart near the center of the field and closer together toward the periphery. In monochromatic light, a series of light and dark circles will be observed (Figs. 370 and 371).

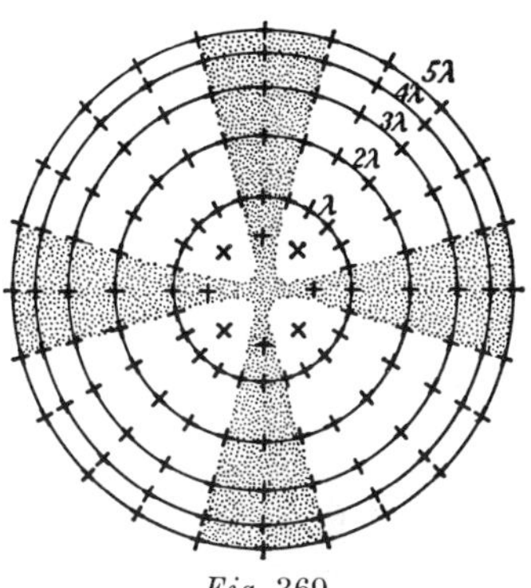

Fig. 369.

Fig. 370.[1]

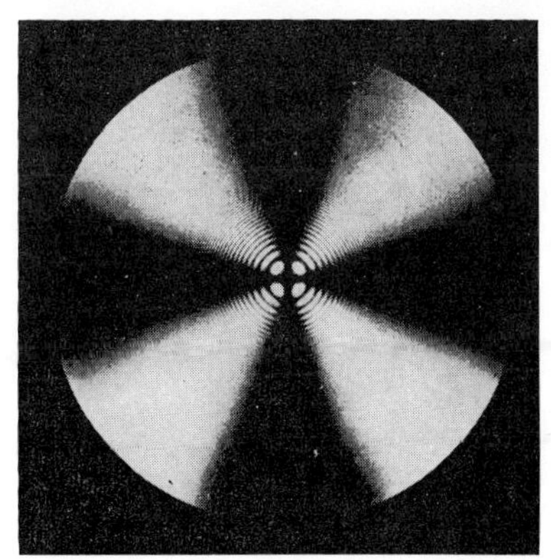
Fig. 371.

It will be further observed that a dark cross lies superimposed upon the isochromatic circles. The cross occurs where the vibration directions of the substance correspond to those of the Nicols, for, as has been pointed out previously, in such instances the field is dark. The isochromatic

[1] Figures 370 to 372, 380 to 383, 386 to 389, and 392 to 396 are from Hauswaldt's "Interferenzerscheinungen im polarisirten Lichte."

circles and the dark cross constitute what is called the *uniaxial interference figure*.

The uniaxial interference figure remains unchanged when the stage is rotated, for all directions through the substance equally inclined to the *c* axis are alike optically. In order to observe interference figures, it is necessary to use an objective of high magnification, and either to remove the eyepiece of the microscope or to insert an auxiliary lens called the *Bertrand lens* into the tube above the analyzer. In the first case, the figure is small and appears far down in the tube. It is, however, usually quite distinct. In the second case, the figure is much larger but generally more hazy.

Some uniaxial substances, which have been subjected to stress, often show upon rotation of the stage a slight separation of the black cross. The figure, thus produced, is biaxial in character.

Fig. 372.

Sections Inclined to the c Axis. Sections of this character show only a partial interference figure in convergent light. The more nearly the section is parallel to the base, the more will the observed figure approximate the normal figure; and the greater the departure from this parallelism, the more the figure will be eccentric and incomplete. This is shown by Fig. 372. When the stage is rotated, the arms of the dark cross move across the field parallel to the cross hairs and in the same direction as the movement of the stage. This observation is of great importance in distinguishing certain uniaxial from biaxial figures (see page 143).

Strength of Double Refraction Determined from Uniaxial Interference Figures. The number of isochromatic circles may serve to estimate the strength of double refraction or birefringence. When sections have the same thickness, substances with strong double refraction will show more rings than those possessing weak birefringence. Thickness also increases the number of rings (Figs. 370 and 371). In extremely thin sections these rings may not be visible. This is especially true of substances with very weak birefringence.

Character of Double Refraction Determined from Uniaxial Interference Figures. The optical character of uniaxial substances cut perpendicular to the *c* axis can usually be determined by using the following test plates: (1) *mica test plate*, (2) *gypsum or selenite test plate*, and (3) the *quartz wedge.* The gypsum test plate and the quartz wedge are more serviceable than the mica plate.

MICA TEST PLATE. If the mica test plate is inserted in the slot of the microscope tube, it will be observed that the interference figure breaks up and two distinct black spots appear near the center of the field. The position of these spots with respect to the slow vibration direction Z or $\mathfrak{c}$ marked on the test plate should be noted. If a line joining these spots is parallel to the Z or $\mathfrak{c}$ direction the substance is optically *negative* (Fig. 373). In optically *positive* substances, the line joining the black spots is perpendicular to the Z or $\mathfrak{c}$ direction (Fig. 374).

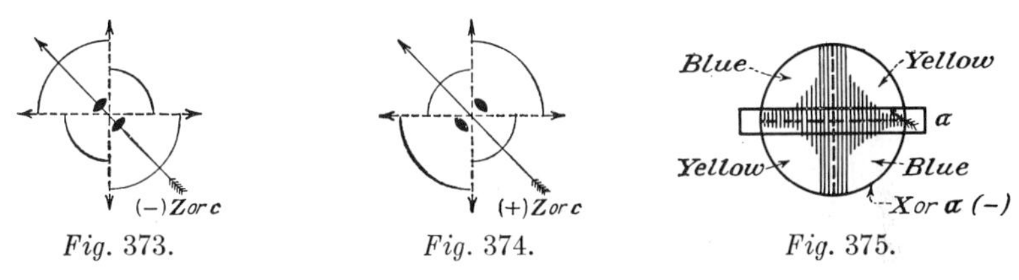

Fig. 373. *Fig.* 374. *Fig.* 375.

GYPSUM OR SELENITE TEST PLATE. When the gypsum or selenite test plate is used, two blue spots appear. If the line joining these blue spots is parallel to the X or $\mathfrak{a}$ direction of the gypsum test plate (fast ray in test plate), the substance is said to be optically *negative* (Fig. 375) and optically *positive* if it crosses the X or $\mathfrak{a}$ direction of the test plate.[1]

QUARTZ WEDGE. If the quartz wedge is slowly pushed into the slot, it will be observed that the interference figure is broken up into two pairs of moving arcs which lie in opposite quadrants. One pair of these arcs will move *outward* or away from the center of the figure while the other pair moves in the opposite direction, that is, *inward* or toward the center. If the outward movement of the arcs is parallel to the Z or $\mathfrak{c}$ direction of the wedge, when the wedge is slowly inserted beginning at the thin end, the substance is optically *negative* (Fig. 376). In optically *positive* substances, the outward movement of the arcs is across or perpendicular to the Z or $\mathfrak{c}$ direction (Fig. 377, page 140).

These observations are based upon the fact that, when like directions in the test plates and in the substances are over one another, the double refraction is increased. When the corresponding directions are unlike, for example, fast ray over slow ray, and vice versa, a reduction in double refraction results.

General Statement Regarding Biaxial Crystals. As indicated on page 120, all crystals of the orthorhombic, monoclinic, and triclinic systems are biaxial and possess three principal optical directions at right

[1] X and Z are now generally used to designate the fast and slow rays, respectively, rather than $\mathfrak{a}$ and $\mathfrak{c}$, and Y instead of $\mathfrak{b}$ for the optic normal, p. 140.

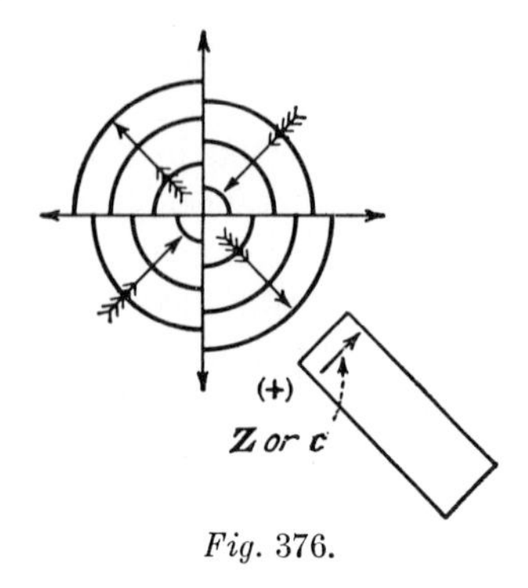

Fig. 376.

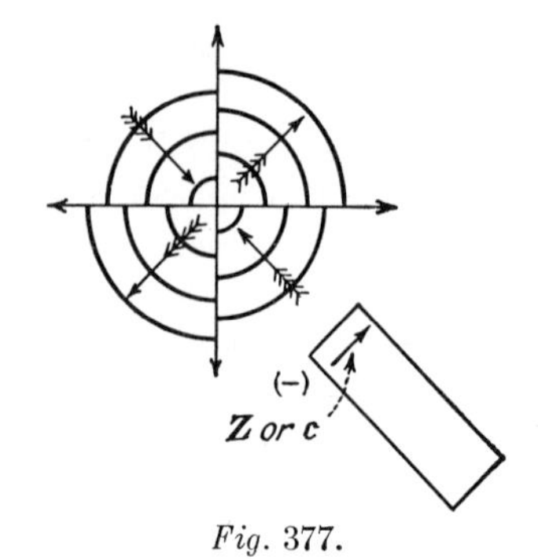

Fig. 377.

angles to each other. The principal optical direction which bisects the acute angle $2V$ between the two isotropic directions, or the optic axes AA', is called the *acute bisectrix* Bx_a (Fig. 378). The *obtuse bisectrix* Bx_o bisects the obtuse angle of the optic axes. These bisectrices are the vibration directions of the rays traveling with the greatest and least velocities. The acute and obtuse bisectrices and the optic axes lie in the same plane, called the *plane of the optic axes.* The direction at right angles to the plane is termed the *optic normal* Y or $\mathfrak{b}$. In the orthorhombic system, the three optical directions, acute bisectrix, obtuse bisectrix, and optical normal (Fig. 378) correspond to the three crystallographic axes. Monoclinic crystals have only one of these directions fixed, namely, by the b crystallographic axis. In the triclinic system, there is no fixed relationship between the orientation of the principal optic directions and the crystallographic axes.

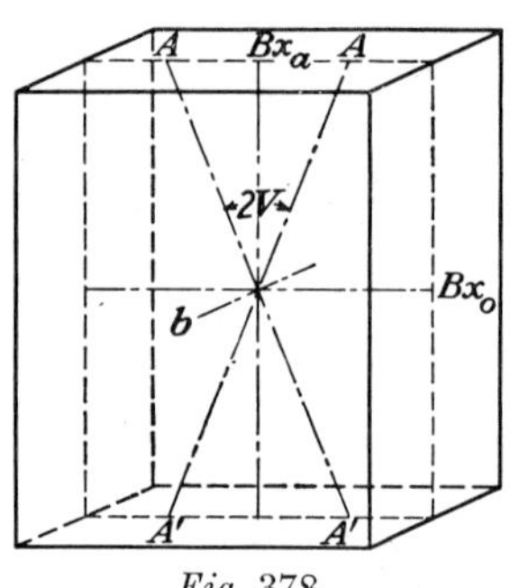

Fig. 378.

Crystals are said to be optically *positive* or *negative,* depending upon whether the acute bisectrix is the vibration direction of the slow (Z or $\mathfrak{c}$) or fast (X or $\mathfrak{a}$) ray, respectively. The direction of the optic normal is commonly designated as Y or $\mathfrak{b}$. Also consult pages 120 and 121.

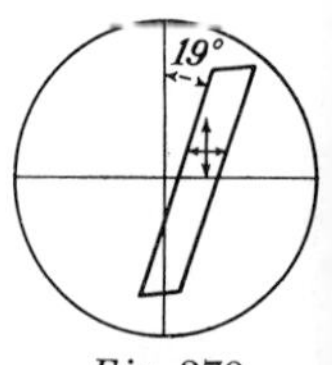

Fig. 379.

Behavior of Biaxial Crystals. *In Parallel Polarized Light with Crossed Nicols.* ANY SECTION. All sections of biaxial crystals, with the exception of those perpendicular to an optic axis, are four times light and four times dark during a complete rotation of the stage. The extinction may be parallel, symmetrical, or inclined to an edge or cleavage of the crystal or section (Figs. 363, 364, and 379). In the case of orthorhombic substances, the extinction is usually parallel or symmetrical. Monoclinic substances possess parallel, symmetrical, and inclined extinctions; that is, sections parallel to the *b* axis have parallel or symmetrical extinction, while all other sections have inclined or oblique extinction. Maximum obliquity is observed on sections perpendicular to the *b* axis. In triclinic substances, all extinctions are inclined.

SECTIONS PERPENDICULAR TO AN OPTIC AXIS. These sections do not extinguish when the stage is rotated between crossed Nicols but remain uniformly illuminated with an interference color of low order. In convergent light, an interference figure is observed (see Figs. 388 and 389, page 143).

In Convergent Polarized Light with Crossed Nicols. SECTIONS PERPENDICULAR TO THE ACUTE BISECTRIX Bx_a. These sections show an interference figure consisting of two series of oval-like curves upon which two dark brushes are superimposed. In the *normal* position, that is, when the plane including the optic axes and the direction at right angles to it

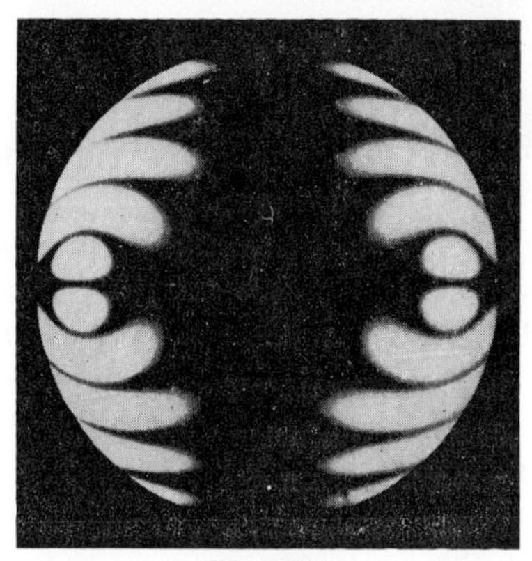

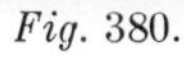

Fig. 380.

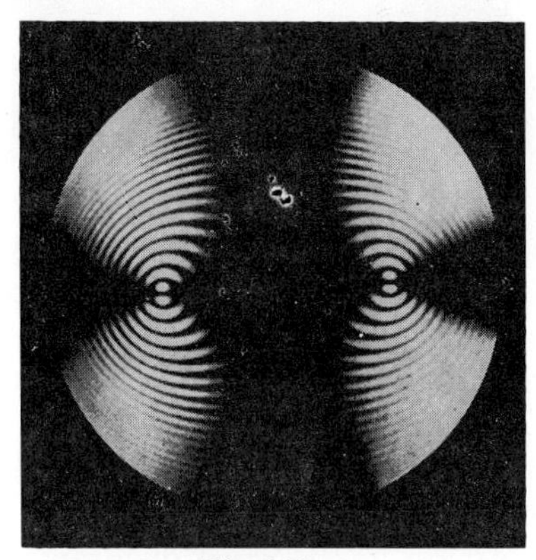

Fig. 381.

are parallel with the cross hairs, the interference figure resembles Fig. 380. In white light the curves are colored, while in monochromatic light they are alternately light and dark. The distance between the optic axes or "eyes" gives some indication of the size of the angle of the optic axes. The closer together the "eyes" are, the smaller is the angle (Fig. 381), and vice versa. The angle of the optic axes is constant for any given substance and is independent of the thickness of the section, provided the temperature remains the same. From the number of curves in the interference figure, some idea of the double refraction may be obtained, for the stronger the double refraction, the larger the number of the curves in the field of vision, provided the sections are the same thickness.

The optical properties of biaxial crystals are very complex, and only an elementary and incomplete explanation of the formation of these interference figures will be given. The black cross or hyperbolic brushes appear wherever the vibration directions of the emergent rays are parallel to those of the Nicols. At all other points of the section, the emergent rays have vibration directions which are inclined to those of the Nicols, and interference of light, as explained on page 134, will, therefore, take place. As these vibration directions change most rapidly around the

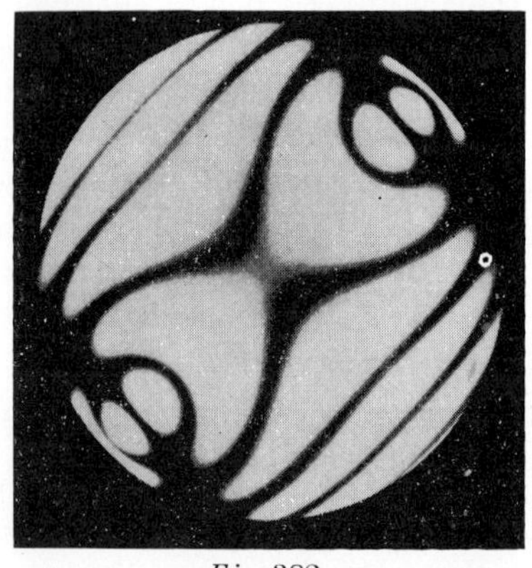

Fig. 382.

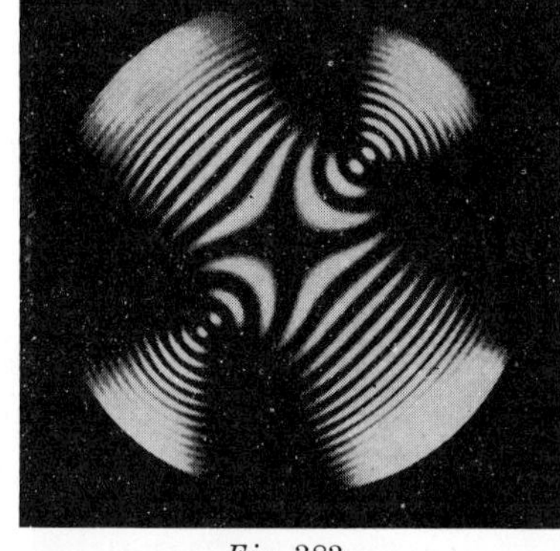

Fig. 383.

optic axes, the curves there will be smaller and closer together than elsewhere. These curves are unaltered as the stage is rotated. The dark brushes, however, change. Figures 382 and 383 show biaxial interference figures in the 45° or *diagonal* position.

The positive and negative character of biaxial crystals with small optic angles $2V$ may be determined from the interference figure by using the mica or gypsum test plates, as described on page 139. When the spots are in the same quadrants as the marked directions on the test plate (Z, mica; or X, gypsum) the substance is negative, and positive in the opposite quadrants.

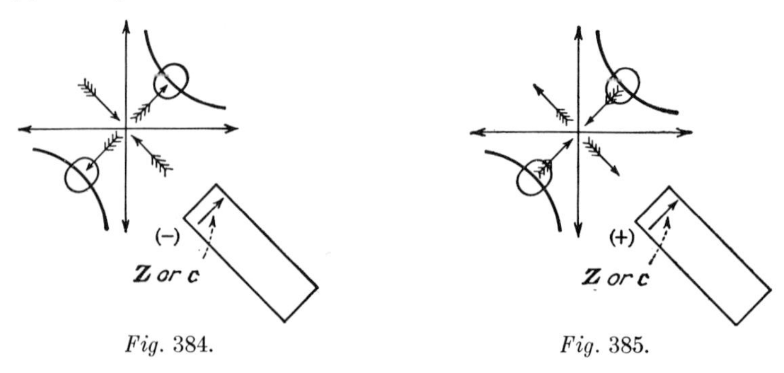

Fig. 384. *Fig.* 385.

The quartz wedge may be used to advantage when the biaxial figure is in the 45° or *diagonal* position (Figs. 382 and 383). The wedge should be slowly inserted, beginning at the thin end, so that the slow direction of the wedge Z or $\mathfrak{c}$ is parallel to the plane of the optic axes. In optically *negative* substances the outward movement of the arcs is parallel to the Z or $\mathfrak{c}$ direction of the wedge (Fig. 384), while in optically *positive* substances it is across or perpendicular to the Z or $\mathfrak{c}$ direction (Fig. 385).

SECTIONS INCLINED TO THE ACUTE BISECTRIX Bx_a. These sections show a partial interference figure, usually only one optic axis or "eye" and a portion of the brushes being visible (Figs. 386 and 387). The brushes always move in a direction opposite to that of the stage.

SECTIONS PERPENDICULAR TO AN OPTIC AXIS. These sections show the emergence of an optic axis, the observed interference figure being illus-

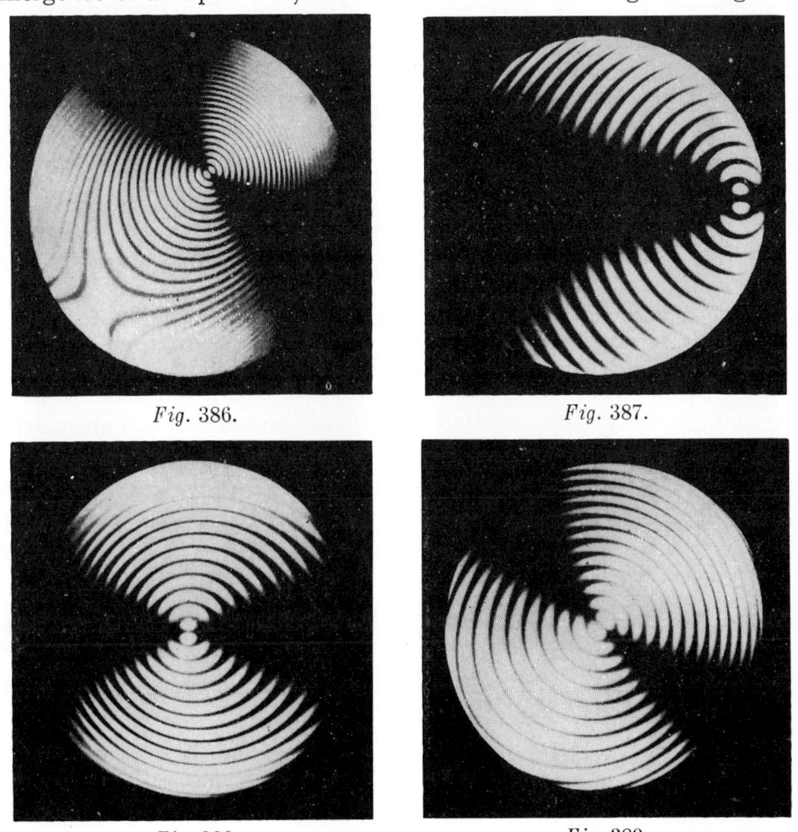

Fig. 386. *Fig.* 387.

Fig. 388. *Fig.* 389.

trated by Fig. 388. This figure does not remain stationary when the stage is rotated, as is the case with interference figures of uniaxial substances (page 137). Figures 388 and 389 show the interference figure in the normal and diagonal positions, respectively. When the interference figure is in the 45° or diagonal position, the convex side of the hyperbolic brush and the more pointed portions of the curves about the optic axis are directed toward the acute bisectrix.

The gypsum test plate may be used to advantage in determining the optical character of the substance when the interference figure is in the diagonal position. If the substance is optically positive, a blue spot appears on the convex side of the hyperbolic brush, provided the test plate is inserted with its X or $\mathfrak{a}$ direction parallel to the plane of the optic axes. In the case of optically negative substances, the blue spot will be observed on the concave side of the brush.

SECTIONS PARALLEL TO THE PLANE OF THE OPTIC AXES. Sections of this character do not, in general, show distinct interference figures, especially if studied in white light.

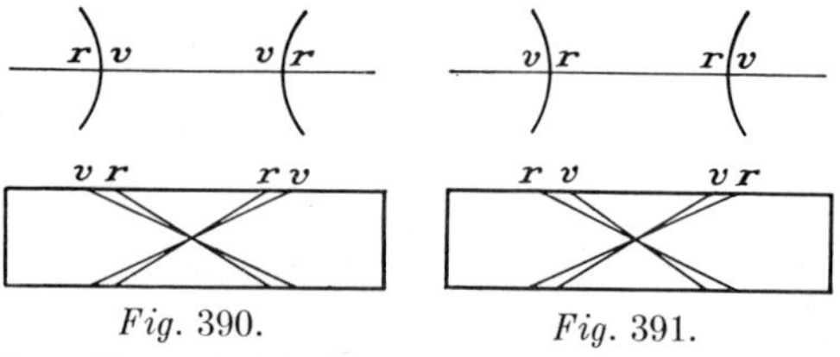

Fig. 390. *Fig.* 391.

Figs. 390 and 391. Sketches of interference figures (upper) and sections showing location of optic axes (lower).

DISPERSION OF THE OPTIC AXES, $r > v$ OR $r < v$. In Fig. 383 illustrating a biaxial interference figure, the size of the angle of the optic axes is indicated by the distance between the centers of the eyes. When white light is used and the interference figures are viewed in the 45° or diagonal position, the hyperbolic brushes show red and blue or violet fringes. These fringes are especially distinct at r and v, as shown in Figs. 390 and 391. This is due to the fact that the size of the angle of the optic axes varies with the color. In some cases, the angle for red is larger than for violet, and vice versa. If red appears on the convex side of the hyperbolic brushes, it means that the optic angle for red is larger than for blue or violet; that is, $r > v$. On the other hand, if violet is observed on the convex side of the brushes, the angle for violet is the larger, namely, $v > r$. That is, the dispersion of the optic axes is directly opposite to what appears to be the case from the position of the colors in the interference figure. This is due to the fact that, from the white light traveling along the optic axes of the various colors, certain components are eliminated and others intensified. Hence, where the axes for red light emerge, say, at r in Figs. 390 and 391, red will have been eliminated and the resultant light will be violet. At v, violet has been lost, and in the interference figure red will appear at the corresponding positions. The observation of the character of the dispersion of the optic axes is best made with the interference figure in the diagonal position on any section where a portion of a hyperbolic brush is distinctly visible near the center of the field. The determination of the character of the dispersion aids materially in identifying biaxial substances.

Optical Rotation. Enantiomorphous crystals, that is, those which have a right- and left-handed development (Figs. 169 and 170, page 56), have a corresponding enantiomorphous internal structure. When plane polarized light passes through such substances in definite directions, the plane of polarization of the emerging light is rotated either to the right or left. This is called *optical rotation* or *rotary polarization.* These substances are said to be *optically active.* Quartz and cinnabar are the most notable optically active minerals. Crystals of tartaric acid, cane sugar, and sodium chlorate are also optically active. In some particulars the optical behavior of substances possessing rotary polarization is unique. Some of the effects in uniaxial crystals, especially as observed on quartz, will be considered briefly.

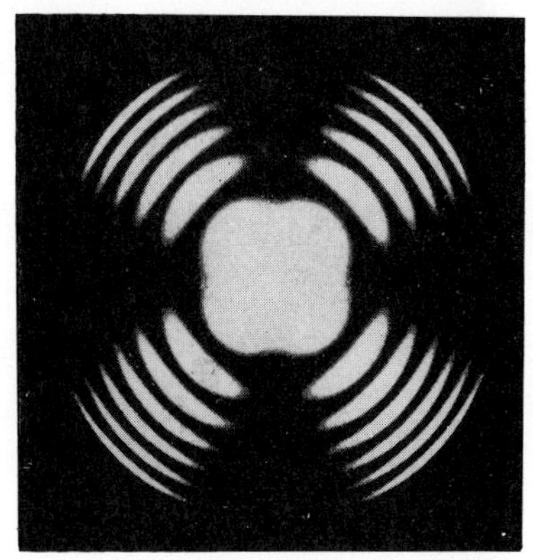

Fig. 392.

Parallel Polarized Light and Crossed Nicols. Sections Cut Perpendicular to the *c* Axis. As the *c* axis in these substances is not an isotropic direction, sections cut perpendicular to it do not extinguish between crossed Nicols but remain uniformly illuminated when the stage is rotated.

Sections Cut Parallel or Inclined to the *c* Axis. These sections behave in the same way as those described on page 133.

Convergent Polarized Light and Crossed Nicols. Sections Cut Perpendicular to the *c* Axis. An interference figure quite analogous to the regular uniaxial interference figure is obtained (Fig. 392). It will be observed that the dark brushes do not extend entirely across the center of the figure. By rotating the upper Nicol, the character of the rotation of polarization may be determined, that is, whether it is to the right or left. If the upper Nicol is rotated in the same direction as that of the rotation of the plane of polarization, the circles of the figure enlarge; but if it is rotated in the opposite direction, the circles contract. By using the mica test plate, a two-armed spiral is obtained, the direction of rotation being indicated by the directions of the arms (Figs. 393 and 394). By placing two sections of quartz of opposite character of the same thickness over one another, a figure with a four-armed spiral results. These are the spirals of Airy (Figs. 395 and 396). The direction of the arms of the spirals indicates the character of the rotation in the lower section. Figures 392 to 396 show interference figures as obtained from thick sections of quartz. These interference figures cannot be observed on sections of quartz of normal thickness (0.03 mm.).

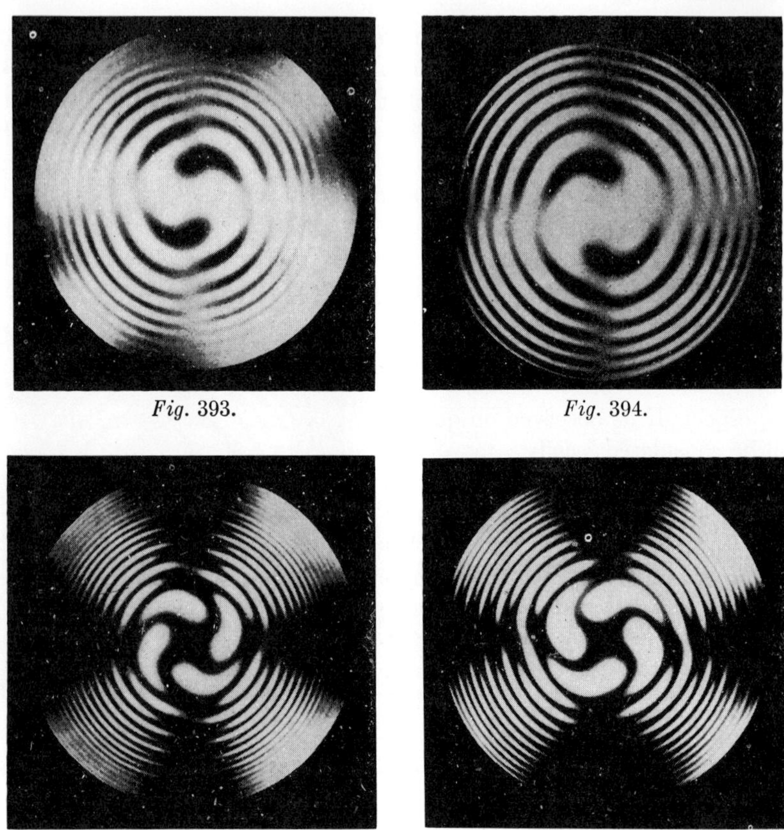

Fig. 393. *Fig.* 394.

Fig. 395. *Fig.* 396.

Twin Crystals. The fact that crystals are twinned is easily recognized in polarized light, especially if they are anisotropic.

Parallel Light and Crossed Nicols. Anisotropic crystals showing twinning do not extinguish uniformly. Certain portions of the crystal may be

Fig. 397.

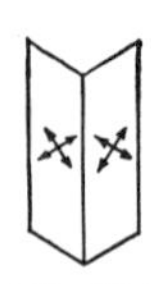

Fig. 398.

Fig. 399.

Fig. 400.

dark, while other portions are light, when the stage is rotated. Figures 397 and 398 show the behavior of contact twins and Fig. 399 that of a section with polysynthetic twinning. Obviously, twinned crystals of isotropic substances will have no effect upon polarized light.

Convergent Light and Crossed Nicols. In properly oriented sections, interference figures may be observed, as shown in Fig. 400.

Pleochroism. The absorption of light in colored sections and crystals of uniaxial and biaxial substances varies with direction. In the case of uniaxial substances, there are two principal colors for transmitted light. These colors are obtained when the light vibrates either parallel or perpendicular to the *c* axis. Uniaxial substances are, therefore, said to be *dichroic*. In biaxial crystals there are three principal colors corresponding to the three principal optical directions at right angles to each other. Biaxial substances are therefore *trichroic*.

Pleochroism is easily recognized under the microscope by first determining the extinction directions of the section or crystal under consideration. The upper Nicol should now be removed and the color observed, and then the stage rotated 90° and the change in color noted. Strongly pleochroic substances show marked changes in color when studied in this way.

Isotropic substances, that is, those which are amorphous or belong to the cubic system, do not show pleochroism.

Summary

BEHAVIOR OF SECTIONS, CRYSTALS, OR FRAGMENTS IN PARALLEL LIGHT BETWEEN CROSSED NICOLS

Behavior	Class	Characteristics	System
All sections remain dark through 360°	Isotropic	(*a*) No regular outline, structure, cleavage, or etch figures	Amorphous
		(*b*) Regular outline, structure, cleavage, and etch figures	Cubic
Not all sections remain dark through 360°. Some are four times light and dark, others remain uniformly light	Anisotropic	(*a*) Isotropic and doubly refractive sections. The first show a uniaxial interference figure in convergent light	Hexagonal Isotropic sections are trigonal or hexagonal in outline
			Tetragonal Isotropic sections are tetragonal or ditetragonal in outline
		(*b*) Sections either extinguish regularly or remain uniformly light. The latter show the emergence of an optic axis in convergent light	Orthorhombic Most sections show parallel or symmetrical extinction
			Monoclinic Sections show parallel, symmetrical, or inclined extinction
			Triclinic All sections show inclined extinction

Order of Procedure and Methods for Recording Observations. In studying sections, crystals, or fragments under the polarizing microscope, the following order for making determinations is suggested:

PARALLEL POLARIZED LIGHT

1. Isotropic or anisotropic.
2. Index of refraction; higher or lower than canada balsam or the liquid in which substance is embedded, if in fragments.
3. Outline of section or crystal. Cleavage cracks.
4. Extinction directions—parallel, symmetrical, or inclined. Measurement of extinction angles.
5. Determination of fast and slow rays.
6. Order of interference colors. Double refraction.
7. Pleochroism.

CONVERGENT POLARIZED LIGHT

1. Uniaxial or biaxial figure. Orientation.
2. If biaxial, note size of optic angle.
3. Positive or negative character.
4. Double refraction.
5. Dispersion.
6. Optical rotation.
7. System. See summary.

Figures 401 and 402 indicate a very good method, suggested by Weinschenk, for recording the various optical properties of substances,

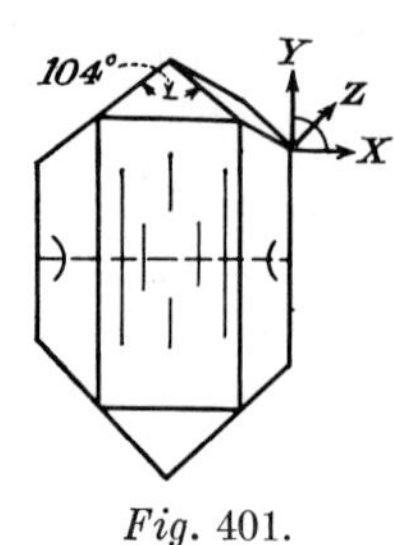

Fig. 401.

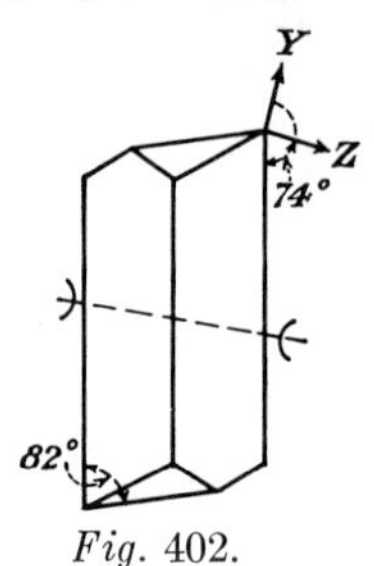

Fig. 402.

as determined under the microscope. In both figures the material represented was in the form of small crystals. The outline of the substance should be sketched and important angles measured and their sizes indicated. The direction of cleavage cracks may be shown as in Fig. 401. The various extinction directions are shown by arrows. The approximate value of the indices of refraction for these directions can be indicated by lines of different widths; that is, light lines indicate low indices, heavy lines high indices. The strength of double refraction is given by the arc enclosing the vibration directions, which may be drawn light or heavy in accordance with the variation from weak to strong double refraction, or one or more arcs may be used. Pleochroism may be shown in connection with the vibration directions, the observed colors being designated. The location of the optic axes, size of the optic angle, and dispersion are all easily indicated.

12 Crystal Structure and X-ray Analysis

Crystals and Crystal Structure. Solids are formed by precipitation from a solution, solidification of a melt, or sublimation from a vapor. In most cases these processes involve crystallization; that is, the atoms assume a definite orderly three-dimensional arrangement. Such solids are crystalline, as opposed to noncrystalline or amorphous substances, in which a regular atomic arrangement is lacking. Just as in wallpaper, where some design is repeated in a two-dimensional pattern, in crystalline solids groups of atoms are repeated in a three-dimensional pattern.

Long before X-ray methods were developed for actually determining this structural arrangement, a rather complete geometrical theory concerning possible atomic arrangements was developed. Many different facts directly or indirectly implied that such structural patterns must exist. Of importance among these facts were the recognition of only six crystal systems and 32 classes of symmetry, the laws of rational indices and constancy of interfacial angles, and the directional properties of crystals, such as cleavage, and especially the optical properties.

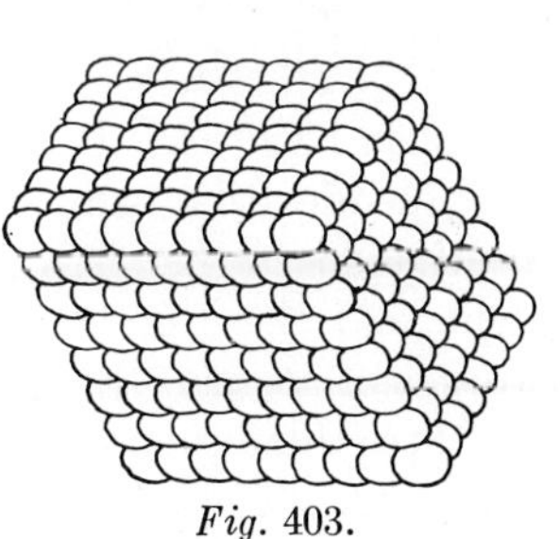

Fig. 403.

Early Theories of Crystal Structure. Although it was long surmised that crystals undoubtedly possess regular internal structure, it was not until toward the close of the seventeenth century that students of crystals began to formulate theories. Thus, Huygens, in 1678, in explaining the double refraction of calcite, advanced views that may be considered as having formed the basis for the development of the subsequent theories of crystal structure. By assuming calcite to be made up of small ellipsoidal particles arranged or packed in a regular manner, Huygens endeavored to explain the crystal form and cleavage of the mineral as well as the variations in its hardness and double refraction with direction. Figure 403 represents the internal structure of calcite as visualized by Huygens.

Later, in 1781, Haüy (Fig. 22, page 14) published a theory of crystal structure which was based principally on cleavage. Haüy assumed that a crystal is made up of a large number of small particles, similar in form and equal in size, which are arranged in parallel order and fill space without gaps. The occurrence of different crystal forms on a crystal, each with rational indices, Haüy explained by *decrescence*, according to which the successive layers decrease regularly, or stepwise, in area (Fig. 404). The particles were considered as being of infinitesimal size, and, hence, apparently smooth crystal faces resulted.

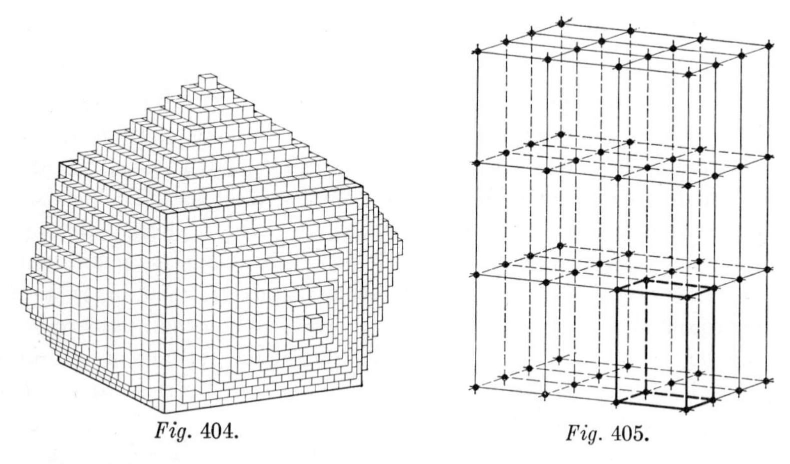

Fig. 404. *Fig.* 405.

Space Lattices. Basic to the conceptions of both Huygens and Haüy was the idea that some unit was repeated in a three-dimensional pattern. As the ideas of modern physics and chemistry developed, it became evident that these crystal units could not be solid particles, but must be groups of atoms. Bravais was the first to point out that there are only 14 three-dimensional patterns according to which these units might be arranged. These 14 patterns are called *space lattices* and are frequently referred to as *Bravais lattices*.

A *space lattice* (Fig. 405) is a regular repetition of points in space at constant intervals for a given direction. All parallel directions are identical, and the environment about any one point is identical to that about every other point. The 14 lattices are distributed among the six crystal systems. Planes may be passed through the points of a lattice, so as to divide space into identical parallelepipeds, known as *unit cells*. Figures 406 to 419 show the unit cells representative of the 14 space lattices.

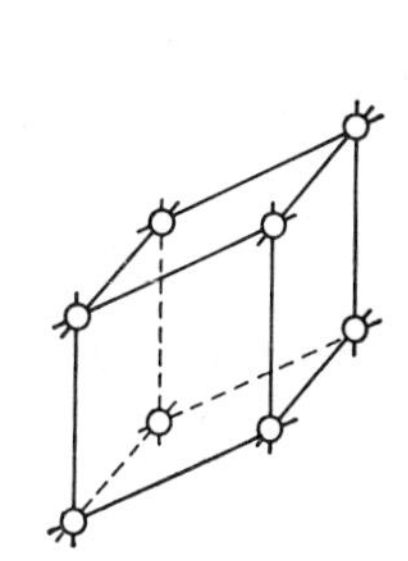

Fig. 406. Triclinic.

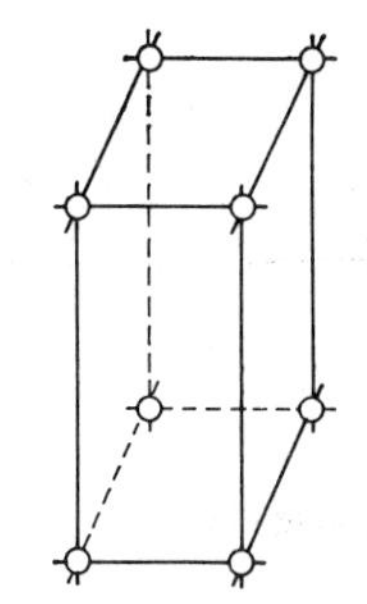

Fig. 407. Simple monoclinic.

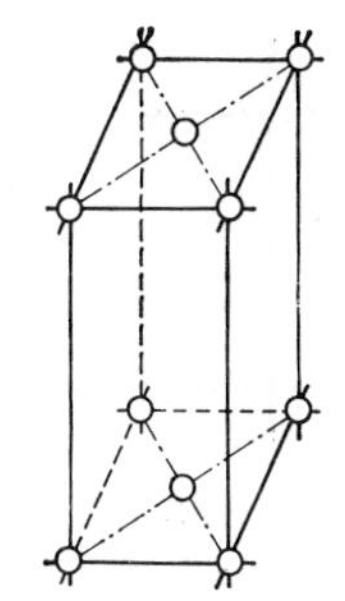

Fig. 408. Base-centered monoclinic.

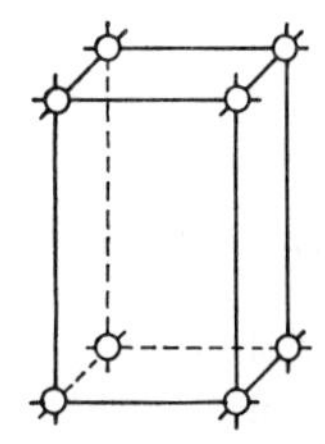

Fig. 409. Simple orthorhombic.

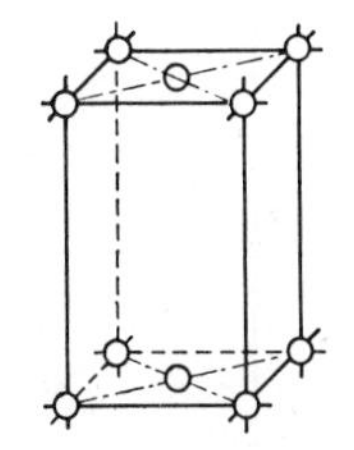

Fig. 410. Base-centered orthorhombic.

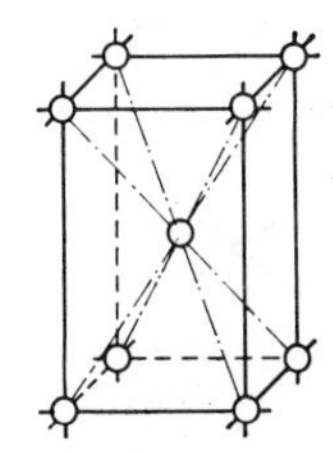

Fig. 411. Body-centered orthorhombic.

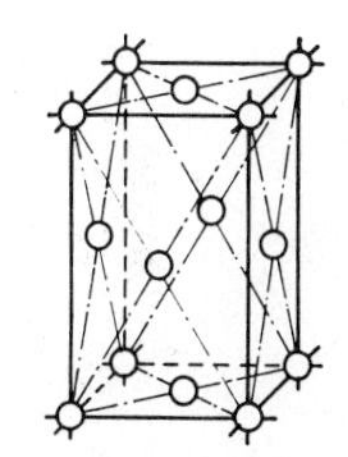

Fig. 412. Face-centered orthorhombic.

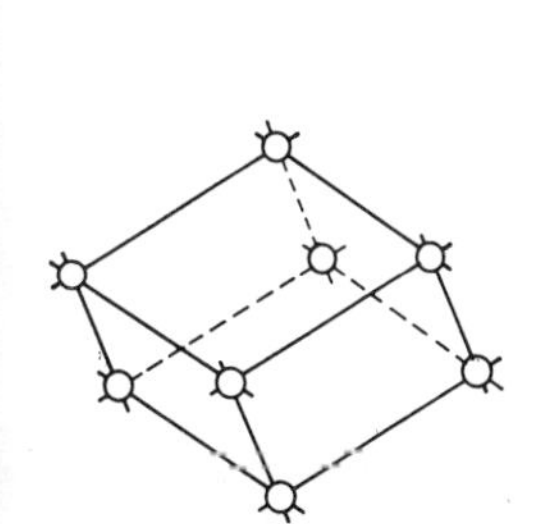

Fig. 413. Rhombohedral.

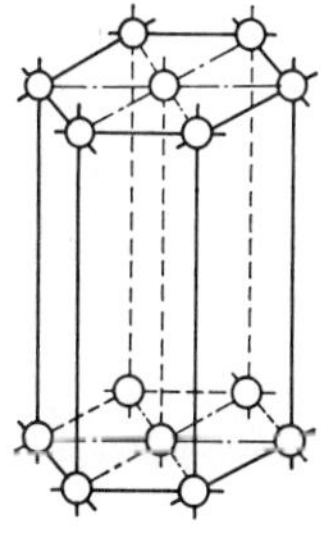

Fig. 414. Hexagonal.

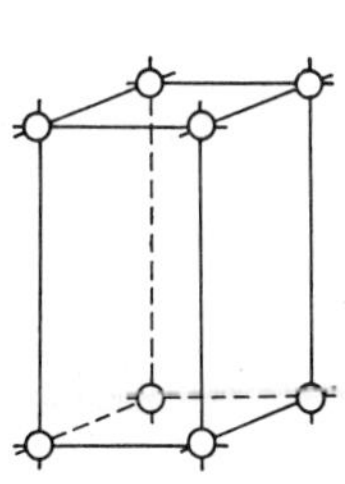

Fig. 415. Simple tetragonal.

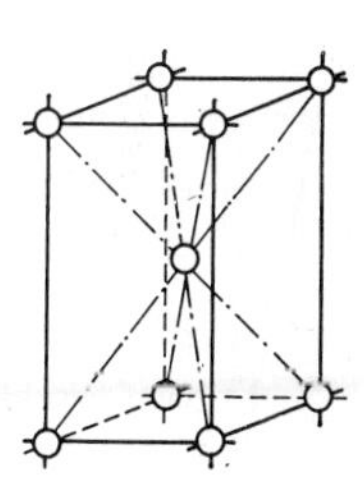

Fig. 416. Body-centered tetragonal.

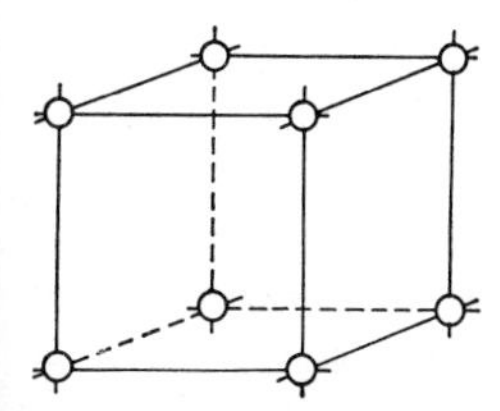

Fig. 417. Simple cubic.

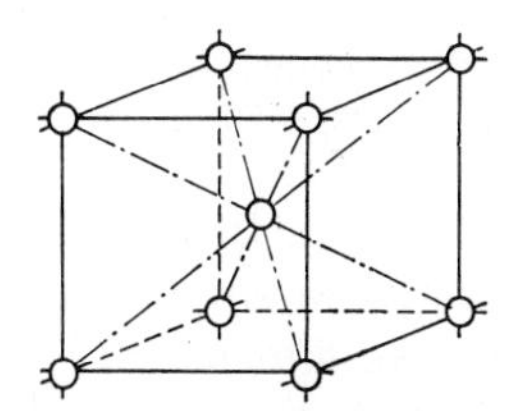

Fig. 418. Body-centered cubic. The 14 unit cells.

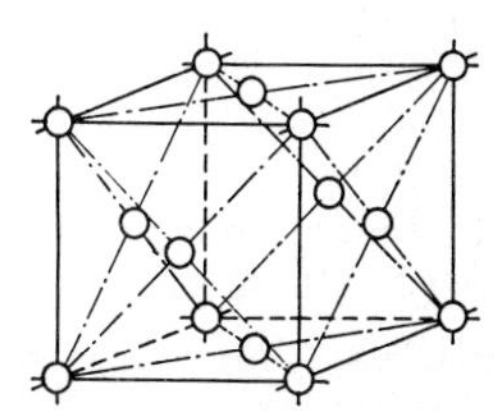

Fig. 419. Face-centered cubic.

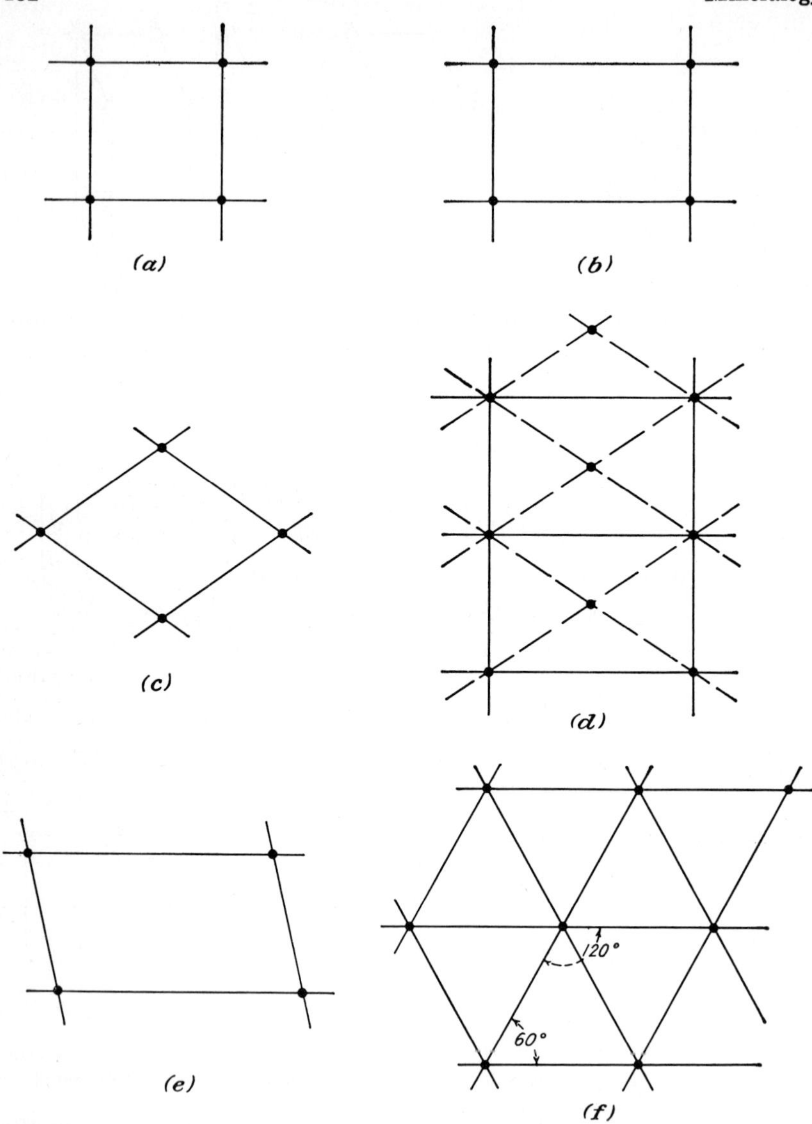

Fig. 420. The only possible two-dimensional lattices: square (*a*), rectangle (*b*), rhombus (*c*), usually described as a centered rectangle (*d*), parallelogram (*e*), and hexagon, a special case of the rhombus with angles of 60° and 120° (*f*).

The existence of only 14 space lattices is capable of simple geometric proof. This is easily illustrated in simplified form for two-dimensional lattices. The only possible two-dimensional lattices are the ones illustrated in Fig. 420. These include the square (*a*), rectangle (*b*), rhombus (*c*) which is usually described as a centered rectangle (*d*), parallelogram (*e*), and the hexagon, a special case of the rhombus, with angles of 60 and 120 degrees (*f*). No other two-dimensional figures can form lattices by regular repetition. This would apply to a figure such as a pentagon; hence there is no pentagonal system, nor can a crystal have a fivefold axis of symmetry.

Following the development of the 14 lattices by Bravais, many other workers were active in formulating a complete theory of crystal structure. Among these were Franckenheim, Sohncke, Groth, Schoenflies, von Fedorov, and Barlow. The last three, working independently and using different methods, all came to the conclusion that there are 230 basic structural patterns possible for crystallizing substances. These are called *space groups* and are discussed on page 155.

As a result of these investigations, in 1904 Groth proposed a definition of a crystal in terms of atomic arrangement which is strikingly similar to our modern conception of crystals, as revealed by X-ray analysis.

Fig. 421. Paul Heinrich von Groth (1843–1927). Professor of mineralogy in the University of Munich (1885–1923). Eminent for his many contributions on chemical and physical crystallography and on the structure of crystals.

Topical Axes. With the development of a theory concerning crystal structure various attempts were made, especially under the leadership of Groth (Fig. 421), to apply the theory to the study of isomorphous substances. Thus, in 1893, Muthmann, in investigating the chemical-crystallographic properties of a series of phosphates and arsenates of ammonium and potassium, endeavored to show that the volumes of the elementary parallelepipeds, or unit cells, of these compounds are not identical but vary with the chemical composition. In order to demonstrate this, Muthmann computed the molecular volumes of the unit cells of the several compounds by combining the specific gravity and the chemical composition, as represented by the molecular weight, with the elements of crystallization (see page 11). In this way, he was able to determine the relative lengths of the edges of the elementary parallelepipeds and note the variations in them for the various compounds of the series. The lengths of the edges Muthmann called the *topical axes.* They were represented by the letters χ, ψ, ω. These axes correspond in direction to the crystallographic axes a, b, c.

At about the same time, and quite independently of Muthmann, Becke and Tutton introduced similar ideas. By Tutton the lengths of the edges of the unit cells were called *molecular distance ratios.* Formulas were developed by these investigators for the calculation of the topical axes for several of the crystal systems. Later, in 1901, Kraus and Mez developed the formulas[1] for all systems and defined the unit of the topical axes as the length of the edge of the cubical unit cell of a substance having a molecular volume of one.

Application of the Topical Axes. The introduction of the idea of the topical axes stimulated interest in the study of structural relations between closely related compounds. As an example of one of the most interesting groups studied for the changes in the topical axes, the series investigated by Slavik, in 1902, may be given (Table 17).

TABLE 17

NH_4I	$N(CH_3)_4I$	$N(C_2H_5)_4I$	$N(C_3H_7)_4I$
Cubic	Tetragonal	Tetragonal	Orthorhombic
V^* = 57.51	108.70	162.91	235.95
χ = 3.860	5.319	6.648	6.093
ψ = 3.860	5.319	6.648	7.851
ω = 3.860	3.842	3.686	4.953

* The molecular volume V is equal to the molecular weight divided by the specific gravity (see p. 153).

These data show that, as the hydrogen in the first compound is successively replaced by CH_3, C_2H_5, and C_3H_7, the relationship between the topical axes is greatly altered. Furthermore, it is in the lengths of χ and ψ, corresponding to the crystallographic axes a and b, that the greatest changes take place. In other words, as the molecular volume becomes larger, χ and ψ change much more than does ω. Observations of this character seemed to confirm the ideas of crystal structure already referred to, and many similar studies were made during the first decade of the twentieth century. It was in this period that Barlow and Pope advanced the theory of *equivalent parameters*, which are obtained by substituting in the formulas for the calculation of the topical axes the total valency of the substance for its molecular weight.

The topical axes gave some clue as to the changes in the structures of chemically related compounds, but these changes could not be expressed precisely, for it was only the relative sizes and not the actual dimensions of the unit cells which were determined. It was assumed that the unit cell was based on the elements of crystallization, as determined from morphological measurements. While in many cases this is true, there are frequent exceptions, both with respect to axial lengths and angles. The

[1] For these formulas, see Groth-Marshall, "An Introduction to Chemical Crystallography," pp. 40–43, John Wiley & Sons, Inc., New York, 1906.

fundamental inadequacy of topical axes, however, was that they did not provide any information about the positions of individual atoms. With the application of X-ray methods it became possible not only to make accurate measurements of the unit cell dimensions and angles, but also to determine the actual atomic arrangement. These methods are described briefly later.

Space Groups and Point Groups. The space lattices possess the maximum symmetry of their respective crystal systems. Thus the lattices do not account for the occurrence of crystal forms with less than the maximum symmetry, such as the tetrahedron and pyritohedron in the cubic system. To explain such crystals, we must assume that, although the lattice framework necessarily has maximum symmetry, the group of atoms repeated at each lattice position may have lower symmetry. In other words, the lattice determines the crystal system, but the particular symmetry class within that system is determined by the symmetry of the atomic group.

In the cubic system there are three space lattices, the simple cube (P), the body-centered cube (I), and the face-centered cube (F). There are five symmetry classes in the cubic system, $m3m$, $m3-$, $\bar{4}3m$, 432, and 23−. Atomic groups possessing any one of these five symmetries may occur in any one of the three cubic lattices, giving rise to 15 *space groups*, designated by the following symbols:

$$\begin{array}{lllll} Pm3m, & Pm3, & P\bar{4}3m, & P432, & P23 \\ Im3m, & Im3, & I\bar{4}3m, & I432, & I23 \\ Fm3m, & Fm3, & F\bar{4}3m, & F432, & F23. \end{array}$$

The first part of the symbol defines the space lattice, and the second part, sometimes called the *point group*, defines the symmetry of the atomic arrangement. The geometrical framework of a crystal (space group) thus consists of a group of symmetry elements (point group) repeated in a three-dimensional pattern (space lattice).

Actually there are more than the 15 cubic space groups listed above. If a crystal possesses a certain plane of symmetry, each group of atoms will likewise possess this same plane. But instead of being a simple reflection plane, with the atoms occurring on either side in mirrored positions, it may be a *glide plane*. Glide planes involve the operation of reflection across the plane, combined with a shift in position parallel to the plane. This shift is called a *translation* and is usually parallel to one of the axes and equal to one-half of the lattice spacing in that particular direction. These glide planes are designated by the letters n, a, b, c, or d, depending upon the direction of the translation. Thus, in addition to the space group $Pm3m$, there are also the following: $Pm3n$, $Pn3m$, and $Pn3n$. Moreover, instead of a simple axis of symmetry, as revealed by the external face development, an atomic group may possess a *screw axis*, in which the angular rotation is combined with a translation parallel to the axis. For a fourfold axis this translation may be $\frac{1}{4}$, $\frac{2}{4}$, or $\frac{3}{4}$ of the lattice spacing in the direction of the axis. Accordingly, in addition to the space group $P432$, there are also $P4_132$, $P4_232$, and $P4_332$, where the symbols 4_1, 4_2, and 4_3 indicate screw axes.

The introduction of such additional space groups in the five symmetry classes of the cubic system raises the total number of cubic space groups to 36. When this same procedure is carried out for all of the six crystal systems, a grand total of 230 space groups is reached. As previously stated, the idea that there are 230 space groups was firmly established on theoretical grounds. This was done long before the development of X-ray methods which could experimentally demonstrate that the atomic arrangements in crystals actually conform to these space groups.

Atomic Groups. A crystal consists of identical atomic groups repeated at the positions of a space lattice. The crystal system and the physical dimensions of the structure are determined by the lattice framework. The particular symmetry revealed by the crystal is determined by the symmetry of the atomic group (point group). Consider, for example, the space group $Pm3m$. At each point of the simple cubic lattice there are located three axial and six diagonal symmetry planes, as well as fourfold, threefold, and twofold axes, and a center of symmetry (Figs. 50 to 54, page 24). If an atom is located in a general position near a lattice point, the various operations of symmetry (that is, reflection across planes, rotation about axes, and inversion across the center) will require 47 additional like atoms. These 48 atoms will form a cluster, with the symmetry $m3m$, surrounding the lattice point. However, if an atom occupies some special position, there may be less than 48 in the group. If it lies on a plane of symmetry, it will coincide with its own reflection, and the symmetry requirements of that plane will be satisfied by the single atom, rather than two. Thus, if all atoms were on symmetry planes, there would be only 24 in the group, instead of 48. Likewise, if atoms lie on axes of symmetry, or at a center of symmetry, the operation of symmetry (rotation or inversion) will require no additional atoms. If atoms lie at the intersection of two or more planes or axes of symmetry, the total number required to form a symmetrical group is further reduced. In the point group $m3m$, instead of 48 atoms, as required in a general position, there may be only 24, 12, 8, 6, 3, or 1 in the various special positions. This last value, 1, is obtained when an atom is located at the origin (corner) of the unit cell. Since the center of symmetry is at the origin, and all the symmetry planes and axes pass through the origin, a single atom thus located satisfies all the symmetry requirements.

In an element, the atomic group may consist of a single atom, as in iron or copper, or of several atoms, as in carbon, sulfur, or tin. In compounds, the proper number of each kind of atom will be arranged in individual groups, each with the same symmetry, all interpenetrating each other, and having the lattice point as a common center. Thus in the mineral apatite ($Ca_5F(PO_4)_3$) the atomic group consists of 10 calcium, 2 fluorine, 6 phosphorus, and 24 oxygen atoms. In some structures, the grouping may not be very obvious. In halite (NaCl) each sodium atom is surrounded by 6 chlorine atoms (Fig. 430). But each Cl is equidistant from 6 Na atoms, so that only ⅙ of a Cl belongs to any one Na. Thus the group may be considered as $NaCl_{6/6}$.

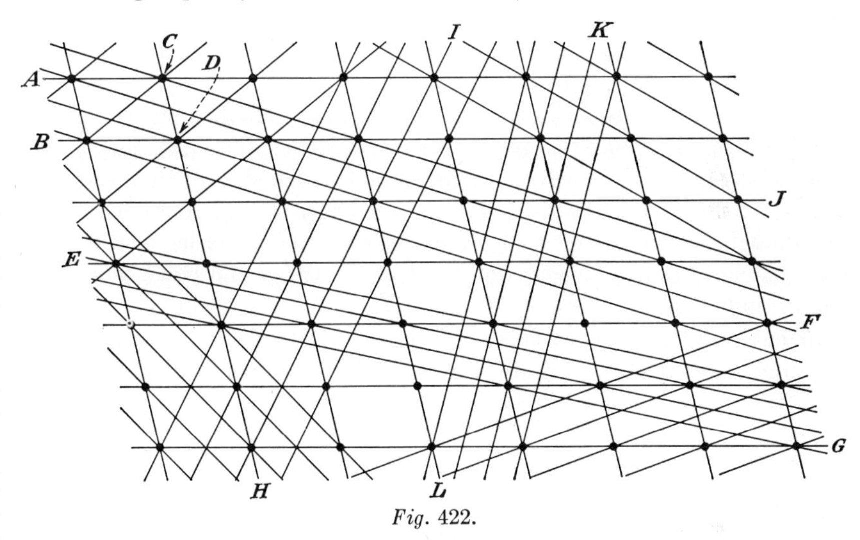

Fig. 422.

Atomic Planes. A crystal is based on a three-dimensional framework or lattice. In such a lattice it is always possible to pass a large number of parallel equidistant planes. This is most easily illustrated with a two-dimensional example. Figure 422 shows a few of the many possible sets of parallel equidistant lines passing through the points of a lattice whose unit is the parallelogram *ABCD*. The entire lattice is built up by repetition of this parallelogram, in which the distances *AB* and *AC* can be considered as unit axial lengths for the lattice. It will be observed that each of the sets of parallel lines, when referred to the unit parallelograms, has intercepts which can be expressed as the ratio of two integers. Thus the set *BC* has the intercepts 1 : 1; *HI*, 2 : 1; *LK*, 3 : 1; *LF*, 1 : 2; *IJ*, $1 : \bar{1}$; *AF*, $1 : \bar{2}$; *EG*, $1 : \bar{3}$; and *EH*, $2 : \bar{1}$. Since all lines pass through lattice points, these intercept ratios are necessarily rational numbers and can be designated by Miller indices.

In the three-dimensional lattices similar sets of parallel equidistant planes are present. Crystal faces are always parallel to such planes;

hence they must have rational indices. Likewise, for a given lattice, the angular relationships between planes are fixed. Thus, the laws of *rational indices* and of the *constancy of interfacial angles* are both explained.

Nature of X Rays. Two years after the development of the idea of topical axes by Muthmann, X rays were discovered in 1895 by Roentgen, at that time professor of physics in the University of Würzburg. Although these new rays were intensively and critically studied, their exact nature remained in doubt for nearly two decades.

It had been noticed that in some respects X rays resemble light, while in others they seemed to differ from light. As the study of X rays progressed, it became evident that if some method could be devised whereby they could be diffracted and reflected it might then be possible to determine their fundamental character.

Studies involving the passage of X rays through small openings seemed to indicate that if they consist of transverse waves like light, they must possess extremely short wave lengths, in fact, much shorter than those of light. The wave lengths of light are of the order of 1×10^{-5} cm., and it was thought that those of X rays must be either of the order 1×10^{-8} or 1×10^{-9} cm., that is, about one ten-thousandth of the wave length of sodium light.

In Table 18 the different types of electromagnetic waves are given with the *approximate* ranges of the wave lengths as determined at present.

TABLE 18. ELECTROMAGNETIC WAVES

Type of Wave	Range of Wave Lengths
Cosmic	4 to 6.7 million millionths of 1 cm. (4×10^{-12} to 6.7×10^{-12} cm.)
γ rays	560 million millionths to 1 thousand millionths of 1 cm. (560×10^{-12} to 1×10^{-9} cm.)
X rays	0.1 to 45 hundred-millionths of 1 cm. (0.1×10^{-8} to 45×10^{-8} cm., angstroms, Å.)
Extreme ultraviolet	0.45 to 1.3 millionths of 1 cm. (0.45×10^{-6} to 1.3×10^{-6} cm.)
Ultraviolet	1.3 to 35 millionths of 1 cm. (1.3×10^{-6} to 35×10^{-6} cm.)
Visible light	35 to 77 millionths of 1 cm.* (35×10^{-6} to 77×10^{-6} cm.)
Heat	77 millionths to 3 hundredths of 1 cm. (77×10^{-6} to 3×10^{-2} cm.)
Short electromagnetic	3 hundredths of 1 cm. to 1 meter (3×10^{-2} to 1×10^{2} cm.)
Radio	1 to 30,000 meters (1×10^{2} to 3×10^{6} cm.)
Long electromagnetic	30,000 meters to thousands of kilometers

* The wave lengths of visible light are generally expressed in *millimicrons*, mμ (millionths of a millimeter). Thus, these wave lengths vary from 350 mμ for violet light to 770 mμ for red light at the extreme ends of the visible spectrum. The wave lengths of X rays are given in terms of angstrom units, Å. (1 hundred-millionth of a centimeter, *i.e.*, 10^{-8} cm.).

The classification is somewhat arbitrary, definite dividing lines being impossible since the different types of waves may overlap greatly. It will be noted that the waves of visible light occupy a very small section of this so-called wave spectrum.

Fig. 423. Max F. F. von Laue (1879–). For many years professor of theoretical physics at the universities of Berlin and Göttingen. Winner of the Nobel prize for physics in 1914. Pioneer investigator of crystal structure by X-ray methods.

Laue's Discovery. In studying the nature of X rays, Laue came to the conclusion that (1) if the points in the space lattices are to be considered as atoms, and (2) if X rays are like light but possess very short wave lengths, comparable to the distances between the atoms, a crystal should act toward X rays as a three-dimensional diffraction grating. In this case, diffraction effects should take place and interference phenomena result when X rays are transmitted through a crystal. In 1912, Laue (Fig. 423), in conjunction with Friedrich and Knipping, tried this epoch-making experiment.[1] Its success showed that the assumption of a regular internal atomic arrangement in crystals was justified and that it might be possible to develop methods for investigating this arrangement. Moreover, the experiment proved that X rays and light are fundamentally the same, but differ in wave lengths (see Table 18), and demonstrated that there was now a means available for studying this radiation.

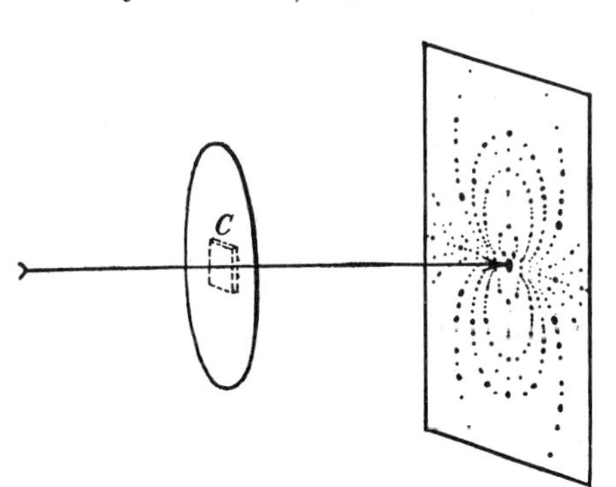

Fig. 424. General plan for obtaining Laue photograph. (*Adapted from Rinne.*)

Laue Method. In the Laue experiment a beam of heterogeneous or polychromatic X rays was transmitted through an oriented section of a crystal (Fig. 424). The emergent rays consist of a strong undeviated beam and of fainter beams, diffracted by the different layers of atoms which act as gratings. These beams were allowed to fall upon a photographic plate, forming a sym-

[1] The experiment was made in Munich, where Sohncke and Groth had long been active in developing and teaching theories of crystal structure, and where the noted physicists Roentgen and Sommerfeld were also located as professors in the university. Furthermore, it was in Munich that the researches were made by Muthmann, which, in 1893, led to the development of the idea of the topical axes.

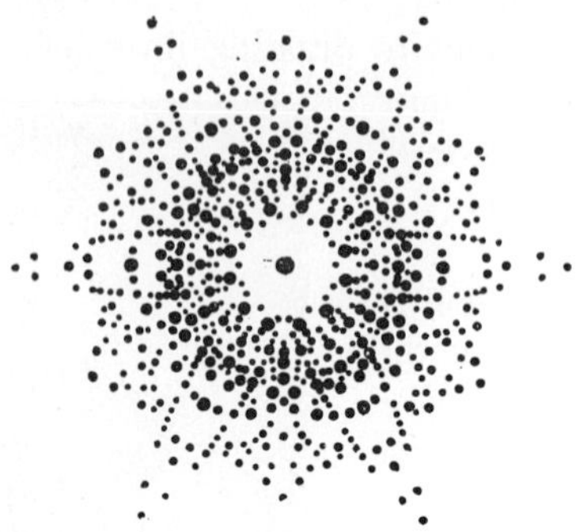

Fig. 425. Laue photograph of beryl taken parallel to the vertical sixfold axis. (*After Rinne.*)

metrical grouping of spots. These are known as *Laue photographs* or *Laue diagrams* (Fig. 425). The spots are caused by diffraction or "reflection" of the incident beam by internal atomic planes.

Symmetry of Laue Photographs. Since the positions of the internal planes depend upon the symmetry of the crystal, the arrangement of the reflections from these planes, as shown by the spots in the photograph, must possess a corresponding symmetry (Fig. 425). If the X-ray beam travels along a fourfold symmetry axis the photograph will show fourfold symmetry. The geometrical conditions are such, however, that a center of symmetry is always indicated by a Laue photograph, whether or not it is present in the crystal. Thus, while there are 32 classes of symmetry, only 11 classes can be distinguished in Laue photographs. This same limitation applies to all other X-ray methods, although the rotating crystal methods (page 167) may make further distinctions if glide planes and screw axes are present. Supplementary evidence concerning symmetry, such as face development, etch figures, rotary polarization, and piezoelectricity, is of importance in determining the symmetry.

Fig. 426. Sir William Henry Bragg (1862–1942). For many years director of the Royal Institution of Great Britain and of the Davy-Faraday Research Laboratory, London. Winner (with his son, W. L. Bragg) of the Nobel prize for physics in 1915. Eminent for researches in the field of crystal structure.

Bragg Method. Shortly after Laue announced that X rays could be diffracted by crystals, W. H. Bragg (Fig. 426) and W. L. Bragg (Fig. 428, page 161) (father and son) studied the effect of reflecting a beam of monochromatic X rays from a crystal face. They determined the position of the reflected beam by means of an ionization chamber, although now photographic plates are usually used for this purpose. In this method the X-ray beam falls upon a crystal face at a small glancing angle, and the crystal is slowly turned so that the angle of incidence is increased. The angles at which reflections occur are determined. By means of the formula given below, the Braggs showed that it was possible to calculate the actual distance between the successive layers of atoms parallel to the crystal face.

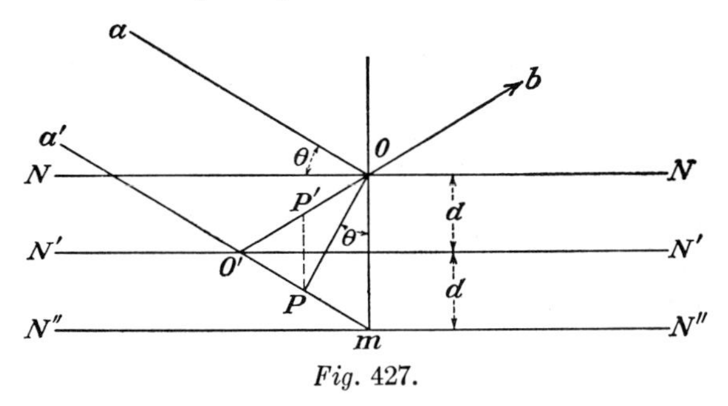

Fig. 427.

In Fig. 427, let a and a' represent part of a beam of X rays, of wave length λ, impinging at an angle θ upon successive atomic layers NN, $N'N'$, $N''N''$. The distance between these layers is d. The incident beam may penetrate hundreds of thousands of these layers, and a very small portion of the beam will be diffracted or reflected by each layer. If, in a particular direction Ob, the reflections from successive layers are all in phase, they will reinforce one another and together make up a beam of sufficient intensity to be detected. The conditions under which this will occur are as follows: Let Ob and $O'b$ represent reflections from the first two layers. The difference in path between aOb and $a'O'b$ is $P'O$, for

$$aO = a'O' + O'P = a'O' + O'P',$$

but

$$P'O = Pm = Om \sin \theta = 2d \sin \theta.$$

Thus the path difference between the reflections from the first two layers is equal to $2d \sin \theta$. This same relationship holds for the reflections from all succeeding layers. Accordingly, when the path difference of the superimposed reflections, such as Ob and $O'Ob$, is λ or $n\lambda$, they will all be in phase and the reflected beam will have a maximum intensity. This can be expressed by

Fig. 428. Sir William Lawrence Bragg (1890–). Director of the Davy-Faraday Research Laboratory of the Royal Institution of Great Britain, since 1954. Distinguished investigator of the structure of crystals and solids by X-ray methods.

$$n\lambda = 2d \sin \theta.*$$

The path difference between reflections from successive layers becomes greater as the angle θ increases. Accordingly, there is a series of angles for which the path difference will be, successively, λ, 2λ, 3λ, and so forth.

* The angle θ is called the *Bragg angle*.

The reflections occurring at these angles are known as reflections of the first, second, and third orders, respectively. In the above equation, the order of reflection is indicated by n, which is always a whole number. If the path difference varies even very slightly from $n\lambda$, complete destructive interference occurs. For this reason, these reflections do not represent merely positions of maximum intensity, but they are sharply defined and are separated by regions in which no reflections are observed.

The procedure used by the Braggs was to obtain reflections of several orders from a few simple faces, such as the cube, dodecahedron, and the octahedron, and calculate the spacings for each of these planes. With this information, together with the relative intensities of the various reflections, the spatial relations of the atoms within the crystal could be deduced.

This method by itself is applicable only to the analysis of rather simple structures. Among the crystals studied by the Braggs were halite ($NaCl$), fluorite (CaF_2), sphalerite (ZnS), diamond (C), and pyrite (FeS_2). The method requires oriented single crystals of moderate size, free from twinning and imperfections.

In modern practice, reflections from a given plane are not designated as first order, second order, etc., but rather by using multiple Miller indices. Successive orders of reflection from the 100 planes are written 100, 200, 300, etc.; from the 110 planes as 110, 220, 330, etc.; from the 111 planes as 111, 222, 333, etc. This is equivalent to considering a second-order reflection as a first-order reflection from the halved spacing $d/2$, or a third-order reflection as a first-order reflection from a spacing $d/3$, etc.

Crystal Structure of Halite. By applying the method just described to the study of halite ($NaCl$), the Braggs were able to determine the atomic arrangement. In the cubic system, the spacings of the 100, 110, and 111 planes are in the ratio of $1 : \frac{1}{\sqrt{2}} : \frac{1}{\sqrt{3}}$. The Braggs found that the first reflections from these three planes occurred at angles corresponding to spacings in the ratio of $\frac{1}{2} : \frac{1}{2\sqrt{2}} : \frac{1}{\sqrt{3}}$. This was interpreted by assuming that the first-order reflections from 100 to 110 were missing and that the reflections obtained were actually 200, 220, and 111, which do have spacings with the observed ratio. The missing first-order reflections can be explained if identical planes occur midway between the regular 100 and 110 planes. A study of Fig. 429 shows that in the proposed structure this is exactly what occurs.

The unit cell of halite is a cube whose edge has a length of 5.628×10^{-8} cm., or 5.628 Å. (angstrom units) (Fig. 430). In determining the cell contents, it should be noted that only one atom, the one at the center, belongs entirely to the unit cell shown. Those at the corners are shared

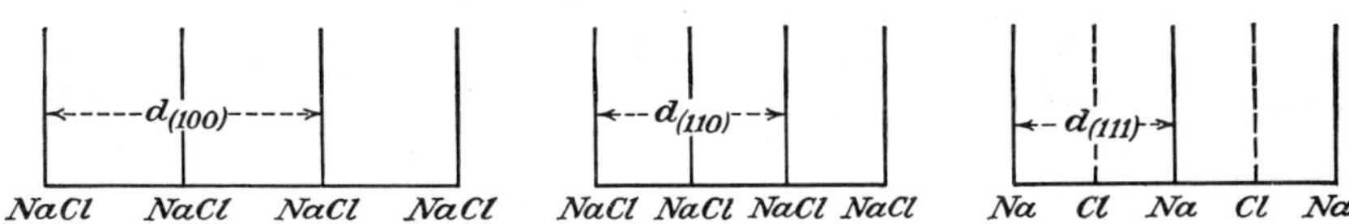

Fig. 429. Relative distances between successive layers of atoms in halite (NaCl) parallel to faces of the cube (100), rhombic dodecahedron (110), and octahedron (111), respectively.

by eight adjacent cells, those at the middle of the edges by four cells, and those at the center of the faces by two cells. Hence, in counting the atoms in the unit cube, these are rated as only one-eighth, one-fourth, and one-half, respectively. Thus, the unit cube contains four Na and four Cl atoms. However, no NaCl molecule is present. Each Na^+ ion is surrounded by 6 Cl^- ions, and each Cl^- by 6 Na^+. Hence, the unit cell is said to contain four *formula weights* of NaCl. The number of formula weights is commonly designated by the letter Z. Thus for halite, $Z = 4$.

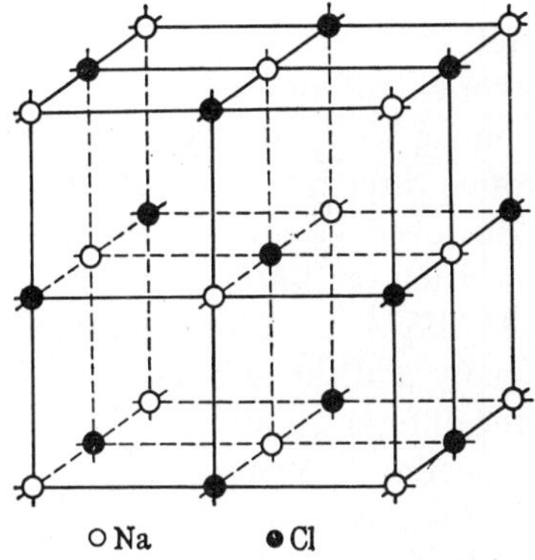

Fig. 430. Unit cell of halite (NaCl).

Powder Method. Although the Bragg method is now seldom used, the equation developed by the Braggs, $n\lambda = 2d \sin \theta$, is basic to all the other methods. Important among these is the *powder method*, developed independently in this country by Hull and in Europe by Debye and Scherrer. This differs from the Laue and Bragg methods in that an oriented crystal is not necessary. This is of distinct advantage, especially in cases where well-formed crystals are not available. As shown by the Braggs, reflection of X rays of a definite wave length λ will occur from a set of parallel planes with spacing d, at a definite angle θ. The spacing d is inherent in the crystal itself and cannot be controlled. Accordingly, if either λ or θ is also fixed, the other must be capable of variation. In the Laue method, with a stationary crystal and therefore fixed values of θ, reflections are obtained because in the general radiation used appropriate values of λ are present. The Bragg equation cannot be applied in this case, since the value of λ for any given reflection is unknown. In the powder method, a known wave length λ is used, and the appropriate values of θ are obtained by chance. If the sample consists of a sufficient number of tiny randomly oriented crystal particles, all possible values of θ for many planes will be represented. Thus, among the grains of a powdered cubic substance, some grains will be in proper position for reflection from the 100 plane, some for 110, some for 111, etc.

The Bragg method could be used to record photographically, on a single film, successive reflections *A*, *B*, and *C*, from the cubic planes 100,

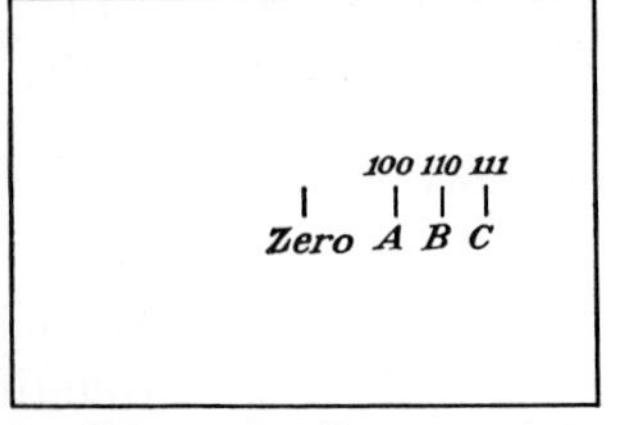

Fig. 431. Schematic diagram of Bragg reflections.

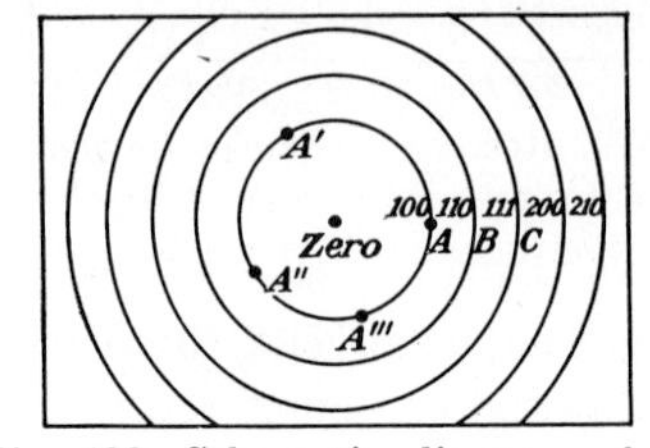

Fig. 432. Schematic diagram of corresponding powder-photograph reflections.

110, and 111 (Fig. 431), but the crystal would, of course, have to be reoriented for each successive exposure. If a powder sample is used, among the many reflections obtained simultaneously, there will be the same three reflections *A*, *B*, and *C*, at exactly the same angles (Fig. 432). However, because of the random orientation, not only will grains be in position for 100 planes to reflect at *A*, but also at all points on the circle A', A'', A'''. This condition will hold also for reflections 110, 111, and as many additional ones as might be recorded. The successive reflections for different planes will thus lie on concentric cones, which register on a flat film as concentric circles, surrounding the zero point, where the undeviated X-ray beam strikes the film.

An important advantage of the powder method over the Bragg method is that a much larger number of reflections may be obtained. In order to realize this advantage fully, the reflections usually are not recorded on a flat film, but on one bent in the form of a cylinder (Fig. 433). A much greater angular range of reflections is obtained by this arrangement. The film is in the form of a narrow strip (Fig. 434). Only limited portions of the cones of reflection are thus recorded. The reflections appear as lines of varying curvature on the film. Each line on the pattern corresponds to a definite crystal plane, with its own characteristic spacing. The powder sample is mounted on the cylinder axis. It is commonly molded in the form of a tiny rod, and in order to increase the randomness of orientation of the powder particles, a mechanism may be provided to rotate the sample during the exposure. The X-ray beam passes through a slit system consisting of two pinholes, about 0.5 mm. in diameter. Holes are cut in the film both for the entering and the exit beams.

Because comparatively few powder particles contribute to any given reflection, much longer exposures are necessary than for the Bragg method. But since the operation of the powder camera is entirely automatic, requiring no attention during exposure, this is of no special consequence.

The film is in the form of a cylinder during the exposure, and consequently the distance of any line from the zero beam is a measure of the angle 2θ for that particular reflection. Since a known value of λ is used, it is thus possible to compute by means of the Bragg equation the actual spacing of the set of planes producing any reflection.

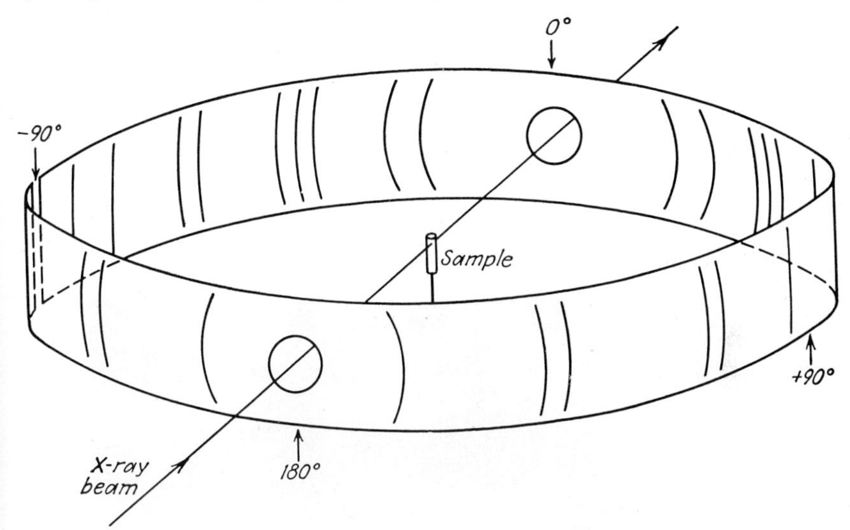

Fig. 433. General plan for obtaining powder photographs.

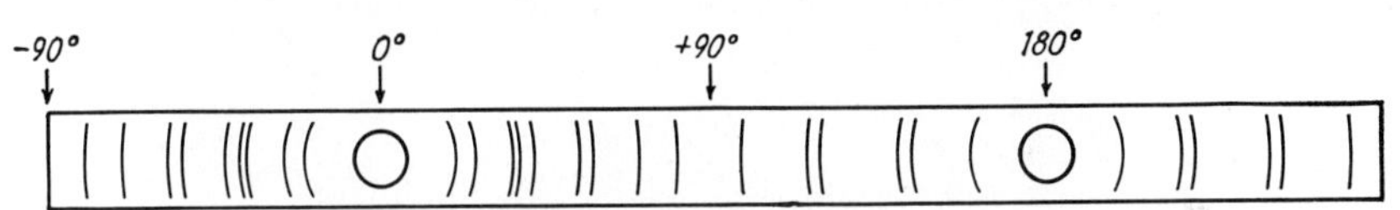

Fig. 434. Powder photograph, or diffraction pattern.

If a powder photograph is to be used for determining the structure of the substance, it is necessary to identify each line of the pattern in terms of the particular crystal plane which produced the reflection. This means that the Miller indices of the plane responsible for a given reflection must be determined, and this process is called *indexing* the film.

In the cubic system, this indexing of the reflections is a comparatively simple process, for the ratios of the various interplanar spacings are constant. Thus, no matter what the actual dimensions of the unit cells, the ratios of the cubic spacings 100, 110, 111, etc., are always in the ratio of $1 : \frac{1}{\sqrt{2}} : \frac{1}{\sqrt{3}}$, etc. Various graphical methods are used for indexing cubic films. In the case of hexagonal and tetragonal substances, the ratios of the spacings of planes parallel to the c axis are constant, but those of the planes inclined to c vary with the axial ratio. This makes indexing more difficult than for cubic substances. Charts are available, extending over a range of axial ratios, for use in the identification of the reflections. For the orthorhombic, monoclinic, and triclinic systems, it is almost impossible to identify the reflections from the powder photograph alone. The unit-cell dimensions and angles ordinarily must be determined by other means.

In addition to indexing the powder photograph, it is also necessary to determine the relative intensities of the reflections. This is usually done visually. However, a nonphotographic method of recording powder patterns is also available. This makes use of a Geiger counter spectrometer. The reflections from the powder sample are received in a Geiger counter, amplified, and recorded. The resulting graph shows a series of peaks corresponding to the lines of the powder photograph. The heights of these peaks give a very accurate measure of the relative intensities of the various reflections.

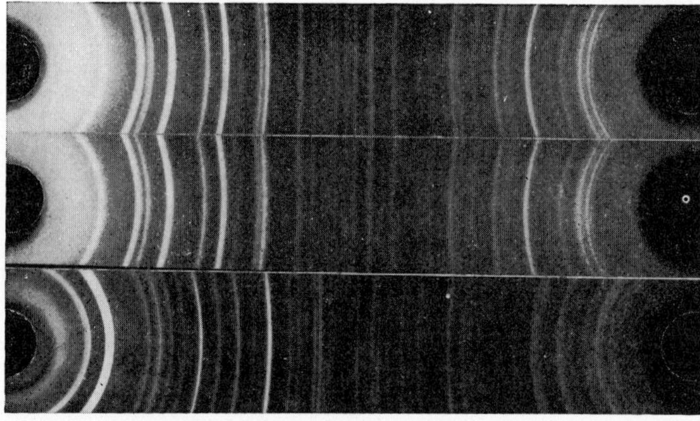

Fig. 435. Powder photographs of natural (top) and synthetic rubies, which are identical, and of rose quartz.

The diffraction patterns obtained from most substances are distinctive and unique, and even though the reflections are not identified, the pattern offers a positive means of identification. Figure 435 shows three powder photographs. That the crystalline character of natural and synthetic ruby is the same is clearly indicated by their identical patterns, while the totally different pattern of quartz is characteristic of all varieties of that mineral. One distinct advantage of identification by the X-ray powder pattern is that only a very small amount of material is required for the sample and the sample is not destroyed in the experiment.

Although this method is referred to as the powder method, the sample does not necessarily have to be in the form of a powder. All that is required is that it be fine grained and with random orientation. An ordinary copper wire may give as good a powder photograph as a sample composed of fine copper fillings. Also, if the sample is fine grained, but does not have random orientation of the grains, certain distinctive effects are produced in the powder photographs. This is of great importance in the study of preferred orientations found in fibers and in drawn wires and rolled-metal sheets.

The sample used for a powder photograph may contain more than one constituent. These different constituents may be merely a mixture, they may be chemically combined, or they may be present as a solid solution. The powder photograph readily distinguishes between these three possibilities. The pattern from a mixture is a composite one, with the lines of each individual substance occurring in their normal positions. The relative proportions of each substance present in the mixture are indicated by the relative intensities of the lines of its pattern.

If two constituents have combined chemically to form a new compound, the resulting powder pattern is different from that of either constituent alone and is characteristic of the compound.

One substance A may have some of substance B dissolved in it. The powder photograph in this case will show the typical pattern of A, but with a slight shift in the positions of the lines. This shift corresponds to either an increase or a decrease in the unit-cell dimensions, depending upon whether the atoms of B are larger or smaller than those of A. These distinctions are very important in the field of metallurgy, where the three cases of (1) mixture, (2) compound, and (3) solid solution are frequently encountered among various alloys.

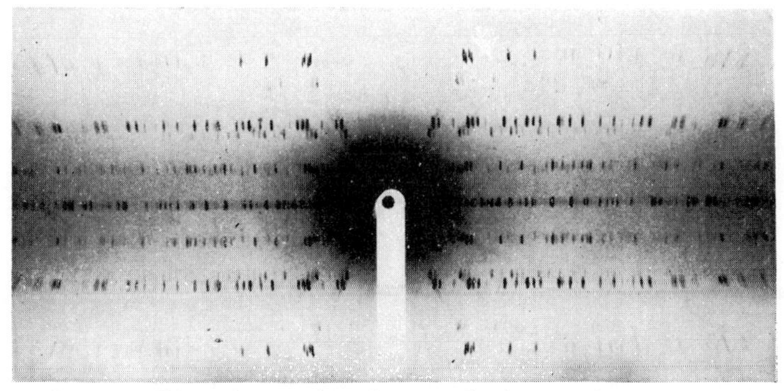

Fig. 436. Rotation photograph of atacamite.

Rotation Methods. In these methods a single small crystal is rotated about some important crystallographic direction. Monochromatic X rays are used. As the crystal rotates, reflections will be obtained from all planes that come into proper position. The number of reflections is large, especially when a cylindrical film is used. The reflections are arranged in horizontal rows or layers, as in Fig. 436 [atacamite, $Cu_2(OH)_3Cl$]. Each layer is composed of reflections from planes having one Miller index in common. Thus, if a crystal is being rotated about the *c* axis, the row of spots passing through the center of the film, called the zero layer, consists entirely of reflections from *hk*0 planes. The first layer, directly above and below, has all *hkl* and $hk\bar{l}$ reflections, followed by *hk*2, etc.

The spacing between the layers is a function of the unit-cell spacing in the direction of the axis of rotation. Thus with an orthorhombic crystal, rotation about the three crystal axes gives the dimensions of the unit cell, and with this information it is possible to index all reflections completely. Graphical methods are commonly used for identification of the reflections.

In rotation photographs, especially with crystals of lower symmetry, totally different planes may have nearly identical spacings, and difficulty is encountered in distinguishing their reflections. If instead of being rotated through 360°, the crystal is oscillated through a small known angle, it is possible to avoid this confusion. This is known as the *oscillation method.* A series of photographs is taken, each representing an oscillation through a definite angular range, until all reflections are recorded. Only a limited number of reflections appear on a given film, and these can be correlated with the angular position of the crystal for that particular exposure.

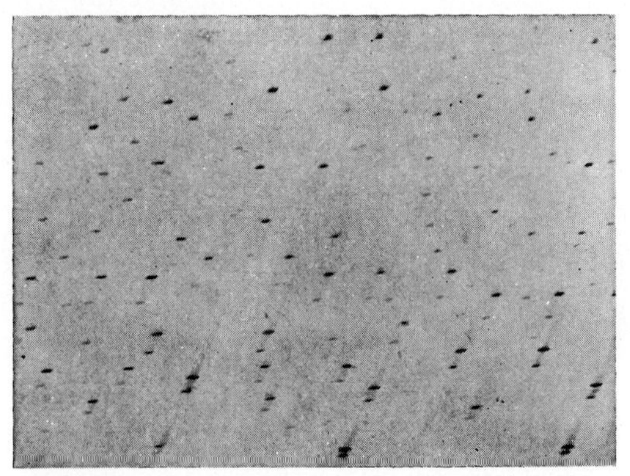

Fig. 437. Weissenberg photograph of atacamite.

Moving-film Methods. Various methods have been developed which are a great improvement over the ordinary rotation or oscillation methods. The most common of these is the *Weissenberg method.* A rotation photograph is first taken to determine the position of the layer lines. A movable screen makes it possible to record each layer on a separate film. During the exposure, while the crystal is rotating, the cylindrical film is moved parallel to the rotation axis. The reflections of a single layer are thus spread out over the film (Fig. 437). The pattern of reflections obtained is capable of direct interpretation, both with respect to the crystal system and the symmetry. The assignment of Miller indices to each reflection is simple, and the symmetry about the rotation axis is immediately apparent. Characteristic extinctions due to centered lattices and to glide planes and screw axes are clearly revealed. This method is equally applicable to all crystal systems.

In the *precession method* the crystal is not rotated, but is tilted with respect to the incident X-ray beam with a precessing motion, thus bringing successive crystal planes into position to reflect. A flat film is used, and the reflections are recorded without any distortion of their symmetry.

Summary of X-ray Methods. The essential features of the methods of X-ray analysis just described may be summarized as follows:

ORIENTED CRYSTALS OR CRYSTAL PLATES ARE USED

Laue Method. Transmission of white X rays through stationary oriented specimen.

Bragg Method. Reflection of monochromatic X rays from a single rotating crystal face. Of special value in the accurate determination of interplanar spacings.

Rotation and Oscillation Methods. Reflection of monochromatic X rays from a large number of internal crystal planes, which are brought into proper position for reflection by rotation of the crystal.

Weissenberg Method. Oriented crystal is rotated, but the film moves during the exposure. An improvement over the normal rotation method and especially useful for crystals of low symmetry, namely those of the orthorhombic, monoclinic, and triclinic systems.

Precession Method. Oriented crystal is tilted in all azimuths with respect to the X-ray beam, giving an undistorted representation of the symmetry. Applicable to all crystal systems.

UNORIENTED POWDERED SPECIMENS ARE USED

Hull, Debye–Scherrer, or Powder Method. Transmission of monochromatic X rays through finely powdered specimens. The random positions of the powder particles furnish the proper orientations for reflections from many planes. Very important in identification and in the determination of structures of substances not occurring in good crystals.

Interpretation of X-ray Data. In an X-ray investigation of a crystalline substance, data of four kinds may be obtained:

1. The crystal system and symmetry class (always subject to lack of direct evidence as to presence or absence of a center of symmetry).

2. The dimensions of the unit cell, calculated from the interplanar spacings of known crystal planes. In the monoclinic and triclinic spacings the interaxial angles must also be determined. This is possible by the use of moving-film methods.

3. Characteristic missing or forbidden reflections. These are of two types and reveal

a. Type of lattice—whether simple or centered.
b. Presence of glide planes and screw axes.

4. Relative intensities of the reflections from the various planes. These intensities are dependent upon the positions of the atoms within the unit cell.

When the unit-cell dimensions and angles are known, it is possible to

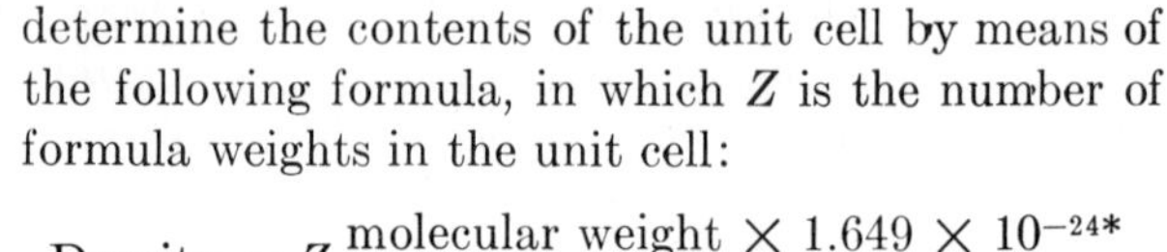

determine the contents of the unit cell by means of the following formula, in which Z is the number of formula weights in the unit cell:

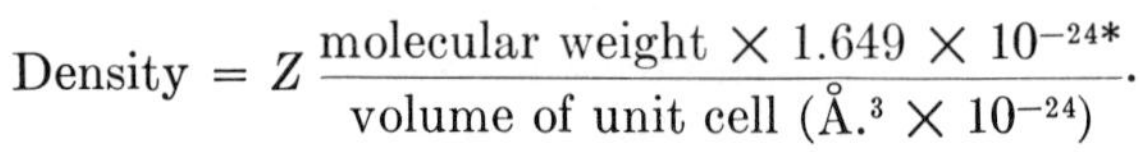

$$\text{Density} = Z\,\frac{\text{molecular weight} \times 1.649 \times 10^{-24}*}{\text{volume of unit cell } (\text{Å.}^3 \times 10^{-24})}.$$

Fig. 438. Friedrich Rinne (1863–1933). Professor of mineralogy in the University of Leipzig (1909–1928). Investigator of the fine structure of crystals.

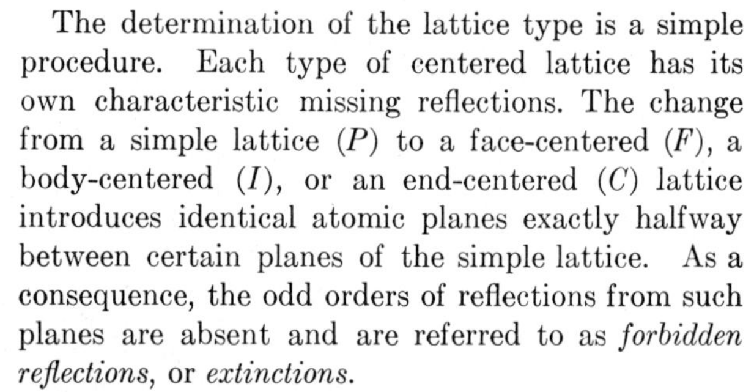

The determination of the lattice type is a simple procedure. Each type of centered lattice has its own characteristic missing reflections. The change from a simple lattice (P) to a face-centered (F), a body-centered (I), or an end-centered (C) lattice introduces identical atomic planes exactly halfway between certain planes of the simple lattice. As a consequence, the odd orders of reflections from such planes are absent and are referred to as *forbidden reflections*, or *extinctions.*

The rhombohedral lattice (R) is most conveniently treated as a centered hexagonal lattice. In this case additional atomic planes are introduced at one-third and two-thirds of the spacings of certain planes of the simple hexagonal lattice. This likewise causes some reflections to be absent.

The characteristic extinctions for centered lattices are as follows:

Simple lattice (P)	None
Face-centered lattice (F)	All planes where $h + k$, $h + l$, or $k + l$ is odd
Body-centered lattice (I)	All planes where $h + k + l$ is odd
End-centered lattice (C)	All planes where $h + k$ is odd
Rhombohedral lattice (R) (Referred to hexagonal axes)	All planes where $h - k - l$ is not divisible by three

The recognition of glide planes and screw axes is likewise a simple matter. Depending upon the position of the plane and the direction of the glide, certain characteristic extinctions are produced. In a similar manner, dependent upon the direction of the screw axis and the amount of translation, typical extinctions due to the screw axis are always observed. In this way it is possible to distinguish between certain space groups, such as $Pm3m$, $Pn3m$, and $Pn3n$, or $P432$, $P4_132$, and $P4_232$.

Intensities of X-ray Reflections. Whenever an atomic group is located at the lattice points, rather than a single atom, additional atomic

* The value of 1.649×10^{-24} is the weight in grams of one unit of molecular (or atomic) weight.

planes of varied composition are introduced at fractional distances between the regular lattice planes. This causes variable interference relations. Some reflections may be intensified, some may be weakened, and some may be completely eliminated. These variations in intensities of the various reflections are very important.

Having determined the space group and the unit-cell contents, the final step in the determination of the structure is to find the actual locations of the atoms in the unit cell. The symmetry requirements of the space group place definite limitations on the possible positions. The variations in the intensities of the reflections themselves, in some cases, may give a clue as to the atomic positions. Information concerning interatomic distances and common atomic groupings is of great importance. A plausible structure is set up, and the theoretical intensities of reflections to be expected from this proposed arrangement are compared with the intensities actually obtained. If the proposed arrangement is correct, there will be close agreement between the calculated and observed intensities. If there is only approximate agreement, it may be that certain adjustments in the positions of some atoms will provide a satisfactory correlation between the calculated and observed intensities. If there is no agreement, an entirely new atomic arrangement must be sought. In the determination of the correct structure, the variations in the intensities of the different reflections are significant. The strong, weak, and missing reflections must all be explained by the proposed structure.

Crystal Structures of Elements. Many of the elements have simple structures. The face-centered cubic arrangement (Fig. 419, page 151) is observed on 24 elements, including copper, silver, gold, and platinum. A body-centered cubic structure (Fig. 418, page 151) has been found for 17 elements. Iron at ordinary temperatures has this type of structure. Twenty-nine elements, including zinc, have a hexagonal arrangement. This hexagonal type and the face-centered cubic arrangement represent the two ways in which spheres of equal size may be most closely packed together. These are referred to as hexagonal and cubic close packing, respectively (Figs. 439 and 440). However, the hexagonal elements depart more or less from the axial ratio $c/a = 1.633$ for ideal close packing.

The submetallic elements arsenic, antimony, and bismuth, all occurring as minerals, have more complicated structures, based on rhombohedral lattices.

Two nonmetallic elements occur as minerals, namely, the two forms of carbon, diamond and graphite, and sulfur. Diamond is cubic and has a structure in which the carbon atoms are located both at the face-centered positions and at the corners of a tetrahedron within the cube (Fig. 441). The length of the edge of the unit cell containing eight atoms of carbon is

Fig. 439.

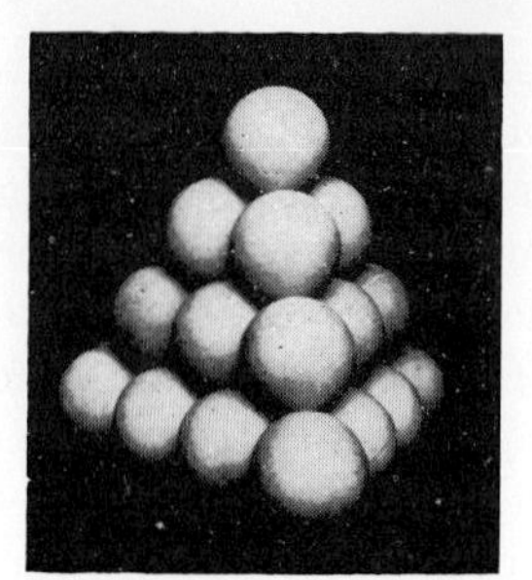

Fig. 440.

3.57×10^{-8} cm., or 3.57 Å. The cell contents are designated by the letter Z, and the length of the cube edge by a_o. Thus, for diamond, $Z = 8$; $a_o = 3.57$ Å.

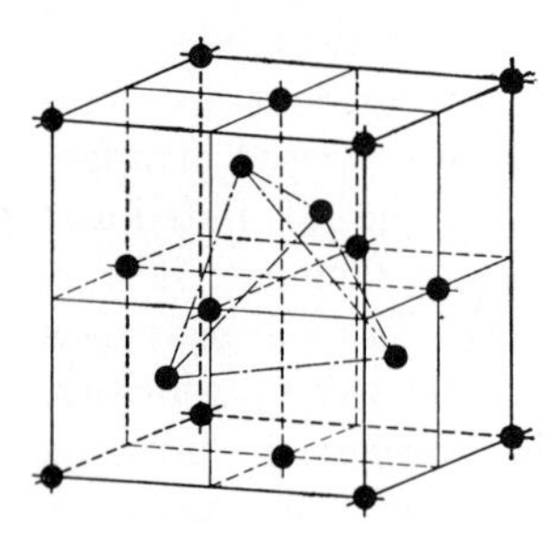

Fig. 441. Unit cell of the diamond, C.

In diamond each C atom is surrounded tetrahedrally by four other C atoms at equal distances. These form four interlocking sets of closely bonded layers of atoms parallel to the octahedral planes and perpendicular to the four trigonal axes.

Graphite has a related structure, in which each C atom is also surrounded by four others, but three of these are closer and lie nearly in the same plane, while the fourth is at a greater distance (see Fig. 442). This arrangement gives layers of closely bonded C atoms parallel to the base and perpendicular to the trigonal c axis.

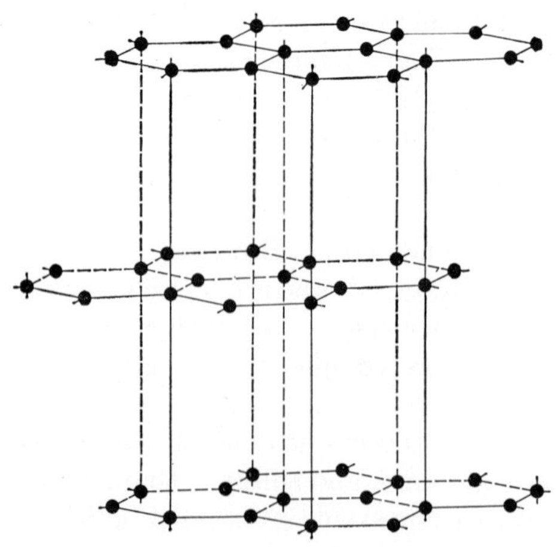

Fig. 442. Model showing the widely separated parallel layers of carbon atoms in graphite.

Sulfur has a very large orthorhombic unit cell containing 128 atoms, which are grouped into S_8 molecules in the form of a puckered ring.

Structures of Compounds. The number of different types of structures among the minerals is large. A few of the more common types, observed on important minerals, will be described.

Galena (PbS). The lead atoms occupy the corners and face centers of the cubic cell, while the sulfur atoms are located at the middle of the edges and at the cube center (Fig. 443). This arrangement is similar to that of the sodium and chlorine atoms in halite (NaCl), which has already been described on page 163. Obviously galena and halite are not isomorphous, for they are chemically dissimilar. The term *isostructural* is used in such a case. This type of structure is also observed on the minerals alabandite (MnS) and cerargyrite (AgCl), as well as on numerous compounds not occurring as minerals. In galena the side of the unit cube has a length of 5.94 Å., in alabandite it is 5.22 Å., and in cerargyrite, 5.55 Å.; $Z = 4$ for each one.

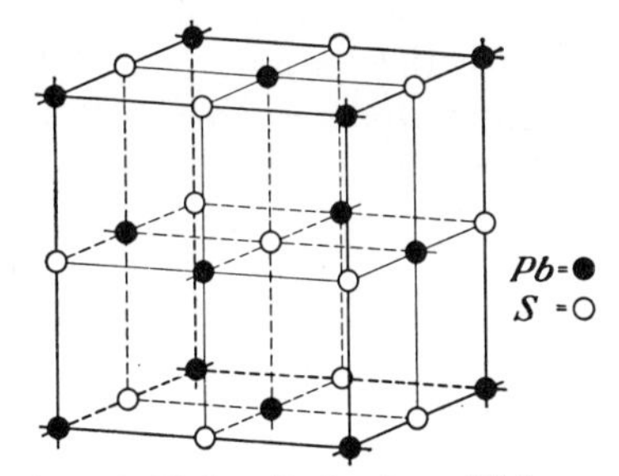

Fig. 443. Unit cell of galena, PbS.

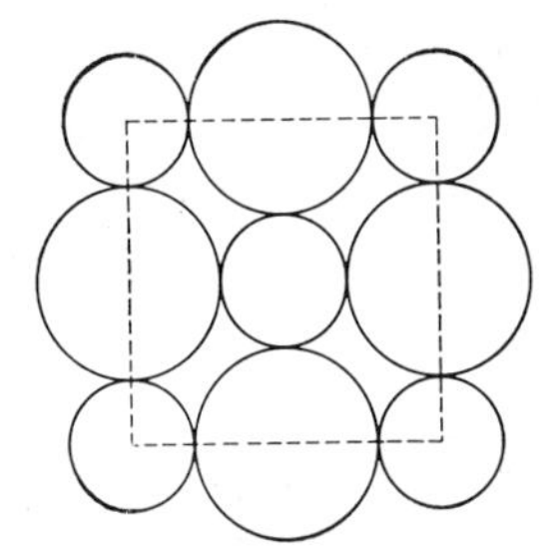

Fig. 444.

In these structure diagrams no attempt is made to show the relative sizes of the atoms. The symbols ○ and ● merely represent the centers of the atoms. If relative sizes were to be shown, the structure of galena, for example, as given in Fig. 443, would appear as in Fig. 444, which indicates the arrangement of the smaller lead atoms and the larger sulfur atoms parallel to the unit cube face. This diagram does not imply, of course, that the atoms are solid spheres.

Fluorite (CaF_2). The crystal structure of fluorite is illustrated by Fig. 445. The calcium atoms have the same positions in this structure as those of lead in galena (Fig. 443), while the atoms of fluorine occupy the centers of the eight smaller cubes into which the unit cell as a whole is divided by the planes parallel to the three intersecting sides. As shown in the figure, the fluorine atoms form a small cube within the face-centered cube lattice of calcium. $Z = 4$; $a_0 = 5.46$ Å.

Sphalerite (ZnS). Figure 446 illustrates the crystal structure of the mineral sphalerite, the zinc atoms being placed in the same manner as those of lead and calcium in Figs. 443 and 445, respectively. The four sulfur atoms occupy the alternate centers of the eight smaller cells into which the unit cell as a whole can be divided (see Fluorite). The sulfur atoms form a tetrahedron within the unit cube. $Z = 4$; $a_0 = 5.41$ Å.

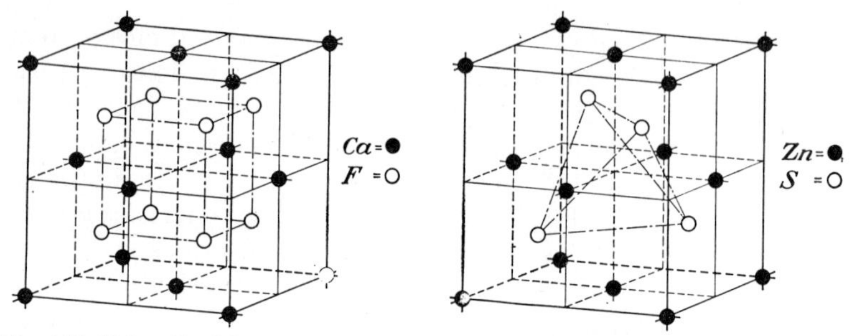

Fig. 445. Unit cell of fluorite, CaF_2. *Fig.* 446. Unit cell of sphalerite, ZnS.

Pyrite (FeS_2). The iron atoms in pyrite are in the cubic face-centered positions (Fig. 447), just as are the lead, calcium, and zinc atoms in Figs. 443, 445, and 446, respectively. Since the formula is FeS_2, the unit cube must contain twice as many sulfur atoms as iron. Pairs of sulfur atoms are located at the middle of the edges and at the center of the cube. $Z = 4$; $a_0 = 5.42$ Å.

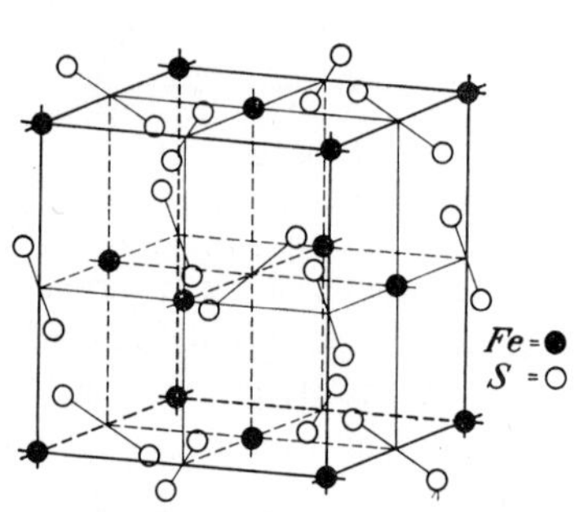

Fig. 447. Unit cell of pyrite, FeS_2.

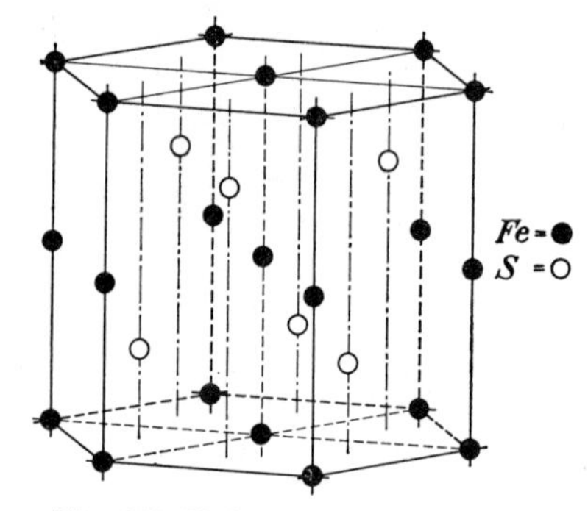

Fig. 448. Unit cell of pyrrhotite, FeS.

Pyrrhotite (FeS). Pyrrhotite is hexagonal, and the atomic arrangement is shown in Fig. 448. The complete hexagonal prism is not taken as the unit cell but rather the parallelepipeds indicated by the lines crossing the basal pinacoid. Thus two entire cells, and two half-cells are shown. The iron atoms are located at the corners and at the middle of the vertical edges of the unit cells, and two sulfur atoms are within each cell. $Z = 2$, and the lengths of the horizontal and vertical edges are 3.44 Å. and 5.80 Å., respectively, or $a_0 = 3.43$ Å. and $c_0 = 5.79$ Å.

Cassiterite (SnO_2). The unit cell of cassiterite is tetragonal. The tin atoms have a body-centered arrangement, and the oxygen atoms are located within the cell, as shown in Fig. 449. $Z = 2$; $a_0 = 4.74$ Å. and $c_0 = 3.19$ Å. Rutile (TiO_2) has a similar structure: $Z = 2$; $a_0 = 4.59$ Å. and $c_0 = 2.96$ Å.

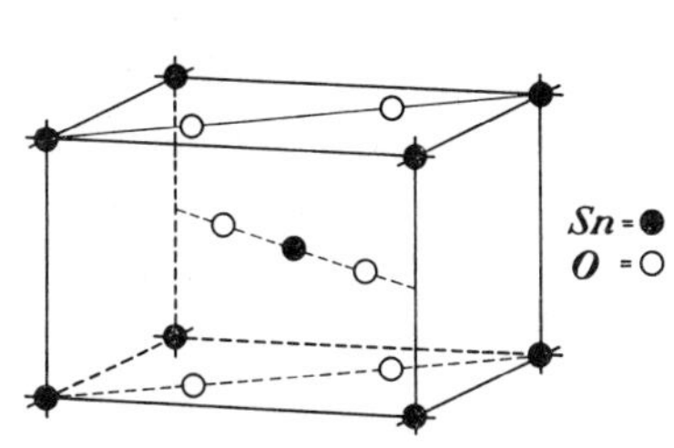

Fig. 449. Unit cell of cassiterite, SnO_2.

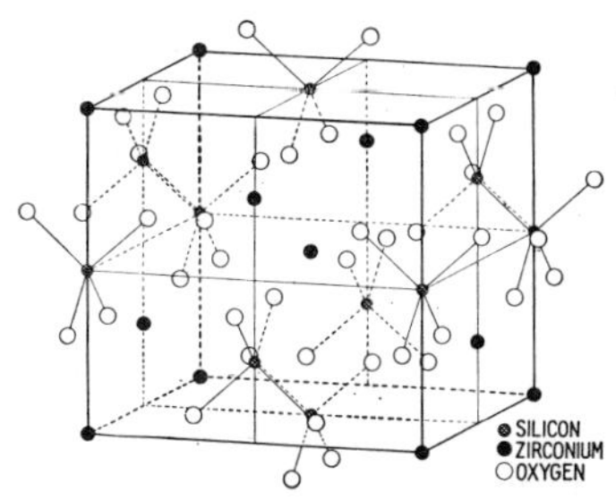

Fig. 450. Unit cell of zircon, $ZrSiO_4$.

Zircon ($ZrSiO_4$). Zircon is tetragonal. The structure is built up of Zr^{+4} and clearly defined $(SiO_4)^{-4}$ ions. Each silicon atom is surrounded by four oxygen atoms, arranged tetrahedrally (Fig. 450). $Z = 4$; $a_0 = 6.60$ Å. and $c_0 = 5.98$ Å.

Value of X-ray Analysis. The earlier investigations of crystal structure were limited to the elements and to comparatively simple compounds. With new methods and greatly improved techniques, together with the rapidly accumulating knowledge concerning crystal-chemical relationships, it is possible to determine the structures of crystals with complex chemical compositions and with low symmetry.

As indicated on page 171, the determination of the atomic positions involves setting up a trial structure, and then determining if the theoretical X-ray reflections to be expected from this proposed structure correspond to those actually obtained. The intensities of the X ray reflected by different atoms are proportional to the number of electrons in each atom. Thus an atomic arrangement may be shown by a two-dimensional projection on any given plane, in the form of contour lines representing electron density. Enormous quantities of data may be involved, and modern electronic devices are used in the calculations, and in the projection of the resulting electron densities on a screen.

During the years which have passed since Laue's discovery, great progress has been made. The general theories of crystal structure based upon space groups have been confirmed. There is a greater understanding of the properties which are unique to crystallized substances. The new field of crystal chemistry (see page 184) is concerned with the relationships between crystal structure and both the chemical and physical properties.

Many problems in mineralogy have been studied. Important data concerning isomorphism, polymorphism, solid solutions, hardness, cleavage, twinning, indices of refraction, and crystal growth have been obtained. Crystal-structure data have been of value in verifying and in correcting formulas of some minerals. The interpretation of the chemical compositions of the silicate minerals, long a baffling problem to the mineralogist, has been greatly clarified (see page 357). X-ray analysis is also being used in research and industry in the study of the structure, composition, and properties of many substances, such as metals, alloys, textile fibers, ceramic materials, cements, pigments, semiconductors, silicones, rubber, soaps, greases, and numerous other complex organic substances.

The unit-cell dimensions and atomic arrangements of hundreds of crystalline substances have been determined. But of greater importance than the description of crystal structures is our increasing knowledge concerning the solid state. Much of the older physics, whether dealing with gases and liquids or solids, was based on the mass behavior of ions, atoms, and molecules. The new methods provide a means of studying the individual ions, atoms, and molecules in crystalline solids. As a consequence, our understanding of the fundamental properties of matter is being greatly enlarged.

13 Chemical Mineralogy and Crystal Chemistry

Most minerals have compositions corresponding to chemical compounds. A few occur as elements, and these are said to be *native*, as *native* gold, *native* copper, and *native* sulfur.

It is often difficult to prepare substances in the laboratory which can be characterized as chemically pure. In nature, minerals usually form in complex environments, and practically never do the compositions correspond to an ideal chemical formula. This explains why the term *characteristic chemical composition* is used in the definition of a mineral on page 6.

Fig. 451. Samuel L. Penfield (1856–1906). Professor of mineralogy in Yale University (1893–1906). Distinguished American chemical mineralogist.

Chemical Formulas. The determination of the principal chemical constituents of a mineral can frequently be made most rapidly by blowpipe methods. These methods are discussed in detail in the next chapter. The determination of the quantitative composition of minerals belongs to the domain of chemistry, the usual methods of the analytical chemist being employed. The formulas representing the chemical composition of minerals are calculated in exactly the same way as for any other chemical substance. For example, an analysis of chalcopyrite from Müsen, Germany, gave Laspeyres the following results:

	I Analysis, per Cent		II Atomic Weights		III Combining Ratios	IV	V
Cu..........	34.89	÷	63.54	=	0.5491	1.021	1
Fe..........	30.04	÷	55.85	=	0.5378	1.000	1
S...........	34.51	÷	32.07	=	1.0768	2.002	2
	99.44						

By dividing the percentages (I) of the various constituents by the atomic weights (II) of the same, their combining ratios (III) are obtained. These can then be expressed in approximate whole numbers (IV), from which the following ratio results: Cu : Fe : S = 1 : 1 : 2 (V).

It will be noted that the sum in column I does not total 100 per cent. A complete analysis would have shown traces of other elements, but they have no bearing on the identification of the mineral as chalcopyrite.

In the case of more complex minerals where the composition is indicated by giving the percentages of the various oxides present, the procedure is the same, with the exception that the molecular weights of the oxides, that is, the sum of the atomic weights of the elements in the same, are used. Thus, Brax in analyzing a beryl from Paavo, Finland, obtained the following:

	I Analysis, per Cent		II Molecular Weights		III Combining Ratios	IV	V
SiO_2	66.37	÷	60.1	=	1.1043	5.846	6
Al_2O_3	19.26	÷	101.9	=	0.1889	1.000	1
BeO	14.01	÷	25.0	=	0.5604	2.967	3
	99.64						

These oxides therefore combine in the following ratio: BeO : Al_2O_3 : SiO_2 = 3 : 1 : 6, from which the formula $3BeO.Al_2O_3.6SiO_2$ or $Be_3Al_2Si_6O_{18}$ is obtained for beryl.

Percentage Composition. When the formula of a mineral has been established, it is possible to calculate what percentages of the various constituents should theoretically be present. Indeed, the degree of purity of a mineral may often be easily estimated by comparing an analysis with the theoretical percentage composition, calculated from the generally accepted formula. Referring again to the mineral chalcopyrite, the formula of which was calculated above as $CuFeS_2$, we may determine its theoretical percentage composition by ascertaining the percentage the combining weight of a given constituent is of the molecular weight of the mineral as a whole. Thus,

Constituents	Atomic Weights	Combining Ratios	Combining Weights	Proportion of Molecular Weight of Mineral		Theoretical Percentage Composition
Cu	63.54	1	63.54	$\frac{63.54}{183.53}$	=	34.62
Fe	55.85	1	55.85	$\frac{55.85}{183.53}$	=	30.43
S	32.07	2	64.14	$\frac{64.14}{183.53}$	=	34.95
			183.53 (Molecular weight of mineral)			100.00

Using $Be_3Al_2Si_6O_{18}$ as the formula for beryl, the theoretical percentage composition of the various constituents may be calculated as follows:

Constituents	Molecular Weights	Combining Ratio	Combining Weights	Proportion of Molecular Weight of Mineral		Theoretical Percentage Composition
SiO_2........	60.1	6	360.6	$\frac{360.6}{537.5}$	=	67.09
Al_2O_3......	101.9	1	101.9	$\frac{101.9}{537.5}$	=	18.96
BeO.......	25.0	3	75.0	$\frac{75}{537.5}$	=	13.95
			537.5 (Molecular weight of mineral)			100.00

Names. Although chemical names may be assigned to minerals, it has long been common practice to designate them by special or mineralogical names. These mineral names are given for various reasons. In some instances, as in the case of *celestite,* the name refers to the light-blue color which is commonly observed on this mineral. *Azurite* also has reference to color, namely, a deep azure blue; *vesuvianite* to Mount Vesuvius, where first found; and *tetrahedrite* to its crystallization in tetrahedrons. *Argentite* is so called because it is a compound of silver (argentum). *Magnesite* is a compound of magnesium. *Scheelite* is named after Scheele, a Swedish chemist, and *wollastonite* after Wollaston, an English scientist. It is thus seen that in some instances outstanding physical or chemical properties have been incorporated in the names, whereas in other cases the minerals have been named after distinguished scientists or after the locality where first found.

Classification of Minerals. The chemical composition of a mineral is of basic importance in any scheme of classification, for the properties of minerals vary with the chemical composition. In order to emphasize this, it will be well to review briefly the periodic system of chemical elements. In 1869 the Russian chemist Mendelyeev published a classification of elements in which they were arranged in order of their increasing atomic weights. This classification is given in Table 19. In the various groups there are elements which possess similar properties. For example, in group II, calcium, strontium, and barium are found directly under one another. These elements are very closely related to each other chemically. The carbonates of these three elements, $CaCO_3$, $SrCO_3$, and $BaCO_3$, have strikingly similar physical and chemical properties. These carbonates occur in nature as the minerals aragonite, strontianite, and witherite, respectively. All of them crystallize in the orthorhombic system, for their crystal structures are also very similar. The relation-

Table 19. Periodic Classification of the Elements

Periods	Group O	Group I	Group II	Group III	Group IV	Group V	Group VI	Group VII	Group VIII
1		1 Hydrogen H = 1.008							
2	2 Helium He = 4.00	3 Lithium Li = 6.94	4 Beryllium Be = 9.02	5 Boron B = 10.82	6 Carbon C = 12.01	7 Nitrogen N = 14.01	8 Oxygen O = 16.00	9 Fluorine F = 19.00	
3	10 Neon Ne = 20.18	11 Sodium Na = 23.00	12 Magnesium Mg = 24.32	13 Aluminum Al = 26.97	14 Silicon Si = 28.06	15 Phosphorus P = 30.98	16 Sulfur S = 32.07	17 Chlorine Cl = 35.46	
4	18 Argon A = 39.94	19 Potassium K = 39.10	20 Calcium Ca = 40.08	21 Scandium Sc = 45.10	22 Titanium Ti = 47.90	23 Vanadium V = 50.95	24 Chromium Cr = 52.01	25 Manganese Mn = 54.93	26 Iron Fe = 55.85 27 Cobalt Co = 58.94 28 Nickel Ni = 58.69
	—	29 Copper Cu = 63.54	30 Zinc Zn = 65.38	31 Gallium Ga = 69.72	32 Germanium Ge = 72.60	33 Arsenic As = 74.91	34 Selenium Se = 78.96	35 Bromine Br = 79.92	—
5	36 Krypton Kr = 83.7	37 Rubidium Rb = 85.48	38 Strontium Sr = 87.63	39 Yttrium Y = 88.92	40 Zirconium Zr = 91.22	41 Columbium Cb = 92.91	42 Molybdenum Mo = 95.95	43 Technetium Tc = 99.0	44 Ruthenium Ru = 101.7 45 Rhodium Rh = 102.9 46 Palladium Pd = 106.7
	—	47 Silver Ag = 107.88	48 Cadmium Cd = 112.41	49 Indium In = 114.76	50 Tin Sn = 118.70	51 Antimony Sb = 121.76	52 Tellurium Te = 127.61	53 Iodine I = 126.92	—
6	54 Xenon Xe = 131.3	55 Cesium Cs = 132.91	56 Barium Ba = 137.36	57 Lanthanum* La = 138.92	72 Hafnium Hf = 178.60	73 Tantalum Ta = 180.88	74 Tungsten W = 183.92	75 Rhenium Re = 186.31	76 Osmium Os = 190.2 77 Iridium Ir = 193.1 78 Platinum Pt = 195.2
	—	79 Gold Au = 197.2	80 Mercury Hg = 200.61	81 Thallium Tl = 204.39	82 Lead Pb = 207.21	83 Bismuth Bi = 209.00	84 Polonium Po = 210.0	85 Astatine At = 211.0	
7	86 Radon Rn = 222	87 Francium Fr = 223	88 Radium Ra = 226.05	89 Actinium† Ac = 227.05				—	—

* Numbers 57 to 71 include the rare earths, as follows: 57 lanthanum (La), 58 cerium (Ce), 59 praseodymium (Pr), 60 neodymium (Nd), 61 promethium (Pm), 62 samarium (Sm), 63 europium (Eu), 64 gadolinium (Gd), 65 terbium (Tb), 66 dysprosium (Dy), 67 holmium (Ho), 68 erbium (Er), 69 thulium (Tm), 70 ytterbium (Yb), 71 lutecium (Lu).

† The following are the heavy radioactive elements; 93 to 98 are synthetic: 89 actinium (Ac), 90 thorium (Th), 91 proactinium (Pa), 92 uranium (U), 93 neptunium (Np), 94 plutonium (Pu), 95 americium (Am), 96 curium (Cm), 97 berkelium (Bk), 98 californium (Cf).

ship between chemical composition and crystal structure is known as crystal chemistry; see page 184.

Table 20 gives the molecular weights, the specific gravities, several important angles, and the elements of crystallization of the minerals aragonite, strontianite, and witherite.

It is observed that the specific gravities increase regularly with the molecular weights. The size of corresponding prism and dome angles on crystals of these three minerals is of the same character. A close examination, however, reveals small but regular differences. This is also true of the elements of crystallization. In both cases, nevertheless, the fact that the values, although among themselves slightly different, are of the same order is at once noticed.

TABLE 20

Formula	Molecular weights	Specific gravity	Angles		Elements of crystallization		
			Prism $110\wedge 1\bar{1}0$	Dome $011\wedge 0\bar{1}1$	*a*	*b*	*c*
Aragonite, $CaCO_3$.....	100.1	2.9	63°48′	71°33′	0.6228	:1:	0.7204
Strontianite, $SrCO_3$......	147.6	3.7	62°41′	71°48′	0.6089	:1:	0.7237
Witherite, $BaCO_3$.....	197.4	4.3	62°12′	72°16′	0.5949	:1:	0.7413

Isomorphism. *Minerals with analogous chemical compositions which crystallize with similar structures and hence have similar crystal forms are said to be isomorphous.* It is common for such substances to show gradations in chemical composition as well as in physical properties, such as specific gravity and indices of refraction. An analysis of strontianite will frequently show the presence of calcium and barium replacing some of the strontium. The atoms of these three elements are randomly distributed in the structural positions of the positive metal ions. This is a type of solid solution, and is also known as *isomorphous replacement.* The term *replacement* does not refer to a change in composition subsequent to formation. It means that as the crystal is growing, chemically similar atoms of nearly the same size may proxy for one another in identical structural positions. The amount of replacement may be slight, or it may be extensive.

Since Fe^{+2} and Mn^{+2} are nearly the same size, $FeCO_3$ and $MnCO_3$ in the calcite group (see page 326) form a complete series, with all proportions of Fe and Mn. The formula $(Fe,Mn)CO_3$ indicates that Fe predominates over Mn, while $(Mn,Fe)CO_3$ indicates the reverse. On the other hand, Ca^{+2} and Mg^{+2} are quite different in size, hence in $CaCO_3$ only a very small amount of Mg may replace Ca. However, it is possible for Ca and Mg to alternate regularly in the structure, forming a definite compound $CaMg(CO_3)_2$, called dolomite.

The garnet group (page 363) is a good illustration of isomorphous replacement. The composition is best expressed by the formula $M_3''M_2'''(SiO_4)_3$. In this formula, M'' may be calcium, magnesium, ferrous iron, or manganese. M''' indicates ferric iron, aluminum, or chromium. Usually one of the elements in each of these groups predominates, the others being present in varying amounts. It is common practice to differentiate six distinct varieties of garnet depending upon the elements which predominate, as shown in the following table:

Fig. 452. Gustav Tschermak (1836–1927). For many years professor of mineralogy and petrography in the University of Vienna. Noted for his many important contributions, especially those on the isomorphism of the feldspars.

Grossularite	$Ca_3Al_2(SiO_4)_3$
Pyrope	$Mg_3Al_2(SiO_4)_3$
Spessartite	$Mn_3Al_2(SiO_4)_3$
Almandite	$Fe_3Al_2(SiO_4)_3$
Uvarovite	$Ca_3Cr_2(SiO_4)_3$
Andradite	$Ca_3Fe_2(SiO_4)_3$

Between these compositions there are many gradations, but in every instance the composition can be referred to the general formula $M_3''M_2'''(SiO_4)_3$.

A more complex type of isomorphous replacement is illustrated by the plagioclase feldspars, in which albite ($NaAlSi_3O_8$) and anorthite ($CaAl_2Si_2O_8$) are the end members. Between them are intermediate members whose composition and properties vary regularly from that of albite on the one hand to that of anorthite on the other. This is clearly shown by the following table:

Albite,	$NaAlSi_3O_8(Ab)$	Ab_9An_1
Oligoclase,	Ab_9An_1	Ab_7An_3
Andesine,	Ab_7An_3	Ab_1An_1
Labradorite,	Ab_1An_1	Ab_3An_7
Bytownite,	Ab_3An_7	Ab_1An_9
Anorthite,	Ab_1An_9	$CaAl_2Si_2O_8(An)$

In this case there is a dual replacement, which is best shown when the formulas of the end members are written $NaAlSiSi_2O_8$ for albite and $CaAlAlSi_2O_8$ for anorthite. This replacement consists of Ca^{+2} for Na^{+1}, large ions, and of Al^{+3} for Si^{+4}, small ions.

Isomorphous replacement is not limited to the positive ions, but may also occur with the negative ions. The mineral apatite has the formula

$Ca_5F(PO_4)_3$. In various members of the apatite group (page 350) the F may be replaced by Cl or OH, and the PO_4 by AsO_4 or VO_4.

Polymorphism. A chemical substance may crystallize with different structural arrangements under different conditions of pressure and temperature, although other factors may also be involved. This is called *polymorphism*. Thus Ag_2S crystallizes in the cubic system above 180°C. and is called argentite. If formed below that temperature, the crystals are monoclinic, and are called acanthite. Argentite crystals cooled below 180° undergo an internal atomic rearrangement, and become a mosaic of monoclinic units. They retain the original cubic shape and are called *paramorphs* of acanthite after argentite (see page 276).

One unusual feature of polymorphism is that two or more different structures of a given substance may both exist under normal conditions. Common mineral examples are as follows:

Carbon	Diamond—cubic Graphite—hexagonal
$CaCO_3$	Calcite—hexagonal Aragonite—orthorhombic
FeS_2	Pyrite—cubic Marcasite—orthorhombic
TiO_2	Rutile—tetragonal Anatase—tetragonal Brookite—orthorhombic

With two forms, the substances are said to be dimorphous, with three, trimorphous. In these cases only one arrangement can be truly stable for a given temperature and pressure; the others must be metastable, although they may exist for indefinitely long periods. The change from a metastable to a more stable form can frequently be brought about by heating. Such treatment changes aragonite to calcite, and both anatase and brookite to rutile.

Usually the differences in structural arrangement among polymorphs of the same substance are relatively slight. Thus orthorhombic aragonite is decidedly pseudohexagonal. The chief difference between it and hexagonal calcite is a slight rotation of the CO_3 groups. The low and high forms of quartz, called α and β, respectively, have very similar structures. Above 573°C. there is a sixfold axis of symmetry. Below 573° the atoms shift slightly to positions with only a threefold axis of symmetry. This internal rearrangement occurs without any visible external change. Quartz crystals with twelve equally developed $10\bar{1}1$ faces are usually considered to have formed above 573° as β quartz, while those having positive and negative $10\bar{1}1$ rhombohedrons with unequal development indicate formation below 573°, as α quartz.

In addition to the α and β forms of quartz, there are also formed at much higher temperatures two other modifications of SiO_2, called cristobalite and tridymite. Once formed, these are stable at ordinary temperatures. However, their stability is attributed to the presence of foreign ions, and they do not represent pure SiO_2; see page 298.

CRYSTAL CHEMISTRY

The isomorphous series $CaCO_3$, $SrCO_3$, and $BaCO_3$ has already been described (page 181). It might be expected that $CaSO_4$, $SrSO_4$, and $BaSO_4$ would also form an isomorphous series. Their compositions are analogous and they crystallize in the same system. However, the crystal structure of $CaSO_4$ differs from that of $SrSO_4$ and $BaSO_4$; hence these three sulfates do not form an isomorphous series. Likewise NaCl and CsCl are chemically analogous, and both are cubic, but they have different structures and are not isomorphous. It is apparent that more than chemical analogy is necessary to cause substances to crystallize with similar structures. The atomic arrangement does not depend solely upon the number and kinds of atoms present, but also upon the relative sizes of the atoms and the nature of the bonding forces between them. Crystal chemistry is concerned with the nature of these relationships.

The process of crystallization involves the fitting together of identical atoms or groups of atoms in various three-dimensional patterns. For a given substance these patterns are very precise, and the laws of rational intercepts and of constancy of interfacial angles are the direct result of this precision.

Early crystallographers speculated about the relationship between crystal form and chemical composition, but no real understanding was possible until the discovery of X-ray methods by which the positions of the individual atoms in a crystal can be determined. Variations in the sizes of different atoms was demonstrated by the Braggs (page 162). In their pioneer study of the structures of the alkali halides, they found that in the two series of isomorphous compounds NaF-NaCl-NaBr-NaI and NaCl-KCl-RbCl there is a progressive increase in the sizes of the unit cells. This must mean that both the positive ions Na, K, and Rb and the negative ions F, Cl, Br, and I increase in size with increasing atomic number. The size of an atom is expressed as its "radius." The use of this term does not imply that the atom must be a sphere. If two atoms are in contact in a crystal, the distance between their centers is the sum of the radii of the two atoms.

The structures of a sufficient number of crystals have been determined to provide reasonably accurate values for the radii of many of the elements. The radius for a given element varies with the valence. Thus Fe (metal), Fe^{+2}, and Fe^{+3} have radii of approximately 1.25 Å., 0.93 Å., and 0.67 Å.; S^{-2}, S, and S^{+6} have the values 1.74 Å., 1.04 Å., and 0.34 Å., respectively.

The term *coordination* refers to the number of atoms which surround a given atom. Thus in metallic copper, each Cu atom is surrounded by 12 other Cu atoms; hence Cu has twelvefold coordination. In NaCl, both the Na and Cl have sixfold coordination, that is, each Na is surrounded by 6Cl, and each Cl by 6Na.

In addition to the relative sizes of atoms and their coordination, there is another factor of great significance in determining the structural arrangement, namely, the type of bonding. Four groups representing different types of bonding are recognized, and these are characterized by the varying behavior of the electrons. The inert gases, such as neon and argon, whose atoms have complete outer shells of electrons, are neutral, and do not form compounds. All other elements have atoms with incomplete outer shells. These may gain or lose electrons by electron transfer, thus producing negative or positive ions, or they may have the outer shells filled by sharing of electrons. The four types of bonding are as follows:

Metallic:	Free electrons	Undirected bonds
Ionic:	Electron transfer	
Homopolar or covalent:	Electron sharing	Directed bonds
Molecular:	Discrete molecules held together by electrons; weak residual forces hold molecules together	

It should be pointed out that there may be gradations from one type to another, and different types may be present in a given structure. Among minerals, the first three types are the most common.

Metallic Bonding. In metals the electrons are more or less free. The bonding forces are not specifically directed. The structures can be described as close-packed assemblages of spheres, resulting in a high coordination number. Many metals are either cubic or hexagonal close-packed (see page 171). Each atom is surrounded by 12 others at equal distances. Other metals are cubic body-centered, which is slightly less close-packed, with a coordination number of 8. In some metals, such as zinc and cadmium, the distances between atoms are not quite the same in all directions, and the binding is less metallic in character. This is even more true for the semimetals arsenic, antimony, and bismuth.

Ionic Bonding. Many minerals have crystals of the ionic type, which is characterized by a transfer of electrons. Thus in a crystal of NaCl, each Na atom gives up an electron, forming a Na^+ ion (cation), while each Cl receives an electron, forming a Cl^- ion (anion). In ionic crystals electrical neutrality requires that each anion be surrounded by cations, and each cation by anions. The relative sizes and number of anions and cations are very important in determining the structural arrangement.

Compounds with an equal number of anions and cations are designated as type AB. Among these a coordination of 12 is impossible, for there is no arrangement which can place 12 cations around each anion and 12 anions around each cation. If both are nearly the same size, as in CsCl, a coordination of 8 may occur. CsCl has a structure with 8 Cs ions at the corners of a cube, with a Cl ion at the center, or vice versa. The NaCl type of structure (Fig. 430) occurs with a greater difference in size between cation and anion. Here each Na^+ is surrounded by $6Cl^-$, and each Cl^- by $6Na^+$. This structure is quite common, and is observed in such chemically different minerals as halite (NaCl), periclase (MgO), and galena (PbS). These three minerals are not isomorphous, but rather are said to be isostructural.

With different numbers of anions and cations, many other types are possible. A common structure among type AB_2 compounds is that of the mineral fluorite, CaF_2. Fluorite has the Ca^{+2} ions at a face-centered cubic arrangement, and the F^- are at the centers of the eight smaller cubes into which the unit cell is divided by the three principal planes of symmetry. Each Ca is surrounded by 8F, and each F by 4Ca (Fig. 445). The mineral cassiterite, SnO_2, is tetragonal; its structure is shown in Fig. 449. Still more complex ionic crystals include corundum (Al_2O_3) and spinel ($MgAl_2O_4$).

Since the O^{-2} anion is relatively large compared with most metal cations, many ionic compounds containing oxygen have structures with close-packed arrangements of oxygen, with the metal cations among the interstices in various types of coordination. The large oxygen is also important in determining the shape of some of the common anion radicals. In the carbonate group $(CO_3)^{-2}$, the tiny C^{+4} is at the center of an equilateral triangle of three oxygens, somewhat closer together than usual. In the SO_4, PO_4, and SiO_4 groups, the somewhat larger S, P, or Si atoms are at the centers of tetrahedral groups of four oxygens (Figs. 602 and 603, page 357). The metal cations occur between such groups. The silicates, which form the largest group of minerals, are of this type, and their structures are discussed on pages 357 to 360.

Homopolar or Covalent Bonding. Among minerals there are few examples of strictly homopolar compounds. These are characterized by sharing of electrons. A neutral carbon atom has only four outer electrons. In the diamond, each of these four is shared with neighboring atoms, thus completing the outer shell of eight electrons. The dimorphous forms of ZnS, sphalerite and wurtzite, and zincite, ZnO, are other examples of this type of bonding. These have more open structures than either metallic or ionic types, and a fourfold coordination is common.

It should be pointed out that the last groups of minerals described under ionic bonding, those with the radicals CO_3, SO_4, PO_4, and SiO_4, are actually intermediate between ionic and homopolar bonding. In $CaCO_3$, for example, although consisting of Ca^{+2} and $(CO_3)^{-2}$ ions, there is not the simple transfer of electrons such as occurs in Na^+Cl^-. To form the CO_3^{-2} ion, the three oxygens must share four electrons received from the carbon, and two electrons from calcium, as shown by the formula $Ca^{+2}C^{+4}O_3^{-6}$. Accordingly, such compounds have both ionic and covalent characteristics.

Molecular Structures. Few minerals have structures which are molecular, although this type is very common among organic compounds. Crystals of orthorhombic sulfur are built up from S_8 molecules, which have the form of a puckered ring. The mineral senarmontite, Sb_2O_3, has definite Sb_4O_6 molecules, eight of which are arranged in a cubic cell; As_2O_3 has a similar structure. Graphite has a sheet structure, in which an individual sheet can be regarded as a single molecule of indefinite extent.

The type of bonding in a crystal is very closely related to many of its physical properties, such as hardness, melting point, solubility, index of refraction, and conductivity. However, these relationships are too complex to be included in an elementary discussion.[1]

[1] See R. C. Evans, "Crystal Chemistry," Cambridge University Press, London, 1939; or C. W. Stillwell, "Crystal Chemistry," McGraw-Hill Book Company, Inc., New York, 1938.

14 Formation and Occurrence of Rocks and Minerals

The materials at the earth's surface may be divided into the *lithosphere*, *atmosphere*, *hydrosphere*, and *biosphere* (living matter). The lithosphere is composed of minerals, which occur in more or less complex assemblages called rocks. In considering the origin and occurrence of primary minerals, we are concerned with the lithosphere, although the atmosphere, hydrosphere, and biosphere are involved in the formation of secondary minerals.

The average composition of the lithosphere has been estimated from thousands of chemical analyses. These show that over 98 per cent of the lithosphere is made up of only eight chemical elements, as follows: oxygen (46.60), silicon (27.72), aluminum (8.13), iron (5.00), calcium (3.63), sodium (2.83), potassium (2.59), and magnesium (2.09). Of the many useful metals, only aluminum, iron, and magnesium are in this list of the eight most common elements.

The science of *geochemistry*, or chemistry of the earth, discusses the origin of mineral deposits and considers the manner in which the chemical elements are combined and distributed. It also attempts to explain the processes of differentiation and concentration which took place in the formation of the earth, and the subsequent changes which have produced the rocks and minerals as they now exist.

THE STRUCTURE OF THE EARTH

Theories concerning the structure of the earth are based on evidence obtained from various sources. Among these sources are (1) the composition of meteorites, on the assumption that they are similar to earth materials; (2) the propagation of earthquake waves, which reveal differences in the density and elasticity of the earth at various depths; and

(3) the existence of the earth's magnetic field. From these observations it is assumed that the earth is made up of concentric shells, first a nickel-iron *core*, comparatively small in volume, and at least in part molten; second, a solid shell, called the *mantle*, making up the greater portion of the earth, and having a composition corresponding to the basic rock peridotite (see page 199); and third, a relatively thin outer *crust*, that is, the *lithosphere*.

LITHOSPHERE

The rocks of the lithosphere are chiefly igneous rocks which have been formed by the crystallization of molten material called *magma*. The composition of these rocks is usually expressed not in terms of the percentages of the chemical elements present but rather in the percentages of their oxides, such as SiO_2, Al_2O_3, FeO, and Na_2O. This is also the practice in the case of individual minerals. For example, the formula of the mineral olivine, Mg_2SiO_4, may be written as $2MgO.SiO_2$; that of anorthite, $CaAl_2Si_2O_8$, as $CaO.Al_2O_3.2SiO_2$; and albite, $NaAlSi_3O_8$, as $Na_2O.Al_2O_3.6SiO_2$.

Igneous rocks and silicate minerals may be classed as *acid*, *intermediate*, or *basic*. The significance of these terms is to indicate the relative percentage of silica (SiO_2) present. Thus a rock high in silica (over 65 per cent) is termed an acid, between 65 per cent and 52 per cent an intermediate, and below 52 per cent a basic rock. Likewise, both olivine and anorthite would be classed as basic minerals, while albite would be considered an acid mineral.

The rocks of the crust beneath the great ocean basins are chiefly basalt, a basic rock. In the continental areas and the Atlantic basin granitic rocks overlie the basaltic layer. Relatively thin and irregular patches of secondary rocks, sediments, and metamorphic rocks occur in the continental areas.

MAGMATIC PROCESSES

Subsequent to the primary differentiation during the formation of the earth, there have been complex alterations and rearrangements of the materials of the earth's crust. At various periods volcanic eruptions and extensive lava flows have occurred at the surface, as well as the injection of molten rock into the upper levels of the crust. These actions are the result of the melting of previously existing rocks at moderate depths. The magma is the primary source of the minerals at the earth's surface An important part of geochemistry deals with magmatic processes.

MAGMATIC DIFFERENTIATION

The crystallization of a magma is a very complex process. A single pure substance has a definite melting point. Above this point it is a liquid; below this point it crystallizes and becomes solid. In contrast, a mixture of molten materials, such as a magma, has no definite crystallization temperature. It is a high-temperature solution, and when it cools, the substance with the highest melting point does not necessarily crystallize first, but rather the least soluble constituent, followed by the more soluble ones. The least soluble constituents are certain ores and basic minerals, low in silica, such as olivine and anorthite. The acid minerals, such as albite and quartz, are the most soluble and hence among the last to crystallize. This sequence of formation is known as *fractional crystallization*, or *magmatic differentiation.*

Although the temperatures and the compositions of the lava and of the gases escaping from active volcanoes can be determined, such information is not available concerning the magma below the surface. Observations on the rocks resulting from the cooling of the magma are usually restricted to a few natural outcrops or man-made exposures.

Because of (1) the complex composition of the magma, (2) the attendant high temperatures and pressures, and (3) the unlimited time factor involved in the chemical reactions and in the crystallization of the magma, it is difficult to determine the magmatic processes by experiment in the laboratory.

ACTION OF VOLATILE CONSTITUENTS

The magma normally contains gaseous constituents which are called *volatiles, fugitive constituents*, or *mineralizers.* These gaseous constituents cannot escape because of the confining pressure. The most important and abundant of these volatiles is water vapor, with lesser amounts of carbon dioxide, and of chlorine, fluorine, boron, and sulfur compounds. These volatiles play a very important part in the complex series of changes which take place when the temperature and the pressure of the magma are reduced. These changes may be as follows:

1. The volatiles do not enter appreciably into the minerals which crystallize first, but are concentrated in the residual material. The volatiles eventually form a magmatic water phase and finally a *hydrothermal phase.*

2. The volatiles lower the temperature of crystallization and greatly increase the fluidity and the chemical reactivity of the residual magma, and the pressure of the expanding gases tends to force magmatic material into the adjacent rocks.

3. These volatiles may be important in reactions between the magma and the country rock (*contact metamorphism*, see page 193), and are also involved in the concentration of certain ore minerals. If near the surface, the volatiles may escape and form sublimates, or contaminate the ground water, as in some hot springs.

Pneumatolysis is a general term that has been applied to the formation of minerals in an igneous rock or in the fissures of the adjoining wall rock by gases or vapors emanating from the igneous mass.

ORDER OF CRYSTALLIZATION FROM THE MAGMA

The first major silicate minerals to crystallize from the magma are basic minerals, low in silica, such as olivine and basic plagioclase. Non-silicate minerals, that is, sulfides and oxides of iron, copper, nickel, chromium, and titanium, as well as platinum and diamond, may be associated with the basic silicate minerals. Next to crystallize are the intermediate silicates. The acid minerals, such as orthoclase, mica, and quartz, crystallize last.

This sequence of crystallization explains the formation of different rock types from one magma. The basic minerals crystallizing first will form a rock of basic type. The resulting residual magma has a composition different from the original magma and will form an intermediate type of rock to be followed later by an acid type. If there is complete crystallization or differentiation in one place, without orogenic disturbance, the resulting igneous mass may show a zoned or layered structure. These various types do not necessarily represent sharply defined and separate phases but rather a gradation from one type to the other. If, however, the pressures during the crystallizing process are sufficient to cause movement of the still molten material, there will be a *spatial distribution* with the later acid rocks more or less widely separated from the basic rock which was formed first.

PEGMATITE STAGE

After the major portion of the magma has crystallized, the residue is greatly enriched in the volatile constituents, the chief of which is water vapor. Consequently, when the temperature is reduced sufficiently to allow liquid water to exist, a very hot and highly concentrated aqueous solution, known as *magmatic water*, is formed. This magmatic water still contains SiO_2, Al_2O_3, Na_2O, and K_2O. In addition there is a concentration of many of the less common elements, which were minor constituents of the original magma. This magmatic water is more fluid than the magma, and is often injected into the adjacent rocks causing vein-like bodies known as *pegmatite dikes* to be formed. The major constituents of these dikes may resemble granitic rocks. For example, a granite may be composed of quartz, orthoclase (high temperature feldspar), and muscovite, while a pegmatite dike might contain quartz, microcline (low temperature feldspar), and muscovite. However, there may be a marked difference in the texture of these rocks. In granite, the orthoclase, mica, and quartz may be present as very small grains, whereas in a pegmatite, the microcline usually occurs in large crystals, the mica in sheets, and the quartz in masses. These large crystals form because of the greater fluidity of the magmatic water compared to the viscous magma. Some pegmatites are very simple in composition, while others are very complex. Typical pegmatite minerals are tourmaline, beryl, lithium mica, topaz, spodumene, monazite, uraninite, wolframite, and columbite. Pegmatites of basic composition also occur in nature but they have a finer texture and do not contain an abundance of accessory minerals.

Fig. 453. Paul Niggli (1888–1953). Professor of mineralogy and petrography in the University of Zürich, Switzerland (1920–1953). Eminent as an investigator and contributor to mineralogical and geological sciences.

HYDROTHERMAL STAGE

Following the pegmatite stage, there may be a hydrothermal stage of mineral deposition of great importance. Many important ores occur in hydrothermal veins near magmatic intrusions. The physical relationship of these veins to the magma is not fully understood. Hydrothermal veins are composed almost entirely of nonsilicate minerals. They may be classified as follows:

1. *Hypothermal veins*—deposited at great depths, with high pressures and temperatures of 300 to 500°C. These veins may contain cassiterite, wolframite, scheelite, molybdenite, and native gold.

2. *Mesothermal veins*—deposited at intermediate depths with lower pressures and temperatures of 200 to 300°C. Pyrite, chalcopyrite, arsenopyrite, galena, sphalerite, and tetrahedrite are typical of these veins. Quartz and carbonates often occur as gangue minerals.

3. *Epithermal veins*—deposited nearer the surface with temperatures of 50 to 200°C. These veins may contain cinnabar, stibnite, marcasite, pyrite, and at times, native gold. Associated gangue minerals are quartz opal, calcite, fluorite, and barite.

A mineral-bearing solution, usually at elevated temperature, may react with and dissolve wholly or in part a mineral and simultaneously deposit another in its place. Thus, galena (PbS) and other sulfides are deposited from solution and at the same time replace the limestone with which the solution is in contact. The texture or structure of the original mineral is often retained by the replacing substance. This process of solution and replacement is known as *metasomatism* and is an important factor in the formation of many ore deposits.

SUBLIMATION

Extrusive magmas may discharge volatile material, and minerals called *sublimates* may be formed, as is the case around volcanic vents or fumaroles. Halite ($NaCl$), sal-ammoniac (NH_4Cl), sulfur (S), boric acid (H_3BO_3), and ferric chloride ($FeCl_3$) have been formed in this manner. In the vicinities of volcanoes small scales of hematite (Fe_2O_3) are frequently found resulting from the interaction of volatile $FeCl_3$ and water vapor. Thus $2FeCl_3 + 3H_2O = Fe_2O_3 + 6HCl$. Comparatively small amounts of material are deposited by sublimation.

Sublimation does not ordinarily occur in connection with intrusive magmas, since the gases do not escape to the surface. However, if the magma intrudes near the surface, the temperature of the ground water may be raised sufficiently to cause hot springs and geysers. The water of these springs and geysers is not magmatic water, but there is some evidence that in Yellowstone Park it actually contains some volatile material from the magma.

SUMMARY

A summary of the complex series of events which may be caused by an intrusive magma together with examples of the minerals formed at different stages is given in Table 21. In the case of quickly cooled extrusive magmas, this differentiation cannot take place, and since the volatiles escape, there are no pegmatite or hydrothermal phases. Volcanic rocks and lava flows contain comparatively few minerals and are of very little economic importance.

CONTACT METAMORPHISM

Profound changes take place in the rocks which have been intruded by a magma. These changes are limited to a narrow zone at the contact of the magma and the intruded rock. The results constitute what is termed *local, thermal,* or *contact metamorphism.* This type of metamorphism is most pronounced in the vicinity of batholiths, stocks, dikes, and intrusive sheets, that is, wherever older rocks, especially impure limestones and shales, have been subjected to the action of igneous intrusions. The changes are due to the heat, the pressure, and the volatiles of the magma. By the action of contact metamorphism on impure limestones, wollastonite, garnet, graphite, vesuvianite, and epidote may be formed. The minerals olivine, diopside, tremolite, spinel, phlogopite, and chondrodite may result if the limestone contains considerable magnesium. In a few localities as many as one hundred minerals have been formed in impure carbonate rocks under the influence of contact metamorphism. The minerals andalusite and cordierite are the result of the action of contact metamorphism upon shales. The minerals formed under these conditions are termed *contact metamorphic minerals.*

The term *granitization* is employed to describe the processes by which preexisting sedimentary and metamorphic rocks have been changed into

TABLE 21. GENERAL SEQUENCE OF CRYSTALLIZATION FROM AN INTRUSIVE MAGMA

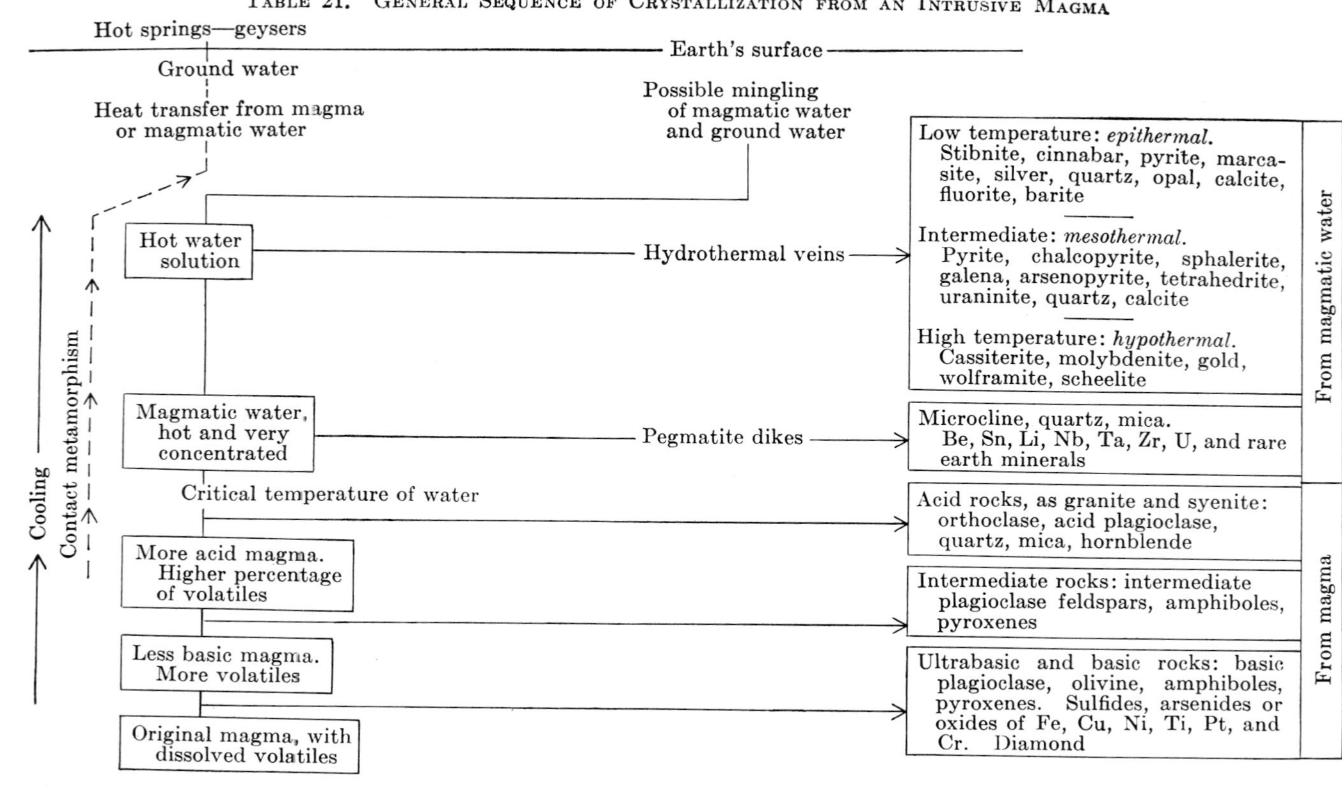

rocks of granitic mineral composition and texture without passing through a molten stage. While the possibility of such alterations is generally conceded, especially at igneous contacts, there is not complete agreement as to the extent of the alterations, the temperatures involved, and the various agencies and mechanism necessary to bring about such a transformation.

REGIONAL METAMORPHISM

A second type of metamorphism affects large areas and is due chiefly to the pressures of mountain-building or orogenic processes. Heat and water also play an important part. This action is called *dynamic* or *regional metamorphism.* There may be recrystallization without change in mineral composition, as in the change of limestone to marble, or of sandstone to quartzite. A granite may be altered to a granite gneiss, with no change in minerals present but with the mineral grains flattened or elongated, giving a coarsely laminated texture. New and characteristic minerals may develop in such metamorphosed rocks, for example, andalusite, kyanite, sillimanite, staurolite, some garnets, and epidote.

SECONDARY MINERALS

The minerals which crystallize from a magma or from magmatic water are termed *primary* minerals. The minerals which are formed from previously existing minerals by processes which involve the hydrosphere, atmosphere, and biosphere are called *secondary* minerals. The chief agent is *meteoric* water, that is, the water which falls on the earth as rain or snow. It includes the water in oceans, lakes, streams, and ground or surface water.

Meteoric water containing dissolved gases from the atmosphere and living organisms from the biosphere plays both destructive and constructive roles. Minerals may be chemically altered, or they may be dissolved, transported and precipitated, or carried in solution to the ocean or salt lakes and later deposited as new minerals. The action of ground water on rocks and minerals is an important phase of *weathering,* which is discussed on page 208.

Secondary minerals may be produced by the following methods:

1. Chemical weathering, chiefly oxidation, hydration, and carbonation.
2. Solution and deposition by water containing dissolved carbon dioxide.
3. Solution and deposition by hot springs and geysers.
4. Leaching of soluble minerals, with concentration of insoluble constituents.
5. Evaporation of water in salt lakes and oceans.
6. Formation of minerals by the action of living organisms.

1. *Chemical Weathering.* Ground water containing dissolved oxygen and carbon dioxide from the atmosphere may react with and change the composition of minerals. For example, native copper or copper sulfide minerals may be changed to the copper carbonates, malachite ($Cu_2(OH)_2CO_3$) and azurite ($Cu_3(OH)_2(CO_3)_2$). A sulfide may also be altered to a sulfate, as galena (PbS) to anglesite ($PbSO_4$). Hydration may occur, as when anhydrite ($CaSO_4$) is changed to gypsum ($CaSO_4.2H_2O$).

The process called *secondary enrichment* is of great importance in the concentration of copper ores. At the surface minerals may occur very sparingly, but extend to a considerable depth. They may be dissolved at the surface in the zone of oxidation by descending water and then precipitated at lower levels. Very rich mineral deposits may be formed if the surface is continually eroded, so that the zone of oxidation moves progressively downward.

2. *Solution and Deposition by Water Containing Carbon Dioxide.* When ground water containing dissolved carbon dioxide from the atmosphere comes in contact with limestone, calcium carbonate ($CaCO_3$) readily passes into solution as the soluble bicarbonate, $CaH_2(CO_3)_2$. By this action, extensive caverns have been formed in many limestone regions. The bicarbonate is unstable, and the reaction may be reversed. The carbon dioxide is then lost and the insoluble calcium carbonate is again formed, and in many cases is deposited as *stalactites* and *stalagmites* in caves or in banded masses called *cave onyx* or *onyx marble.* The insoluble calcium carbonate may also be deposited around springs or in the beds of streams or lakes, in a cellular form called *calcareous tufa.*

3. *Hot Springs and Geysers.* Minerals that are comparatively insoluble in cool water may be dissolved by hot water below the surface and then be precipitated at the surface. Typical examples are in Yellowstone Park. In the southern section of the park, the hot water ascends through siliceous rocks and contains silica (SiO_2), which is deposited around the geysers as *geyserite,* a variety of opal ($SiO_2.xH_2O$). In the northern section, the hot water ascends through carbonate rocks, and large terraces of *travertine* ($CaCO_3$) are formed. The deposits of travertine at Tivoli, near Rome, Italy, have been worked for centuries for structural and ornamental purposes.

4. *Leaching of Soluble Material and Concentration of Insoluble Minerals.* Residual deposits of some minerals are very important. Among these are the clay minerals, which are chiefly hydrous aluminosilicates, formed by the weathering of silicate minerals containing aluminum (see kaolin, page 402). In tropical or semitropical regions with alternating wet and dry seasons, *laterites* may be formed. These are red soils, with a high content of ferric oxide (Fe_2O_3) which may actually form iron ores. In a similar

way, bauxite, high in alumina (Al_2O_3), may be formed. Such deposits constitute the major source of aluminum. Various oxides of manganese may also be concentrated in this manner.

5. *Evaporation.* The ocean contains large quantities of chemical compounds in solution, of which the chlorides, sulfates, carbonates, and borates of sodium, magnesium, calcium, and potassium are the most abundant. At various geologic periods the ocean water in closed basins evaporated, and large deposits of gypsum, anhydrite, and halite were formed. Minerals which are the result of evaporation are known as *evaporites.* In some cases, as at Stassfurt, Germany, where evaporation went to completion, the more soluble magnesium and potassium salts were also deposited (see page 320). The deposits from lakes in arid regions not only contain gypsum and halite but also have important quantities of sodium carbonate and sulfate and of borates. Both bromine and metallic magnesium are produced commercially from ocean water.

6. *Minerals Formed by Living Organisms (Biosphere).* Although calcium carbonate and silica are usually present only in minute quantities in lakes and oceans, certain organisms have the ability to extract these compounds from the water and then secrete them to form the hard parts of their bodies. Mollusks, corals, and crinoids do this with calcium carbonate ($CaCO_3$), forming either calcite or aragonite. Extensive deposits of limestone have been formed by the accumulation of the remains of these organisms. Sponges, Radiolaria, and diatoms secrete silica ($SiO_2.xH_2O$), giving rise to *diatomaceous earth, flint, chert,* and some varieties of *chalcedony.* Limonite and sulfur may be the result of the action of certain bacteria. The large deposits of sodium nitrate in Chile are thought to be of organic origin. Coal and petroleum have been formed from plant and animal remains, but, as stated on page 6, they lack characteristic chemical compositions and do not qualify as minerals.

ROCKS

The earth's crust or lithosphere consists of rocks which are composed of minerals (page 189). While approximately 2,000 mineral species have been described, the number considered as important rock-forming minerals can be restricted to a relatively small number, possibly not more than 20. Those of utmost importance would most likely include the following: feldspars, feldspathoids, pyroxenes, amphiboles, micas, olivine, epidote, garnets, chlorite, talc, serpentine, kaolinite and related clay minerals, quartz, hematite, magnetite, calcite, dolomite, gypsum, anhydrite, and halite.

Any mineral or aggregate of minerals comprising an important part of the earth's crust may be termed a *rock.* A rock may consist of a single component as, for example, a sandstone or limestone (see page 6). In the majority of rocks, however, two or more minerals are present as is illustrated in the case of granite where the three principal constituents are quartz, orthoclase or microcline, and mica or hornblende. To illustrate the relationship between minerals and rocks, the minerals might be compared to the letters of the alphabet and the rocks to the words.

Depending upon origin, three main groups of rocks may be differentiated. The *igneous* rocks are those which have resulted from the solidification of a molten or liquid mass, called a magma. The *sedimentary* rocks, on the other hand, were deposited in water, either as fragments carried mechanically or as chemical precipitates, whereas the *metamorphic* rocks were developed from either the igneous or sedimentary types by geological agencies including heat, pressure, and the chemical action of water.

Igneous Rocks

If the magma is permitted to cool slowly, it will in time become supersaturated with reference to certain chemical compounds which then separate or crystallize out to form the various minerals. The important rock-forming minerals of igneous rocks comprise (1) the *essential* and (2) the *accessory* minerals. The former are those present in large amounts and whose presence has a direct influence upon the character and name of the rock. This division would include feldspars, pyroxenes, amphiboles, micas, nepheline, leucite, olivine, and quartz. The accessory minerals, as the name indicates, are those present in small amounts. They do not affect appreciably the character of the rock. The more important ones would include magnetite, ilmenite, pyrite, pyrrhotite, apatite, zircon, rutile, and sphene.

Fig. 454. Auguste Michel-Lévy (1844–1911). For many years professor in the Collège de France, Paris. Distinguished for his researches on rock-forming and synthetic minerals.

Those igneous rocks which are formed from magmas that have reached the surface are termed *extrusive* or *volcanic.* Owing to the escape of dissolved gases and the more rapid rate of cooling, rocks of this type are characterized by fragmental, glassy, cellular, or extremely fine-grained (felsitic) textures. Magmas, on the other hand, that have solidified at depths produce rocks that are termed *plutonic* or *intrusive.* They have cooled very slowly and consequently possess larger and better developed crystal grains. They are said to have a granular or granitoid texture.

In many instances the texture of an intrusive rock is sufficiently coarse to permit the identification of all the essential minerals with the naked eye. A porphyritic texture results when large crystals (phenocrysts) are embedded in a finer grained or glassy ground mass. These rocks are commonly referred to as porphyrics.

The field classification of igneous rocks is a dual one, based upon both the grain or texture and the mineral composition. If a rock contains over 65 per cent of silica (SiO_2), it is classed as an *acid* rock. These are usually light-colored and contain an abundance of orthoclase or microcline, some acid plagioclase, quartz, and a subordinate amount of ferromagnesium minerals. Examples of this type are granite, granodiorite, rhyolite, aplite, and pegmatite. The *basic* rocks are generally dark colored and contain less than 52 per cent of SiO_2. In these there is a larger amount of the ferromagnesium minerals, some plagioclase feldspar and olivine, but little or no quartz. Gabbro, peridotite, pyroxenite, hornblendite, and basalt are a few examples of basic igneous rocks. The intermediate types are those whose SiO_2 content is somewhere between 52 and 65 per cent and are represented by syenite, diorite, trachyte, and andesite. A summary of some of the more important igneous rocks is given in Table 22. It should be noted, however, that in nature the transition from one type of rock into another is gradual. The various

TABLE 22. LABORATORY CLASSIFICATION OF COMMON IGNEOUS ROCKS

	Orthoclase or microcline acid ←—		Plagioclase intermediate —→		Feldspar-free basic	
Dark constituent	Mica or hornblende		Hornblende or augite		Augite, hornblende, or mica	
Distinguishing mineral	+Quartz	−Quartz	−Quartz	+Olivine	−Olivine	+Olivine
Granular texture	Granite*	Syenite†	Diorite‡ Dolerite§	Gabbro	Pyroxenite Hornblendite	Peridotite
Felsitic texture	Rhyolite ←Felsite→	Trachyte	Andesite	Basalt (Trap)	Augitite	Limburgite
Glassy texture	Obsidian Pitchstone		Tachylyte (basaltic glass)			
Cellular texture	Pumice		Scoria			
Fragmental texture	Felsitic tuff and breccia			Basaltic tuff and breccia		

* If the amount of plagioclase exceeds that of orthoclase, the term *granodiorite* is preferred. Its fine-grained equivalent is *quartz latite*.

† If approximately equal amounts of orthoclase and plagioclase are present, the rock is termed *monzonite*. Its fine-grained equivalent is *latite*.

‡ If quartz is present, the rock is called *quartz diorite* or *tonalite*. Its fine-grained equivalent is *dacite*.

§ The texture of dolerite is intermediate between granular and felsitic. It includes the rock type known as *diabase*.

types do not show the sharp distinctions that might be inferred from the rulings in the diagram. Any one of the listed types may have a porphyritic variety.

From an inspection of Table 22 it will be seen that a rock with a granular texture is called a *granite* when it contains orthoclase or microcline, a dark constituent, and quartz, while a rock with the same texture without the quartz is known as a *syenite*. *Rhyolite* and *trachyte* are mineralogically the equivalents of granite and syenite but possess a felsitic rather than granular texture. *Diorite*, on the other hand, is a granular rock consisting essentially of acid plagioclase[1] and hornblende, while *gabbro* contains basic plagioclase, augite, and frequently some olivine. The term *dolerite* may be employed for those fine-grained types of diorite-gabbro rocks when it is impossible to determine with the naked eye whether the dark constituent is hornblende or augite. *Andesite* and *basalt* are the felsitic equivalents of diorite and gabbro, respectively.

Dike Rocks. Frequently penetrating the larger rock bodies will be found fissures containing intrusions of igneous material. These occurrences are known as *dikes*. They are of later origin than the rock penetrated and may be either extremely acid or very basic in character. The acid or light-colored dikes include *aplite* and *pegmatite*, while the general term *lamprophyre* has been suggested for all the basic types. Aplite is an extremely fine and even-grained rock consisting largely of quartz, microcline or orthoclase, with a very subordinate amount of dark material. Pegmatite, while possessing in general the same mineral composition as the aplite, has, on the contrary, an exceedingly coarse and uneven texture. In the formation of pegmatites mineralizers play an important role. The concentrated residual fluids and dissolved vapors from the magma form magmatic water. This is more fluid than the viscous magma, and permits crystals of greater size to form, and explains the concentration of certain accessory minerals which are so abundant in some pegmatites. The later hydrothermal solutions frequently alter the original mineral components of a dike by dissolving some of the constituents and reacting with others, with the result that many new species are formed. A list of a few of the more common accessory minerals in pegmatites would include tourmaline, beryl, topaz, fluorite, spodumene, amblygonite, monazite, uraninite, wolframite, and columbite. While in most cases aplite and pegmatite have the general mineral composition of granite or granodiorite, there are instances where they are more closely related mineralogically to syenite, diorite, or gabbro. Syenitic pegmatites have been described containing numerous zirconium, titanium, and

[1] The terms *acid* and *basic* plagioclase refer to silica content (see p. 410). Thus oligoclase with 63.3 per cent SiO_2 is an acid, while labradorite, containing 53.0 per cent SiO_2, is a basic plagioclase.

rare-earth minerals. The basic dikes are not so well crystallized, nor do they, as a rule, contain the wealth of accessory minerals which characterizes the acid types.

Sedimentary Rocks

These are all of secondary origin, having been derived from the disintegration of older rocks through the action of agencies included under the comprehensive term *weathering* (page 208). That portion of the mineral matter which is carried away in solution may at some later period be deposited either through strictly chemical action, by slow evaporation, or through processes involving organic life.

Sedimentary rocks are characterized by a parallel or bedded structure. In these rocks the layers may vary in thickness, and the individual grains of the materials making up the rock may show considerable variation in composition and size. They form widely extended deposits which, generally speaking, are without great vertical dimensions, especially when compared with some of the massive igneous formations. A field classification based on origin would divide the sedimentary rocks into three main groups: (1) the *mechanical*, (2) the *chemical*, and (3) the *organic sediments*. The more important mechanical sediments would include shale, sandstone, arkose, graywacke, conglomerate, and breccia; while formations of anhydrite, gypsum, and salt would be classified as chemical deposits (evaporites). Those of organic origin would include coal, most limestones, and possibly chert and flint as well.

Shale. The finest particles carried mechanically by the water, and generally referred to as mud or silt, when reaching the sea, settle quickly, owing to the action of the soluble salts in the ocean water. These deposits, when consolidated, yield a very fine and even-grained rock, possessing a good parting parallel to the bedding, which is known as *shale*. The chief components are clay minerals, quartz, mica, and feldspar, although these constituents cannot be distinguished with the naked eye. The sizes of the particles comprising a shale vary from less than 0.002 mm. (clay particles) to about 0.02 mm. (silt). As the amount of quartz and the size of the grain increase, the shale gradually passes over into a sandstone. The colors of shale may vary from green to gray and in some instances may even be black (*carbonaceous shale*). From some of the shales of northwestern Colorado and adjacent states oil is recovered, and in several instances the quantity amounts to 30 or 40 gallons per ton of rock. These are termed *oil shales.* The oil can be obtained by distillation at a low temperature (about 400°C.) and paraffin wax and ammonium sulfate recovered from the residue as by-products.

Sandstone. When particles of sand varying in size from 0.02 to 2 mm. become consolidated, *sandstone* results. The individual components are usually rounded and consist essentially of quartz. When considerable feldspar is present, the rock is spoken of as feldspathic sandstone or *arkose* (over 25 per cent feldspar). The cementing material varies greatly in both amount and character. In some instances it is silica, although calcium carbonate, clay, iron oxide, or calcium sulfate may serve as the binding material. The most durable sandstones for structural purposes are those with a siliceous cement. Those containing iron oxide show, however, the greatest variation in color. When a sandstone is used for structural purposes, it should always be placed with the bedding planes in a horizontal position, ensuring thereby greater strength and durability. A thinly bedded argillaceous sandstone is called a *flagstone,* while the term *freestone* is applied to those homogeneous types which occur in thick beds and can be worked in all directions with equal ease.

A *graywacke* is a sandstone-like rock of grayish or greenish color, consisting of quartz, feldspar, and angular fragments of rocks embedded in a chloritic and micaceous groundmass. It has also been called a *microbreccia.*

A *conglomerate* is a rock term applied to rounded, water-worn pebbles of various sizes which are held in a matrix of finer materials. If the fragments are sharp and angular instead of rounded, the term *breccia* is employed. Breccias are quite common in limestone regions where the movement along a fault plane has crushed the rock to various degrees of fineness. These are known as *friction breccias* in contrast to *volcanic breccias* which are composed of consolidated, angular fragments of igneous material.

Limestone and Dolomite. A *limestone* is a sedimentary rock consisting essentially of calcium carbonate with minor amounts of magnesium carbonate, silica, clay, iron oxide, or carbonaceous material. The majority of limestones were formed by organisms such as Foraminifera, brachiopods, corals, mollusks, and crinoids, which have secreted calcium carbonate taken from the waters and utilized the material to form shells and skeletons. The pressure of superimposed rocks has, in many instances, largely destroyed its original fossiliferous character. The variety known as *oölitic limestone* is composed of small rounded grains of concretionary nature. With an increase in the content of magnesium carbonate, limestone gradually passes over to a *dolomitic limestone,* which is a mixture of dolomite and calcite, and finally to a *normal dolomite,* which theoretically contains 54.35 per cent $CaCO_3$ and 45.65 per cent $MgCO_3$. Normal dolomite is both slightly heavier and harder than the limestone and will not effervesce so freely when treated with cold, dilute acids. Many dolomites are believed to be the result of magnesium solutions of sea water or circulating ground water reacting upon limestones, as indicated by the equation $2CaCO_3 + MgCl_2 = CaMg(CO_3)_2 + CaCl_2$.

A classification of the common sedimentary rocks is shown in Table 23.

TABLE 23. LABORATORY CLASSIFICATION OF COMMON SEDIMENTARY ROCKS

<table>
<tr><th>Texture</th><th colspan="4">Rounded</th><th colspan="2">Angular</th></tr>
<tr><td>Coarse</td><td colspan="2">Conglomerate (pebble aggregates)</td><td colspan="2">Graywacke (gray color; quartz, feldspar, rock particles)</td><td colspan="2">Breccia (fragments of minerals or rocks)</td></tr>
<tr><td>Medium</td><td colspan="2">Sandstone (quartz grains)</td><td colspan="4">Graywacke
Arkose (usually fragments of quartz and feldspar)</td></tr>
<tr><td rowspan="4">Fine (individual grains often indistinguishable)</td><td rowspan="2">Earthy</td><td>Clay rocks
H* = 1–3</td><td colspan="2">React with HCl
H = 1–4</td><td colspan="2">Silica rocks
H = 6–7</td></tr>
<tr><td>Clays</td><td colspan="2">Chalk
Marl</td><td colspan="2">Diatomaceous earth</td></tr>
<tr><td>Dense</td><td>Shale</td><td colspan="2">Limestone
Dolomite (reacts when powdered)
Onyx marble</td><td colspan="2">Sandstone
Chert—light color (novaculite)
Flint—dark color</td></tr>
<tr><td>Cellular</td><td>—</td><td colspan="2">Travertine
Calcareous tufa</td><td colspan="2">Geyserite</td></tr>
<tr><td rowspan="2"></td><td colspan="2">Sulfates</td><td>Has taste</td><td>Phosphate</td><td>Organic</td><td>Iron ores</td></tr>
<tr><td>H = 2
Gypsum</td><td>H = 3½
Anhydrite</td><td>H = 2–3
Halite or rock salt</td><td>Phosphate rock</td><td>Coal
Peat
Asphalt</td><td>Hematite
Limonite</td></tr>
</table>

* H = hardness.

Metamorphic Rocks

Magmatic intrusions, or the pressure and heat accompanying orogenic processes (see page 205), may produce profound physical and chemical changes in igneous and sedimentary rocks. These changes may include recrystallization, change in texture or structure, or may involve the formation of new minerals. The rocks thus formed are classified as *metamorphic*. They possess certain features which resemble both the igneous and sedimentary types. Many are coarsely crystalline in character and in this respect are similar to intrusive igneous rocks. Others possess a banded structure caused by certain minerals of like character being brought together in parallel layers. This parallel arrangement is termed *schistose* or *foliated structure*. Some of the important rock types resulting from the action of regional metamorphism (page 195) include gneiss, various schists, metaquartzite, slate, and marble.

Gneiss. This is a coarsely laminated rock which generally has the mineral composition of granite or granodiorite. The intermingled grains of quartz and feldspar are separated by layers of the dark constituent.

The banding may extend in straight parallel lines or be curved and bent. Gneisses differ from schists in that they are more coarsely laminated and contain a larger amount of feldspar. They usually represent an altered igneous rock, such as granite, or some other feldspathic type, although they may also have originated from a coarse feldspathic sandstone or conglomerate. Gneisses are of widespread occurrence, especially in the older geological formations.

Schists. These are finely laminated metamorphic rocks which split readily along planes that are approximately parallel. Depending upon the character of the prevailing mineral, five common types are easily differentiated, namely, quartz, mica, chlorite, talc, and hornblende schists. In *mica schist* the scales are so arranged that the cleavage directions are all parallel, thus producing a rock of pronounced schistose structure. In addition to mica and more or less quartz and feldspar, well-developed crystals, known as *porphyroblasts* or *metacrysts*, of garnet, kyanite, andalusite, and staurolite are also frequently present. Next to the gneiss, mica schist is the most abundant metamorphic rock. Usually it is the result of the metamorphism of a fine-grained sedimentary deposit, such as clay or shale. In *chlorite schist* the chief component is the green granular or scaly mineral chlorite. In many instances it has been formed from some basic igneous rock, such as gabbro or basalt. In the case of *talc schist*, the predominating mineral is talc, which gives the rock a characteristic soapy feel. As talc is a magnesium silicate it can be developed only from the feldspar-free igneous rocks, which have high magnesium content, or, if of sedimentary origin, from impure dolomites. A schist composed essentially of some member of the amphibole group, as hornblende, actinolite, tremolite, or glaucophane, is known as *amphibolite*. *Hornblende schist* is the most important member of the amphibolites. As the black slender prisms of hornblende are all arranged with their long direction parallel to the schistosity, these schists cleave readily and show a marked silky luster. In many instances the hornblende schist has been derived from a basic igneous rock, such as a gabbro, and represents a higher grade of metamorphism than a chlorite schist.

Fig. 455. Charles Palache (1869–1954). Professor of mineralogy in Harvard University (1912–1941). American crystallographer and mineralogist.

Metaquartzite.[1] This is a very firm compact rock consisting of interlocking quartz grains. It is the result of the intense metamorphism of a

[1] *Metaquartzite* is a truly metamorphosed and recrystallized sandstone, while *orthoquartzite* has been applied sometimes to a sandstone with a siliceous cement.

sandstone in which the silica cement has been crystallized and becomes an integral part of the quartz grains. In an ordinary sandstone it will be seen that the fracture always follows the cement, that is, the fracture follows grain boundaries, while in a true metaquartzite it passes through the recrystallized grains.

Slate. This is an exceedingly fine-grained rock which breaks very easily in thin broad sheets. The cleavage, as a rule, does not correspond to the bedding planes of the shale, from which most slates were derived, but cuts these planes at various angles. In mineral composition the slates consist essentially of quartz and mica (variety sericite), with subordinate amounts of chlorite, hematite, or graphite, which contribute the green, red, and black colors, respectively. Purple slates owe their color to a combination of green chlorite and red hematite. Some slates contain a large amount of calcite or dolomite. Slates containing a considerable amount of iron carbonate have a tendency to develop a brown color (limonite) on exposure and are termed *fading slates* in the building trade.

Marble. Strictly speaking, the term *marble* includes limestones or dolomites which have been recrystallized and can be polished. The term, however, is used somewhat loosely and not infrequently includes limestones that will take a polish and can be used for decorative purposes, irrespective of their recrystallized character. Scales of mica and chlorite, arranged in wavy streaks or bands, are frequently present which add to the attractiveness of the stone but, when present in large amounts, interfere with the continuity of the polish and lower its resistance to atmospheric agencies when placed in exposed positions. Marbles show great variation in texture and color. Statuary marbles demand the purest and whitest varieties, while ornamental types show strongly contrasted color effects. For structural purposes uniformity of color is rather essential. Contrasting colors of marble slabs used as flooring in public places should be selected of types of approximately the same hardness in order that the wear will be uniform over the entire surface. Marbles are not so widely distributed as limestones and are confined almost entirely to metamorphic areas.

A laboratory classification of the common metamorphic rocks is shown in Table 24.

TABLE 24. LABORATORY CLASSIFICATION OF COMMON METAMORPHIC ROCKS

Foliated Texture	Nonfoliated Texture
Gneiss (coarsely laminated)	Metaquartzite
Schists (finely laminated)	Marble (calcite or dolomite)
Varieties: mica, quartz, chlorite, talc	
Schists (amphibolites)	Serpentine
Varieties: hornblende, tremolite, actinolite, glaucophane	
Slate (perfect cleavage)	Hornfels (baked shale or slate)

OCCURRENCE OF MINERALS

Minerals may be found either *disseminated* throughout other minerals or rocks (Fig. 456), or they may occur *attached* as crystals (Fig. 457) or adhering as crusts or in layers on other minerals or rocks. When found disseminated they sometimes exhibit crystal forms, although they are most frequently observed in irregular particles or grains. Disseminated

Fig. 456. Disseminated crystals of orthoclase (sanidine) in trachyte.

Fig. 457. Attached crystal of quartz.

crystals are generally *doubly* or *fully terminated.* Crusts of compact calcite, so commonly observed coating the exposed surfaces of limestone in cracks or coating pebbles in stream beds, are illustrative of the attached occurrence. Under favorable conditions crystals frequently form with one end well developed and with the other end adhering to the rock or mineral on which it was formed. Attached crystals are generally only *singly terminated* (Fig. 457).

Fig. 458. Vein of asbestos in serpentine.

Fig. 459. Banded vein of sphalerite (dark), fluorite, and calcite.

Cracks or crevices filled with mineral matter are spoken of as *veins* (Fig. 458). When a vein consists of several minerals deposited in layers or bands, it is termed a *banded vein* (Fig. 459). Veins may be *symmet-*

rically or *unsymmetrically banded,* depending upon whether or not the same minerals are encountered in passing from opposite walls of the vein to the center. The character of veins, as to their width and constituents, varies greatly in different localities. In some instances the width and mineral contents will continue practically unchanged over considerable distances laterally and vertically, whereas in other cases marked changes take place (Figs. 460 and 461). When a vein consists principally of unimportant or valueless material, which, however, contains some mineral of value disseminated throughout it, the former is spoken of as the *gangue.* Thus, in a gold-bearing quartz vein, quartz is obviously the gangue mineral. The term *lode* is used for a highly mineralized area consisting of a series of parallel or branching veins.

Fig. 460. Quartz vein with copper (dark).

Fig. 461. Vein of smaltite and calcite (light).

Veins have been formed principally as the result of deposition of mineral matter from solution. These solutions may have been descending or ascending in character, while in some instances their flow may have been largely lateral. Where veins trending in different directions cross, owing to a possible difference in the character of the solutions from which they were formed, mineralization is usually most pronounced. In fact, it is well known that the richest mineral deposits, or what are frequently called *bonanza ores,* are to be expected at the intersection of veins. An *ore* may be defined as a mineral deposit of economic importance. The term ore is commonly applied to metallic minerals.

Geodes are cavities lined with mineral matter, which frequently consists of well-developed crystals. Quartz and calcite geodes are not uncommon (Fig. 462). Some geodes are large enough to be designated as caves. Thus, the "crystal" cave on the island of Put-in-Bay in Lake Erie is a huge geode containing crystals of celestite ($SrSO_4$). Similarly, large geodes lined with quartz crystals are found in the Alps of Switzerland. The term *vug* is sometimes used for geode.

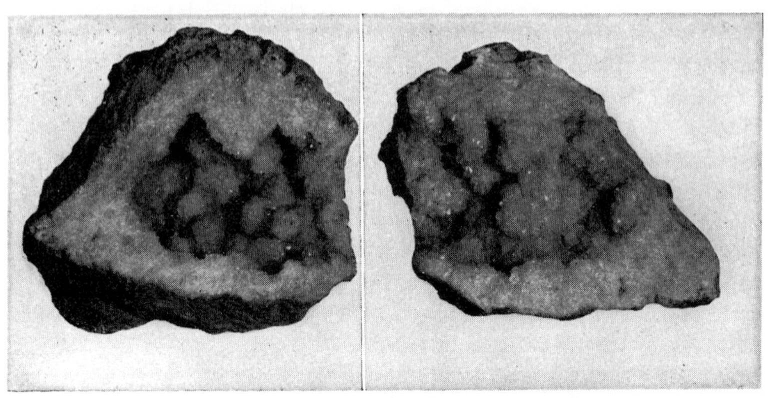

Fig. 462. Broken geode of quartz crystals.

When crystals or minerals are found in the places where they were formed, we may speak of them as occurring *in situ*. They are also said to be found in the parent or mother rock. When found in the sands and gravels of streams or of other bodies of water, as the result of transportation, they are said to occur in *secondary deposits* or *placers*. When gold is found in a quartz vein, it may be said to be observed *in situ*, but when it is recovered from the sands and gravels of a stream or lake, we refer to it as *placer* gold. There are also platinum, diamond, and cassiterite placers.

DECOMPOSITION AND WEATHERING OF MINERALS

As soon as minerals are formed and are exposed to atmospheric conditions, they are subject to change. This is known as *weathering*, and it may be either physical or chemical in nature. Among the forces producing physical weathering are the alternate expansion and contraction due to temperature fluctuations, the tremendous expansive force of freezing water, and the abrasion of mineral particles through movement by water, ice, and wind. The chemical agencies include moisture, oxygen, and carbon dioxide in the air and various acids in the soil. Profound changes may be brought about. In some cases the alteration takes place rather rapidly, while in others it may proceed very slowly. All minerals are, however, sooner or later acted upon. The changes are the result of processes familiar to students of chemistry. Some of the more important are solution, oxidation, reduction, hydration, and carbonation. In most instances several of these processes may have been effective simultaneously or successively.

PSEUDOMORPHS

Not infrequently crystals alter in such a way that the external form of the original specimen is retained. For example, goethite (hydrated iron oxide) is sometimes found in the form of crystals which were originally pyrite (FeS_2). That is, by means of oxidation and hydration pyrite has been altered to goethite without destroying the external crystal form. Such altered crystals are called *pseudomorphs,* and in the case just referred to, they are known as pseudomorphs of *goethite after pyrite.* There are several interesting types of pseudomorphs.

Paramorphs. In these an atomic rearrangement has taken place, without the chemical composition being changed. Paramorphs are possible only in the case of polymorphous substances. Thus, rutile (TiO_2), tetragonal, after brookite (TiO_2), orthorhombic. Also, calcite ($CaCO_3$), hexagonal, after aragonite ($CaCO_3$), orthorhombic.

Alternation Pseudomorphs. The change in composition may involve the loss of some constituents, the addition of new ones, or there may be a partial exchange. Gypsum ($CaSO_4.2H_2O$) after anhydrite ($CaSO_4$), malachite ($Cu_2(OH)_2CO_3$) after cuprite (Cu_2O), kaolinite ($Al_2(OH)_4Si_2O_5$) after orthoclase ($KAlSi_3O_8$), and chlorite after garnet are excellent illustrations of pseudomorphs of this type.

Substitution Pseudomorphs. Sometimes the replacing mineral has no chemical relation to the original substance. Good illustrations are the pseudomorphs of quartz (SiO_2) after fluorite (CaF_2) and quartz after calcite ($CaCO_3$).

Incrustation Pseudomorphs. At times a mineral may be deposited upon the crystal form of another and completely enclose it—thus, smithsonite ($ZnCO_3$) on calcite ($CaCO_3$). Incrustation pseudomorphs of quartz on fluorite are sometimes of such a character as to permit the crust of quartz with the cubical casts of fluorite to be removed intact. In some cases the removal of the first mineral has taken place simultaneously with the deposition of the incrusting substance.

15 | Qualitative Blowpipe Methods

Whenever possible it is advisable to determine minerals at sight, that is, by means of their physical properties, occurrences, and associates. It frequently becomes necessary, however, to supplement these observations by simple, confirmatory chemical tests. These reactions, obtained largely at high temperatures by the proper use of the blowpipe, are referred to as *blowpipe reactions.* The chemist in his laboratory can increase the number of his reagents at will, and naturally his field of operation is larger than that of the student equipped with a blowpipe, who relies upon a limited number of reagents and the effects produced when minerals are subjected to the oxidizing or reducing action of a flame. The ease with which many blowpipe tests are obtained and the small amount of apparatus and reagents required have made these reactions popular with both the mineralogist and geologist.

Fig. 463. George J. Brush (1831–1912). For many years a professor in Yale University. Distinguished for the application of blowpipe and chemical methods in the determination of minerals.

The equipment which is necessary may be limited to the following apparatus and reagents.

APPARATUS

Blowpipe. The best type consists of a brass or nickel-plated slightly conical-shaped tube *a* (Fig. 464) about 18 cm. in length, into the larger end of which fits a mouthpiece of hardened rubber *b*. At the opposite end a hollow cylindrical chamber *c* serves to collect the moisture which condenses in the tube. A side tube *d* joins the air chamber at right angles and is equipped with a platinum tip *e*, in the center of which is a smooth hole 0.4 to 0.6 mm. in diameter.

Lamps. Where illuminating gas is available, the most convenient form of lamp is the bunsen burner equipped with an additional inner tube which is flattened at the upper end and cut off obliquely (Fig. 465). The supply of gas should be so regulated that a luminous flame about 4 cm. in height results. Where gas is not available, lamps may be secured which burn either liquid (alcohol, olive oil, lard oil) or solid (tallow, paraffin) fuel. By the addition of a small amount of turpentine to the alcohol the luminosity as well as the reducing power of the flame are greatly increased. A candle flame may also be used to advantage.

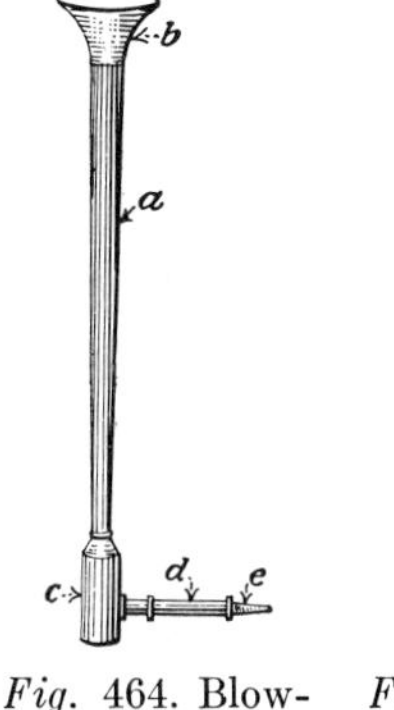

Fig. 464. Blowpipe.

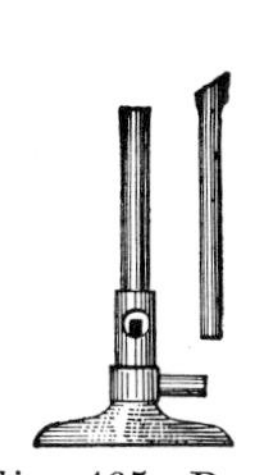
Fig. 465. Bunsen burner with inner tube.

Forceps. Plain iron, or better still platinum-tipped, forceps are indispensable for testing the fusibility of minerals as well as for noting flame colorations.

Charcoal. Rectangular blocks of charcoal about 10 by $2\frac{1}{2}$ by $1\frac{1}{4}$ cm. are useful supports during the fusion of the assay. Likewise, films are often condensed and deposited on the cooler portion of the support. Charcoal made from willow, pine, or basswood is usually recommended.

Plaster Tablets. These are made by preparing a thin paste of plaster of paris and water and spreading it over an oiled glass plate until a uniform thickness of about 5 mm. is secured. Before the plaster has hardened, the surface is ruled by a knife into rectangular divisions 10 cm. long and about 5 cm. wide. These tablets are especially well adapted for the condensation of iodide sublimates.

Platinum Wire. No suitable substitute has been found to replace platinum wire for flame colorations and bead tests. The wire should be No. 27 or 28 B. & S. gauge, about 10 cm. long. One end should be fused into a piece of glass tubing.

Hammer and Anvil. A small hammer weighing about 75 grams with a wire handle is recommended; also a block of steel 4 cm. square and 1 cm. thick for crushing material to be tested.

Agate Mortar and Pestle. The mortar should be at least 4 cm. in diameter. It is used for pulverizing material.

Diamond Mortar. The mortar should be of tool steel, about 4 cm. square, and possess a cylindrical cavity to receive the pestle. It is indispensable in crushing minerals to a fairly fine powder.

Open and Closed Tubes. Hard-glass tubing, 12 to 14 cm. in length and about 5mm. inside diameter, is employed either open at both ends to note the effect of a current of heated air upon the mineral, or closed at one end for the detection of volatile acids.

Merwin Flame-color Screen. This is a celluloid screen, 7½ by 12½ cm., consisting of three colored strips, one blue, one violet, and one blue over violet. The strips are so stained as to absorb the orange and yellow portions of the spectrum. This screen is extremely useful in the examination of flame colorations and is far superior to the "blue" and "green glass" formerly employed for the same purpose.

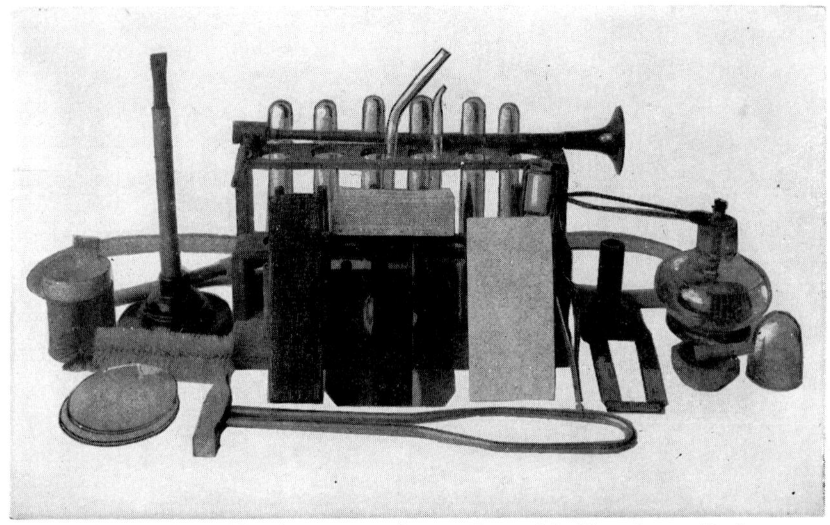

Fig. 466. Assembly of apparatus frequently used in blowpipe methods.

Other articles for blowpipe work which need no detailed description are the following:

Test Tubes. 12 cm. in length and 15 mm. in diameter; pyrex glass preferred.

Test-tube Stand, Test-tube Brush and Holder.

Magnet. Horseshoe type.

Watch Glasses. 5 cm. in diameter.

Glass Funnel and Filter Paper. Bunsen rapid-filtering funnel, 65 mm. in diameter.

File. Triangular for cutting glass tubing.

Pliers. Serviceable in breaking and cutting fragments of minerals.

Figure 466 shows an assembly of the more important blowpipe apparatus.

DRY REAGENTS

These reagents should be kept in wide-mouthed glass bottles.

Sodium Carbonate (Na_2CO_3) *or Sodium Bicarbonate* ($NaHCO_3$).

Employed extensively in the decomposition of minerals. Also as a flux in a bead test.

Borax ($Na_2B_4O_7.10H_2O$). When fused in a loop of platinum wire it is used for bead tests. Borax glass is fused and pulverized borax.

Microcosmic Salt or Salt of Phosphorus ($HNaNH_4PO_4.4H_2O$). Also used for bead tests. Upon heating, water and ammonia are liberated and the salt is transformed to sodium metaphosphate ($NaPO_3$).

Test Papers. Blue and red litmus for alkaline and acid reactions. Yellow turmeric paper for the detection of boracic acid and zirconium.

Potassium Bisulfate ($KHSO_4$). Used in fusions for decomposing minerals.

Bismuth Flux. An intimate mixture of 1 part by weight of KI, 1 part of $KHSO_4$, and 2 parts of S (*von Kobell's flux*). When used on the plaster support many elements yield highly colored iodide sublimates.

Boracic Acid Flux. Consists of 3 parts of finely pulverized $KHSO_4$ and 1 part of powdered fluorite (CaF_2) (*Turner's flux*). Employed for the detection of boron in silicates.

Potassium Nitrate (KNO_3). When used with a fusion mixture it accelerates oxidation.

Granulated Tin and Zinc. Used in acid solutions to effect reduction.

Magnesium Ribbon. For the detection of phosphoric acid.

Fig. 467. Wolfgang Franz von Kobell (1803–1882). For many years professor of mineralogy in the University of Munich. Noted for his many contributions in the field of blowpipe methods.

LIQUID REAGENTS

Work in the field demands that the number of reagents, and especially those of the liquid type, be reduced to a minimum. Under these conditions it is possible to restrict the number of wet reagents to ammonia, a 10 per cent solution of cobalt nitrate, and the common acids HCl, HNO_3, and H_2SO_4. In the laboratory it is far better to augment this number in order to extend materially the range of operations.

Alcohol. 95 per cent ethyl alcohol.

Ammonium Hydroxide (NH_4OH). One part of the concentrated alkali diluted with 2 parts of water.

Ammonium Molybdate ($(NH_4)_2MoO_4$). Dissolve 50 grams of MoO_3 in a mixture of 200 cc. of water and 40 cc. of NH_4OH (sp. gr. 0.90). The solution should be kept warm. The liquid is then filtered and poured with constant stirring into a mixture of 200 cc. of HNO_3 (sp. gr. 1.42) and 300 cc. of water.

Ammonium Oxalate ($(NH_4)_2C_2O_4.2H_2O$). 20 grams dissolved in 500 cc. of water.

Ammonium Polysulfide ($(NH_4)_2S_x$). Add flowers of sulfur to fairly concentrated ammonia and saturate the solution with H_2S. The flask should be cooled with running water while being charged with H_2S. Keep stopper in bottle when not in use.

Barium Chloride ($BaCl_2.2H_2O$). 30½ grams dissolved in 500 cc. of water.

Calcium Hydroxide (Lime Water) ($Ca(OH)_2$). Prepared by shaking CaO with water and decanting the clear liquid.

Cobalt Nitrate ($Co(NO_3)_2.6H_2O$). One part of the crystallized salt is dissolved in 10 parts of water and the solution kept in dropping bottles.

Dimethylglyoxime ($C_4H_8O_2N_2$). Prepare a saturated solution in 50 per cent alcohol to which a small amount of ammonia has been added.

Disodium Hydrogen Phosphate (Sodium Phosphate) ($Na_2HPO_4.12H_2O$). 30 grams dissolved in 500 cc. of water.

Ferrous Sulfate ($FeSO_4.7H_2O$). Solution prepared as needed.

Hydrobromic Acid (HBr). Prepared by passing H_2S through a solution of liquid bromine in water until the red color of the bromine disappears. The flask should be cooled with running water while being charged. Decant the clear solution.

Hydrochloric Acid (HCl). The chemically pure concentrated acid is diluted with an equal volume of water.

Hydrogen Peroxide (H_2O_2). 3 per cent solution. Keep in amber-colored bottle.

Lead Acetate ($Pb(C_2H_3O_2)_2.3H_2O$). 47½ grams dissolved in 500 cc. of water.

Nitric Acid (HNO_3). Used either in its concentrated form, or 1 part of the acid is diluted with 2 parts of water.

Nitrohydrochloric Acid (Aqua Regia). A mixture of 3 parts of concentrated HCl and 1 part of concentrated HNO_3.

Potassium Ferricyanide ($K_3Fe(CN)_6$). 27½ grams dissolved in 500 cc. of water.

Potassium Ferrocyanide ($K_4Fe(CN)_5.3H_2O$). 26½ grams dissolved in 500 cc. of water.

Potassium Hydroxide (KOH). The "sticks" should be kept in well-stoppered bottles and dissolved in water when needed.

Silver Nitrate ($AgNO_3$). 21½ grams dissolved in 500 cc. of water. The solution should be kept in amber-colored bottles.

Sodium Nitroferricyanide ($Na_2Fe(NO)(CN)_5$). Solution should be prepared as needed.

Stannous Chloride ($SnCl_2.2H_2O$). Solid reagent.

Sulfuric Acid (H_2SO_4). Used at times in its concentrated form, also diluted with 6 parts of water. In diluting, the acid should be added very slowly to the water.

On account of the ease with which blowpipe reactions may be obtained and the simplicity of the equipment necessary, various portable sets suitable for field work have been arranged. One of the best is the blowpipe set, illustrated in Fig. 468.

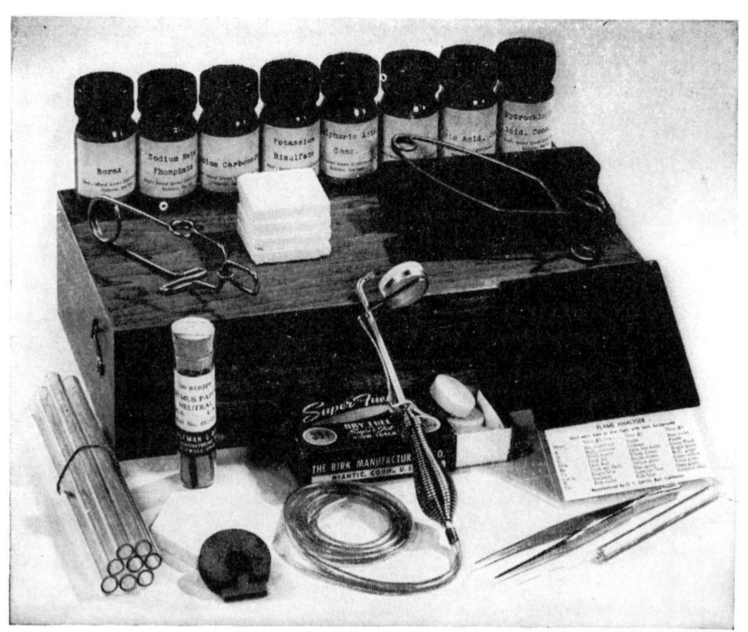

Fig. 468. Blowpipe kit suitable for field use. (*Arranged and sold by Ward's Natural Science Establishment, Rochester, New York.*)

STRUCTURE AND USE OF THE FLAME

Structure of the Flame. The structure of the flame is essentially the same whether produced by burning a gaseous, a liquid, or a solid fuel. If a small luminous flame of the bunsen burner is examined carefully, it will be noted that four more or less distinct zones are present (Fig. 469). Immediately above the burner is a dark cone *a*, consisting primarily of unburned gases. Surrounding the dark zone and extending beneath the luminous mantle is a small, blue, nonluminous zone *b*. The strongly luminous region *c*, which emits a bright yellow light, constitutes the largest portion of the luminous flame.

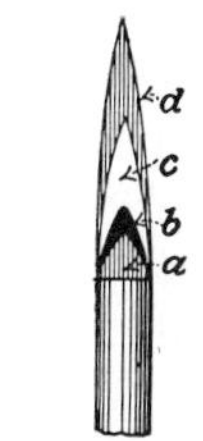

Fig. 469. Structure of luminous flame.

In general, luminosity may be due to three causes operating either separately or jointly in increasing the light-producing property of a flame. These causes are (1) the temperature of the flame, (2) the density of the flame gases, and (3) the presence of solid particles which are heated to incandescence. In the case of the bunsen burner the luminosity is unquestionably due to the presence of solid particles of carbon. The illuminants, which determine the light-giving property of a coal-gas flame, are the unsaturated hydrocarbons, such as ethylene (C_2H_4), acetylene (C_2H_2), and benzene (C_6H_6). Owing to the heat of combustion these hydrocarbons undergo dissociation. Ethylene breaks down, giving acetylene and hydrogen, while the acetylene yields carbon and hydrogen, thus explaining the cause of the luminosity. The equations expressing this dissociation may be written as follows:

$$C_2H_4 \rightarrow C_2H_2 + H_2$$
$$C_2H_2 \rightarrow 2C + H_2$$

Finally surrounding the luminous mantle we have an outer, nonluminous, invisible zone *d*, in which, owing to the oxygen of the air, there is almost complete oxidation yielding as end products CO_2 and H_2O.

The bunsen flame may be modified by inserting an inner tube which is flattened at one end and cut off obliquely, so that the blowpipe flame can be directed downward. The tube also acts as a support for the blowpipe.

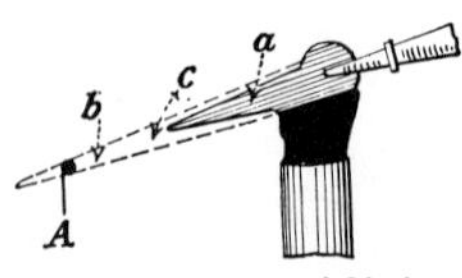

Fig. 470. Oxidizing flame.

Oxidizing and Reducing Flames. The oxidizing blowpipe flame is produced by inserting the tip of the blowpipe into the luminous flame, which should be about 4 cm. in height and blowing a gentle but steady current of air. The flame is directed slightly downward and immediately becomes nonluminous, with the possible exception of a very small luminous region above the blowpipe tip. Two well-defined nonluminous zones are readily produced, *a* and *b* (Fig. 470). The nonluminosity of this flame may be explained by the dilution and cooling effect of the air introduced into the flame gases, thus preventing the dissociation of the hydrocarbons which is so essential for the production of luminosity. Not only does the flame become nonluminous, but it is also reduced in size. Since the same amount of gas is consumed and the ultimate end products are the same in both cases, the heat liberated would likewise be the same in both instances. As the nonluminous flame is smaller, it follows that the average temperature of this flame must necessarily be higher than that of the luminous flame. The zone *a* is slightly reducing in character owing to the presence of CO in this region. For oxidation purposes the substance to be tested should be placed as indicated by the position of the loop *A* (Fig. 470). When placed in this position, the highly heated substance readily unites with the oxygen of the atmosphere.

The oxidizing blowpipe flame is also frequently employed in testing the fusibility of minerals. The hottest portion of this flame is to be found at *c* (about 1500°C.). In testing for fusibility, the fragment, which should extend beyond the tip of the forceps, should be thin, possess sharp edges, and be held in the hottest portion of the flame. If the sharp outlines are rounded, the mineral is said to be fusible. The degree of fusibility may be roughly determined by comparison with the fusibility of minerals comprising a standard scale. It is quite important that fragments should be chosen of approximately the same size. The generally accepted *scale of fusibility* is composed of the following six minerals, beginning with the most fusible. This is Penfield's modification of von Kobell's scale.

Stibnite fuses readily in a candle flame, also in a closed tube (525°C.).

Chalcopyrite fuses in the luminous gas flame but with difficulty in a closed tube (800°C.).

Almandite (garnet) fuses readily in the blowpipe flame, infusible in the luminous gas flame (1050°C.).

Actinolite: edges are readily rounded in the blowpipe flame (1200°C.).

Orthoclase: edges are fused with difficulty in the blowpipe flame (1300°C.).

Bronzite: only the sharpest splinters are rounded by fusion (1400°C.).

Quartz is sometimes added to this list, representing a mineral that is infusible in the blowpipe (1710°C.).

The reducing blowpipe flame is produced by placing the blowpipe tip just outside the flame while blowing a gentle current of air (Fig. 471). The flame is tilted sideways but retains its luminosity. A fragment held in the luminous portion of this flame will suffer reduction by virtue of the hot carbon particles of the flame and the CO that surrounds the luminous zone. Thus, by simply shifting the position of the blowpipe and regulating the strength of the blast, entirely opposite chemical effects may be produced. The purity of the oxidizing and reducing flames may be readily tested by dissolving a few small particles of MnO_2 in a borax bead on a platinum wire. In the oxidizing flame the color of the bead should be reddish violet, while in the reducing flame the color should entirely disappear.

Fig. 471. Reducing flame.

Scope of the Chemical Reactions. The reactions to be described will be presented in the following order:

1. Reactions on plaster-of-paris tablet.
    a. Assay heated per se.
    b. Assay heated with reagents.

2. Reactions on charcoal support.
   a. Assay heated per se.
   b. Assay heated with reagents.
3. Flame colorations.
4. Bead tests.
5. Heating in open tube.
6. Heating in closed tube.
7. Special tests.
8. Summary of chemical and blowpipe tests.

REACTIONS ON PLASTER TABLET

On account of their smooth white surface, infusibilty, conductivity, and porosity, plaster tablets are one of the most important supports for blowpipe work. They can be employed with both solid and liquid reagents. The tablets are cheaply and easily made, and their cleanliness in handling has added to their popularity.

Per Se Reactions. A small depression to hold the assay is made in the lower portion of the tablet and the support held in an inclined position. Unless otherwise stated, the oxidizing blowpipe flame is then directed upon the assay. The volatile constituent, either the metal itself or an oxide of the metal, or a mixture of metal and oxide, is driven off by the heat and deposited upon the cooler portions of the support. Should the material be difficult to retain on the support because of decrepitation, a paste should be made of the finely powdered substance with water and heat applied gradually. The per se tests are given as shown in Table 25.

While some characteristic coatings are thus obtained by merely heating the substance per se, the use of reagents greatly increases the number of elements which can be easily differentiated. The reagents usually employed on the plaster support are bismuth flux, ammonium polysulfide, hydrobromic acid, and cobalt nitrate.

Reactions with Bismuth Flux and Ammonium Polysulfide. One part of the powdered mineral is intimately mixed with 3 parts of bismuth flux (consisting of 2 parts S, 1 part KI, and 1 part $KHSO_4$) and heated on a plaster support. In nearly every instance, highly colored, volatile iodide coatings are obtained which condense on the cooler parts of the tablet. Similarly colored sublimates can be easily differentiated by the use of ammonium polysulfide, which transforms the iodide films to sulfides. Table 26 summarizes the most satisfactory iodide reactions.

Combination of Elements. On account of the difference in the degree of volatility of the iodides, it is not difficult at times to determine more than one element, capable of giving iodide coatings, at a single operation. Thus, in the case of jamesonite ($Pb_4FeSb_6S_{14}$), when the powder is heated slowly with bismuth flux, the peach-red antimony iodide coating is the

TABLE 25. PER SE REACTIONS ON PLASTER TABLET

Indication	Color of coating	Remarks
Cadmium	Near assay, reddish brown to greenish yellow. At a distance brownish black	Film is due to an oxide, is permanent, and is best obtained from metallic cadmium
Carbon	Brownish black, nonvolatile coating	Obtained from those carbonaceous materials yielding volatile sooty deposits. Example, asphalt
Molybdenum	In oxidizing flame, near assay, yellowish white, crystalline coating of MoO_3	When touched with reducing flame, white coating is immediately changed to deep blue. Example, ammonium molybdate
Arsenic (metal)	White over brownish black, very volatile coating	Garlic odor is also noted, due probably to small amount of arsine
Arsenic (sulfide)	Yellowish to reddish-brown coating tinged with black	Coating is volatile. Not very distinct
Mercury	Drab gray, extremely volatile sublimate	Example, HgO
Selenium	Cherry red to crimson in thin layers. Black near assay where coating is very thick. Flame is colored indigo blue	Sublimate is due to metal, is volatile, and yields reddish fumes with odor of rotten horse-radish. Example, metallic selenium
Tellurium	Volatile brown to black coating, at times with narrow fringe of blue near assay	A drop of conc. H_2SO_4 added to brown coating and gently heated yields a pink spot of tellurium sulfate. Example, metallic tellurium
Silver*	Faint yellowish coating near assay. When touched with reducing flame, becomes brownish and mottled	Coating is permanent and requires high heat. Reduced metal may also be noted. Example, $AgNO_3$
Gold*	Slightly purple to rose-colored coating near and under the assay	Requires very intense heat and is best seen when tablet is cold

* Not very distinct; wet tests for these elements are more satisfactory.

TABLE 26. IODIDE SUBLIMATES ON PLASTER TABLET

Indication	Color of coating	Remarks
Arsenic	Lemon to orange-yellow coating	A drop of $(NH_4)_2S_x$ on coating yields yellow ring. Single drop of NH_4OH dissolves ring completely
Antimony	Orange to peach-red sublimate	A drop of $(NH_4)_2S_x$ on coating produces orange-red ring, which is not completely dissolved by single drop of NH_4OH
Lead	Chrome-yellow coating	$(NH_4)_2S_x$ applied to film yields black spot, often surrounded by reddish cloud
Thallium	Orange-yellow film near assay, with purplish black band at distance. Entire coating ultimately changes to yellow	$(NH_4)_2S_x$ applied to yellow coating gives chocolate-brown spot
Bismuth	Chocolate-brown with underlying crimson. Yellowish on outer margins	When subjected to ammonia fumes, brown coating changes to orange yellow and then to cherry red
Mercury	Combination of scarlet, yellow, and greenish black	If strongly heated, predominating color is greenish black
Silver*†	Slightly yellowish coating near assay. Somewhat similar to the per se reaction	Requires intense heat. When touched with reducing flame becomes pinkish brown and somewhat mottled
Selenium†	Reddish brown to scarlet	Reddish fumes given off. Flame is colored indigo blue
Tellurium†	Purplish brown to black coating	A drop of concentrated H_2SO_4 added to coating and gently heated yields a pink spot

* Not so satisfactory as a wet test.
† Same as per se test.

first to appear at a distance from the assay. As the temperature is increased, the less volatile chrome-yellow coating of lead iodide forms near the assay. The use of ammonium polysulfide can also be used to advantage to detect such a combination. Near the assay a black spot with a reddish cloud indicates the presence of lead, while at a distance a well-defined red antimony ring is obtained. Iodides of the same or nearly the same degree of volatility are deposited together producing a compound coating with a resultant color which may serve to indicate the individual components.

Reactions with Hydrobromic Acid. The porosity of the plaster tablet lends itself readily to the application of the liquid reagent hydrobromic acid. To the assay, placed in a slight depression as heretofore, is slowly added 6 to 8 drops of the acid. The liquid is quickly absorbed by the support and returned as needed to the assay when the latter is heated with the blowpipe flame. Hydrobromic acid can be prepared by passing H_2S through a mixture of bromine in water until the red color of the liquid bromine disappears. The elements not previously recorded, which yield bromide reactions, are copper and iron.

TABLE 27. BROMINE REACTIONS ON PLASTER TABLET

Indication	Color of coating	Remarks
Copper	Volatile, purplish coating, mottled with black	On standing frequently changes to yellow. Flame is colored green
Iron	Rust-colored spots, color fades on standing	Nonvolatile and deposited near assay

Of the two reactions indicated in Table 27, that for copper is the more important, as the reagent alone develops a slight reddish stain on the tablet which may be mistaken for a trace of iron. In addition to the copper and iron reactions, molybdenum, bismuth, lead, and mercury may also produce the following colored films with HBr:

Molybdenum. Volatile, blue to bluish-green coating.

Bismuth. Volatile, yellow or crimson sublimate.

Lead. Canary-yellow film.

Mercury. Volatile, yellow coating.

Cobalt Nitrate Reactions. Crystallized cobalt nitrate is dissolved in 10 parts of water and kept in convenient dropping bottles. The application of this reagent is restricted to white or light-colored, infusible minerals. Fusible compounds would invariably yield blue cobalt glasses. The pulverized mineral is placed on a plaster tablet and strongly ignited with the oxidizing flame; a drop or two of cobalt nitrate is then added and the assay intensely heated a second time. Upon cooling, the assay may be seen to have assumed a definite color due to combination with the cobalt oxide. If the mineral is sufficiently porous to absorb the cobalt nitrate, the liquid can be applied directly to the fragment without previous pulverization. Cobalt nitrate reactions are especially serviceable in the detection of aluminum and zinc. See Table 28.

TABLE 28. COBALT NITRATE REACTIONS

Indication	Color	Remarks
MgO and minerals containing it*	Pink or pale-flesh red	Best seen when cold. Example magnesite
Al_2O_3 and compounds containing it. Zinc silicates	Blue	Examples, kaolinite, hemimorphite
ZnO and minerals containing it	Bright green	Can be applied to mineral fragment or to white coating on charcoal. Example, smithsonite
——	——	——
SnO_2, Sb_2O_3	Bluish green	Should be applied to white coating on charcoal
TiO_2	Yellowish green	Should be applied to the white powder

* As the color change is slight, the wet test is more satisfactory.

REACTIONS ON CHARCOAL SUPPORT

When plaster tablets are not available or when it is desirable to verify the presence of an element, recourse may be had to the charcoal support, for the reactions obtained on plaster and charcoal supplement each other. Plaster is the better conductor, and the sublimates formed are found nearer the assay. Charcoal, on the other hand, aids the reducing flame whenever reduction is desired. Care must be exercised not to mistake the ash of the charcoal for a sublimate. The ash will form near the assay where the heat has been intense and will not obscure the grain of the charcoal; sublimates, on the other hand, tend to conceal the grain.

Per Se Reactions. A small depression is made near the edge of the charcoal and the assay is heated slowly with the oxidizing flame, while the support is held in an inclined position to catch the sublimate formed. If the assay decrepitates (snaps) when heated, it should be finely pulverized and moistened with a drop of water. The films produced when heat is applied slowly are mainly oxides, as is shown by Table 29.

In addition to the above, white sublimates may result from the volatilization of the chlorides of copper, lead, mercury, ammonium, and the alkalies.

Since the charcoal support does not lend itself readily to the use of liquids, solid reagents such as bismuth flux and sodium carbonate are frequently employed.

TABLE 29. SUBLIMATES ON CHARCOAL

Indication	Color and character	Remarks
Arsenic	White (As_2O_3), very volatile coating	Deposits at distance from assay. Garlic odor often noted
Antimony	Near assay, dense white coating (Sb_2O_3, Sb_2O_4). At distance, bluish	Less volatile than arsenic coating
Cadmium	Near assay—black to reddish brown (CdO). At distance, yellowish green	Very thin deposits may appear iridescent
Molybdenum	Pale yellow (MoO_3), hot; white, cold; crystalline	When touched with reducing flame, becomes dark blue. Copper red (MoO_2) coating surrounding assay
Lead	Dark yellow (PbO) hot; pale yellow, cold. At distance, bluish white	At times mixed with white sulfite and sulfate of lead
Bismuth	Orange-yellow (Bi_2O_3), hot; lemon yellow, cold. At distance, white	Distinguished from lead by bismuth flux test
Zinc	Canary yellow (ZnO), hot; white, cold when Na_2CO_3 is added to assay	When moistened with $Co(NO_3)_2$ and heated, becomes grass green
Tin	Faint yellow (SnO_2), hot; white, cold	When moistened with $Co(NO_3)_2$ and heated, becomes bluish green
Selenium	Near assay, steel gray with metallic luster. At distance, white (SeO_2) tinged with red (Se)	Coating colors the flame blue. Characteristic odor
Tellurium	Near assay, white (TeO_2). At distance, gray (Te) or brownish	Imparts pale-green color to reducing flame
Thallium	White (Tl_2O), very volatile	Coating colors flame bright green

Reactions with Bismuth Flux. The reactions of the elements with bismuth flux on charcoal are, on the whole, rather unsatisfactory with the following two exceptions:

Lead. Greenish-yellow film.

Bismuth. Yellowish-white sublimate with crimson border.

Reactions with Sodium Carbonate. The effect of heating the assay with Na_2CO_3 on charcoal is to increase the reducing action of the hot charcoal. This is due to the formation of reducing gases, such as CO and possibly gaseous sodium. Under this treatment a number of substances are reduced to the metallic condition. The assay is mixed with 3 parts of anhydrous Na_2CO_3 together with some powdered charcoal obtained from the pit made to support the assay. After heating with the reducing flame for several minutes the fusion is ground with water in an agate mortar and the color, malleability, or magnetism of the reduced particles noted. In addition to reduced metal, some substances yield a sublimate, while others are volatilized so quickly that no reduced metal is formed.

Summary of Na_2CO_3 Reactions. The reactions of the common elements fall under three divisions.

Reduced Metal without Sublimate.

MALLEABLE BUTTONS. Cu, Ag, Au.

Copper. Confirm by dissolving in HNO_3 and note deep-blue color when solution is made alkaline with NH_4OH.

Silver. Dissolve in HNO_3 and note white precipitate when a drop of HCl is added. The precipitate is soluble in NH_4OH.

Gold. Confirm by dissolving in aqua regia, evaporate almost to dryness, and dissolve the residue in a little water. Add a few drops of freshly prepared $SnCl_2$. Finely divided precipitate is formed which renders the solution purple by transmitted light and brownish by reflected light (Cassius purple test).

$$2AuCl_3 + 3SnCl_2 = 3SnCl_4 + Au_2$$

MAGNETIC PARTICLES. $FeFe_2O_4$, Co, Ni.

Iron. Dissolve in HNO_3, add a few drops of potassium ferrocyanide. Dark-blue precipitate will be formed.

Cobalt. Dissolve in borax bead on end of platinum wire. Note blue color.

Nickel. Dissolve in HNO_3 and make alkaline with NH_4OH. Add several cubic centimeters of alcoholic solution of dimethylglyoxime. Bright-red precipitate is produced.

Reduced Metal with Sublimate.

Antimony. Dense white coating near assay. Gray brittle button.

Lead. Sulfur-yellow coating. Gray malleable button.

Bismuth. Lemon-yellow sublimate. Reddish white, brittle button.

Tin. White coating near assay, yellow while hot. White malleable button.

Sublimate without Metal.

Arsenic. White volatile film. Garlic odor.

Zinc. White film, yellow while hot.

Cadmium. Reddish-brown to orange sublimate with tarnish colors.

Selenium. Steel-gray coating and reddish fumes with characteristic odor.

Tellurium. White coating with reddish or dark-yellow border.

Molybdenum. White coating, changed to dark blue when exposed to the reducing flame.

Sodium carbonate can also be profitably employed in the detection of sulfur, manganese, chromium, and phosphorus.

Test for Sulfur. The powdered sulfide, mixed with 3 to 4 parts of anhydrous Na_2CO_3, is thoroughly fused on a charcoal support. In the case of sulfates, some powdered charcoal should be added to the Na_2CO_3. After fusion, the mass (Na_2S) is removed from the support and crushed. One-half of the powder is then placed upon a clean silver coin, and several drops of water are added. A dark-brown or black stain (Ag_2S) indicates sulfur, provided selenium and tellurium are absent. To check this sulfur test, the remaining powder is placed on a watch glass. Several drops of water are then added, followed by a drop or two of freshly prepared sodium nitroferricyanide ($Na_2Fe(NO)(CN)_5$). An intense red-purple coloration is indicative of sulfur. As there is a tendency for the fusion to sink into the charcoal, the same pit should be used but once.

Tests for Manganese and Chromium. Powdered manganese compounds should be mixed with a small amount of KNO_3 and placed in a shallow depression made in a charcoal support. Sodium carbonate is then spread over this mixture. The blowpipe flame is directed for a brief period on a given spot until incipient fusion takes place. Upon cooling, this fused area assumes a bluish-green color due to the formation of sodium manganate (Na_2MnO_4). Long fusion is to be avoided, as the manganate loses its color, owing to reduction brought about by the charcoal. If copper is present, this test cannot be used for manganese.

Chromium compounds when fused with Na_2CO_3 and KNO_3 in a manner similar to that indicated for manganese yield yellow-colored fusions (Na_2CrO_4). Instead of performing the fusion on charcoal, manganese or chromium compounds may be dissolved in a Na_2CO_3 bead held in a loop of platinum wire. Under the influence of the oxidizing flame of the blowpipe the bead will assume the color indicated above.

Tests for Phosphorus. Phosphates of aluminum and the heavy metals should be fused with 2 parts of Na_2CO_3 on charcoal and the powdered fusion then ignited in a test tube with magnesium ribbon. The phosphorus is thereby converted into a phosphide (Mg_3P_2), which upon the addition of a few drops of water liberates the unpleasant, garlic-like order of phosphine (PH_3) which produces a black coloration when brought in contact with filter paper moistened with $AgNO_2$.

Phosphates of the alkalies and alkaline earths may be ignited with magnesium ribbon directly without previous fusion. This test for phosphorus cannot be relied upon in the presence of arsenic or antimony.

A more reliable test for phosphorus is the following: The phosphate is dissolved in HNO_3 (if insoluble, fusion with Na_2CO_3 should precede solution in acid) and a portion of the filtrate added to an equal volume of ammonium molybdate solution. Upon standing or upon slightly warming, a yellow precipitate of ammonium phosphomolybdate will be formed. (Vanadium and arsenic in the pentavalent condition give similar tests with ammonium molybdate.)

FLAME COLORATIONS

A number of compounds and especially those of the alkalies and alkaline earths impart to the nonluminous flame of the bunsen burner, or to the oxidizing flame of the blowpipe, characteristic colors which may be used for their identification. As the intensity of the flame coloration depends upon the volatility of the salt used, and inasmuch as chlorides are generally more volatile than other compounds, the best results are ordinarily obtained by moistening the powder with HCl. In a few instances moistening with H_2SO_4 is preferable. The powder is introduced into the bunsen flame by means of a clean platinum wire, or a very thin splintery fragment of the mineral, moistened with acid, may be held by the forceps in the nonluminous portion of the oxidizing blowpipe flame. Fusible metals and arsenic should not, however, be heated in contact with platinum-tipped forceps. To detect alkalies in silicates, decomposition may be brought about by mixing the assay with an equal volume of powdered gypsum or CaO before introducing into the hottest portion of the bunsen flame. It is even possible at times to detect the individual components when several flame-coloring elements occur together. This may be accomplished by making use of (1) the spectroscope, or (2) the difference in degree of volatility of the constituents present, or (3) colored screens.

Spectroscope. For blowpipe work the direct-vision pocket spectroscope is very useful. The best instruments are provided with a scale and a comparison prism by means of which the spectrum of an unknown substance can be directly compared with that of a known substance. When a colored flame is observed through a spectroscope, light-colored lines are perceived upon a dark background. The color, position, and grouping of the lines are used as the basis for the recognition of the elements.

Difference in Volatility. In a mixture the flame-coloring constituents can often be detected readily without the use of the spectroscope by noting the *difference in the degree of volatility of the components.* In general the alkalies (Na, K, Li) are more volatile than the alkaline earths (Ca, Ba, Sr), and by holding the platinum wire about 1 mm. from the outer nonluminous bunsen flame sufficient heat is encountered to volatilize the alkalies, while insertion in the hotter portion of the flame is necessary to detect the alkaline earths.

Colored Screens. These are also extensively employed in analyzing flame mixtures. Screens composed of colored glass or celluloid transmit certain rays while others are entirely absorbed. Thus, blue glass absorbs certain red and green rays together with those of yellow. One of the most effective screens on the market at present is the *Merwin flame color screen.* This celluloid screen is composed of three colored divisions, one blue, one violet, and one blue over violet. The strips are stained so as to absorb the orange and yellow portions of the spectrum. Observations should be made through all three divisions of the screen. In Table 30, flame colorations will be recorded as seen with and without the Merwin color screen. The numbers refer to the divisions of the screen. Observations are made against a dark background, holding the screen close to the eyes.

BEAD TESTS

The oxides of many metals form complex compounds with characteristic colors when dissolved at a high temperature in borax ($Na_2B_4O_7.10H_2O$) or microcosmic salt (salt of phosphorus)($HNaNH_4PO_4.4H_2O$). Sodium carbonate bead is also used, especially in testing for manganese, and the sodium fluoride bead in testing for uranium. The support usually employed for this work is a No. 28 B. & S. gauge platinum wire about 10 cm. long which has been fused into the end of a piece of glass tubing. Unoxidized metals as well as compounds of sulfur, arsenic, and antimony should be roasted until the volatile constituents have been removed and the residue converted into an oxide.

A small circular loop made at the end of the platinum wire is heated and then touched to the borax or microcosmic salt. Sufficient material will adhere to form a clear colorless glass, when heated before the blowpipe flame. In the case of the microcosmic salt bead the heat should be applied slowly as the material has a tendency to drop from the wire, owing to the escape of water and ammonia. By touching the hot bead to a few particles of the finely crushed oxide, and again heating in the oxidizing flame of the blowpipe, solution and coloration of the fusion will frequently result. The color of the bead should be noted after it has been subjected to the oxidizing flame[1] and again after the reducing flame has been applied. The action of the reducing flame may be greatly accelerated by dissolving a small particle of SnO or $SnCl_2$ in the bead. The

[1] A particle of KNO_3 added to the bead aids oxidation.

TABLE 30. FLAME COLORS

Indication	Flame color	Through Merwin screen	Remarks
Calcium*	Yellowish red	1. Flash of greenish yellow 2. Faint green 3. Flash of crimson	Invisible through green glass. Calcium minerals become alkaline upon ignition
Strontium*	Crimson	1. Invisible 2. Invisible 3. Crimson	Strontium minerals become alkaline upon ignition. If to solution of Sr salt a few drops of $BaCl_2$ are added, red color (Sr) will appear *after* green of Ba. Sr solutions yield white precipitate when a few drops of H_2SO_4 are added. (Distinction from Li)
Lithium*	Carmine	1. Invisible 2. Invisible 3. Crimson	Lithium minerals do not become alkaline upon ignition. If to solution of Li salt a few drops of $BaCl_2$ are added, red color (Li) will appear *before* green of Ba
Potassium*	Pale violet	1. Blue violet 2. Deep red-violet 3. Red violet	Purplish red through blue glass. Spectroscope is necessary to distinguish between potassium, rubidium, and cesium
Sodium*	Intense yellow	1. Invisible 2. Invisible 3. Invisible	Flame color should be intense and persistent to indicate sodium mineral. Invisible through blue glass
Copper oxide } Copper iodide }	Emerald green		Tinged with azure blue when moistened with HCl
Manganese chloride	Yellowish green	1. Emerald 2. Pale blue-green 3. Pale lavender	Coloration of short duration. Other manganese tests are more satisfactory
Tellurium } Antimony }	Pale green		
Thallium	Grass green		
Phosphorus	Pale bluish green	1. Green 2. Invisible 3. Red violet	Should be moistened with concentrated H_2SO_4. Color not very distinct

* Important reactions.

TABLE 30. FLAME COLORS (*Concluded*)

Indication	Flame color	Through Merwin screen	Remarks
Boron*	Yellowish green	1. Bright green 2. Faint green 3. Faint green	For borates decomposed by H_2SO_4: To mineral placed in porcelain dish, add alcohol and concentrated H_2SO_4, apply match. Note yellowish green color of flame. For borates not decomposed by H_2SO_4: Mix powder with 3 parts of boracic acid flux (3 parts $KHSO_4$, 1 part CaF_2), introduce into flame by means of hot platinum wire. Flash of green will be seen, due to BF_3
Barium*	Yellowish green	1. Bright green 2. Faint green 3. Faint green	Barium minerals become alkaline upon ignition. Have rather high specific gravity.
Molybdenum	Faint yellowish green		If in form of oxide or sulfide. Color not very distinct
Zinc	Bluish green		Appears as bright streaks in outer part of flame
Copper chloride*	Azure blue	1. Bright green 2. Bluish green 3. Bluish green	Flame is tinged with emerald green
Selenium	Indigo blue		Accompanied by characteristic odor
Arsenic	Livid blue		Characteristic garlic odor
Lead	Pale azure blue		Tinged with green in outer parts

* Important reactions.

colors observed with the microcosmic salt are not in every instance identical with those of the borax. In general the tests obtained with the borax flux are more delicate, while the microcosmic salt fusions yield a greater variety of colors. The removal of the bead from the support for preservation may be accomplished by simply straightening the wire. In Table 31 the colors listed are those of the cold beads obtained from the unmixed oxides.

Of the beads enumerated, the first eight are extremely serviceable. In order to detect Ni in the presence of Co, or any other oxide which ordinarily would obscure the nickel test, the procedure should be as follows: Dissolve several beads in HNO_3 and add NH_4OH until the solution becomes alkaline. To filtrate add several cubic centimeters

TABLE 31. BEAD COLORATION

Oxide of	Borax bead		Microcosmic salt bead	
	Oxidizing flame	Reducing flame	Oxidizing flame	Reducing flame
Mn*	Reddish violet	Colorless	Violet	Colorless
Co	Blue	Blue	Blue	Blue
Cu	Blue-green	Opaque red	Blue-green	Opaque red
Ni	Reddish brown	Opaque gray	Straw to reddish yellow	Yellow to reddish yellow
Fe	Yellow	Pale green	Colorless to yellow	Colorless to pale violet
Cr†	Yellowish green	Emerald green	Emerald green	Emerald green
U‡	Yellow	Pale green to colorless	Yellowish green	Bright green
V	Yellowish green	Emerald green	Light yellow	Emerald green
Ti	Colorless	Brownish violet	Colorless	Violet
Mo	Colorless	Brown	Colorless	Pure green
W	Colorless	Yellow to yellowish brown	Colorless	Fine blue
Si	Colorless	Colorless	Insoluble skeleton	Insoluble skeleton

* The Na_2CO_3 bead for manganese gives a blue-green color under oxidizing conditions, which is more satisfactory in the presence of interfering elements.

† The Na_2CO_3 bead for chromium is yellow in color under oxidizing conditions.

‡ The NaF bead on a platinum wire fluoresces with a bright yellow-green color under ultraviolet light.

of an alcoholic solution of dimethylglyoxime. A scarlet precipitate indicates Ni. This is an extremely delicate test.

$$Ni(NO_3)_2 + 2NH_4OH + 2C_4H_8N_2O_2 = (C_8H_{14}N_4O_4)Ni + 2NH_4NO_3 + 2H_2O.$$

OPEN-TUBE REACTIONS

Hard-glass tubing, 15 to 20 cm. long and about 5 mm. in diameter, is employed in blowpipe work to note the effects of a current of air when permitted to pass over a highly heated substance. These open tubes should be bent slightly near one end in order to hold more conveniently the material which should be in a powdered condition to expose the maximum amount of surface. The tube is held in an inclined position in the flame; apply heat first above the assay to ensure a good current of air through the tube and then directly under the mineral (Fig. 472). In most instances oxidation results and the volatile material either escapes in the form of a gas with a characteristic odor, or a sublimate is formed which

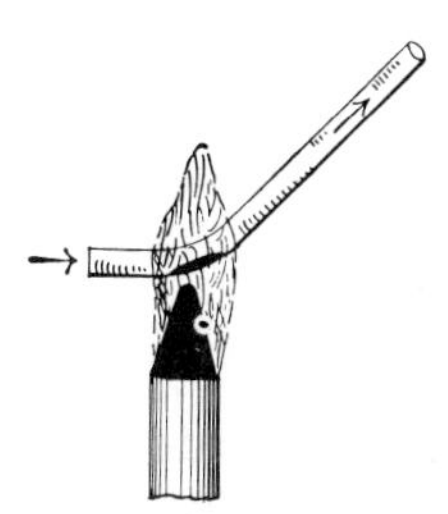

Fig. 472. Heating in open tube.

TABLE 32. SUBLIMATES

Indication	Character of the coating	Remarks
Arsenic Arsenides Sulfides of arsenic	White, crystalline, and volatile sublimate (As_2O_3). Crystals are minute octahedrons	Metallic mirror of arsenic or yellow coating of arsenic sulfide indicates too rapid heating
Antimony Sulfides of antimony	Dense white fumes which partly escape and partly condense as white powder. Both Sb_2O_3 and Sb_2O_4 are formed	Sb_2O_3 is white, slowly volatile and crystalline. Sb_2O_4 is non-volatile
Bismuth sulfide	White, nonvolatile powder ($Bi_2(SO_4)_3$)	Fusible to yellow drops
Bismuth (free from sulfur)	Brown while hot; yellow when cold (Bi_2O_3)	Sublimate is fusible
Tellurium Tellurides	Snow white, nonvolatile sublimate (TeO_2)	Upon heating fuses to colorless drops
Lead chloride	White, particularly volatile sublimate (Pb_2OCl_2)	Fusible to yellow drops
Lead sulfide	Nonvolatile, white powder formed near assay ($PbSO_4$)	Fusible to yellow drops, white when cold
Selenium Selenides	Near assay, steel gray, volatile coating consisting of radiating needles (SeO_2)	At distance reddish due to finely divided Se
Molybdenum oxide or sulfide	Yellow when hot, white when cold (MoO_3)	Collects near assay as mass of delicate crystals
Mercury Amalgam	Minute, gray, metallic globules. Volatile (Hg)	Globules unite by rubbing with strip of paper

deposits upon the cooler portions of the tube. The temperature should be increased gradually so as not to volatilize the substance in an unoxidized condition. The results of open-tube tests may be summarized as shown in Table 32 on page 231.

Gases with Characteristic Odors

Odor of burning sulfur with bleaching properties. The gas liberated is SO_2. The test is very delicate and is extremely useful in testing for sulfur and sulfides. If oxidation is not complete, because of too rapid heating or an insufficient air supply, free sulfur may also deposit on the sides of the tube.

Garlic Odor. Produced when arsenic compounds are rapidly heated and not completely oxidized.

Odor of Rotten Horse-radish. Obtained from selenium compounds when volatilized.

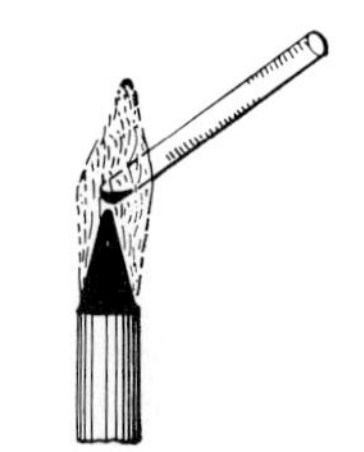

Fig. 473. Heating in closed tube.

CLOSED-TUBE REACTIONS

Closed-tube reactions are carried out in hard-glass tubes about 10 cm. long and 6 cm. in diameter, which are closed at one end. The assay is introduced in the form of small fragments and heat applied gradually. The object of this treatment is to note the effect of heat without oxidation as the air is practically entirely excluded (Fig. 473). These are known as the per se tests. Closed tubes may also be profitably employed in heating the assay with $KHSO_4$.

Per Se Tests

The application of heat alone may produce such phenomena as:

Change in Appearance or Character of Assay.

Change in Color. The more important minerals thus affected are as follows:

Copper minerals. Blue or green, become black when hot; black, cold.

Zinc minerals. White or colorless, become pale yellow when hot; white, cold.

Manganese and cobalt minerals. Pink, become black when hot; black, cold.

Lead and bismuth minerals. White or colorless, become dark yellow to brown when hot; pale yellow to white, cold.

Iron minerals. Green or brown, become black when hot; black, cold.

Hematite. Dark red, becomes black when hot; dark red, cold.

Fusion. Only minerals with a fusibility below one and one-half in the scale of fusibility melt when heated in a closed tube per se.

Carbonization. Indicating organic substances.

LUMINESCENCE. Some minerals when heated to a temperature below redness and viewed in a dark room will be seen to emit colored light. Many varieties of fluorite when heated to 150°C. emit a purple or green light.

DECREPITATION. Alkali chlorides, galena, and other minerals snap and break down to a fine powder when heated. This behavior is usually the result of unequal expansion or due to the presence of water held mechanically.

MAGNETIZATION. Iron minerals frequently become magnetic upon the application of heat.

Formation of Gases in the Tube.

CARBON DIOXIDE. Colorless and odorless gas. A drop of lime water held in a loop of platinum wire becomes turbid. Indicates carbonates.

OXYGEN. A glowing splinter takes fire when held in the tube. Indicates peroxides, nitrates, chlorates, bromates, or iodates.

AMMONIA. Characteristic odor and alkaline reaction. More pronounced when heated with Na_2CO_3. Indicates ammonium salts or organic compounds containing nitrogen. If the latter, the mass usually chars.

Formation of Sublimates.

TABLE 33. COLORLESS OR WHITE SUBLIMATES

Indication	Character of sublimate	Remarks
Water	Colorless, volatile liquid which forms on the cooler part of the tube	Indicates water of crystallization or hydroxyl. Neutral if pure, may show acid or alkaline reaction
Ammonium salts	White, very volatile	
Lead chloride	White, fusing to yellow drops	
Mercurous chloride	White, yellow when hot	Sublimate is infusible
Mercuric chloride	White, yellow when hot	Sublimate is fusible
Antimony oxide	White, fusible	Sublimate consists of needle-like crystals
Arsenic oxide	White, volatile	Sublimate consists of octahedral crystals
Tellurium oxide	Pale yellow, hot; colorless to white globules, cold	Obtained from tellurium and a few of its compounds

TABLE 34. COLORED SUBLIMATES

Indication	Character of sublimate	Remarks
Sulfur Some sulfides	Brownish red liquid, hot; pale yellow crystalline solid, cold	Due to the formation of free sulfur
Sulfides of arsenic	Dark red liquid, hot; reddish yellow solid, cold	From realgar, orpiment, and sulfarsenites
Sulfides of antimony	Black when hot; reddish brown when cold. Sb_2OS_2 is formed	From sulfides and sulfantimonites
Sulfide of mercury	Brilliant black solid	Yields a red powder when rubbed
Selenium Selenides	Black fusible globules. Red when rubbed	Sublimate forms only at high temperature
Arsenic Arsenides	Brilliant black sublimate. Gray and crystalline near heated end	Garlic odor noted when tube is broken below mirror and gently heated
Mercury Amalgam	Minute gray metallic globules	Globules unite when rubbed
Tellurium Tellurides	Black fusible globules	Sublimate forms at high temperature

Reactions in Closed Tube with $KHSO_4$

The detection of volatile acids may be accomplished by *gently* heating the assay with an equal volume of $KHSO_4$.

TABLE 35. COLORED GAS EVOLVED

Indication	Character of gas	Remarks
Nitrates Nitrites	Reddish brown with pungent odor	Gas liberated is NO_2
Chlorates	Yellowish green fumes with odor of chlorine	Gas liberated is ClO_2
Iodides	Violet vapors accompanied by a black metallic sublimate	Iodine is set free
Bromides Bromates	Heavy brownish red vapor with pungent odor	Bromine is liberated. Best seen when tube is held against a white background

TABLE 36. COLORLESS, ODOROUS GAS EVOLVED

Indication	Character of gas	Remarks
Sulfates Sulfites	Suffocating odor with bleaching properties	Gas is SO_2
Chlorides	Colorless gas which fumes strongly when in contact with NH_4OH	Gas is HCl
Fluorides	Gas which etches the tube above the assay	Gas is HF
Sulfides	Gas with odor of decayed eggs. Blackens lead acetate paper	Gas is H_2S
Acetates	Gas with odor of vinegar	Gas is $C_2H_4O_2$

TABLE 37. COLORLESS, ODORLESS GAS EVOLVED

Indication	Character of gas	Remarks
Carbonates	A drop of lime water held in a loop of platinum wire becomes turbid	Gas is CO_2
Oxalates	A gas which burns with a blue flame	Gas is CO

SPECIAL TESTS

In this section reactions will be listed which do not conveniently fall under any of the previous divisions. They are nevertheless extremely useful in mineralogical determinations. The reactions given below are to be considered as individual tests and not in any way related to one another.

Tests for Calcite and Aragonite. 1. Powdered calcite when boiled 1 to 5 minutes in a 5 to 10 per cent solution of cobalt nitrate remains white or in the presence of organic matter becomes yellowish, while aragonite turns violet owing to the formation of a basic cobalt nitrate. This is commonly known as *Meigen's test.* The change in color is more readily detected by washing the powder by decantation after boiling. Inasmuch as barium or strontium carbonate and precipitated basic magnesium carbonate give the same reactions as aragonite, and dolomite the same as calcite, it is absolutely necessary first to establish the fact that one is dealing with one of the modifications of $CaCO_3$ before applying the cobalt nitrate test. This test cannot be applied to powdered mixtures of calcite and aragonite.

2. Leitmeier and Feigl have shown that a cold solution of $MnSO_4$ and Ag_2SO_4 produces a black color ($MnO_2 + Ag$) on powdered aragonite in

a few seconds, but on calcite only after several minutes. The same reagent can be used on microsections, but the action is slower. Strontianite and witherite give the same reactions as aragonite; dolomite, the same as calcite. The reagent is prepared by adding 1 gram of solid silver sulfate to a solution of 11.8 grams of $MnSO_4.7H_2O$ in 100 cc. of water. The solution is boiled, allowed to cool, and filtered. One or two drops of dilute Na(OH) are added, and after 1 to 2 hours the precipitate is filtered. Keep in brown bottle.

Tests for Calcite and Dolomite. 1. Calcite dissolves in acetic acid with a brisk evolution of CO_2, while dolomite is not appreciably affected by the cold acid.

2. J. Lemberg has noted that powdered calcite is colored violet within a few minutes when treated with a solution of aluminum chloride and extract of logwood, while dolomite remains unchanged. The reaction is caused by the precipitation upon the calcite of $Al(OH)_3$ which absorbs the dye and acts as a mordant. To observe the color change, the powder should be washed by decantation. The Lemberg solution is prepared by boiling for 20 minutes a mixture of 4 grams of $AlCl_3$, 6 grams extract of logwood, and 60 grams of water, with constant stirring and with the addition of the amount of water lost by evaporation. Aragonite gives same reaction as calcite.

TABLE 38

Indication	Color of solution	Remarks
Titanium	Violet	Best seen when evolution of H_2 ceases
Tungsten	Dark blue	Color due to heavy precipitate which upon standing settles to bottom
Columbium	Pale blue	Color fades with addition of water
Vanadium	Blue, green, finally blue-violet	Metallic zinc should be used instead of tin
Titanium *	Amber-colored solution	The fused mass should be dissolved in 1:1 H_2SO_4 solution
Vanadium *	Reddish-brown solution	Dissolve fusion in HNO_3

* Instead of using a reducing agent for the detection of titanium and vanadium, H_2O_2 in an acid solution can be employed. The oxidation reactions are more delicate than the corresponding reduction tests.

3. Mahler suggested the use of a dilute solution of copper nitrate. On boiling for a few minutes with powdered calcite, a brisk effervescence is followed by a green coloration of the particles. Dolomite similarly treated is not affected.

Test for Cassiterite (SnO_2). As the usual colors of cassiterite are various shades of yellow, brown, or black, a change in the appearance of the mineral can be utilized for its detection. This can readily be accomplished by placing fragments of cassiterite in a test tube on top of granulated metallic zinc and adding dilute HCl. The nascent hydrogen liberated reduces the SnO_2, and after a few minutes the cassiterite becomes coated with a thin gray layer of metallic tin.

Reduction Tests with Metallic Tin and HCl. Rapid tests for the elements titanium, tungsten, columbium, and vanadium may be carried out by dissolving the Na_2CO_3 fusion in HCl and adding a few fragments of metallic tin. The hydrogen evolved reduces the salts of the rarer elements producing colored solutions or precipitates which are used to detect the presence of the element involved. Table 38 indicates the changes referred to.

SUMMARY OF CHEMICAL AND BLOWPIPE TESTS FOR THE MORE IMPORTANT ELEMENTS

For convenience of reference the most reliable tests for the various elements are here summarized. The wet chemical tests included in this summary are often extremely useful and supplement the dry reactions.

Aluminum (Al)

1. *Ignition with Cobalt Nitrate.* Infusible light-colored aluminum minerals when moistened with a drop or two of cobalt nitrate and intensely ignited assume a blue color. Zinc silicates give a similar reaction but yield a white coating when heated with Na_2CO_3 on charcoal.

2. *Precipitation with Ammonia.* When an acid solution containing aluminum is rendered alkaline with NH_4OH, a white gelatinous precipitate of $Al(OH)_3$ is formed. This precipitate is readily dissolved in a warm KOH solution. $Fe(OH)_3$ (red) is precipitated under the same condition but is insoluble in KOH.

Ammonium (NH_4)

Heating in Closed Tube. When boiled with a solution of KOH, or heated with Na_2CO_3 or CaO, ammonia is evolved which is recognized by its odor, alkaline reaction, and white fumes when brought in contact with HCl.

Antimony (Sb)

1. *Sublimate on Plaster Tablet.* Antimony minerals mixed with bismuth flux and heated on a plaster support yield an orange- to peach-

red sublimate. A drop of $(NH_4)_2S_x$ upon the coating produces an orange-red ring.

2. *Sublimate on Charcoal.* When heated with the oxidizing flame on charcoal, a dense white sublimate of Sb_2O_3 is formed near the assay. The coating is volatile and bluish in thin layers. The fumes have no distinctive odor (difference from arsenic).

3. *Heating in Open Tube.* Most antimony minerals yield dense white fumes which partly escape and partly condense as a white powder.

4. *Heating with Concentrated Nitric Acid.* HNO_3 oxidizes antimony and its sulfides to metantimonic acid, which is a white precipitate, insoluble in both water and HNO_3.

Arsenic (As)

1. *Sublimate on Plaster Tablet.* Arsenic minerals mixed with bismuth flux and heated on a plaster support yield a lemon-yellow sublimate. A drop of $(NH_4)_2S_x$ on the coating produces a yellow ring.

2. *Sublimate on Charcoal.* Arsenic, arsenides, and sulfides of arsenic heated with the oxidizing flame on charcoal give a very volatile white coating of As_2O_3 which deposits at some distance from the assay. The fumes have a characteristic garlic odor.

3. *Heating in Open Tube.* Arsenic, arsenides, and sulfides of arsenic produce a white, volatile, and crystalline sublimate of As_2O_3. Too rapid heating may yield a metallic mirror instead of the oxide.

4. *Heating in Closed Tube.* Arsenic and arsenides give a bright metallic mirror. When the tube is broken below the mirror and heated, a garlic odor will be noted. Arsenates should be mixed with powdered charcoal to cause reduction.

5. *Precipitation as Ammonium Magnesium Arsenate.* With few exceptions arsenic minerals are oxidized to arsenic acid (H_3AsO_4) when boiled with concentrated HNO_3. Make the solution alkaline with NH_4OH and filter. To the filtrate add a few cubic centimeters of magnesia mixture ($MgCl_2$ and NH_4Cl), shake, and let stand. White crystalline $MgNH_4AsO_4$ will precipitate.

Barium (Ba)

1. *Flame Test.* When moistened with HCl, many barium minerals impart a yellowish-green color to the flame (coloration quite similar to boron).

2. *Alkaline Reaction and High Specific Gravity.* Barium compounds, with the exception of silicates and phosphates, are characterized by rather high specific gravities and alkaline reaction on moistened turmeric paper after strong ignition.

3. *Precipitation as Barium Sulfate.* A few drops of dilute H_2SO_4 will precipitate white $BaSO_4$, insoluble in dilute acids. This test distinguishes barium from boron and phosphorus minerals which also color the flame green.

Beryllium (Be); also Called Glucinum

There are no characteristic dry reactions for beryllium. As beryllium usually occurs as a silicate with aluminum, the material must be fused with Na_2CO_3; acidified with HCl and evaporated to dryness; again acidified with HCl and the aluminum and beryllium chlorides filtered from the insoluble silica.

Beryllium compounds resemble very closely aluminum in their chemical reactions. A few distinguishing tests are the following:

1. *Precipitation as Basic Carbonate.* Ammonium carbonate added to a solution of a beryllium salt produces a white precipitate of beryllium carbonate, readily soluble in an excess of the reagent (difference from Al). Upon boiling the solution, beryllium is precipitated as white basic carbonate.

2. *Precipitation as Beryllium Hydroxide.* Dissolve $Al(OH)_3$ and $Be(OH)_2$ in HCl, oxidize with HNO_3, add NH_4OH to nearly neutralize. Then add hot solution of $NaHCO_3$ and boil. $Be(OH)_2$ goes in solution, $Al(OH)_3$ is precipitated. Acidify filtrate, boil, and Be is precipitated as $Be(OH)_2$ by NH_4OH.

3. *Oxine Test for Beryllium.* Aluminum and beryllium can be separated with 8-hydroquinoline (oxine). A slightly acid solution of the NH_4OH precipitate of aluminum and beryllium is warmed to 60°C. and treated with an excess of acetic acid solution of oxine. Ammonium acetate is added until a permanent precipitate is obtained. After settling, the aluminum compound ($(C_9H_6ON)_3Al$) is filtered. The beryllium in the filtrate is precipitated from a hot solution with NH_4OH as beryllium hydroxide.

Bismuth (Bi)

1. *Sublimate on Plaster Tablet.* When mixed with bismuth flux and heated on a plaster support, bismuth minerals yield a chocolate-brown coating, which is changed to a bright red when exposed to strong ammonia fumes.

2. *Bismuth Flux on Charcoal.* Upon charcoal the mineral mixed with bismuth flux produces a yellowish sublimate with crimson border.

3. *Reduction on Charcoal.* Bismuth compounds mixed with Na_2CO_3 on charcoal give a lemon-yellow coating with white border and reddish-white brittle buttons.

4. *Precipitation as Bismuth Oxychloride.* If water is added to an HCl solution, which has been evaporated almost to dryness, a white precipitate of BiOCl is formed.

Boron (B)

1. *Flame Test.* Some boron minerals yield a yellowish-green flame when heated alone, but the majority require the application of H_2SO_4 or boracic acid flux. If decomposable by H_2SO_4, boron compounds burn with a yellowish-green flame [owing to the formation of basic acid methyl ester ($B(OCH_3)_3$)] when placed in an evaporating dish with alcohol and concentrated H_2SO_4 and ignited. Borates not decomposable by H_2SO_4 should be mixed with 3 parts of boracic acid flux (3 parts $KHSO_4$, 1 part CaF_2) and introduced into the flame on a clean platinum wire. A flash of green indicates the liberation of the volatile boron fluoride (BF_3).

2. *Turmeric-paper Test.* If turmeric paper is moistened with a dilute HCl solution of boron and dried, it assumes a reddish-brown color. If it is then moistened with NH_4OH, a bluish-black or grayish-blue spot results, depending upon the amount of turmeric and boric acid present. It is advisable to run a blank test at the same time. As acid solutions of zirconic, titanic, tantalic, columbic, and molybdic acids also color turmeric paper brown, this test for boron can be employed only in their absence.

Bromine (Br)

1. *Heating in Closed Tube with Potassium Bisulfate.* When a bromide is heated with $KHSO_4$ and MnO_2, heavy brownish red vapors of bromine are liberated.

2. *Precipitation as Silver Bromide.* A white precipitate of AgBr (soluble in NH_4OH) is formed when $AgNO_3$ is added to a dilute HNO_3 solution of a bromide.

Cadmium (Cd)

1. *Heating on Plaster Tablet per Se.* Near the assay there is formed a reddish-brown to greenish-yellow coating. At a distance it is brownish black. It is best obtained from the metal.

2. *Heating on Charcoal.* When heated on charcoal, cadmium yields a film which is reddish brown near the assay and yellowish green at a distance. Very thin deposits show an iridescent tarnish.

3. *Precipitation as Cadmium Sulfide.* Hydrogen sulfide precipitates from neutral, alkaline, or not too strongly acid solutions yellow cadmium sulfide, soluble in hot dilute H_2SO_4 and in a saturated solution of sodium chloride.

Calcium (Ca)

1. *Flame Test.* After being pulverized and moistened with HCl, many calcium minerals color the nonluminous flame yellowish red. The color should not be confused with the redder and more persistent strontium flame. When viewed through the Merwin color screen, calcium appears as a flash of greenish yellow through division 1 (distinction from lithium and strontium).

2. *Precipitation as Calcium Oxalate.* Ammonium oxalate added to an ammoniacal solution of calcium produces a white precipitate of calcium oxalate (CaC_2O_4). This precipitate will also form in a very slightly acid solution. Barium and strontium also yield white oxalate precipitates.

3. *Precipitation as Calcium Sulfate.* A few drops of dilute H_2SO_4 added to a calcium salt dissolved in a small volume of dilute HCl precipitates $CaSO_4$. Upon the addition of water and the application of heat the precipitate dissolves (distinction from barium and strontium). The solubility of $CaSO_4$ in acid solution is greatly decreased by the addition of ethyl alcohol. In testing for calcium in apatite or phosphate rock the sulfate test should be used.

Carbon (C)

1. *Heating in Closed Tube.* When heated, hydrocarbons such as asphaltum, albertite, or bituminous coals yield oils and tarry compounds which condense on the sides of the tube. The residue, if any, is mainly carbon. If carbon is present as a carbonate, decomposition is effected with the liberation of CO_2 which renders a drop of limewater on a loop of platinum wire turbid.

2. *Effervescence with Acids.* The solution of carbonates in dilute acids takes place with brisk evolution of CO_2. In some instances the acid should be heated, but care must be exercised not to mistake boiling for liberation of CO_2.

Cerium (Ce)

1. *Oxidation with Hydrogen Peroxide.* If a cerous salt is treated with a slight excess of NH_4OH and then with H_2O_2, the white precipitate becomes reddish orange in color, $CeO_3.nH_2O$, which on boiling is changed to yellow $Ce(OH)_4$. To remove interfering elements proceed as follows: Fuse with Na_2CO_3 and evaporate the HCl solution to dryness. Take up with dilute HCl and filter. Precipitate the cerous oxalate from the dilute acid solution by means of ammonium oxalate. Filter and dissolve the precipitate in warm concentrated HCl. Make ammoniacal with NH_4OH, and white cerium precipitate is formed. Upon oxidation with H_2O_2, its color is changed to reddish orange.

2. *Oxidation with Lead Peroxide and Nitric Acid.* Boil and allow to settle; cerous salts yield orange-colored solutions, owing to the formation of ceric nitrate.

Chlorine (Cl)

1. *Flame Coloration with Copper Oxide.* If a hot salt of phosphorus bead saturated with CuO is brought in contact with a chloride and then heated in the nonluminous flame, copper chloride will be formed which will tinge the flame azure blue. Bromine gives a similar reaction.

2. *Liberation of Chlorine.* If a chloride is mixed with $KHSO_4$ and a small amount of MnO_2 and then heated in a closed tube, free chlorine is set free. AgCl and silicates containing chlorine require fusion with Na_2CO_3.

3. *Precipitation as Silver Chloride.* A few drops of $AgNO_3$ added to a chloride in a dilute HNO_3 solution precipitates white curdy AgCl, soluble in NH_4OH. This is an extremely delicate test. Minerals insoluble in HNO_3 should be fused with Na_2CO_3. Bromine and iodine give similar reactions.

Chromium (Cr)

1. *Bead Tests.* Chromium colors borax and microcosmic salt beads green, in both the oxidizing and reducing flames.

2. *Fusion with Sodium Carbonate on Platinum Wire.* When chromium compounds are dissolved in a Na_2CO_3 bead to which has been added a particle of KNO_3, the fusion is colored a light yellow in the oxidizing flame; yellowish green in reducing flame.

3. *Precipitation as Lead Chromate.* Fuse with Na_2CO_3 and KNO_3 on charcoal. Leach with water, make slightly acid with acetic acid, and add a few drops of lead acetate. A yellow precipitate of lead chromate will be formed.

4. *Oxidation to Perchromic Acid.* Dissolve the fusion in water and acidify with dilute H_2SO_4. To the cold solution add H_2O_2, and a blue color of H_3CrO_8 is obtained. Perchromic acid is very unstable, and the color may last but a few seconds.

Cobalt (Co)

Bead Tests. Cobalt imparts a blue color to the borax and salt of phosphorus beads, in both the oxidizing and reducing flames. When copper and nickel interfere, fuse the bead on charcoal with a particle of metallic tin. Copper and nickel are reduced to the metallic condition, and the blue color of cobalt will appear.

Columbium (Cb); also Called Niobium

Reduction with Tin. Finely powdered columbates are decomposed when heated to dull redness with $KHSO_4$ in a test tube. When decomposition is complete, rotate and incline the tube so that the melt may solidify as a thin crust on the sides. Add HCl, some metallic tin, and boil. Reduction takes place, and a light-blue color due to columbium will appear. The color becomes much fainter upon the addition of water. With zinc instead of tin the blue color changes to brown.

Copper (Cu)

1. *Sublimate on Plaster Tablet.* When moistened with HBr and heated on a plaster support, copper minerals yield a volatile purplish coating, mottled with black.

2. *Flame Test.* Oxides of copper color the flame emerald green, while moistening with HCl produces an intense azure blue.

3. *Bead Test.* Under the influence of the oxidizing flame, borax and microcosmic salt beads are green when hot and bluish green when cold. In the reducing flame, Cu_2O is formed which colors the beads an opaque red.

4. *Reduction to Metal on Charcoal.* When heated with a mixture of Na_2CO_3 and charcoal, copper minerals yield globules of metallic copper. Sulfides should first be roasted before reducing.

5. *Blue Solution with Ammonium Hydroxide.* An acid copper solution made alkaline with NH_4OH assumes a deep-blue color. Nickel solutions are light blue.

Fluorine (F)

1. *Etching Glass Tube.* When mixed with 4 or 5 parts of $KHSO_4$ or with sodium metaphosphate (obtained by fusing salt of phosphorus), and then heated in a closed tube, many powdered fluorides liberate HF, which etches the glass. In addition a ring of SiO_2 may form in the upper part of the tube. The etching of the glass may be seen to best advantage by breaking the closed end of the tube, washing out its contents, and drying the tube over a flame, when the glass will appear clouded.

2. *Flame Test.* Fluorides mixed with $KHSO_4$ and tourmaline, and introduced into the bunsen flame on a platinum wire, give a flash of green due to the volatilization of BF_3.

Glucinum (Gl). See Beryllium

Gold (Au)

1. *Sublimate on Plaster per Se.* Upon intense and prolonged ignition on the plaster support, gold gives a slight purple-to-rose-colored coating near and under the assay. It is best seen when the tablet is cold.

2. *Cassius Purple Test.* Gold dissolves readily in concentrated nitro-hydrochloric acid (aqua regia) with the formation of auric chloride

($AuCl_3$). Evaporate the solution almost to dryness, and dissolve the residue in a little water. If a few drops of freshly prepared stannous chloride are now added, a finely divided precipitate will form which is purplish in transmitted and brownish in reflected light. This is known as the *Cassius purple test* for gold and is extremely delicate. The color is due to a mixture of colloidal gold and tin hydroxide. Ferrous salts also precipitate gold at ordinary temperatures from neutral or acid solutions (distinction from platinum).

3. *Alloy with Silver.* Yellow flakes are isolated, wrapped in silver foil, and heated. Dissolve the silver in HNO_3, absorb the filtrate with filter paper, and heat residue in crucible. A spongy, yellow residue indicates gold.

Hydrogen (H)

Water in Closed Tube. When minerals containing water of crystallization or the hydroxyl radical are heated in a closed tube, water is set free which condenses on the cold portions of the tube. More intense heat is necessary to liberate the hydroxyl radical. The water which may be neutral toward test papers is often acid in reaction but rarely alkaline.

Iodine (I)

1. *Heating with Potassium Bisulfate.* Iodides when heated in a closed tube with $KHSO_4$ liberate violet vapors, often accompanied by a metallic sublimate of iodine.

2. *Precipitation as Silver Iodide.* A few drops of $AgNO_3$ added to an iodide in a dilute HNO_3 solution precipitates AgI, nearly insoluble in ammonia (distinction from chlorine and bromine).

Iron (Fe)

1. *Magnetic upon Ignition.* Although a few iron minerals (magnetite, pyrrhotite) are magnetic before heating, the majority become magnetic when heated in the reducing flame and allowed to cool. Cobalt and nickel minerals react in a similar manner.

2. *Borax Bead Test.* In the oxidizing flame iron colors the borax bead yellow when cold. In the reducing flame a pale green results.

3. *Precipitation as Ferric Hydroxide.* If an acid solution containing ferric iron is made ammoniacal with NH_4OH, a reddish-brown precipitate of $Fe(OH)_3$ is formed. To obtain the iron in the ferric condition, a few drops of HNO_3 should be added to the HCl when dissolving the mineral.

4. *Test for Ferrous and Ferric Iron.* If an iron mineral is dissolved in a nonoxidizing acid as HCl or H_2SO_4, the valence of the iron in solution will be the same as in the original mineral (except sulfides). If a few drops of potassium ferricyanide are added to a solution of ferrous iron,

a dark-blue precipitate will be formed. Ferric iron, on the other hand, gives a similar precipitate with potassium ferrocyanide. Potassium sulfocyanate (KCNS) gives a blood-red color (but no precipitate) when added to a ferric solution. Nitric and chloric acids give red color with KCNS, but color is destroyed by heat.

Lead (Pb)

1. *Sublimate on Plaster Tablet.* When mixed with bismuth flux and heated on a plaster support, lead minerals yield a chrome-yellow coating. A drop of $(NH_4)_2S_x$ applied to the film gives a black spot.

2. *Bismuth Flux on Charcoal.* Upon charcoal, lead minerals, mixed with bismuth flux, produce a greenish-yellow film.

3. *Reduction on Charcoal.* Mixed with Na_2CO_3 on charcoal, lead compounds give a yellowish coating and gray malleable globules.

4. *Precipitation as Lead Sulfate.* From a dilute HNO_3 solution, lead may be precipitated as white insoluble $PbSO_4$ upon the addition of a few drops of H_2SO_4.

Lithium (Li)

Flame Test. Lithium imparts a carmine-red coloration to the flame. The color is more volatile and not so persistent as that of strontium. If to a solution of lithium salt a few drops of $BaCl_2$ are added, the red color of lithium will appear before the green of barium; strontium will appear after the green. Lithium minerals do not become alkaline upon ignition (distinction from strontium). In testing silicates, it is necessary to mix the assay with powdered gypsum and introduce it into the flame on a platinum wire.

Magnesium (Mg)

1. *Ignition with Cobalt Nitrate.* Infusible and light-colored magnesium minerals assume a pale pink color when moistened with a drop or two of cobalt nitrate and intensely ignited. This test is unsatisfactory at times, and the following wet reaction must then be employed.

2. *Precipitation as Ammonium Magnesium Phosphate.* If hydrogen sodium phosphate (Na_2HPO_4) is added to a strongly ammoniacal solution, magnesium is precipitated as ammonium magnesium phosphate (NH_4MgPO_4). The precipitate is white and crystalline and may appear only after shaking and standing for a short time. In order to remove interfering elements proceed as follows: The HCl solution containing a few drops of HNO_3 is boiled and then made alkaline with NH_4OH. This will precipitate Fe, Al, and Cr, if present. To the ammoniacal filtrate add ammonium oxalate to remove Ca, Ba, and Sr. To the filtrate, Na_2HPO_4 is then added to test for magnesium.

Manganese (Mn)

1. *Borax Bead Test.* Manganese colors the borax bead reddish violet in the oxidizing flame but becomes colorless in the reducing flame. Salt of phosphorus gives a similar reaction, but the test is not so sensitive.

2. *Fusion with Sodium Carbonate on Platinum Wire.* When dissolved in a Na_2CO_3 bead in the oxidizing flame to which a grain of KNO_3 has been added, manganese compounds color the fusion a bluish green owing to the formation of sodium manganate (Na_2MnO_4).

3. *Heating in Closed Tube.* Some of the higher oxides yield oxygen upon heating or when dissolved in HCl evolve chlorine.

4. *Oxidation to Permanganic Acid.* Boil with concentrated HNO_3 and PbO_2, and allow the lead oxide to settle. The supernatant solution will be purplish from the permanganic acid formed. The same result may be obtained by the use of potassium periodate (KIO_4) in a nitric acid solution.

Mercury (Hg)

1. *Sublimate on Plaster Tablet.* When mixed with bismuth flux and heated on a plaster support, mercury minerals produce a coating which is usually a combination of scarlet, yellow, and greenish black.

2. *Heating in a Closed Tube.* When mixed with 3 parts of dry Na_2CO_3 and heated, metallic mercury will volatilize and condense as globules on the sides of the tube.

3. *Precipitation by Copper.* A clean copper wire immersed in a mercury solution becomes covered with a deposit of metallic mercury.

Molybdenum (Mo)

1. *Sublimate on Plaster and Charcoal.* When heated per se with the oxidizing flame, some molybdenum compounds yield MoO_3, which is yellow when hot and white when cold. When touched with the reducing flame, the white coating is changed to a deep blue. If a charcoal support is used, a copper-red sublimate will also be noted surrounding the assay, which is best seen in reflected light.

2. *Treatment with Concentrated Sulfuric Acid.* If a molybdate is treated with a few drops of concentrated H_2SO_4 and an equal amount of water in a porcelain dish and evaporated until it fumes strongly, the mass, upon cooling, is colored intensely blue. A drop of alcohol added at this point will hasten the color reaction. The color will disappear upon the addition of water. Molybdenite (MoS_2) must be oxidized, either by boiling to dryness with HNO_3 or by roasting, before it can be tested in this manner.

3. *Formation of Molybdenum Thiocyanide.* To a dilute solution of a molybdate which has been treated with tin and HCl, add some KCNS

in solution. Note the red color. By shaking with ether, the color can be concentrated in the ether extract.

Bead Test. The salt of phosphorus bead in the reducing flame is colored green.

NICKEL (Ni)

1. *Bead Tests.* Nickel colors the borax bead in the oxidizing flame a reddish brown, while the salt of phosphorus bead is yellow.

2. *Pale-blue Solution with Ammonium Hydroxide.* A fairly concentrated acid solution of nickel will become pale blue upon adding an excess of NH_4OH. The color is not so dark a shade as that produced by copper.

3. *Precipitation with Dimethylglyoxime.* Dissolve the mineral in HNO_3, and make the solution alkaline with NH_4OH. Filter if necessary, and to the filtrate add several cubic centimeters of an alcoholic solution of dimethylglyoxime. A scarlet precipitate ($C_8H_{14}N_4O_4Ni$) indicates nickel.

NIOBIUM (Nb). SEE COLUMBIUM

NITROGEN (N)

1. *Heating in Closed Tube.* Nitrates heated in a closed tube with $KHSO_4$ liberate reddish-brown fumes of NO_2.

2. *Brown-ring Test.* Acidify the solution with a few cubic centimeters of dilute H_2SO_4, then add twice its volume of concentrated H_2SO_4. Cool and add fresh concentrated $FeSO_4$ solution so that it forms a separate layer on top. A brown ring will form at the junction of the two liquids. Iodides and bromides give similar rings which interfere with the test.

OXYGEN (O)

1. *Heating in Closed Tube.* Some of the higher oxides as MnO_2 and $KClO_3$ liberate oxygen which causes a glowing splinter to take fire.

2. *Evolution of Chlorine.* If HCl is added to some of the higher oxides, free chlorine is liberated which is recognized by its odor and bleaching properties.

PHOSPHORUS (P)

1. *Reduction with Magnesium Ribbon.* Phosphates of aluminum and the heavy metals should be fused with Na_2CO_3 and the powdered fusion ignited in a test tube with Mg ribbon. The phosphorus is converted into a phosphide which, upon the addition of a few drops of water, liberates phosphine (PH_3), recognized by its unpleasant garlic odor and ability to produce a black coloration when brought in contact with filter paper moistened with $AgNO_3$. Phosphates of the alkalies and alkaline earths may be ignited with Mg ribbon directly without previous fusion. This test is not satisfactory if arsenic or antimony is present.

2. *Precipitation with Ammonium Molybdate.* The phosphate is dissolved in HNO_3 (if insoluble, fusion with Na_2CO_3 should precede solution in acid) and a portion of the filtrate added to an excess of freshly prepared ammonium molybdate solution. Upon standing or slightly warming, a yellow precipitate of ammonium phosphomolybdate will be formed. If heated to boiling, other elements if present may be precipitated. Vanadium and arsenic in the pentavalent condition give similar tests with ammonium molybdate.

Platinum (Pt)

1. *Brownish-red Solution with Potassium Iodide.* Isolate and dissolve several scales of platinum in concentrated aqua regia and evaporate to dryness. Redissolve in HCl and evaporate to a thick paste. Dilute with water and then add a few drops of H_2SO_4 and a crystal of KI. The solution assumes a brown color. This test will not detect traces of platinum in the presence of large quantities of iron.

2. *Precipitation of Potassium Platinic Chloride.* Add KCl to a concentrated portion of the paste obtained, as indicated in test 1. Yellow crystals of K_2PtCl_6, insoluble in 80 per cent alcohol, will be precipitated.

Potassium (K)

1. *Flame Test.* Volatile potassium compounds impart a pale-violet color to the nonluminous flame. If obscured by sodium, view the flame through a thick blue glass or a Merwin color screen. Through blue glass the flame appears purplish red, while through the Merwin screen the coloration is blue-violet through division 1 and red-violet through divisions 2 and 3. In testing silicates it will be necessary to mix the assay with powdered gypsum and introduce it into the flame on a platinum wire.

2. *Precipitation as Potassium Platinic Chloride.* If hydrochlorplatinic acid, H_2PtCl_6, is added to a concentrated slightly acid solution of potassium, a yellow crystalline precipitate of K_2PtCl_6 will be formed.

Selenium (Se)

1. *Sublimate on Plaster Tablet.* When heated on the plaster tablet per se, selenium gives a coating which is cherry-red to crimson in thin layers and nearly black in thick deposits. When volatilized, the fumes are reddish and have the odor of rotten horse-radish.

2. *Flame Test.* When volatilized, selenium imparts an indigo-blue coloration to the flame.

Silicon (Si)

1. *Salt of Phosphorus Bead.* Silica does not dissolve readily in the salt of phosphorus bead but forms an insoluble translucent skeleton.

2. *Gelatinization with Acid.* Finely powdered silicates, which are completely soluble in HNO_3 or HCl, form a gelatinous mass of silicic acid when evaporated almost to dryness.

3. *Fusion with Sodium Carbonate.* Insoluble silicates should be fused with 3 to 4 parts of Na_2CO_3 and dissolved in HCl. Evaporate to complete dryness and redissolve the bases with fairly concentrated HCl. SiO_2 remains insoluble and may be removed by filtering the solution.

4. *Qualitative Separation of Common Elements in Silicates.* Fuse mineral with 3 parts of Na_2CO_3, if insoluble. Dissolve fusion in dilute HCl, evaporate to dryness, and bake. Redissolve in dilute HCl with a little concentrated HNO_3 and filter. Residue is SiO_2. Make filtrate alkaline with NH_4OH and boil. Precipitates: $Fe(OH)_3$ and $Al(OH)_3$. $Al(OH)_3$ is soluble in KOH. To filtrate add $(NH_4)_2C_2O_4$ and boil. Precipitate: CaC_2O_4. To the cold ammoniacal filtrate add Na_2HPO_4. Precipitate: $MgNH_4PO_4.6H_2O$.

Silver (Ag)

1. *Reduction on Charcoal.* When silver minerals are heated on charcoal with 3 parts of Na_2CO_3, they are readily reduced to malleable metallic globules. If sulfur, arsenic, or antimony is present, roasting should precede reduction in order to volatilize these constituents.

2. *Precipitation as Silver Chloride.* If to an HNO_3 solution of a silver mineral a few drops of HCl are added, a white curdy precipitate of AgCl will be formed. This precipitate is soluble in ammonia.

Sodium (Na)

1. *Flame Test.* Sodium imparts an intense and prolonged yellow color to the flame. The color is invisible through a thick dark-blue glass or the Merwin screen. Silicates of sodium should be mixed with gypsum and introduced into the flame on a platinum wire.

2. *Alkaline Reaction.* With the exception of silicates, phosphates, and borates, sodium minerals become alkaline upon ignition.

Strontium (Sr)

1. *Flame Test.* Strontium imparts a crimson color to the flame, which is more persistent than that of lithium and is invisible through division 1 of the Merwin screen (distinction from calcium). If a few drops of $BaCl_2$ are added to a solution of a Sr salt, the red color (Sr) will appear after the green of Ba; lithium will appear before the green.

2. *Alkaline Reaction upon Ignition.* With the exception of silicates and phosphates, strontium minerals give upon ignition an alkaline reaction with turmeric paper (distinction from lithium).

3. *Precipitation as Strontium Sulfate.* From a strontium-bearing solution, $SrSO_4$ is precipitated upon the addition of a few drops of dilute H_2SO_4 (distinction from lithium).

Sulfur (S)

When Present as Sulfides

1. *Heating in Open Tube.* Powdered sulfides are oxidized when heated in an open tube. SO_2 is set free and is recognized by its pungent odor and acid reaction with litmus paper.

2. *Heating in Closed Tube.* When heated in a closed tube, some sulfides liberate a portion of their sulfur, which condenses as a dark-red liquid when hot and changes to a crystalline yellow solid when cold.

3. *Fusion with Sodium Carbonate.* Fuse with 3 to 4 parts of Na_2CO_3 and place a portion of the fusion on a silver coin. Moisten with a few drops of water. A dark-brown to black spot indicates sulfur, provided selenium and tellurium are absent. To another portion of the fusion placed in a watch glass, add several drops of water and a drop or two of freshly prepared sodium nitroferricyanide. An intense purple color is indicative of sulfur.

4. *Oxidation with Nitric Acid.* Hot concentrated HNO_3 oxidizes sulfides to sulfates, liberating some free sulfur, which rises to the surface. A few drops of $BaCl_2$ added to the filtrate precipitate the sulfur as white $BaSO_4$.

When Present as Sulfates

5. *Fusion with Sodium Carbonate.* Mix the sulfate with an equal volume of powdered charcoal and 3 volumes of Na_2CO_3. Fuse and test as indicated in test 3.

6. *Precipitation as Barium Sulfate.* Sulfates soluble in HCl are precipitated as $BaSO_4$ upon the addition of $BaCl_2$.

Tellurium (Te)

1. *Sublimate on Plaster Tablet.* Tellurides heated per se, or with bismuth flux on a plaster support, yield a purplish-brown coating. A drop of concentrated H_2SO_4 added to the film and gently heated forms a pink spot.

2. *Sublimate on Charcoal.* When heated on charcoal, a white sublimate of TeO_2 is formed near the assay which resembles Sb_2O_3. The coating is volatile, and when touched with the reducing flame, it colors the flame a pale green.

3. *Test with Concentrated Sulfuric Acid.* When gently warmed with concentrated H_2SO_4, powdered tellurides produce a reddish-violet solu-

tion. The addition of water will cause the color to disappear and a grayish-black precipitate to form.

Tin (Sn)

1. *Reduction on Charcoal.* If fused with an equal volume of powdered charcoal and 2 volumes of Na_2CO_3, tin minerals are reduced, forming minute metallic globules. Upon prolonged ignition, the tin is volatilized and deposits as a white coating of SnO_2. Add a drop of $Co(NO_3)_2$ to the coating and heat. A bluish-green spot results.

2. *Reaction with Metallic Zinc.* Place a fragment of cassiterite (SnO_2) in a test tube on top of granulated metallic zinc and add dilute HCl. After a few minutes the mineral becomes coated with a thin gray layer of metallic tin.

Titanium (Ti)

1. *Reduction with Tin.* After fusion with 3 volumes of Na_2CO_3, the titanium will dissolve in HCl forming $TiCl_4$. Upon boiling with metallic tin, the titanium is reduced to $TiCl_3$, the solution assuming a violet color. If only a small amount of titanium is present, test 2 should be employed.

2. *Oxidation with Hydrogen Peroxide.* Dissolve the Na_2CO_3 fusion in 1 : 1 solution of H_2O and H_2SO_4, and when cold, add water and a few drops of H_2O_2. The solution is colored a pale yellow to orange red, depending upon the amount of Ti in the solution. This reaction depends upon the formation of $TiO_3.xH_2O$ and is exceedingly delicate. Hydrofluoric acid destroys the color.

Tungsten (W)

1. *Reduction with Tin.* After fusion with Na_2CO_3, the sodium tungstate is dissolved in hot water. Columbates are insoluble in water. Filter if necessary and acidify the filtrate with concentrated HCl. An insoluble white precipitate of hydrated tungstic acid ($H_2WO_4.H_2O$) is formed in the cold, which upon boiling turns yellow (H_2WO_4). Upon adding metallic tin and boiling, a dark-blue solution results, which is due to a heavy precipitate ($WO_3 + WO_2$) held in suspension. Dilution with water will not cause the color to disappear (distinction from columbium). Prolonged reduction finally produces a brown color (WO_2).

2. *Salt of Phosphorus Bead.* Colorless in oxidizing flame, blue in reducing flame, becoming red upon addition of $FeSO_4$.

Uranium (U)

1. *Salt of Phosphorus Bead.* Uranium colors the salt of phosphorus bead a yellowish green in the oxidizing flame and a bright green in the

reducing flame. In the borax bead, uranium cannot be distinguished from iron.

2. *Precipitation as Potassium Uranate.* Potassium ferrocyanide produces a brown precipitate $(UO_2)_2[Fe(CN)_6]$ in a slightly acid solution of a uranyl salt, which upon the addition of KOH is changed to the yellow potassium uranate ($K_2U_2O_7$); distinction from cupric ferrocyanide. If iron is present proceed as follows: Dissolve the fusion in aqua regia. Make alkaline with NH_4OH which will precipitate the Fe and U as $Fe(OH)_3$ and $(NH_4)_2U_2O_7$. Upon adding $(NH_4)_2CO_3$ and shaking, the uranium forms a soluble complex salt. Filter and acidify with HCl. Add NH_4OH until alkaline and the uranium is precipitated free from iron. Test precipitate as indicated in test 1.

3. *Fluorescence Test.* A uranium fragment dissolved in a NaF bead on a platinum wire will fluoresce with a bright yellow-green color under ultraviolet light. (Very satisfactory in the absence of columbium, thorium, or cerium.)

VANADIUM (V)

1. *Bead Tests.* Vanadium can usually be detected by the bead colorations. In the borax bead the color is yellowish green in the oxidizing flame and emerald green in the reducing flame, while the microcosmic salt bead is colored light yellow and emerald green, respectively.

2. *Oxidation with Hydrogen Peroxide.* If to an HNO_3 solution of vanadium H_2O_2 is added, pervanadic acid (HVO_4) is formed, which colors the solution orange to reddish brown. Color not destroyed by hydrofluoric acid (see Titanium). A very delicate reaction.

3. *Reduction with Zinc.* Zinc in an acid medium causes reduction of vanadic acid so that the solution turns blue, then green, and finally violet. This test is not so delicate as test 2.

ZINC (Zn)

1. *Sublimate on Charcoal.* When the finely powdered mineral is mixed with Na_2CO_3 and a small amount of charcoal and ignited, zinc is reduced and then quickly oxidized, forming an oxide coating near the assay which is pale yellow when hot, white when cold. A drop of cobalt nitrate added to the sublimate and heated produces a green spot.

2. *Heating with Cobalt Nitrate.* When moistened with a drop of cobalt nitrate and intensely ignited, infusible and light-colored silicates of zinc, such as hemimorphite, usually assume a blue color. ZnO or minerals forming the oxide upon heating, such as $ZnCO_3$, become green.

3. *Precipitation as Zinc Sulfide.* To an ammoniacal solution from which iron and aluminum have been removed, add a solution of sodium sulfide. A white precipitate indicates zinc sulfide.

ZIRCONIUM (Zr)

1. *Turmeric-paper Test.* Fuse with Na_2CO_3 and dissolve in dilute HCl. Turmeric paper dipped in this solution and dried is colored orange to reddish brown (see Boron). It is well to compare the turmeric paper with another strip treated only with HCl and dried.

2. *Precipitation as Phosphate in Acid Solution.* Dissolve the Na_2CO_3 fusion in HCl, boil, and filter. To the acid filtrate add several drops of Na_2HPO_4, and a white precipitate of zirconium phosphate will be formed. No other common metal, except titanium, yields a phosphate insoluble in an acid solution.

16 | Descriptive Mineralogy

INTRODUCTION

Descriptive mineralogy includes a detailed discussion in some systematic order of the crystallographic, physical, optical, and chemical properties of minerals. Characterizing features, associations, occurrences, and uses are also given.

There are several general methods of classifying minerals. In one of these methods, all minerals possessing some element as an important constituent are grouped together irrespective of their chemical and crystallographic relationships. Thus the important iron minerals would be grouped together, as follows:

Fig. 474. James D. Dana (1813–1895). Professor in Yale University (1850–1890) Author of *System of Mineralogy*, a standard reference work on descriptive mineralogy since it first appeared in 1837.

1. Pyrrhotite, FeS	4. Magnetite, $FeFe_2O_4$
2. Pyrite, FeS_2	5. Goethite-limonite, $HFeO_2$
3. Hematite, Fe_2O_3	6. Siderite, $FeCO_3$

Another method groups minerals according to their chemical composition and the principle of isomorphism. This classification has long been in use and was followed in the earlier editions of this text. Due to the great advances made in the last quarter of a century in the study of crystal structure by means of X-ray analysis, the classification has been revised. The revision followed in this edition is based upon the classifications of the seventh edition of Dana's *System of Mineralogy*,[1] two volumes of which have been published, and Strunz's *Mineralogische Tabellen*.[2] Minerals of the simplest composition and crystal structure are

[1] John Wiley and Sons, Inc., New York, 1944 and 1951.

[2] Akademische Verlagsgesellschaft, 3d ed., Geest & Portig K. G., Leipzig, 1957.

discussed first, while those of greatest complexity are treated last. Eight classes are easily arranged, as follows:

1. Native elements.
2. Sulfide and sulfo minerals.
3. Oxides and hydrated oxides.
4. Halides.
5. Nitrates, carbonates, and borates.
6. Sulfates, chromates, molybdates, and tungstates.
7. Phosphates, arsenates, and vanadates.
8. Silicates.

Fig. 475. Alfred Lacroix (1863–1948). Professor of mineralogy in the Museum d'Histoire Naturelle de France, Paris (1893–1948). Authority on the minerals of France and Madagascar.

Within each of these classes the various minerals are arranged, as far as possible, in groups having similar crystal structures and analogous chemical compositions. The importance of the minerals is indicated by the character of the type used, thus **QUARTZ, Willemite,** Greenockite. The minerals in the first two groups are listed in the determinative tables, pages 493 to 661.

In describing the individual minerals, the following order is used:

1. *Name and formula.*
2. *Crystallographic features and structure.*
3. *Important physical properties, such as cleavage, fracture, hardness, specific gravity, luster, color, indices of refraction, etc.*
4. *Chemical composition and properties.*
5. *Varieties, if important.*
6. *Occurrence, associations, and important localities.*
7. *Uses.*

NATIVE ELEMENTS

Of the more than 90 known elements only the following eight occur as solids and uncombined in nature in sufficient quantities to warrant description:

METALS

GOLD	**Au**	Cubic
SILVER	**Ag**	Cubic
COPPER	**Cu**	Cubic
PLATINUM	**Pt**	Cubic

SEMIMETALS

Arsenic	**As**	Hexagonal
Bismuth	**Bi**	Hexagonal

NONMETALS

SULFUR	S	Orthorhombic
DIAMOND	C	Cubic
GRAPHITE	C	Hexagonal

The specific gravities of the nonmetals are low, those of the semimetals range from 5.6 to 10, while those of the metals may be as high as 22. The metals are malleable and ductile.

Metals

Only the four important metallic elements gold, silver, copper, and platinum will be described. The crystal structures of these elements are discussed on page 171. The other native elements iron, mercury, lead, palladium, iridium, osmium, tantalum, and tin are rare in the uncombined state.

GOLD (*Native Gold*), Au.

Cubic, hexoctahedral class—$4/m\ \bar{3}\ 2/m$. Crystals are small, more or less distorted, but only rarely found. The most common forms are the octahedron, cube, and rhombic dodecahedron, occurring either independently or in combination. Skeletal development frequent. Usually in disseminated or rolled scales or grains; also filiform, reticulated, and in large lumps or nuggets (Fig. 476).

Fig. 476. Gold in conglomerate. Western Sonora, Mexico.

Malleable and ductile. No cleavage, hackly fracture. Hardness, 2.5 to 3. Specific gravity, 15.6 to 19.3. Metallic luster. Golden to brassy or light yellow in color depending upon the amount of silver present. Opaque.

Native gold. Generally contains varying amounts of silver (up to 40 per cent); also iron, copper, bismuth, zinc, lead, and tin. Readily fusible, and soluble in nitrohydrochloric acid. Readily acted upon by chlorine and potassium or sodium cyanide. Forms an amalgam with mercury.

Gold occurs widely distributed, but in only a comparatively few places in sufficient quantities to be of economic importance. There are two general types of occurrence, namely, (1) *in situ* and (2) in *secondary deposits*, called *placers*.

Gold occurring *in situ* is usually found disseminated in quartz veins and associated with various sulfide minerals, of which pyrite is the most important. Owing to the decomposition of the associated sulfides, the quartz, where exposed on the surface to the action of percolating water—zone of oxidation—is usually more or less cellular and of a rusty appearance. Such quartz is often called "porous" or "rusty" quartz. Gold is also found disseminated in granites, trachytes, andesites, crystalline schists, sandstones, and conglomerates. The most common associates, aside from quartz and pyrite, are chalcopyrite, galena, stibnite, tetrahedrite, sphalerite, arsenopyrite, tourmaline, and molybdenite, some of which are frequently auriferous.

Free milling gold is usually present in distinctly visible particles and is easily recovered by crushing and washing in a stamp mill and subsequent amalgamation with mercury, the finely crushed material from the mill being allowed to flow over copper plates coated with mercury. Where gold is associated with considerable quantities of the sulfides, the chlorination or cyanide processes may be used, either alone or in connection with amalgamation. In the chlorination process, the auriferous ores are roasted and then subjected to the action of chlorine, which causes the gold to pass into solution. In the cyanide process, the crushed ores, either raw or roasted, are treated with solutions of potassium or sodium cyanide, whereby a soluble double cyanide is formed. The gold can be separated from these solutions by means of electrolysis or zinc dust. These processes permit ores carrying very small amounts of gold to be worked with a profit.

Important localities for the occurrence of gold *in situ* are California, Nevada, South Dakota, Utah, Alaska; Witwatersrand (the Rand) in the Transvaal, Union of South Africa; western Australia; New South Wales; the Ural Mountains; Porcupine district, Ontario.

Placer gold is the result of the disintegration of rocks containing gold *in situ*, that is, disseminated or in veins. As these rocks are reduced by the action of the atmospheric agencies and erosion to sand and gravel, the gold, on account of its very high specific gravity, becomes concentrated in the stream beds in auriferous regions and is found as scales, grains, and nuggets. Especially rich deposits are likely to be found where the velocity of the stream has been checked by a bend in its course or by some obstruction. Placer gold is readily recovered by washing, the sand and gravel being thrown into long wooden troughs called sluices. Through these sluices water flows at a rather rapid rate in order to carry away the lighter rock material. At regular intervals, cross-bars, called riffles, are placed in the trough to check the velocity of the water. This causes the heavy particles to fall to the bottom of the sluices, and since mercury is added from time to time and is also caught by the riffles, an amalgam of gold is formed. From this amalgam, the gold is easily recovered by volatilizing the mercury. In some localities, *hydraulic* mining has been employed in working placer deposits. This does not differ essentially from the above method and consists in directing a large stream of water under high pressure against the bank of the placer in order to loosen the same and wash the sand and gravel down into the sluices. This type of working placers is practicable only where there is an abundant water supply. In regions where the supply of water is limited, dredges are used to advantage.

Gold placers are common in California, Alaska, Colorado, Australia, and Siberia. In practically all noteworthy gold-producing districts, gold has usually been found first in placers, and by subsequent exploration the primary occurrences *in situ* have been located.

Gold is used chiefly for coinage and jewelry. Gold coins of the United States consist of 9 parts of gold and 1 part of copper. For jewelry purposes, copper and silver are alloyed with gold to increase its hardness. The gold content of such alloys is expressed in carats, thus 14-carat gold consists of 14 twenty-fourths gold and 10 twenty-fourths other metals. Gold is also used in scientific and electrical apparatus, photography, gold plating and lettering, and dentistry. See page 454.

For many years the price of gold was $20.67 per troy ounce; on Jan. 31, 1934, it was advanced to $35.

SILVER (*Native Silver*), Ag.

Cubic, hexoctahedral class—$4/m\ \bar{3}\ 2/m$. Crystals usually small and distorted and in parallel groups. Cube and octahedron most common. Also acicular, reticulated, or arborescent; fine threads or wires (Figs. 477 and 478), sometimes matted and resembling tufts or wads of hair; scales, plates, or large masses.

Malleable and ductile. Hardness, 2.5 to 3. Specific gravity, 10 to 12; 10.5 when pure. Metallic luster. Color silver white, usually with yellow-brown, gray, or black tarnish colors. Silver-white streak, shiny. Excellent conductor of heat and electricity.

Native silver often contains varying amounts of gold, up to 28 per cent; also copper, arsenic, antimony, mercury, iron, or platinum.

Occurs commonly with ores of silver, lead, copper, arsenic, cobalt, and nickel, associated with calcite, quartz, barite, or fluorite. Kongsberg, Norway, has furnished a great deal of silver in the form of crystals and large masses, some weighing 750 pounds. The Saxon mines at Freiberg, Marienberg, and Annaberg were for a long time heavy producers; also Mexico, especially Sonora, Durango, Sinaloa; Chile; Peru; and Bolivia. Several of the more important localities in the United States are the Bingham and Tintic districts, Utah; Butte, Montana (from copper ores); Tonopah, Nevada; Coeur d'Alene, Idaho; Aspen, Colorado; Lake Superior copper district, associated with copper, forming "half breeds" (Fig. 479). In large deposits, disseminated and in veins, at Cobalt and vicinity,

Ontario, associated with niccolite, smaltite, erythrite, annabergite, bismuth, and calcite (Fig. 480). A mass of silver weighing 4,402 pounds was removed from the Keeley Mine, South Lorrain, Ontario. Many masses contained 95 per cent silver. Rarely found as nuggets. At Great Bear Lake, Northwest Territories, Canada, silver is associated with uraninite (pitchblende).

Fig. 477. Wire silver with argentite. Porco, Bolivia.

Fig. 478. Wire silver. Cliff Mine, Lake Superior.

Fig. 479. Silver (white) and copper "half breed." Lake Superior district.

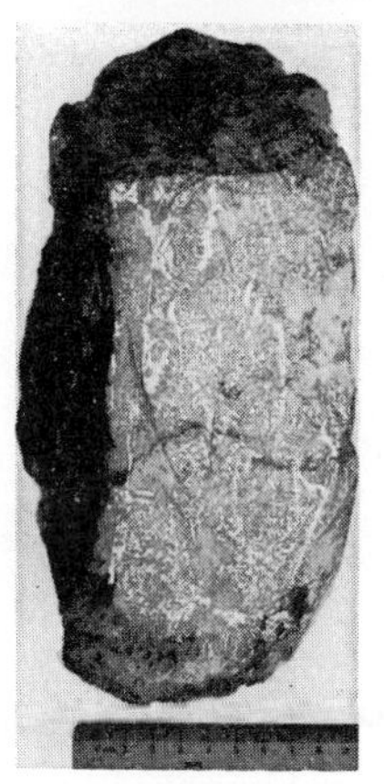

Fig. 480. Silver with calcite. La Rose Mine, Cobalt, Ontario.

Native silver is used for coinage, jewelry, and flat and hollow ware; also in physical, chemical, and surgical apparatus. The price varies greatly. In 1919 it was about $1.11, in 1932 about 28 cents, in 1935 about 64 cents, in 1941 about 35 cents, in 1946 about 80 cents, in 1950 about 74 cents, and in 1958 about 90 cents per troy ounce. Also see page 469.

COPPER (*Native Copper*), Cu.

Cubic, hexoctahedral class—$4/m\ \bar{3}\ 2/m$. Crystals are rather common but usually distorted and in parallel groups. Tetrahexahedrons, rhombic dodecahedron, and cube are the most commonly observed forms (Figs. 481 to 483). Generally in scales, grains, plates, and masses, sometimes weighing tons;[1] less frequently arborescent (Fig. 332, page 115) and filiform.

Hackly fracture. Hardness, 2.5 to 3. Specific gravity, 8.5 to 9. Metallic luster. Ductile and malleable. Color, copper red on fresh fracture. Due to tarnish and decomposition products, color may be

Fig. 481. Crystallized copper (tetrahexahedron). Phoenix Mine, Lake Superior district.

Fig. 482. Crystallized copper (rhombic dodecahedron). Lake Superior district.

Fig. 483. Crystallized copper. Lake Superior district.

superficially black (CuO), red (Cu_2O), green ($Cu_2(OH)_2CO_3$), or blue ($Cu_3(OH)_2(CO_3)_2$). Streak copper red, metallic and shiny. Excellent conductor of heat and electricity.

Native copper is generally almost pure copper; sometimes contains small amounts of silver, arsenic, bismuth, and antimony.

The most important locality for the occurrence of native copper is Keweenaw Peninsula in northern Michigan, where it occurs disseminated, principally in fine grains or scales, or in veins (1) in dark-colored igneous rocks, called melaphyre amygdaloids (variety of basalt) (Fig. 484); (2) in

[1] In 1857 a mass weighing about 420 tons was encountered in the Minnesota mine in Ontonagon County, Michigan.

reddish quartz porphyry conglomerates (Fig. 485); (3) in sandstones; (4) in epidotic beds; (5) in felsitic rocks. The first two occurrences are at present the most important. These ores average about 1 per cent of copper and are easy to treat. By means of crushing, washing, and concentrating with jigs and tables, the metallic copper is readily extracted.

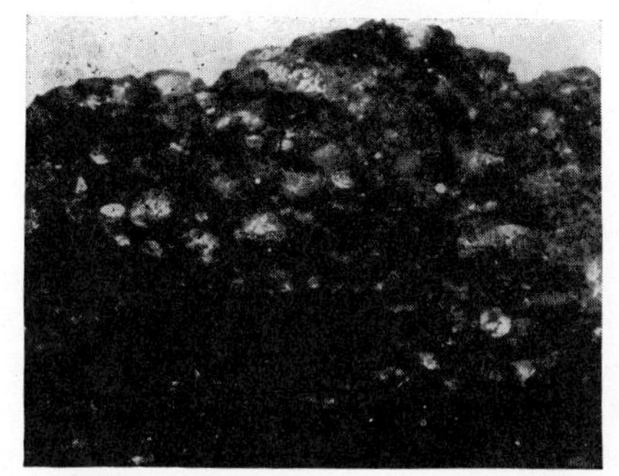

Fig. 484. "Shot" copper. Adventure Mine, Lake Superior district.

Fig. 485. Copper conglomerate. Lake Superior district.

It is then smelted and refined and cast into ingots and sold as "lake" copper. The common associates are calcite, quartz (Fig. 486), datolite, epidote, silver, analcime, and other zeolites. In recent years appreciable amounts of copper were recovered from the tailings of earlier operations by means of a leaching process.

This district was for many years a leading producer of copper. The annual output was, at times, about 175,000,000 pounds. About 60 per cent of the ore treated was conglomerate rock. Owing to the great depth of the mines, the present low copper content of the rock, and the high cost of labor, the mines of the Lake Superior district cannot compete successfully with other copper-producing areas which treat sulfide ores. The annual output has been greatly curtailed and is about 50,000,000 pounds.

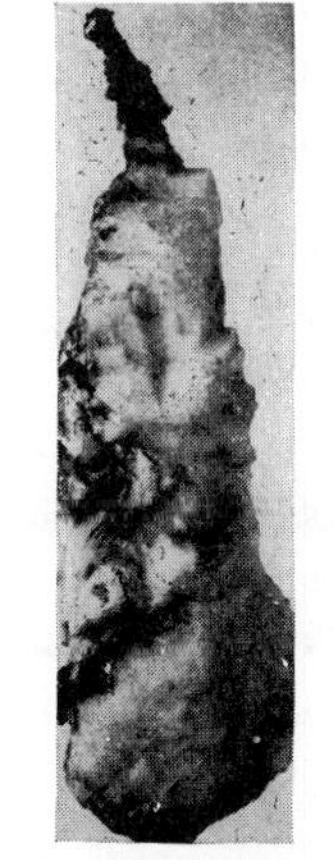

Fig. 486. Copper with calcite and quartz. Lake Superior district.

Native copper also occurs in smaller quantities associated with the other copper minerals—malachite, azurite, cuprite, chalcopyrite, bornite, and chalcocite—especially in Arizona and New Mexico; also in Chile, Bolivia, and Mexico.

Metallic copper is used very extensively in commerce and industry. Large amounts are used in the manufacture of copper wire, nails, and sheets, brass, bronze, electrical and radio apparatus, munitions of war; also for coinage purposes and chemical reagents.

It is said that there are over six hundred uses for copper where it is practically indispensable (see page 452).

The price of metallic copper fluctuates greatly. In 1916 it was about 27 cents, in 1926 about 14 cents, in 1932 as low as 5½ cents, in 1937 about 13 cents, in 1950 about 21 cents, in 1956 a high of 43 cents, and in 1958 about 29 cents per pound.

PLATINUM (*Native Platinum*), Pt.

Cubic, hexoctahedral class—$4/m\ \bar{3}\ 2/m$. Small crystals, generally cubes, but very rare. Usually in scales or grains; also in nuggets.

Hackly fracture. Metallic luster. Opaque. Hardness, 4 to 5. Specific gravity, 14 to 19; melted platinum is 19.7, hammered 21.23. Malleable, ductile, sectile. Silver white to dark gray or black in color. May be magnetic if much iron is present.

Native platinum usually contains iron (up to 28 per cent) and smaller amounts of iridium, rhodium, palladium, osmium, copper, nickel, and at times gold. Infusible at ordinary temperatures, but may be fused and welded with the oxyhydrogen blowpipe. Soluble in hot concentrated nitrohydrochloric acid.

Platinum was first discovered in 1735 in the gold placers of the Pinto River in Colombia, associated with gold, zircon, magnetite, and chromite. In 1822, it was found in the alluvial deposits of Nizhne Tagilski in the Ural Mountains. For many years practically all the world's supply of platinum was obtained from placer deposits, and the Soviet Union was the largest producer. Platinum also occurs in veins associated with chromite and disseminated in peridotite rocks. The nickel-copper ores of the Sudbury district of Ontario and the lode deposits of the Union of South Africa are the chief sources of platinum.

In the United States, small amounts of platinum are found in the black sands of the rivers along the Pacific Coast. Other occurrences are in various districts in the Transvaal and Southern Rhodesia, South Africa; Colombia, and other South American countries; near Bunkerville, Clark County, Nevada; in the gold sands of North Carolina; and in Westphalia, Germany.

Platinum is used very extensively as a catalytic agent in the manufacture of sulfuric, acetic, and nitric acids and in physical, chemical, and electrical apparatus; also in jewelry, pyrography, dentistry, nonmagnetic watches, and surgical instruments. The price of refined platinum has fluctuated greatly. In 1905, it was only 35 cents per gram but gradually increased to \$5.55 in 1918. During the next 10 years, it slowly declined and in 1928 was about \$2.80, in 1936 about \$1.95, in 1948 about \$3.25, and in 1958 about \$1.80 per gram. See also page 467.

Semimetals

The members of this group crystallize in the hexagonal system in pseudocubical rhombohedrons. They are brittle and nonmalleable. Only two semimetals, arsenic and bismuth, will be described. They are rarely uncombined in nature.

Arsenic (*Native Arsenic*), As.

Hexagonal, ditrigonal scalenohedral class—$\bar{3}$ $2/m$. Crystals are pseudocubical rhombohedrons, but very rare. Commonly in compact, scaly, granular, or fine-grained masses with reniform and botryoidal structures (Fig. 487). Often breaks into concentric or onion-like layers.

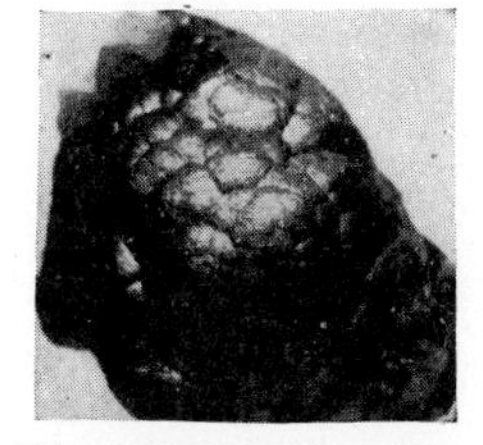

Fig. 487. Arsenic. Andreasberg, Harz Mountains, Germany.

Basal cleavage but usually not conspicuous. Uneven and fine-grained fracture. Hardness, 3 to 4. Specific gravity, 5.6 to 5.8. Metallic luster. Opaque. Tin-white color on fresh fracture surface, tarnishes dark gray to black on exposure. Grayish streak.

Native arsenic often contains antimony, also bismuth, cobalt, nickel, silver, iron, or gold.

Found principally in veins with silver, cobalt, and nickel ores; thus, in the Freiberg mining district of Saxony; Joachimsthal, Bohemia; Kongsberg, Norway; Mexico; Chile; China Creek, Vancouver Island, British Columbia.

Native arsenic furnishes but a small portion of the arsenic used in commerce and industry. Metallic arsenic is a constituent of shot metal. See page 441.

Bismuth (*Native Bismuth*), Bi.

Hexagonal, ditrigonal scalenohedral class—$\bar{3}$ $2/m$. Rarely in rhombohedral crystals. Usually reticulated, arborescent, platy, or compact masses (Fig. 488).

Fig. 488. Bismuth with calcite and smaltite. Cobalt, Ontario.

Basal cleavage, generally conspicuous. Hardness, 2 to 2.5. Specific gravity, 9.7. Brittle, slightly malleable when heated. Metallic luster. Opaque. Reddish white color, often with brassy tarnish colors. Shiny lead-gray streak.

Native bismuth often contains traces of arsenic, sulfur, selenium, and tellurium.

Not especially abundant but usually in veins associated with silver, cobalt, lead, zinc, and tin ores. Important localities are Freiberg, Saxony; Joachimsthal, Bohemia; Bolivia; Cornwall, England; Cobalt, Ontario; Great Bear Lake, Canada.

Metallic bismuth is obtained from native bismuth and bismuthinite (Bi_2S_3) (page 284) or as a byproduct in the electrolytic refining of lead. The metal is used in the manufacture of easily fusible alloys, such as find application in automatic sprinklers and safety plugs in boilers; also in rifle bullets and thermopiles. The salts of bismuth are used in pharmaceutical preparations, calico printing, and in the manufacture of highly refractive glass. See page 443.

Nonmetals

The three minerals to be described here are of great value in commerce and industry.

SULFUR (*Brimstone*), S.

Orthorhombic, bipyramidal class—$2/m\ 2/m\ 2/m$, is formed below 96°C. (α-sulfur). Crystals are common, showing mostly pyramidal or tabular

Fig. 489.

Fig. 490. Sulfur with calcite. Racalmuto, Sicily.

Fig. 491. Banded sulfur in limestone. Racalmuto, Sicily.

habits (Figs. 489 and 490); also in granular, fibrous, earthy, powdery, or stalactitic masses (Fig. 491).

Indistinct cleavages. Pronounced conchoidal to uneven fracture. Hardness, 1.5 to 2.5. Specific gravity, 1.9 to 2.1. Adamantine luster on crystal faces, otherwise resinous to greasy. Transparent to translucent. White to yellow streak. Usually sulfur yellow in color; also honey yellow or yellow-brown; and, due to impurities, reddish, greenish, or grayish. High indices of refraction, α 1.958, β 2.038, γ 2.245, (+);

$2V = 69°$; $r < v$. Nonconductor of heat; becomes negatively electrified on rubbing. On account of the low conductivity and unequal distribution of heat, cold crystals often crack when held in the hand. When held to the ear, a crackling sound may be heard.

Usually, practically pure sulfur, may contain traces of selenium and tellurium; sometimes mixed with bitumen and clay. Melts at 112.8°C.,

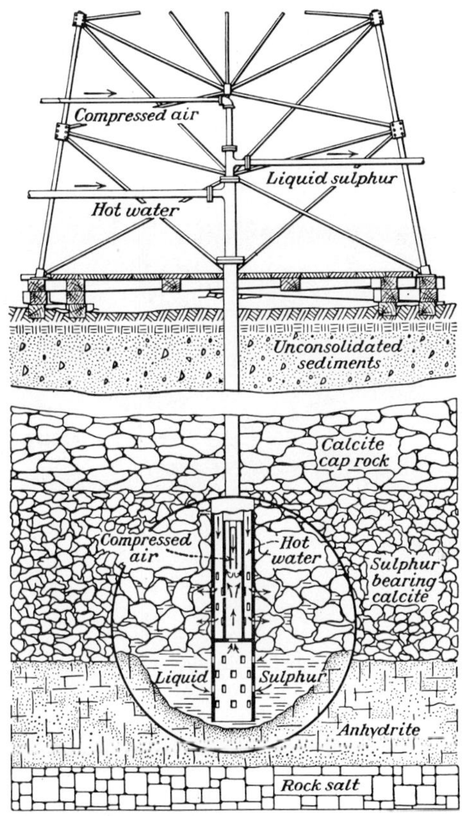

Fig. 492. Cross section of sulfur deposit showing Frasch method. (*Courtesy Texas Gulf Sulphur Company.*)

and at 270°C. burns with a bluish flame to sulfur dioxide. Insoluble in water and acids. Soluble in carbon disulfide.

The large and commercially important deposits occur in sedimentary rocks and are generally the result of the reduction of sulfate minerals, notably gypsum. The common associates are celestite, anhydrite, aragonite, and calcite. In the United States commercial deposits of sulfur occur in the cap rocks of salt domes in the Texas and Louisiana coastal plain. Practically all the American production of sulfur is from this area. The two most important producing localities are the Boling dome in Wharton County, Texas, and the Grande Ecaille dome, Louisiana. Other important deposits occur in Brazoria, Fort Bend, Matagorda, Palangana, and Duval counties, Texas, and in Iberia and Plaquemines parishes, Louisiana. Large mines are at Grande Ecaille, Louisiana, and at Newgulf and Moss Bluff, Texas. The sulfur occurs disseminated and in lenses and cavities in limestones at considerable depths below the surface. The Frasch method is used to recover the sulfur from these deposits. By means of superheated water at a temperature of about

Fig. 493. Molten sulfur being discharged in thin layers upon the top of a vat. It builds up the vat a few inches a day. Completed vat at the left. (*Courtesy Texas Gulf Sulphur Company.*)

320°F. and compressed air the sulfur is melted and forced to the surface and shipped as a liquid, or as a solid after solidifying in large vats (Figs. 492, 493 and 736). It is 99.5 per cent pure. Girgenti, Sicily, has for many years been the chief center of the sulfur industry of Sicily. Sulfur is also found in small quantities around volcanoes, the result of sublimation or interaction of sulfurous vapors; thus, on mounts Vesuvius and Etna, also in Iceland, Japan, and Hawaii. Furthermore, it occurs as the result of decomposition of pyrite and other sulfide minerals. About 92 per cent of the world's production of native sulfur is furnished by the United States.

Important in the manufacture of sulfuric acid, matches, gunpowder, fertilizer, rubber, fungicides, medicines, cement, thermal and electrical insulation, the bleaching of silk, straw, and woolen materials, and in the preparation of wood pulp used in the manufacture of paper. See page 471.

There are two other modifications (β and γ) of sulfur. They crystallize in the monoclinic system, are rare in nature, and are of no commercial importance.

DIAMOND (*Bortz, Ballas, Carbonado*), **C.**

Cubic, hexoctahedral class—$4/m\ \bar{3}\ 2/m$. Usually in crystals or crystal fragments, microscopically small or over 3,000 carats[1] in weight. Most common forms are the octahedron (Fig. 494), rhombic dodecahedron, cube, and hexoctahedron. Crystals are often rounded and distorted. Contact twins according to the spinel law, the twinning plane being parallel to a face of the octahedron, are frequently noted. Sometimes massive, either as crystal aggregates or devoid of external crystal faces.

Fig. 494. Diamond in blue ground. Kimberley, Union of South Africa.

Highly perfect octahedral cleavage. Hardness, 10 (hardest known mineral). The hardness varies markedly on the faces of the different crystal forms and with direction. Specific gravity, 3.15 to 3.53. Greasy adamantine luster (carbonado, dull). Commonly colorless, or slightly yellowish; also yellow, red, green, blue; more rarely black. Transparent to translucent and opaque.

The index of refraction and the dispersion of the diamond are high, n for red light being 2.402, for yellow 2.417, for green 2.427, and for violet 2.465. The dispersion is $2.465 - 2.402 = 0.063$. The characteristic fire is due to this unusually strong dispersion. Anomalous double refraction, caused by internal strains, is often noted. The diamond is an excellent conductor of heat; hence, it is cold to the touch. On the other hand, it is a poor conductor of electricity and becomes positively electrified when rubbed. Many diamonds fluoresce or phosphoresce (page 11) on exposure to ultraviolet, cathode, and X rays or to radioactive emanations. Thus, ultraviolet rays may cause some colorless stones to show a light-blue luminescence, while others may glow with a greenish or yellow color. Similar effects are sometimes observed on exposure to sunlight. By exposure to radium emanations or cyclotron bombardment color changes are induced. The mineral is transparent to X rays, but glass, strass, or paste imitations of the stone are not. An X-ray photo-

[1] The metric carat is 200 mg. It has been in use in the United States since July 1, 1913. See also p. 426.

graph will serve to distinguish the genuine diamond from these imitations (Fig. 495).

Colorless diamonds are pure carbon, for on combustion in an atmosphere of oxygen only carbon dioxide is obtained. Colored stones yield small residues. Spectrographically, 13 elements have been detected, of which calcium, sodium, copper, silicon, aluminum, boron, iron, and magnesium are the most important. Unaffected by acids. Carbonaceous inclusions are frequent.

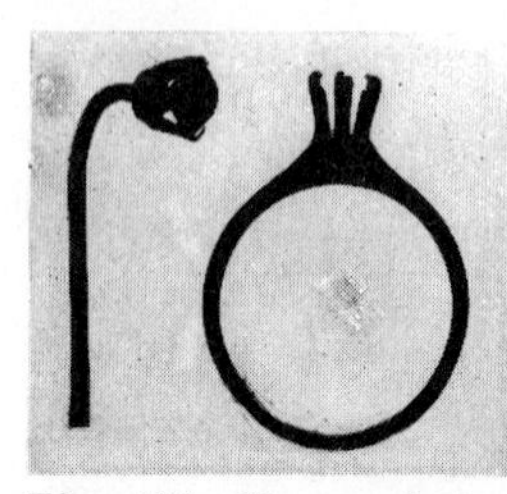

Fig. 495. X-ray photograph of lead-glass imitation (pin) and of diamond (ring).

The diamond has been known from the earliest times and was called *adamas,* that is, *the invincible,* by the ancients. According to the uses to which diamonds are put, they are classified as (1) *gem diamonds* and (2) *industrial diamonds.* These varieties are described in detail on pages 270 and 272.

India and Borneo were the earliest sources of the diamond. In India the diamond was found in three principal localities: (1) in the Madras Presidency of southern India; (2) farther north, in a large area between the Mahanadi and Godavari rivers; and (3) in Bundelkhand in central India. The diamonds were found in alluvial deposits and in a conglomerate, neither of which, of course, represented the original source. In Borneo the most important locality is near the town of Pontianak. At present the annual production of diamonds in India and Borneo is very small.

Tradition has it that diamonds were first discovered in Brazil in 1670, in the gold washings, but they were not positively identified until 1721. The provinces of Minas Gerais and Bahia are the most important producers. The deposits in Brazil are secondary, and the diamond is associated with such minerals as gold, kyanite, tourmaline, pyrope garnet, zircon, and some heavy ore minerals. The Brazilian deposits were very productive between 1721 and 1870, but the present yield is small. It is said that 1,666,569 carats were exported between 1732 and 1871.

In 1867, diamonds were discovered on the south shore of the Orange River, near Hope Town in southern Africa; at present, Africa, as a whole, furnishes over 95 per cent of the world's production. At first, they were found in the "river diggings," that is, in the sands and gravels of the streams, especially the Orange, Vaal, and Modder rivers. About three years later, diamonds were discovered in primary deposits, known as "dry diggings," upon the plateau between the Vaal and Modder rivers. Here the occurrence of the diamond is restricted to limited areas, elliptical or circular in outline and varying from 20 to 700 and more meters in diameter (Figs. 496 and 497). On the surface the diamonds were found in a soft, decomposed material known as the *yellow ground.* At depth the diamond-bearing areas constrict, and the yellow ground is underlaid by a hard, basic magnesian rock, known as kimberlite (variety of peridotite) or the *blue ground.* These areas are of volcanic origin and are called *pipes* or *diamond pipes.* In the diamond-bearing kimberlite about forty minerals are found, among which are the pyrope garnet, called *cape ruby,* kyanite, olivine, and zircon.

Originally, the diamonds were easily recovered from the soft yellow ground by simply washing away the lighter constituents and sorting the diamonds from the concentrates. Formerly, the harder blue ground was brought to the surface in large lumps and generally exposed in the open

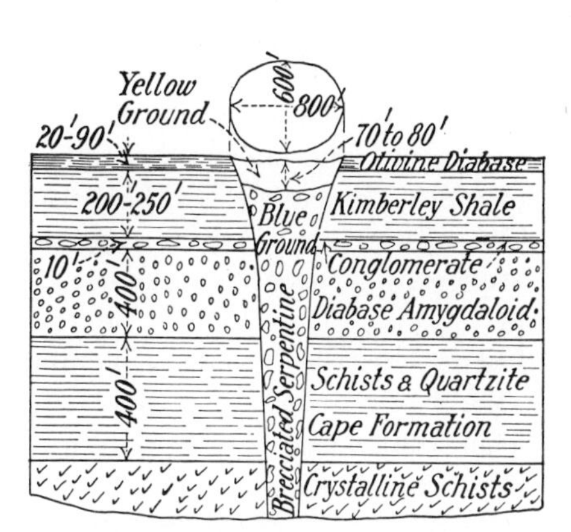

Fig. 496. Ideal section through the Kimberley Mine, Union of South Africa.

Fig. 497. Early view of Kimberley Mine, now partially filled with water.

fields, "depositing floors," to the action of the atmospheric agencies. In due time, the material could be easily crushed. It was then washed and concentrated and passed over oscillating tables covered with grease, called "sorters" or "greasers." The use of these tables is based upon the fact that of all the minerals in the concentrates grease sticks most tenaciously to the diamond. At most of the large mines, the blue ground is crushed and concentrated immediately after being mined. In general, the diamond content of a load of blue ground (1,600 pounds) is less than ¼ carat. The heavy media sink-and-float method and electrostatic separators for the recovery of the diamonds are used at the Premier and Williamson mines. At large mines, electromagnetic separators are generally in use.

Kimberley is the center for gem diamonds in South Africa. Five important mines, the Kimberley, De Beers, Du Toitspan, Bultfontein, and Wesselton, are located in its vicinity. Other important mines are the Jagersfontein, in the Orange Free State, and Premier, in the Transvaal near Pretoria. The Premier was for many years the largest known diamond mine. It covers about 80 acres (see Fig. 728, page 448). The Williamson Mine at Mwadui, in Tanganyika, which was discovered in 1941, is reported to be eight times larger than the Premier Mine.

Formerly the diamond pipe mines, of the type just described, furnished most of the world's annual production. At present, however, the annual production of the alluvial deposits of Africa is much greater than that of the pipe mines. As alluvial stones occur in sands and gravel, they are readily concentrated by washing. Subsequent handling is quite similar to that of the diamonds obtained from the pipe mines. The annual world production of diamonds is about 21,500,000 carats, of which industrial stones make up about 80 per cent and gemstones 20 per cent.

The Belgian Congo, Ghana (Gold Coast), Sierra Leone, Angola, Union of South Africa, and South-West Africa are the most important producers of alluvial diamonds in Africa. The production of the Belgian Congo is by far the largest. About 90 per cent of this production is obtained from the deposits known as the *Beceka* (Société Minière de Beceka). The yield of diamonds in some of these alluvial deposits is 5 to 6 carats per cubic meter of gravel; most of these stones are of industrial quality.

Diamonds have also been found in Australia, Liberia, Borneo, India, Venezuela, Brazil, eastern Siberia, British Guiana, Colombia, Mexico, and British Columbia. In the United States occasional diamonds have been discovered in Wisconsin, Indiana, Michigan, California, Georgia, and North Carolina. The most important find of diamonds in the United States was made on Aug. 1, 1906, near Murfreesboro, Pike County, Arkansas. The occurrence here is strikingly similar to that of the principal South African "pipe" mines. Over 48,000 stones have been recovered; the largest weighed 40 carats; about 10 per cent were of gem quality. Operations at Murfreesboro were discontinued long ago. The property is now a tourist's attraction and for a $1.50 fee one is permitted under certain conditions to hunt for diamonds. In March, 1956, a flawless white cleavage fragment weighing 15.31 carats was found.

Microscopic diamonds have been reported in meteorites (Canon Diablo, Arizona).

Gem Diamonds. In general, diamonds of good color and perfection are used for gem purposes. No sharp distinction can be made between the lower quality of gem and the higher quality of industrial diamonds.

The diamond has long been used as a gem, but the ancients were content to polish the natural crystal faces. It is generally claimed that about 1456 the art of cutting facets upon the diamond was invented whereby the *fire* was greatly increased. Many different styles of cutting

Fig. 498. Cullinan diamond. Premier Mine, near Pretoria, Union of South Africa. (Three-fourths original size.)

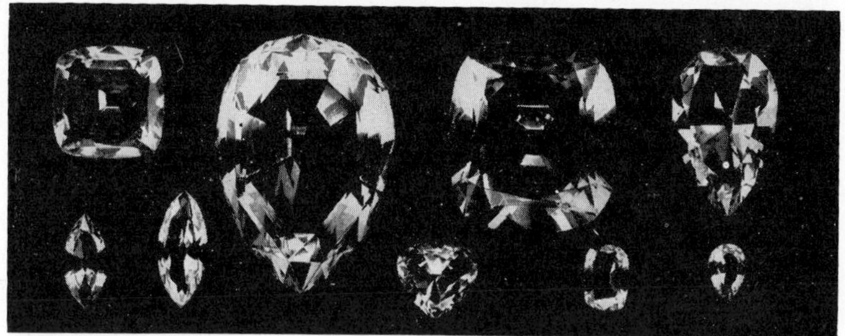

Fig. 499. The largest nine stones cut from the Cullinan diamond. (One-half original size.)

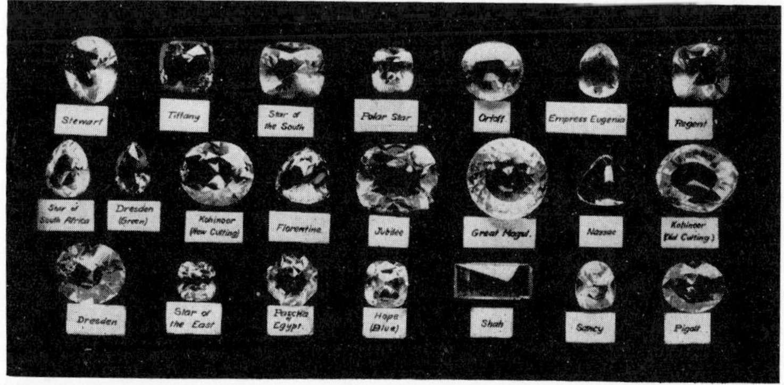

Fig. 500. Photograph of glass models of famous large diamonds. (Approximately one-third original size.)

have been in use at various times, but the *brilliant* and *emerald* cuts have been the most common. At present, various fancy cuts are also used, such as *baguette, cut-corner triangle, epaulet, half-moon, hexagon, keystone, kite, lozenge, marquise, pentagon* or *bullet, square, trapeze, triangle.* These newer cuts are well adapted to the designing of modern jewelry. The baguette, marquise, and square cuts are most popular.

The octahedron, either natural or obtained by cleaving or sawing, is made the basis for the *brilliant* style of cutting. Usually there are 58 facets, but in some cases as high as 74 are cut. Depending upon the character of the rough stone, from a third to one-half of its weight is lost in cutting. Amsterdam and Antwerp are the most important diamond-cutting centers (see Chap. 17).

The largest diamond ever found was the *Cullinan* or *Premier*, also called the *Star of Africa* (Fig. 498), discovered on Jan. 25, 1905, at the Premier Mine, in the Transvaal. This stone weighed 621.2 grams, or 3,106 carats. It measured about 10 by 6.5 by 5 cm. and was a cleavage fragment of a larger stone. It was purchased by the Assembly of Transvaal and presented to King Edward VII and subsequently cut into nine large (Fig. 499) and 96 smaller stones. The largest two stones are called *Cullinan I* and *II* and weigh 530.2 and 317.4 carats, respectively. Some of the other famous cut diamonds and their approximate weights are the *Jubilee*, 245.3 carats; *Kohinoor*, 106 carats; *Orloff*, 195 carats; *Regent*, 137 carats; *Tiffany* (yellow), 128.5 carats; *Hope* (blue), 44.5 carats; *Dresden* (green), 40 carats; *Star of the South*, 125.5 carats (Fig. 500). In January, 1934, the *Jonker* diamond, weighing 726 carats, was found in alluvial diggings on the Elandsfontein farm adjacent to the Premier Mine, near Pretoria. The *Vargas* diamond, weighing 726.6 carats, was discovered in Minas Gerais, Brazil, in July, 1938.

Industrial Diamonds. Those diamonds which are not used as gems find wide application in industry because of their extreme hardness. They vary from well-formed crystals to irregular shapes and from compact masses to semiporous aggregates. Some are clear and transparent, while others are opaque to black. In general, industrial stones are off-color and contain more flaws and inclusions than gem diamonds.

Industrial diamonds, in contrast to gemstones, are entirely consumed by use and consequently must be replaced. They constitute the bulk of the world's annual production of mined diamonds. The center for industrial diamonds in Africa is Johannesburg.

Industrial diamonds may be grouped as follows: (1) *fine industrials*, (2) *bort*, (3) *ballas*, and (4) *carbonado*.

Fine Industrials. These stones are comparable to gem-quality diamonds except in color. They are used for the manufacture of wire-drawing dies and shaped cutting tools.

Bort. Through long usage bort, also called *bortz, boort, boart,* or *bowr,* has come to include irregularly shaped and badly flawed crystals and those with many inclusions (Fig. 501). The term *drilling bort* is restricted to small sound stones used in diamond drill bits (Fig. 502). Diamond drilling is used extensively to determine the location and size of ore bodies and the character of the rocks to be penetrated and hence is of the utmost

Fig. 501. Bort suitable for diamond drills.

Fig. 502. Diamond-drill bit, set with bort.

importance in mining, petroleum, and structural engineering. The lowest grades of diamonds are called *crushing bort.* Its principal use is for crushing into grit or powder for the manufacture of bonded abrasive wheels. Bort is also used for glass cutting, sawing building stone, diamond-set tools, and other industrial purposes.

Ballas is the name given to the spherical aggregates of many small diamond crystals arranged radially and more or less concentrically (Fig. 503). Ballas is extremely hard and very tough and does not cleave

Fig. 503. Ballas, 110 carats, slightly enlarged.

Fig. 504. Carbonado. Brazil.

easily. It has many of the characteristics of carbonado and is therefore well adapted for drilling and industrial purposes. It is obtained principally from Brazil and the Jagersfontein Mine, South Africa.

Carbonado, also called *black diamond* or *carbon,* is an opaque, black or gray, tough and compact variety of diamond (Fig. 504). It has no cleavage. The specific gravity, 3.15 to 3.29, is lower than that of the diamond proper. Bahia, Brazil, is the chief source of carbonado. The largest piece ever found was somewhat heavier than the *Cullinan* diamond. Carbonado was formerly much used in diamond drills for deep boring and in diamond-set lathe tools for the truing of abrasive wheels and for other industrial purposes. For a discussion of *synthetic* or *man-made* diamonds see page 432.

Since the outbreak of the Second World War a better understanding of the properties of diamonds and a sounder technology in their uses have been developed. These advances have led to a manyfold increase in the consumption of industrial diamonds. As a result, outlets have been established for the entire output of the mines, which should give greater stability to the diamond industry as a whole.

GRAPHITE (*Plumbago, Black Lead*), C.

Hexagonal, dihexagonal bipyramidal class—$6/m\ 2/m\ 2/m$. Crystals are small, tabular, and hexagonal in outline but very rare. Usually found in foliated, scaly, granular and compact, or earthy masses (Fig. 505).

Fig. 505. Graphite with calcite. Ticonderoga, New York.

Perfect basal cleavage, yielding very thin and flexible laminae. Hardness, 1 to 2; marks paper and soils the fingers. Greasy feel. Specific gravity, 1.9 to 2.3. Iron black to dark gray in color. Shiny black streak. (Rubbed streak black; molybdenite, greenish.) Opaque. Metallic luster, sometimes dull or earthy. Good conductor of heat and electricity. Transparent to X rays.

Essentially carbon, but not so pure as the diamond. On combustion may yield as much as 20 per cent ash. Not attacked by acids. Graphite brought in contact with metallic zinc in a solution of copper sulfate is quickly copperplated, while molybdenite treated in the same way is only slowly coated. Infusible.

Graphite occurs in large masses and disseminated scales, also in dikes and veins in granites, gneisses, mica schists, and crystalline limestones. In some cases, it is the result of metamorphic action on carbonaceous matter, as in Rhode Island, or it may be due to the reduction of carbureted vapors, as in Ceylon, or of the oxides of carbon, as at Ticonderoga and vicinity in the eastern part of New York State. Common associates are calcite, orthoclase, quartz, pyroxene, garnet, spinel, and amphibole. The principal sources are Ceylon; Madagascar; Chosen (Korea); Sonora,

Mexico; Austria; Czechoslovakia; eastern New York; Chester County, Pennsylvania; Clay County, Alabama; Dillon, Montana; Burnet County, Texas.

Depending upon the size of the particles, graphite is commonly classified as *crystalline* or "*amorphous*." Crystalline graphite includes the *flake*, *chip*, and *lump* varieties. Mexico and Ceylon are the chief sources of amorphous and Madagascar and Ceylon of crystalline graphite.

Artificial graphite is manufactured in large quantities from anthracite coal or petroleum coke in electric furnaces at Niagara Falls, New York, and is used primarily for electrodes.

Graphite is used extensively in the manufacture of crucibles, dynamo and motor brushes, foundry facings, lead pencils, paint, lubricants, and stove polish. See page 449.

SULFIDE AND SULFO MINERALS

Arsenide and telluride minerals also belong to this class, which includes some of the most important economic ore minerals.

A. Sulfide Minerals

Argentite	Ag_2S	Cubic
CHALCOCITE	Cu_2S	Orthorhombic
BORNITE	Cu_5FeS_4	Cubic
GALENA	PbS	Cubic
Alabandite	MnS	Cubic
SPHALERITE	ZnS	Cubic
CHALCOPYRITE	$CuFeS_2$	Tetragonal
PYRRHOTITE	FeS	Hexagonal
Niccolite	NiAs	Hexagonal
CINNABAR	HgS	Hexagonal
REALGAR	AsS	Monoclinic
ORPIMENT	As_2S_3	Monoclinic
STIBNITE	Sb_2S_3	Orthorhombic
PYRITE	FeS_2	Cubic
Cobaltite	CoAsS	Cubic
MARCASITE	FeS_2	Orthorhombic
ARSENOPYRITE	FeAsS	Monoclinic
MOLYBDENITE	MoS_2	Hexagonal
Smaltite	$((Co,Ni)As_{3-x})$	Cubic

B. Sulfo Minerals

Pyrargyrite	Ag_3SbS_3	Hexagonal
Proustite	Ag_3AsS_3	Hexagonal
TETRAHEDRITE	$M_{12}R_4S_{13}$	Cubic
Enargite	Cu_3AsS_4	Orthorhombic
Bournonite	$PbCuSbS_3$	Orthorhombic

A. Sulfide Minerals

This group includes those minerals in which a metal or semimetal is combined with sulfur, as PbS or As_2S_3. If both metal and semimetal are present, the semimetal replaces the sulfur, wholly or in part, in the crystal structure, as in niccolite (NiAs), cobaltite (CoAsS), and arsenopyrite (FeAsS).

Argentite (*Silver Glance*), Ag_2S.

Cubic, hexoctahedral—$4/m\ \overline{3}\ 2/m$, if formed above 180°C.; monoclinic (acanthite) at ordinary temperatures. Crystals are cubical or octahedral in habit, often distorted and in parallel groups (Fig. 506). Crystals are, however, not common. Generally disseminated, coatings, or arborescent.

Fig. 506. Argentite. Batopilas, Mexico.

Hardness, 2 to 2.5. Specific gravity, 7.2 to 7.4. Malleable, sectile; takes an impression. On fresh surface, high metallic luster; but on exposure, soon becomes dull and black. Dark lead-gray color. Shiny lead-gray streak.

Ag_2S. Ag 87.1, S 12.9 per cent. Copper may be present up to 14 per cent. On charcoal fuses with intumescence yielding fumes of sulfur dioxide and a globule of silver.

Commonly in veins associated with silver, cobalt, and nickel minerals; proustite, pyrargyrite, smaltite, niccolite, native silver. Occurs at Comstock Lode and Tonopah, Nevada; Butte, Montana; Aspen, Colorado; Cobalt district, Ontario; Guanajuata and Batopilas, Mexico; Freiberg, Saxony; Joachimsthal, Bohemia; Peru; and Chile.

An important ore of silver. See page 469.

CHALCOCITE (*Copper Glance*), Cu_2S.

Orthorhombic, bipyramidal class—$2/m\ 2/m\ 2/m$, if formed below 105°C.; hexagonal above that temperature. Crystals are tabular or thick prismatic and pseudohexagonal, the prism angle being 119°35′. Striated parallel to the *a* axis. Frequently twinned. Crystals not common. Usually massive—compact, granular, or disseminated.

Hardness, 2.5 to 3. Specific gravity, 5.5 to 5.8. High metallic luster on fresh surface, which soon becomes dull and black. Conchoidal fracture. Color dark lead-gray, often tarnished blue or greenish. Shiny lead-gray streak.

Cu_2S. Cu 79.8, S 20.2 per cent. Usually with varying amounts of iron and silver. Alters to covellite, malachite, and azurite.

Commonly found in veins with bornite, chalcopyrite, tetrahedrite, galena, enargite, pyrite, and covellite. Occurs in large quantities in the Butte district, Montana; Kennecott, Copper River district, Alaska; Ely, Nevada; Miami, Morenci, and Bisbee, Arizona; Bingham, Utah; Sonora, Mexico; Chile; Peru; Tsumeb, South-West Africa; excellent crystals at Cornwall, England, and Bristol, Connecticut; as an impregnation at Mansfeld, Germany.

Chalcocite is an important ore of copper. See page 452.

Stromeyerite, $(Cu,Ag)_2S$, is closely related to chalcocite and difficult to distinguish from it except by chemical means. Not abundant. Associated with copper and silver minerals.

BORNITE (*Purple Copper Ore, Horse-flesh Ore*), Cu_5FeS_4.

Cubic, above 200°C.; orthorhombic, pseudocubic, below 200°C. Cubic and rhombic dodecahedral crystals; very rare. Commonly in compact and granular masses.

Uneven fracture. Hardness, 3. Specific gravity, 4.9 to 5.2. Metallic luster. Color on fresh fracture surface is between bronze and copper red, tarnishing readily and showing brilliant peacock colors. Streak gray-black.

Cu_5FeS_4. Cu 63.3, Fe 11.2, S 25.5 per cent. Frequently contains small amounts of gold and silver.

Occurs with chalcopyrite, chalcocite, enargite, and other copper minerals; also with cassiterite, pyrite, and siderite. Not very common in Europe. Good crystals at Cornwall, England, and Bristol, Connecticut. In large quantities in the Butte district, Montana; Virginia; North Carolina; Plumas County, California; Acton, Canada; Kennecott, Alaska; Chile; Peru; Bolivia.

An important copper ore. See page 452.

GALENA (*Galenite, Lead Glance*), PbS.

Cubic, hexoctahedral class—$4/m\ \bar{3}\ 2/m$. Well-developed crystals are common. Usual forms are the cube (*h*) and octahedron (*o*), independently or in combination; also the rhombic dodecahedron (Figs. 507 to 510). Also skeletal crystals; reticulated and tabular. Most generally in cleav-

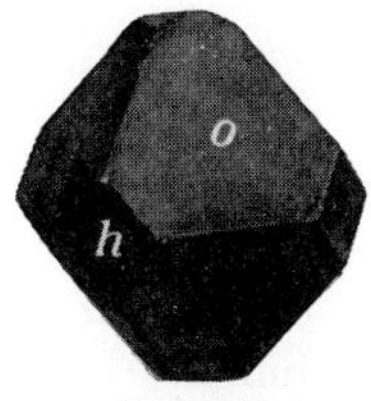

Fig. 507.

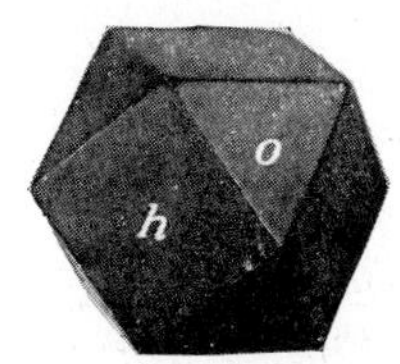

Fig. 508.

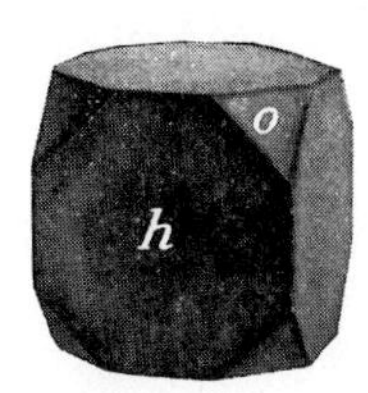

Fig. 509.

age masses; also compact, coarse to fine granular; more rarely stalactitic or fibrous. The internal structure of galena is discussed on page 173.

Fig. 510. Cube of galena. Joplin, Missouri.

Perfect cubical cleavage. Hardness, 2.5. Specific gravity, 7.3 to 7.6. Metallic luster, especially on cleavage surfaces; otherwise rather dull. Lead-gray color. Grayish-black streak.

PbS. Pb 86.6, S 13.4 per cent. Often with small amounts of silver. On this account, galena is an important source of silver. Galena with curved surfaces is apt to carry higher silver values than that with a good cubical cleavage. Antimony, iron, zinc, gold, cadmium, or copper may also be present. Alters to cerussite, anglesite, and pyromorphite.

Found in veins in crystalline rocks associated with sphalerite, chalcocite, pyrite, bournonite, quartz, various silver ores, calcite, fluorite, and barite; often silver-bearing. Thus, at Wallace, Idaho; Leadville, Colorado; Tintic and Park City districts, Utah; Freiberg, Saxony; Přibram, Bohemia; Cumberland, England; Mexico; Chile. Also in large quantities in Missouri, Illinois, Kansas, Wisconsin, and Iowa, in nonargentiferous veins, irregular deposits, or replacement deposits in limestones, with calcite, sphalerite, chalcopyrite, smithsonite, and marcasite. Excellent crystals occur at Joplin, Missouri, and Mineral Point, Wisconsin.

Galena is the chief source of metallic lead. It is also a valuable silver ore. Metallic lead is used extensively in the manufacture of paint, storage batteries, sheets, shot, solder, type metal, easily fusible alloys, and the various compounds of lead. Also see page 458.

Clausthalite (PbSe) and altaite (PbTe) are isomorphous with galena.

Alabandite, MnS.

Cubic, hexoctahedral class—$4/m\ \bar{3}\ 2/m$. Crystals are octahedral in habit, rare. Usually massive. Hardness, 3.5 to 4. Specific gravity, 4. Black color; brownish tarnish. Dirty-green streak. Submetallic luster, ofter dull. Not common. Occurs with manganese minerals; also as furnace product.

SPHALERITE (*Blende, Zinc Blende, Blackjack*), ZnS.

Cubic, hextetrahedral class—$\bar{4}\ 3\ m$. Crystals are common; often highly modified, and distorted or rounded (Fig. 514). Tetrahedrons (*o*) with cube (*h*) or rhombic dodecahedron are most commonly observed (Figs. 511, 512, and 514). Twins according to the spinel law. Generally in cleavable, fine to coarse granular, and compact masses; also fibrous and botryoidal. The internal structure of sphalerite is discussed on page 173.

Highly perfect, rhombic dodecahedral cleavage (Fig. 513). Brittle. Resinous to adamantine luster. Very high index of refraction, $n = 2.37$ for sodium light; high dispersion, 0.197. Hardness, 3.5 to 4. Specific gravity, 3.9 to 4.2. Color varies greatly; when pure, white; commonly,

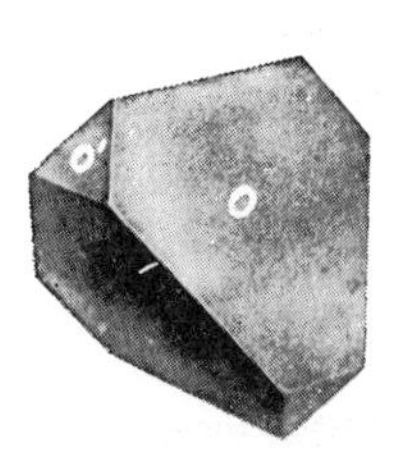

Fig. 511.

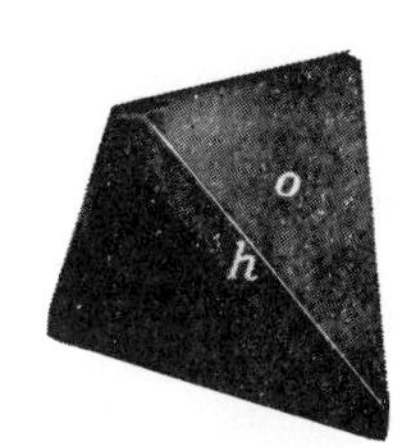

Fig. 512.

Fig. 513. Sphalerite. Cleavage rhombic dodecahedron. Joplin, Missouri.

yellow, red, black, or green. Varieties with high iron content have the darker colors. Transparent to translucent. Streak, white, pale yellow, or brown. Fluorescence or triboluminescence sometimes observed.

ZnS. Zn 67, S 33 per cent. Usually contains iron, up to 26 per cent, also manganese, cadmium, thallium, indium, tin, or mercury.

Fig. 514. Tetrahedral crystals of sphalerite. Joplin, Missouri.

Fig. 515. Sphalerite in chert. Galena, Illinois.

Occurs extensively in dolomitic limestones and other sedimentary rocks, and also in crystalline rocks. Usually associated with galena, chalcopyrite, pyrite, barite, fluorite, siderite, rhodochrosite, and quartz. Commonly in veins and cavities, also in extensive deposits. Important localities are Freiberg, Saxony; Příbram, Bohemia; Binnenthal, Switzerland; Cornwall, England; and Yechigo, Japan.

In the United States, sphalerite is very common in the limestones of Missouri, Kansas, Oklahoma, Wisconsin, Arkansas, Iowa, and Illinois; beautiful crystals at Joplin, Missouri. Also found with lead and silver ores, notably in Montana, Idaho, and Utah. Found in many places in small quantities.

Sphalerite is the chief source of zinc. Metallic zinc, known commercially as *spelter*, is used in large quantities in galvanizing iron and in the manufacture of brass, zinc wire and sheets, shot, dust zinc, and dry cells. The various compounds of zinc are employed extensively as pigments and in chemistry and medicine. Sphalerite is one of the chief sources of cadmium and thallium. Also see page 476.

Wurtzite is the hexagonal modification of ZnS. Crystals are hemimorphic pyramidal, dihexagonal pyramidal class—6 *m m*; quite rare and usually not well developed. Generally massive, fibrous, or as banded crusts. Associated with or disseminated in sphalerite. Formed from sphalerite at 880 to 1020°C. depending upon the iron content. The lower inversion temperature is for high iron content (17.06 per cent).

Greenockite, CdS. Hexagonal, dihexagonal pyramidal class—6 *m m*. Small hemimorphic crystals, rare. Usually as earthy coating. Hardness, 3 to 3.5. Specific gravity, 4.9 to 5. Yellow or brown in color. Streak, yellow or reddish. Resinous adamantine luster. Translucent.

CdS. Isomorphous with wurtzite. Cd 77.8, S 22.2 per cent.

Not common. With zinc minerals at Příbram, Bohemia; Joplin district, Missouri; Franklin, New Jersey.

Quite common as a furnace product.

CHALCOPYRITE (*Copper Pyrites, Yellow Copper Ore*), $CuFeS_2$.

Tetragonal, scalenohedral class—$\bar{4}$ 2 *m*. Bisphenoidal crystals resembling tetrahedrons and octahedrons, often distorted and difficult to interpret. Commonly in compact or disseminated masses.

Uneven fracture. Hardness, 3.5 to 4. Specific gravity, 4.1 to 4.3. Brass to golden yellow in color. Tarnishes to various blue, purple, and blackish tints; often iridescent. Greenish-black streak.

$CuFeS_2$. Cu 34.6, Fe 30.4, S 35 per cent. Contains at times small but valuable amounts of gold and silver; also selenium, thallium, indium, and arsenic.

Most common copper mineral. Usually with pyrite, sphalerite, bornite, galena, tetrahedrite, chalcocite, malachite, azurite, quartz, and calcite. Occurs at Falun, Sweden; Rio Tinto, Spain; Cornwall, England; Sudbury district, Ontario; Rouyn district, Quebec; Chile; Butte district, Montana; Bingham, Utah; Bisbee, Arizona; Ducktown, Tennessee; French Creek, Pennsylvania; San Miguel County, New Mexico; Prince William Sound, Alaska.

A very important ore of copper. See page 452.

PYRRHOTITE (*Magnetic Pyrites*), **FeS.**

Hexagonal, dihexagonal bipyramidal class—$6/m\ 2/m\ 2/m$. Crystals are tabular or pyramidal, but not common. Usually massive, granular, or lamellar. For a discussion of the internal structure of pyrrhotite, see page 174.

Inferior basal cleavage. Brittle. Hardness, 3.5 to 4. Specific gravity, 4.5 to 4.6. Metallic luster. Opaque. Bronze yellow to bronze red in color, tarnishing easily to dark brown. Streak, grayish black. Powder frequently attracted by the magnet.

FeS. Fe 63.5, S 36.5. Usually deficient in iron, as given by the formula $Fe_{1-x}S$, where x varies between 0 and 0.2. Nickel, cobalt, manganese, and copper are often present. The variety *troilite*, which occurs in meteorites, conforms closely to FeS.

Usually as a magmatic segregation in basic igneous rocks such as gabbros, norites, and peridotites, and commonly associated with pyrite, chalcopyrite, pentlandite, and galena. Pyrrhotite also occurs in pegmatites, contact metamorphic deposits, and veins. Important localities are Kongsberg, Norway; Finland; Bodenmais, Bavaria; Stafford and Ely, Vermont; Ducktown, Tennessee; Gap Mine, Lancaster County, Pennsylvania. In the Sudbury district of Ontario, pyrrhotite occurs in large quantities with pentlandite ((Fe,Ni)S) and chalcopyrite ($CuFeS_2$). The pentlandite is usually finely disseminated in the pyrrhotite.

An important source of nickel. See page 464.

Niccolite (*Copper Nickel*), **NiAs.**

Hexagonal, dihexagonal bipyramidal class—$6/m\ 2/m\ 2/m$. Crystals are rare. Nearly always massive, reniform, with columnar structure, or disseminated.

Uneven fracture. Hardness, 5 to 5.5. Specific gravity, 7.3 to 7.7. Metallic luster. Light copper red in color, tarnishes brown or grayish. Often coated with a green crust of annabergite ($Ni_3As_2O_8.8H_2O$). Streak, brownish black.

NiAs. Ni 43.9, S 56.1 per cent. May contain small amounts of iron, cobalt, antimony, and sulfur.

Commonly associated with nickel, cobalt, and silver ores, thus in the Freiberg district of Saxony; Joachimsthal, Bohemia; Cobalt and Gowganda districts, Ontario; in smaller quantities at Franklin, New Jersey; Custer County, Colorado.

A nickel ore. See page 464.

Breithauptite (NiSb) is isomorphous with pyrrhotite and niccolite.

Millerite (*Capillary Pyrites*), NiS. Hexagonal, ditrigonal pyramidal class—$3\ m$. Very fine slender crystals, often in radial groups. Frequently matted together like a wad or tuft of hair. Also as a coating.

Hardness, 3 to 3.5. Specific gravity, 5.5. Metallic luster. Brass to bronze yellow in color, often with gray iridescent tarnish. Greenish-black streak.

NiS. Usually quite pure. Ni 64.7, S 35.3 per cent.

Never found in large quantities. Usually as matted or tuffed masses in cavities in limestones with calcite, dolomite, and sphalerite in Missouri, Iowa, Wisconsin.

Minor source of nickel.

Pentlandite, $(Fe,Ni)_9S_8$. Cubic, hexoctahedral class—$4/m\ \bar{3}\ 2/m$. Rarely as crystals, usually as grains or granular masses. Hardness, 3.5 to 4. Specific gravity, 4.6 to 5. Metallic luster. Usually light bronze yellow in color. Streak, bronze brown. Nonmagnetic.

$(Fe,Ni)_9S_8$. Composition varies.

Occurs in large quantities in the Sudbury district, Ontario, with pyrrhotite and chalcopyrite. Only sparingly elsewhere.

Most important source of nickel.

Covellite, CuS. Hexagonal, dihexagonal bipyramidal class—$6/m\ 2/m\ 2/m$. Crystals are thin tabular, but rare. Usually as compact, fine-grained masses; also as coatings or crusts.

Perfect basal cleavage. Thin plates, flexible. Hardness, 1.5 to 2. Specific gravity, 4.7. Blue-black color. When rubbed, indigo blue. Often iridescent. Lead-gray to black shiny streak. Submetallic to resinous luster.

CuS. Usually nearly pure. Cu 66.4, S 33.6 per cent.

Usually the result of the decomposition of copper minerals, such as chalcopyrite, bornite, and chalcocite. Occurs at Butte, Montana; Kennecott, Alaska; Bor, Serbia; as a sublimation product on Mount Vesuvius.

Of minor importance as a copper ore.

CINNABAR (*Natural Vermilion*), HgS.

Hexagonal, trigonal trapezohedral class—3 2. Extremely small, highly modified crystals; rhombohedral or thick tabular in habit. Trigonal trapezohedral faces are rarely observed. Penetration twins quite common. Usually in fine-grained masses, crystalline crusts, or powdery coatings. (See Figs. 171 and 172, page 56.)

Perfect prismatic cleavage. Hardness, 2 to 2.5. Specific gravity, 8 to 8.2. Adamantine to dull luster. Slightly sectile. Extremely high indices of refraction, ω 2.91, ϵ 3.26, sodium light, (+). In thin plates transparent, otherwise opaque. Color varies with impurities and structure and may be scarlet, brownish red, brown, black, or lead-gray. Scarlet to reddish-brown streak. If moistened with HCl and rubbed on clean copper, a silver-white streak is produced.

HgS. Hg 86.2, S 13.8 per cent. May contain bitumen, clay, and ferric oxide.

Cinnabar is found in veins, disseminated, or in irregular masses in sedimentary rocks, quartzites, trachytes, porphyries, and serpentine. Usual associates are native mercury, pyrite, marcasite, realgar, calcite, stibnite, quartz, and opal. In sandstones at Almaden, Spain; in shales and dolomites in Idria, Italy; Moschellandsberg, Bavaria; excellent crystals in Kweichow, China; Chile; Peru; in serpentine at New Almaden, Altoona, and New Idria, California; Terlinqua, Texas; Pike County, Arkansas; Douglas County, Oregon; and Idaho, Nevada, and Alaska.

Cinnabar is the chief source of metallic mercury which is used extensively in commerce and industry. See page 463.

REALGAR, AsS.

Monoclinic, prismatic class—$2/m$. Crystals are usually short prismatic. Occurs also in granular and compact masses and as incrustations and coatings.

Cleavages parallel to clinopinacoid and orthoprism. Conchoidal fracture. Sectile. Hardness, 1.5 to 2. Specific gravity, 3.5. Resinous luster.

Aurora-red to orange-yellow in color. Orange-yellow streak. Transparent to translucent. α 2.49, β 2.60, γ 2.62, $(-)$; $2V$ = about 40°, all for lithium light; $r > v$, very strong.

AsS. As 70.1, S 29.9 per cent. Alters to orpiment.

Occurs with ores of silver and antimony and is usually associated with orpiment. Frequently disseminated in clay or dolomite; also as a sublimation product and as a deposit from hot springs.

Some notable localities are Kapnik and Felsöbánya, Rumania; Joachimsthal, Bohemia; Allchar, Macedonia; Binnenthal, Switzerland; Mount Vesuvius, Italy; Mercur, Utah; Yellowstone Park; Nye County, Nevada; Snohomish County, Washington.

ORPIMENT (*Auripigment, Arsenical Gold Ore*), As_2S_3.

Monoclinic, prismatic class—$2\ m$. Crystals are short prismatic, often pseudo-orthorhombic, but not common. Usually in foliated or granular masses, sometimes as crusts.

Cleavage parallel to clinopinacoid. Flexible but not elastic. Slightly sectile. Hardness, 1.5 to 2. Specific gravity, 3.5. Resinous to pearly luster. Lemon-yellow color and streak. Translucent to opaque. Very much like realgar, but differs in color. α 2.4, β 2.81, γ 3.02, $(-)$; $2V$ = 76°, all for lithium light; very strong double refraction; $2E = 70°$; $r > v$, strong.

As_2S_3. As 61, S 39 per cent. Often formed from realgar, with which it is commonly associated.

Formation and occurrence are the same as for realgar.

Excellent specimens are rather common, but the mineral is not important commercially. The artificial compound is used as a pigment and in dyeing and tanning.

STIBNITE (*Antimonite, Gray Antimony*), Sb_2S_3.

Orthorhombic, bipyramidal class—$2/m\ 2/m\ 2/m$. Crystals common, prismatic, and highly modified (Fig. 516), often vertically striated, bent, or twisted; also in radial aggregates; bladed (Fig. 517), columnar, granular and compact masses.

Cleavage parallel to brachypinacoid. Slightly sectile. Metallic luster. Hardness, 2. Specific gravity, 4.65. Lead gray in color and streak. Often tarnishes black; iridescent.

Sb_2S_3. Sb 71.4, S 28.6 per cent. Sometimes contains gold, silver, lead, iron, and copper in small amounts. Fuses easily in candle flame.

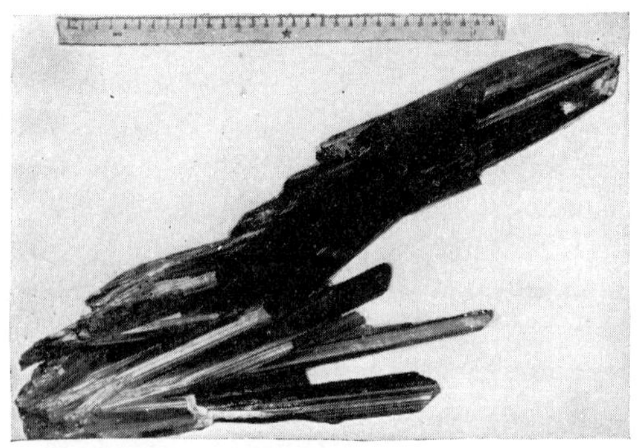

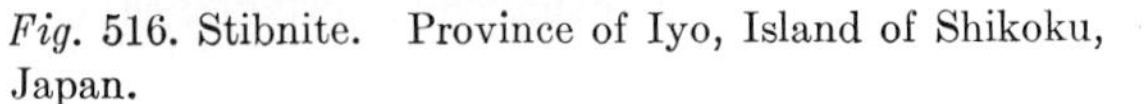

Fig. 516. Stibnite. Province of Iyo, Island of Shikoku, Japan.

Fig. 517. Bladed stibnite. Kremnitz, Hungary.

Found in veins with quartz and various antimony minerals resulting from the decomposition of stibnite. Also with realgar, orpiment, galena, barite, cinnabar, sphalerite, and gold. Occurs in Saxony, Bohemia, Siberia, Algeria, Bolivia, Mexico, and Hunan Province, China. Excellent crystals have been obtained from the Island of Shikoku, Japan. The chief American localities are Idaho, Nevada, Oregon, Alaska, California; also Washington, Arkansas, and Montana.

Stibnite is the chief source of metallic antimony and its compounds. China, Bolivia, and Mexico are the principal sources of metallic antimony. Metallic antimony is used principally in the manufacture of antimonial lead for storage batteries, cable coverings, and in various alloys, such as type, babbitt, and britannia metals. Some of the compounds are used in rubber goods, as pigments in paints and enamels, and in medicinal preparations (see also page 440).

Bismuthinite (Bi_2S_3) resembles stibnite very closely. Heavier than stibnite; specific gravity, 6.8. Bi 81.2, S 18.8 per cent. Important occurrences in Bolivia and Mexico. Not common.

PYRITE (*Fool's Gold, Iron Pyrites*), **FeS_2.**

Cubic, dyakisdodecahedral class—$2/m\ \bar{3}$. Crystals are common, often large. The common forms are the cube, octahedron, and pyritohedron (Figs. 518 and 520); frequently distorted and highly modified. Crystal faces, especially those of the cube, often show striations conforming to the symmetry of the dyakisdodecahedral class (Fig. 521). Penetration twins

Fig. 518. Pyrite crystals—octahedron, striated cube, cube and octahedron, pyritohedron.

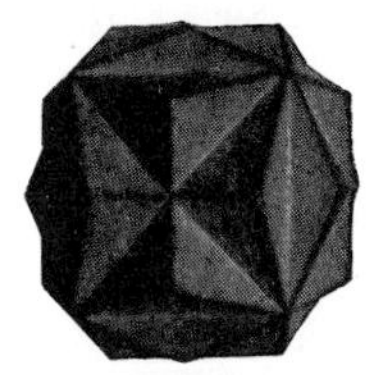

Fig. 519.

of pyritohedrons with the twinning plane parallel to a face of the rhombic dodecahedron (Fig. 519) are sometimes called crystals of the "iron cross." Also massive and disseminated; granular, reniform, botryoidal, stalactitic. For a discussion of the internal structure of pyrite, see page 174.

Uneven fracture. Hardness, 6 to 6.5. Specific gravity, 5.0 to 5.2. Brittle. Metallic luster. Opaque. Pale brassy to golden yellow in color, sometimes with brown or variegated tarnish colors. Greenish to brownish-black streak.

Fig. 520. Pyrite. Bingham Canyon, Utah.

Fig. 521. Pyrite striated cubes. Leadville, Colorado.

FeS_2. Fe 46.6, S 53.4 per cent. May contain cobalt, nickel, copper, arsenic, and gold in varying amounts. Decomposes readily, especially in a moist atmosphere. Limonite and goethite are the usual decomposition products, although various sulfates and sulfuric acid sometimes result. Pseudomorphs of goethite after pyrite are quite common. Pyrite is more stable than marcasite, the orthorhombic modification of FeS_2 (see page 286).

Pyrite is the most common sulfide mineral and, hence, is found very widely distributed. It occurs in rocks of all ages. Its mode of occurrence varies greatly. Usually associated with other sulfides, such as galena, chalcopyrite, sphalerite, and arsenopyrite; also with calcite, siderite, hematite, and magnetite. Commonly found in quartz with native gold. As nodules and concretions in many slates, sandstones, and coals.

Excellent crystals are found in the Freiberg district, Saxony; Příbram, Bohemia; Schemnitz, Czechoslovakia; enormous deposits carrying gold and silver at Rio Tinto, Spain. In the United States, especially good crystals occur at Franklin, New Jersey; Central City Mine, Gilpin County, and elsewhere in Colorado; French Creek, Pennsylvania. Large deposits of massive pyrite occur in Tennessee, Virginia, New York, California, and Wisconsin.

Pyrite is used principally as a source of sulfur dioxide in the manufacture of sulfuric acid, and of sulfate of iron, known as *copperas*. Pyrite is also a source of gold. See also page 455.

Cobaltite (*Cobalt Glance*), **CoAsS.**

Cubic, tetrahedral pentagonal dodecahedral class—2 3. Usually as small, well-developed crystals showing either the cube or pyritohedron. Sometimes both in combination. Cube faces striated, as shown in Fig. 521. More rarely compact and granular.

Cubical cleavage. Uneven fracture. Brittle. Hardness, 5.5. Specific gravity, 6 to 6.4. Metallic luster. Opaque. Silver-white color, at times with a reddish tinge; grayish if much iron is present. Often with a pink coating of erythrite ($Co_3(AsO_4)_2.8H_2O$). Grayish-black streak.

CoAsS. Co 35.4, As 45.3, S 19.3 per cent, usually with iron up to 12 per cent, due to admixture of pyrite or magnetite; nickel up to 3 per cent.

Generally with the cobalt minerals; also with pyrrhotite, chalcopyrite, pyrite, galena, magnetite. Occurs at Tunaberg, Sweden; Skutterud and Nordmark, Norway; Cornwall, England; Cobalt district, Ontario.

An important source of cobalt. See page 451.

Minerals closely related to pyrite and cobaltite are sperrylite ($PtAs_2$), hauerite (MnS_2), gersdorffite (NiAsS), and ullmannite (NiSbS).

MARCASITE (*White Iron Pyrites, Spear Pyrites*), **FeS_2.**

Orthorhombic, bipyramidal class—$2/m\ 2/m\ 2/m$. Crystals usually tabular or short columnar; elongated and striated parallel to *a* axis. Often twinned, resembling cocks' combs or spearheads (Figs. 522 and 523). Commonly massive; fine granular, stalactitic, reniform, and globular; often with radial structures.

Hardness, 6 to 6.5. Specific gravity, 4.8 to 4.9. Metallic luster. Pale-brass yellow to steel-gray in color, darker after exposure. Usually lighter in color than pyrite. Streak, greenish black.

FeS_2. Fe 46.6, S 53.4 per cent. Contains at times arsenic and copper. Marcasite is formed from highly acid solutions at low temperatures, while pyrite has a greater temperature range of formation and may be deposited from slightly acid, neutral, or alkaline solutions. Marcasite alters more readily than pyrite, forming limonite and melanterite. Powdered marcasite dissolves in concentrated nitric acid with separation of sulfur, while pyrite does not.

Fig. 522. Marcasite. Ossegg, Bohemia.

Fig. 523. Marcasite. Ossegg, Bohemia.

Not so abundant as pyrite. When massive, difficult to distinguish from pyrite. Frequently with pyrite, galena, calcite, fluorite, and sphalerite. Common as concretions in marl, clay, limestone, and coal. In chalk marl at Folkestone and Dover, England; Bohemia; Saxony; with sphalerite, galena, and calcite at Joplin, Missouri; Mineral Point, Wisconsin; Galena, Illinois.

Uses same as for pyrite.

Minerals closely related to marcasite are loellingite ($FeAs_2$), glaucodote ($(Co,Fe)AsS$), safflorite ($CoAs_2$), and rammelsbergite ($NiAs_2$).

ARSENOPYRITE (*Mispickel*), FeAsS.

Monoclinic, prismatic class—$2/m$, pseudo-orthorhombic. Often in disseminated, tabular, or short prismatic crystals. Striated parallel to the *a* axis. Sometimes twinned. More generally massive—compact, granular, columnar, or radial.

Hardness, 5.5 to 6. Specific gravity, 5.9 to 6.2. Color, silver-white to light steel-gray, tarnishing brass yellow or gray. Streak, black. Metallic luster.

FeAsS. Fe 34.3, As 46, S 19.7 per cent. Often contains cobalt, nickel, antimony, bismuth, gold, and silver.

Commonly with ores of tin, nickel, cobalt, silver, gold, and lead; also with pyrite, chalcopyrite, and sphalerite. Found at Freiberg, Saxony; in serpentine at Reichenstein, Silesia; Cornwall, England; Tunaberg,

Sweden; in dolomite in Binnenthal, Switzerland; in gold-bearing quartz veins at Deloro, Hastings County, and Cobalt and Porcupine districts, Ontario; Franconia, New Hampshire; Floyd and Montgomery counties, Virginia; Franklin, New Jersey; Lead, South Dakota; Leadville, Colorado; Idaho; Montana.

Used principally as a source of white arsenic or arsenious oxide, the arsenic of commerce. If present in paying quantities, gold, silver, and cobalt are recovered. See also page 441.

MOLYBDENITE, MoS_2.

Hexagonal, dihexagonal bipyramidal class—$6/m\ 2/m\ 2/m$. Rarely in tabular or prismatic hexagonal crystals (Fig. 524). Generally in disseminated scales or grains; sometimes in foliated or granular masses.

Fig. 524. Molybdenite. Wakefield, Quebec.

Excellent basal cleavage. Flexible. Greasy feel. Marks paper. Blue-gray in color (graphite is black). Hardness, 1 to 1.5. Specific gravity, 4.75 (graphite 1.9 to 2.3). Greenish streak on glazed porcelain (graphite shiny black).

MoS_2. Mo 59.9, S 40.1 per cent.

Generally disseminated in granites, especially those associated with tin ore deposits; also in syenites, gneisses, pegmatites, and aplites. Commonly with cassiterite, wolframite, topaz, epidote, fluorite, scheelite, and chalcopyrite. Large crystals occur in Renfrew County, Ontario. Important occurrences in Saxony and Bohemia; Cornwall, England; Queensland and New South Wales, Australia; Copper and Blue Hill, Maine; Westmoreland, New Hampshire; Crown Point, Chelan County, Washington; Pitkin and Climax, Colorado; Sulfur Gulch, near Questa, New Mexico; and Bingham, Utah. Colorado and Utah are the largest producers of molybdenite.

Chief source of molybdenum and its compounds. Used in the manufacture of steel and iron castings and in "high-speed" tools. See page 463.

Calaverite, $AuTe_2$. Monoclinic, prismatic class—$2/m$. Crystals columnar and striated parallel to the *b* axis, but rare. Generally granular to compact.

Conchoidal fracture. Hardness, 2.5. Specific gravity, 9.3. Brass-yellow to silver-white in color; may tarnish yellowish. Metallic luster. Yellowish to greenish streak.

$AuTe_2$. Au 44, Te 56 per cent. Usually contains silver up to about 4 per cent.

Most common gold telluride. Associated with sylvanite ($(Au,Ag)Te_2$). Occurs at the Stanislaus Mine, Calaveras County, California; Cripple district, Colorado. Kalgoorlie, Western Australia.

An ore of gold.

Other telluride minerals are petzite ($(Ag,Au)_2Te$) and hessite (Ag_2Te).

Skutterudite Group

This group includes arsenides of both nickel and cobalt (M), with the proportions varying from MAs_3 to MAs_2. The high arsenic end-members are skutterudite ($(Co, Ni)As_3$) and nickel-skutterudite ($(Ni,Co)As_3$). It commonly occurs as smaltite ($(Co,Ni)As_{3-x}$) and chloanthite ($(Ni,Co)As_{3-x}$), with x having a value between 0.5 and 1.0. The members of this group are practically indistinguishable on the basis of physical properties. Only smaltite will be described.

Smaltite, ($(Co,Ni)As_{3-x}$).

Cubic, dyakisdodecahedral class—$2/m\ \bar{3}$. Crystals generally cubic or octahedral in habit, but rare. Usually massive—compact or granular (Fig. 525).

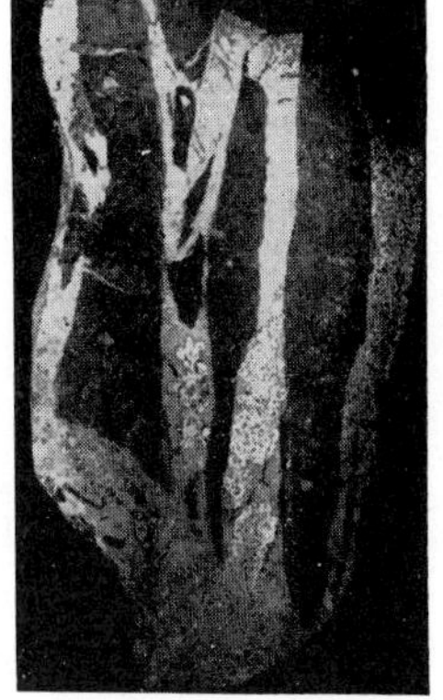

Fig. 525. Smaltite in veins of calcite (light). Cobalt, Ontario.

Uneven fracture. Brittle. Hardness, 5.5 to 6. Specific gravity, 6.4 to 6.6. Metallic luster. Opaque. Tin-white to light steel-gray in color. Tarnishes dull. Often coated with erythrite ($Co_3(AsO_4)_2.8H_2O$). Grayish-black streak. Garlic odor when struck with a hammer.

($(Co,Ni)As_{3-x}$). Usually with varying amounts of iron, bismuth, and sulfur. Iron may amount to 12 per cent, causing higher specific gravity.

Usually with cobalt, nickel, and silver ores; also with native bismuth, barite, siderite, calcite, quartz, arsenopyrite. Thus, in the Freiberg district, Saxony; Cornwall, England; Tunaberg, Sweden; La Motte Mine, Missouri; Cobalt, Gowganda, and Sudbury districts, Ontario, and Great Bear Lake, Northwest Territory, Canada (Fig. 525).

An important source of cobalt. See page 451.

B. Sulfo Minerals

In the minerals of this group the semimetals act like the metals in the crystal structure. Thus, proustite (Ag_3AsS_3) may be interpreted as a double sulfide, $3Ag_2S.As_2S_3$.

Pyrargyrite (*Dark-ruby Silver Ore, Dark-red Silver Ore*), Ag_3SbS_3.

Hexagonal, ditrigonal pyramidal class—3 *m*. Crystals resemble those of proustite; rare. Usually massive—compact, disseminated, crusts or bands.

Conchoidal fracture. Hardness, 2.5 to 3. Specific gravity, 5.8. Submetallic to metallic adamantine luster. Dark red to lead gray in color; thin splinters in transmitted light are deep red. Cherry- to purple-red streak. ω 3.084, ε 2.881, for lithium light; (−).

Ag_3SbS_3. Ag 59.7, Sb 22.5, S 17.8 per cent. Usually contains a little arsenic.

Occurrence similar to that of proustite but more abundant. Found in veins with other silver ores, calcite, and galena. Thus, in the Freiberg district, Saxony; Příbram, Bohemia; Guanajuato and Sonora, Mexico; Chile; Colorado; Nevada; Arizona; Cobalt, Ontario.

An important ore of silver. See page 469.

Proustite (*Light-ruby Silver Ore, Light-red Silver Ore*), $\mathbf{Ag_3AsS_3}$.

Hexagonal, ditrigonal pyramidal class—3 *m*. Crystals often small, highly modified, and difficult to interpret. Hemimorphic development sometimes distinct. Generally massive—disseminated, in crusts or bands.

Conchoidal fracture. Hardness, 2 to 2.5. Specific gravity, 5.5. Brilliant adamantine to dull submetallic luster. Translucent to transparent. Color and streak, scarlet to vermilion. ω 3.088, ε 2.792 for sodium light; (−).

Ag_3AsS_3. Ag 65.4, As 15.2, S 19.4 per cent. At times contains some antimony.

Occurs with pyrargyrite in veins with other silver minerals, galena, and calcite. Occurs at Freiberg, Saxony; Joachimsthal, Bohemia; Chañarcillo, Chile; Guanajuato, Mexico; Peru; Cobalt, Canada; various places in Colorado, Nevada, Idaho.

An ore of silver. See page 469.

TETRAHEDRITE (*Gray Copper Ore*), $\mathbf{M_{12}R_4S_{13}}$.

Cubic, hextetrahedral class—$\bar{4}\ 3/m$. Excellent crystals showing tetrahedral development, often highly modified. Commonly massive—granular, disseminated. See Figs. 103 to 106, page 35.

Uneven fracture. Hardness, 3 to 4.5. Specific gravity, 4.5 to 5.1. Metallic luster, sometimes dull. Opaque. Steel-gray to iron-black color, often with tarnish colors. At times coated with chalcopyrite or sphalerite. Streak black, or reddish brown.

Composition varies greatly. M is usually predominantly copper; lead, silver, mercury, iron, or zinc may be present. R indicates antimony or arsenic. The following varieties are often differentiated—cupriferous and arsenical, *tennantite;* argentiferous, *freibergite;* mercurial, *schwatzite.*

Occurs commonly in veins with chalcopyrite, sphalerite, galena, bournonite, pyrite, quartz, siderite, and barite. Found at Freiberg, Saxony; Clausthal, Harz Mountains, Germany; Příbram, Bohemia; Kapnik, Rumania; Mexico; Chile; Peru; Bolivia; excellent crystals at Bingham, Utah; many places in Colorado, Montana, Nevada, and Arizona.

An important ore of copper and silver. See pages 452 and 469.

Enargite, Cu_3AsS_4.

Orthorhombic, pyramidal class—*m m* 2. Small, prismatic crystals, vertically striated; rare. Usually in compact, granular, or columnar masses.

Perfect prismatic cleavage. Uneven fracture. Hardness, 3. Specific gravity, 4.4. Submetallic luster. Grayish black to iron black in color. In artificial light resembles sphalerite. Streak, black. Opaque.

Cu_3AsS_4. Cu 48.3, As 19.1, S 32.6 per cent. May contain some iron, zinc, and antimony.

In veins with other copper minerals, such as chalcopyrite, bornite, chalcocite, tetrahedrite; also pyrite. Not common in Europe. More extensive in Peru; Argentina; Chile; Bolivia; Mexico; Island of Luzon, Philippines; in large quantities in the copper mines at Butte, Montana; also in San Juan Mountains, Colorado; Tintic district, Utah.

An important ore of copper. Also a source of arsenious oxide. See page 452.

Bournonite (*Cogwheel Ore*), **$PbCuSbS_3$.**

Orthorhombic, bipyramidal class—$2/m$ $2/m$ $2/m$. Thick tabular and prismatic crystals. Frequently twinned, forming *cross* or *cogwheel* crystals. Also in compact and granular masses.

Hardness, 2.5 to 3. Specific gravity, 5.7 to 5.9. On fresh fracture, surface greasy. Metallic luster; crystals are sometimes dull. Steel gray to iron black in color. Dark-gray to black streak.

$PbCuSbS_3$. Pb 42.6, Cu 13.0, Sb 24.6, S 19.8 per cent. Usually contains some arsenic.

Occurs in veins with galena, sphalerite, stibnite, chalcopyrite, tetrahedrite, siderite, and chalcocite at Freiberg, Saxony; Přibram, Bohemia; Kapnik, Rumania; Mexico; Chile; Bolivia; excellent large crystals at Park City, Utah; Yavapai County, Arizona; Montgomery County, Arkansas.

An ore of lead, copper, and antimony. See pages 452 and 458.

The following sulfo minerals are not common: miargyrite ($AgSbS_2$), jamesonite ($Pb_4FeSb_6S_{14}$), stephanite (Ag_5SbS_4), pearceite ($(Ag,Cu)_{16}As_2S_{11}$), polybasite ($(Ag,Cu)_{16}Sb_2S_{11}$).

OXIDES AND HYDRATED OXIDES

Twenty-four minerals belonging to this group will be described.

A. Oxides

WATER (Ice)	H_2O	Hexagonal
QUARTZ	SiO_2	Hexagonal
Cuprite	Cu_2O	Cubic
Zincite	ZnO	Hexagonal
	Hematite Group	
CORUNDUM	Al_2O_3	Hexagonal
HEMATITE	Fe_2O_3	Hexagonal
ILMENITE	$FeTiO_3$	Hexagonal
	Spinel Group	
SPINEL	$MgAl_2O_4$	Cubic
MAGNETITE	$FeFe_2O_4$	Cubic
FRANKLINITE	$(Zn,Mn)Fe_2O_4$	Cubic
CHROMITE	$Fe(Cr,Fe)_2O_4$	Cubic
Hausmannite	$MnMn_2O_4$	Tetragonal
Chrysoberyl	$BeAl_2O_4$	Orthorhombic
	Rutile Group	
RUTILE	TiO_2	Tetragonal
CASSITERITE	SnO_2	Tetragonal
PYROLUSITE	MnO_2	Tetragonal
COLUMBITE	$(Fe,Mn)(Cb,Ta)_2O_6$	Orthorhombic
URANINITE	UO_2	Cubic

B. Hydrated Oxides

OPAL	$SiO_2.nH_2O$	Amorphous
MANGANITE	$MnO(OH)$	Monoclinic
GOETHITE-LIMONITE	$HFeO_2$	Orthorhombic
BAUXITE		
Brucite	$Mg(OH)_2$	Hexagonal
Psilomelane		

A. Oxides

Many of these minerals are very common and of great economic importance.

WATER (*Snow, Ice*), H_2O.

Above 0°C., water is a liquid, hence, amorphous. It is almost colorless, but in large quantities and when pure, it has a bluish tinge. Specific gravity, when pure, at 4°C. and 760 mm. barometric pressure is 1; that of ocean water may be as high as 1.028. When pure, it is without taste or odor. $n = 1.333$.

Water occurs very widely distributed in nature and is an important agency in the disintegration, decomposition, transportation, and formation of minerals. Nearly all minerals are more or less soluble in water, especially if it contains carbon dioxide, humus acid, hydrochloric acid, or oxygen in solution. The ocean water contains about 3.4 per cent of solid matter in solution. Over 30 elements are found in ocean water, and hence, water is frequently called the universal solvent. When water freezes, it expands, the increase in volume being about 9 to 10 per cent and the pressure exerted about 138 tons per square foot. Because of this enormous pressure, freezing water is a most important geological agency, causing the widening of cracks and crevices, thereby extending the zone of activity of water and oxygen and hastening weathering and disintegration.

Fig. 526. Snow crystal. (*After Bentley.*)

On freezing, water forms ice. Snow crystals are formed directly from water vapor and are often very beautiful. They are tabular and hexagonal in outline, dihexagonal pyramidal class, 6 *m m* (?) (Fig. 526), and show great diversity in development. Lake or stream ice consists of crystals arranged in a definite manner, the *c* axes being perpendicular to the extent of the sheet of ice. In glacier ice, however, the ice particles do not possess a definite orientation.

QUARTZ, SiO_2.

Hexagonal, trigonal trapezohedral class—3 2 (below 573°C.). Crystals are very common. They usually consist of a hexagonal prism, which predominates, terminated by faces of a positive and negative rhombohedron

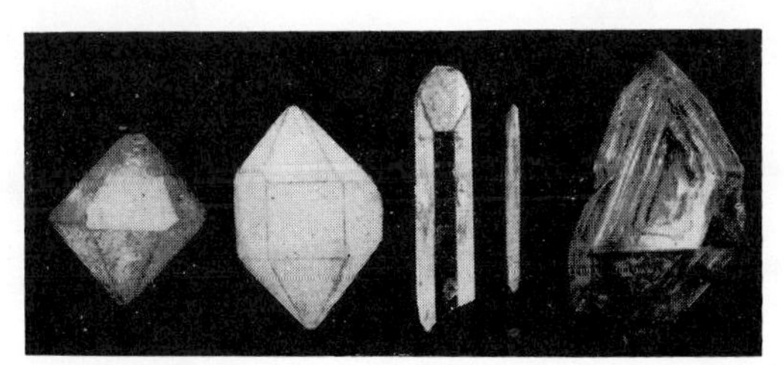

Fig. 527. Quartz crystals—pyramidal, prismatic, long prismatic, tabular, skeletal.

sometimes so developed as to simulate the hexagonal bipyramid of the first order. The pyramid habit is less frequent (Fig. 527). The prism faces are generally horizontally striated. Crystals are sometimes bent, twisted, or greatly distorted. Quartz forms right- and left-handed crystals, which are easily recognized when faces of the trigonal trapezohedron are present (Fig. 528 left, Fig. 529 right). Twins are common. Figure 530 illustrates the common or Dauphiné law, the vertical axis being the twinning axis. Here two right- or left-handed crystals intergrow so that the positive rhombohedron of the one individual coincides with the negative of the other, the c axis being the twinning axis.

Crystals twinned according to the Brazilian law (Fig. 531) consist of a right- and a left-handed individual of the same sign so intergrown that the twinned crystals are symmetrical to planes parallel to faces of the

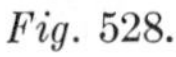

Fig. 528.

Fig. 529.

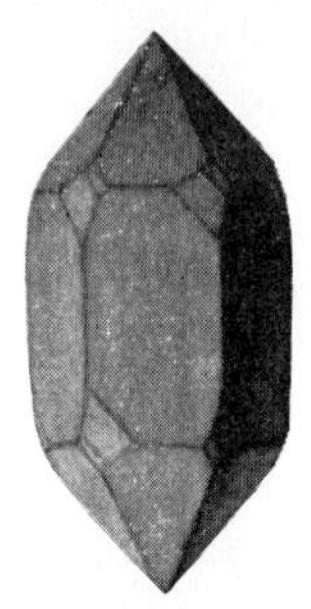

Fig. 530.

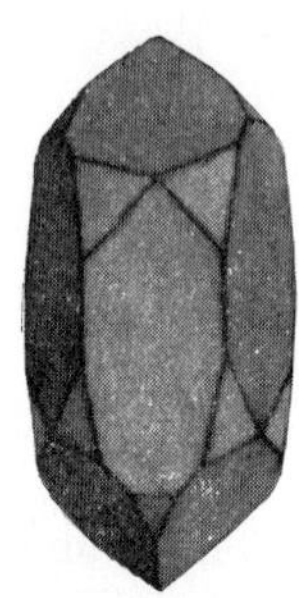

Fig. 531.

prism of the second order. Twins according to several other laws are not uncommon. Crystals sometimes show a skeletal development (Fig. 532).

At times, crystals contain scales of mica or hematite distributed in a regular manner, so that they may be separated into sections or layers. Such crystals are called *cap quartz*. Parallel growths called *scepter quartz*

Fig. 532. Skeletal quartz. Paris, Maine.

Fig. 533. Scepter quartz with phantom. Mursink, Ural Mountains.

(Fig. 533) are also observed. Although quartz is commonly found in distinct crystals, it also occurs in a great variety of massive forms.

According to Wright and Larsen, there are two modifications of quartz. One of these modifications, α quartz, is formed below 573°C. and crystallizes in the trigonal trapezohedral class of the hexagonal system. This modification is the more common. It occurs in veins and geodes, and in some pegmatites, and is here described in detail. The second modification is called β quartz and is formed at temperatures between 573 and 870°C., but upon cooling β quartz inverts to α quartz. β quartz crystallizes in the hexagonal trapezohedral class, often with a bipyramidal habit (Fig. 527). It is found in granites and porphyries and in some pegmatites. These modifications are sometimes termed *low* and *high* quartz, respectively. Tridymite and cristobalite are other modifications of SiO_2 (see page 298).

Indistinct rhombohedral cleavage. Conchoidal fracture. Hardness, 7. Specific gravity, 2.65. Vitreous luster. ω 1.544, ϵ 1.553, (+). Transparent to opaque. Commonly colorless or white; also yellow, red,

Fig. 534. Rock crystal variety of quartz. Dauphiné, France.

Fig. 535. Smoky quartz with muscovite. Paris, Maine.

pink, amethystine, green, blue, brown, and black. Many colors disappear on heating. Streak, white. Some varieties may show luminescence. Exhibits pyroelectric and piezoelectric properties (see page 112).

SiO_2. Si 46.7, O 53.3 per cent. Often contains inclusions of rutile, hematite, chlorite, mica, and liquid and gaseous carbon dioxide. Not attacked by the common acids and infusible before the blowpipe. Common as a pseudomorph after fluorite, calcite, siderite, and wood.

The many varieties of quartz are most conveniently classified as (1) *crystalline*, (2) *cryptocrystalline*, and (3) *clastic.*

Crystalline varieties are vitreous, either crystals or crystalline masses, and but slightly acted upon by potassium hydroxide.

Rock Crystal. Colorless quartz. Excellent crystals are common (Fig. 534).

Amethyst. Various shades of purple or violet.

Rose Quartz. Pink to rose red in color, becoming paler on exposure to light. May show asterism. Usually massive.

Smoky Quartz. Smoky yellow to dark brown. Often called *cairngorm stone* (Fig. 535).

Milky Quartz. Milk white in color. Translucent or nearly opaque. Often with a greasy luster.

Citrine. Yellow, yellow brown, or red brown in color. Unfortunately, often called *topaz, false topaz, Spanish topaz,* or *topaz quartz.*

Aventurine. Contains glistening scales of mica or hematite.

Ferruginous Quartz. Brown or red in color, due to the presence of either limonite or hematite.

Rutilated Quartz. Contains fine interlacing needles of rutile.

Cat's-eye. Grayish or brownish, with an opalescence due to inclusions of fibers or to a fibrous structure.

Tiger's-eye. Yellow brownish in color. Pseudomorphous after crocidolite asbestos. Pronounced chatoyant luster.

Crypotocrystalline varieties are compact and under the microscope show a crystalline structure. More readily acted upon by potassium hydroxide than the crystalline varieties.

Chalcedony. A transparent to translucent variety having a waxy luster. Commonly stalactitic (Fig. 536), botryoidal, concretionary, and lining cavities. White, grayish, brown, blue, and black in color.

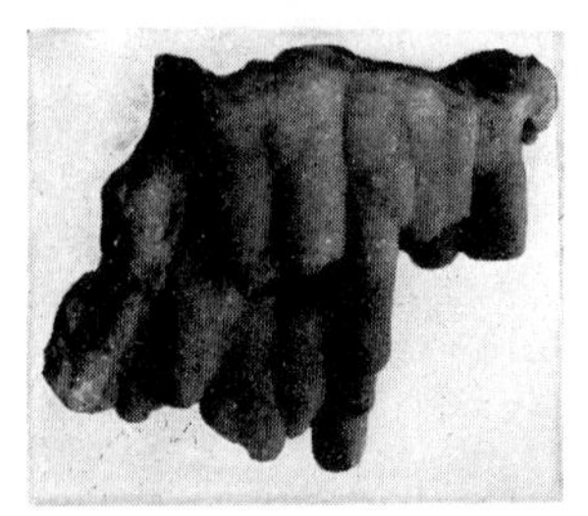

Fig. 536. Chalcedony (stalactitic). Havana, Cuba.

Carnelian or Sard. Commonly reddish chalcedony.

Chrysoprase. Pale yellow-green to apple-green chalcedony.

Heliotrope. Bright- or dark-green chalcedony with small spots of red jasper resembling drops of blood. It is often called *bloodstone.*

Agate. This is chalcedony made up of strata or bands indicating successive stages of deposition. The layers may be differently colored or clouded, giving rise to several varieties, such as *banded* and *clouded* agates.

The banding is usually in parallel but more or less wavy or irregular lines (Figs. 537 and 538). Agates may be white, pale to dark brown, or bluish in color. They are frequently colored artificially. *Moss agate* contains visible inclusions, frequently dendritic or moss-like (Fig. 539).

Onyx. Banded agate with the bands or layers in parallel straight lines, corresponding to layers in even planes (Fig. 538). Onyx is used for cameos.

Jasper. Opaque, and red, yellow, and grayish in color.

Flint. Gray, smoky brown, or brownish black in color. Commonly in nodules with a white coating (Fig. 540). Translucent. Prominent conchoidal fracture.

Chert. Includes varieties with a horn-like appearance (*hornstone*), also impure flints and jaspers.

Clastic varieties of quartz include many of the siliceous fragmental rocks. In some cases, the individual particles are no longer distinct.

Sand. Loose, unconsolidated grains or fragments of quartz.

Sandstone. Consolidated sand. The cementing material may be silica, iron oxide, calcium carbonate, or clay; less commonly, gypsum or barite. *Orthoquartzite* is a sandstone with silica cement. Occurs in a great variety of colors.

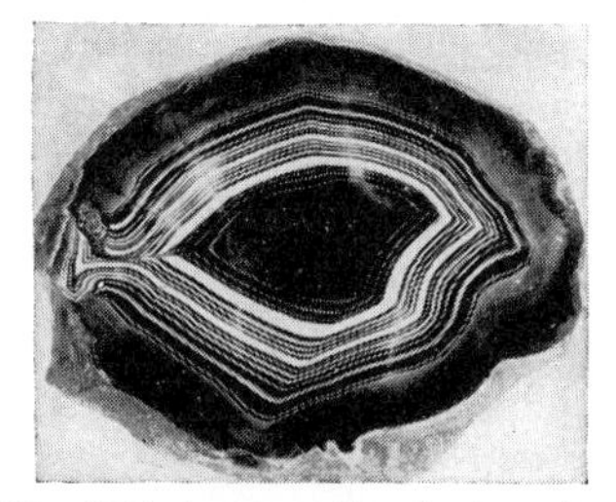

Fig. 537. Agate. South America.

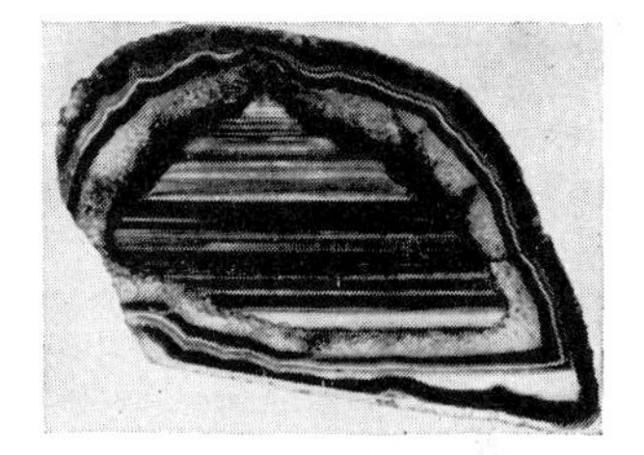

Fig. 538. Agate with onyx in center.

Itacolumite. A flexible sandstone. Contains some mica.

Metaquartzite. Metamorphosed sandstone in which the individual quartz particles are generally not easily recognized by the naked eye.

Next to water, quartz is the most common of all oxides. It is a very important rock-forming mineral, being a constituent of many igneous and sedimentary rocks. It occurs in rocks of all ages and in many ore deposits. It is also found very abundantly as sand and gravel.

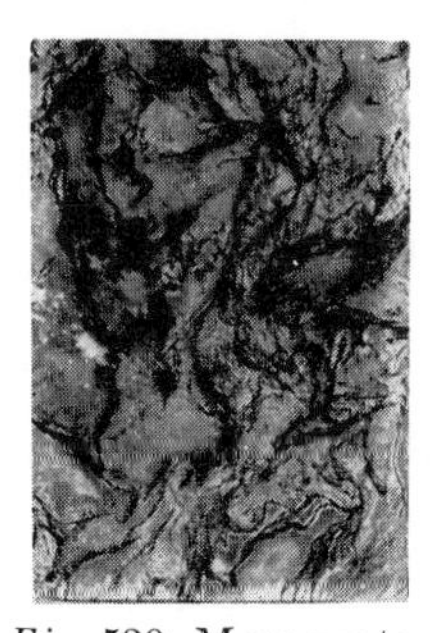

Fig. 539. Moss agate.

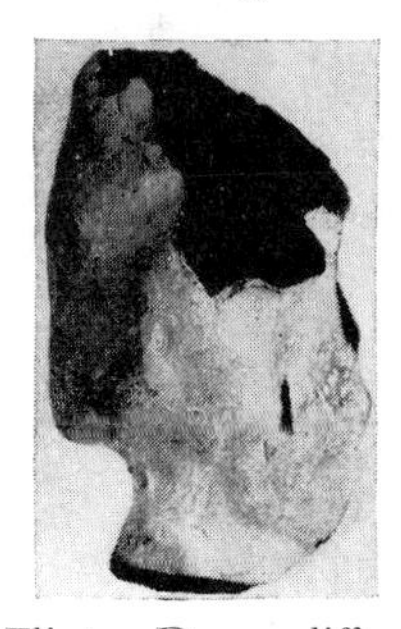

Fig. 540. Flint. Dover cliffs, England.

Rock crystal, amethyst, smoky and rose quartz, aventurine, cat's-eye, tiger's-eye, chalcedony, agate, and jasper are used extensively in jewelry and for ornamental purposes; agate and chalcedony for mortars and pestles; rock crystal for dishes, vases, optical and physical instruments, and chemical and radio apparatus; sand for mortar, plaster, and glass; sandstone and quartzite for building and paving purposes and grindstones; and ground or crushed quartz and flint in wood fillers, pottery, scouring and polishing soaps, and as an abrasive. Large quantities of quartz are also used as a flux in metallurgical processes and in the manufacture of refractories. See also page 468.

Tridymite, SiO_2. Occurs in two modifications. One is hexagonal (β tridymite) and is formed normally between 870 and 1470°C. Below 117°C. it changes to the orthorhombic modification (α tridymite), which occurs in thin tabular crystals with a pseudohexagonal outline. Twin crystals (trillings) are common. Crystals are sometimes arranged in spherical and fan- and wedge-shaped groups.

Basal cleavage. Hardness, 6.5 to 7. Specific gravity, 2.3 (quartz 2.65). Vitreous luster. White, colorless, yellowish or brownish. Translucent to transparent, α1.469, β1.469, γ1.473. Very similar to cristobalite.

First found in the trachyte of Mt. San Cristobal, near Pachua, Mexico. Occurs in cavities of volcanic igneous rocks—obsidian, rhyolite, and andesite. Usually associated with cristobalite. Frequently observed in high-silica refractory materials.

Cristobalite, SiO_2. Tetragonal. Very small pseudocubic crystals, often skeletal and twinned. Cubic above 230°C. Colorless to white. Translucent. Dull luster. Hardness, 6.5. Specific gravity, 2.3. ω 1.484, ϵ 1.487. Occurs in cavities in volcanic igneous rocks, commonly associated with tridymite; also in glass and silica bricks.

Because of the close relationship of the structural arrangement of the various forms of silicon dioxide (SiO_2)—quartz, tridymite, cristobalite—to that of the silicates, these oxides are sometimes grouped with the silicates. See page 359.

Cuprite (*Ruby Copper Ore*), Cu_2O.

Cubic, hexoctahedral class—$4/m\ \bar{3}\ 2/m$. Crystals are common, consisting usually of the cube, octahedron, and rhombic dodecahedron, often in combination. Also, compact, granular, and earthy massive; fine slender needles are called *chalcotrichite* or *plush copper*.

Hardness, 3.5 to 4. Specific gravity, 5.8 to 6.2. Metallic adamantine to dull luster. Indistinct octahedral cleavage. Very high index of refraction, $n = 2.849$. Ruby red to almost black in color. Transparent to opaque. Brownish-red to dirty-brown streak.

Cu_2O. Cu 88.82, O 11.18 per cent. Usually quite pure. Alters readily to malachite, azurite, tenorite (CuO), and native copper. Pseudomorphs of malachite after cuprite are rather common.

Cuprite is a secondary mineral, resulting from the oxidation of various copper minerals. Commonly found with malachite, azurite, native copper, chrysocolla, limonite, and chalcopyrite.

At Chessy, France, it occurs in crystals, partially or completely altered to malachite; also found at Cornwall, England; Dobschau, Hungary; Chile; Peru; Bolivia; Australia; French and Belgian Congo; Tsumeb, South-West Africa; the Ural Mountains. Abundant with other copper ores at Bisbee, Clifton, and Morenci, Arizona; with native copper in the Lake Superior copper district.

An ore of copper.

Zincite (*Red Zinc Ore*), ZnO.

Hexagonal, dihexagonal pyramidal class—6 *m m*. Crystals are hemimorphic and consist of prisms, upper pyramid, and lower basal pinacoid. Natural crystals are very rare. Usually as compact, granular, or foliated masses (Fig. 541).

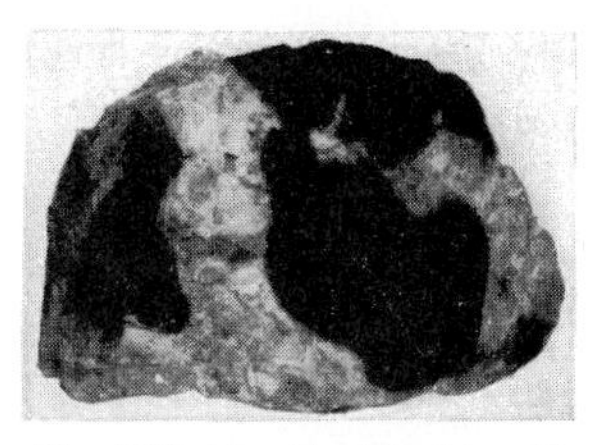

Fig. 541. Zincite (dark) with calcite. Franklin, New Jersey.

Perfect basal cleavage. Hardness, 4 to 4.5. Specific gravity, 5.7. Subadamantine to vitreous luster. High indices of refraction, ω 2.013, ϵ 2.029, (+). Dark red to orange or yellow in color. Reddish to orange-yellow streak. Translucent to opaque.

ZnO. Zn 80.34, O 19.66 per cent. Usually contains some manganese and iron.

Occurs at Franklin and Sterling Hill, New Jersey, in metamorphic limestones associated with franklinite, rhodonite, willemite, sphalerite, rhodochrosite, and calcite. Also in Schneeberg, Saxony; Tuscany; Poland; Spain; Tasmania.

An ore of zinc. See page 476.

Hematite Group

This group includes the isomorphous minerals corundum, hematite, and ilmenite. These are oxides of aluminum, iron, and titanium. They crystallize in the hexagonal system. Hematite is an extremely important economic mineral.

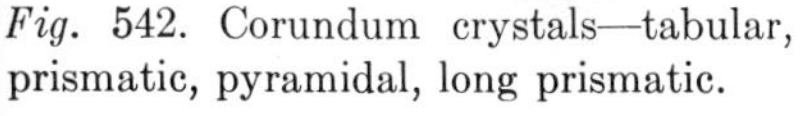

Fig. 542. Corundum crystals—tabular, prismatic, pyramidal, long prismatic.

Fig. 543. Corundum: variety, sapphire. Ceylon.

CORUNDUM (*Sapphire, Ruby, Emery*), Al_2O_3.

Hexagonal, ditrigonal scalenohedral class—$\bar{3}$ $2/m$. Well-developed crystals are common and often rather large. The habit may be pyramidal, rhombohedral, prismatic, or tabular (Figs. 542 and 543). The most common forms are the prism of the second order, unit rhombohedron, bipyramid of the second order, and the basal pinacoid. Large crystals are sometimes rough or rounded, barrel-shaped, and deeply furrowed or striated. Penetration and polysynthetic twins are common, the twinning being parallel to the unit rhombohedron. The basal pinacoid often shows triangular striations. Occurs also in compact, granular, and lamellar masses, showing frequently a nearly rectangular parting or pseudocleavage.

Basal and nearly rectangular rhombohedral partings. Conchoidal fracture. Hardness, 9. Specific gravity, 3.9 to 4.1. Commonly gray, brown, and bluish; also red, blue, yellow, and colorless. Sometimes multicolored. Transparent to translucent. Vitreous luster. ω 1.768, ϵ 1.760, (−). Luminescence is sometimes observed, especially on the gem varieties.

Al_2O_3. Al 52.9, O 47.1 per cent. Crystals are usually quite pure. Small amounts of the oxides of iron, chromium, and titanium may be present as pigments. Emery is generally quite impure.

Several varieties of corundum may be distinguished.

Ruby. This is the transparent deep-red variety. It is highly prized as a gem.

Sapphire. The sapphire proper is a transparent blue corundum. Transparent stones of other colors are called *yellow*, *golden*, or *white sapphires*, and so on. Sometimes the following terms are also used: when green, *oriental emerald;* yellow, *oriental topaz;* violet, *oriental amethyst.* Sapphires are used for gem purposes.

Gem rubies and sapphires frequently show asterism (see page 100) and are called star rubies and star sapphires.

Common Corundum. This includes crystals and compact masses with dull and irregularly distributed colors.

Emery. This is an intimate mixture of corundum, magnetite, hematite, quartz, and spinel. Dark gray to black in color. It was first considered an iron ore. The admixture may be as high as 40 per cent. The hardness may be considerably lower than that of the other varieties, namely, 7 to 9.

Corundum usually occurs disseminated in crystalline limestone and dolomite, gneiss, mica schist, chlorite schist, nepheline syenite, granite, and other crystalline rocks. It is commonly associated with magnetite, mica, chlorite, nepheline, serpentine, and spinel.

The gem varieties are found principally in placer deposits in Ceylon, Burma, Kashmir (Northern India), Thailand, China, Queensland, Ural Mountains, and near Helena, Montana. Rubies and sapphires are highly prized as gems. They are produced artificially in large quantities. Many of these synthetic corundums possess superior colors and when small are often extremely difficult to distinguish from the natural stones (see page 432).

Common corundum is found in extensive deposits associated with peridotite in North and South Carolina and in Georgia; at Raglan and elsewhere in Renfrew County, Ontario, in nepheline syenite; also in Westchester County, New York; Chester County, Pennsylvania; and Chester, Massachusetts. Russia, Madagascar, India, and the Union of South Africa furnish most of the corundum used in industry.

Most of the world's supply of emery is obtained from the islands of Naxos and Samos in the Grecian archipelago and from Asia Minor. On Naxos and Samos it occurs in crystalline limestones and schists. It is also found in the Ural Mountains; Saxony; associated with chlorite and margarite in amphibolite schist at Chester, Massachusetts; in peridotite at Peekskill, New York. Pittsylvania County, Virginia, and Peekskill, New York, are the most important American occurrences of emery.

Ruby and sapphire are used extensively for gem purposes. They are produced artificially in good quality and are used principally as jewels and bearings in watches, in electrical and scientific instruments, and as thread guides in the textile industry, and have important medical and military uses. Synthetic star rubies and sapphires have also been produced since September, 1947. Common corundum and emery are abrasive materials. Artificial Al_2O_3 is produced in large quantities and sold as *alundum*, *aloxite*, *exolon*, and *lionite* (see page 438).

HEMATITE (*Specularite, Specular Iron Ore, Red Iron Ore*), Fe_2O_3.

Hexagonal, ditrigonal scalenohedral class—$\bar{3}\ 2/m$. Crystals are either thin or thick tabular, pyramidal, rhombohedral, or, more rarely, prismatic

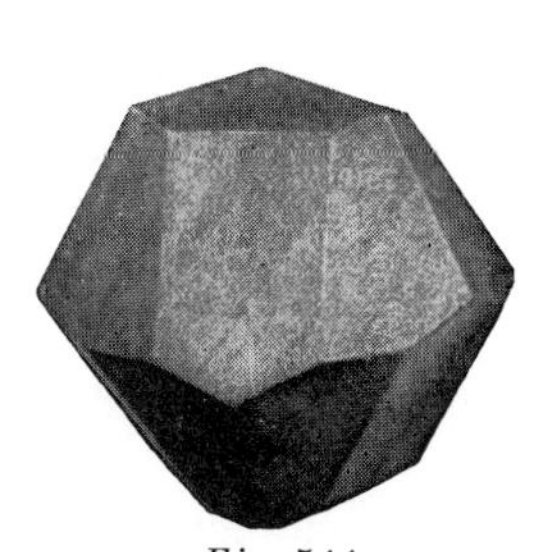

Fig. 544.

Fig. 545. Hematite. Island of Elba.

in habit (Figs. 544 and 545). Tabular crystals are often arranged in rosettes and are then called *iron roses.* The basal pinacoid is frequently striated, owing to polysynthetic twinning. Occurs more abundantly in compact, granular, columnar, fibrous, botryoidal (Fig. 546), reniform, stalactitic, micaceous, oölitic, and earthy masses.

No cleavage, but a rhombohedral parting which is nearly cubical is sometimes observed. Conchoidal to uneven fracture. Hardness, 5.5 to 6.5; earthy varieties are apparently soft. Specific gravity, 4.9 to 5.3. Metallic, splendent, or dull luster. Opaque, except in very thin scales. Commonly steel gray, reddish brown, or iron black in color; sometimes with beautiful tarnish colors. Earthy varieties are red in color. Cherry-red or reddish-brown streak. Sometimes slightly magnetic, owing to the presence of a small amount of magnetite.

Fe_2O_3. Fe 70, O 30 per cent. May contain as much as 7 per cent of titanium dioxide; also ferrous oxide, magnesium oxide, phosphoric acid, silica, and clay. Infusible. Becomes magnetic when heated on charcoal. When powdered, it is slowly soluble in acids. Occurs as a pseudomorph after calcite, siderite, pyrite, and magnetite.

There are several varieties of hematite.

Specularite or Specular Iron Ore. This includes crystals, micaceous, and granular masses with a metallic or splendent luster. Usually steel gray or iron black in color.

Compact or Red Hematite. Compact masses, often with a radial fibrous structure. Submetallic to dull luster. Iron black or brownish red in color.

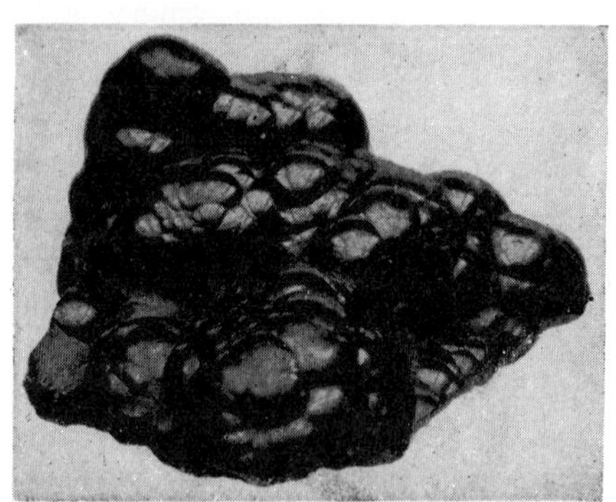

Fig. 546. Hematite (kidney ore). Cumberland, England.

Kidney Ore. Reniform masses, usually with smooth, shiny surfaces (Fig. 546).

Red Ocher. This includes earthy varieties, which are very soft and have a dull luster. Often contains considerable clay or sand.

Argillaceous Hematite. Hard and compact varieties, which are generally quite impure due to admixtures of much clay, sand, or jasper. Brownish black, reddish brown, or red in color.

Oölitic or Fossil Iron Ore. This variety possesses an oölitic structure and frequently contains fossil remains.

Martite. Hematite occurring in octahedrons, pseudomorphous after magnetite.

Hematite is the most important iron ore. It occurs (1) in independent deposits, sometimes of great thickness and extent; (2) as an accessory mineral in many igneous rocks, such as granite and syenite; (3) in cracks and crevices, usually with quartz; (4) as an inclusion in many minerals; thus, in feldspar, quartz, and carnallite; (5) as a sublimation product in lavas; thus, on Vesuvius and Etna; (6) sometimes it is the result of contact metamorphism.

Excellent crystals are found on the island of Elba, in the Mediterranean Sea; the Saint Gotthard district, Switzerland (iron roses); Arendal, Norway; Långban and Nordmark, Sweden; Cumberland, England.

Enormous deposits of hematite occur in the rocks, chiefly of Huronian and Archean ages, in the Lake Superior region of northern Michigan, Minnesota, Wisconsin, and Canada. There are seven well-defined iron ranges or districts in this region: namely, *Marquette* in Michigan; *Menominee* and *Gogebic* in Michigan and Wisconsin; *Mesabi*, *Vermilion*, and *Cuyuna* in Minnesota; *Michipicoten* in Ontario, Canada. This region produces about 95,000,000 long tons of iron ore annually. Most of the ore is mined by power shovels operating in huge open pits. This ore includes both the hard and soft varieties. Oölitic or fossiliferous hematite occurs at Clinton, New York, and in large quantities in eastern Tennessee and northern Alabama. Birmingham, Alabama, is the center of an important district, which has furnished about 8,000,000 long tons annually. Important deposits of hematite also occur in Missouri, Wyoming, and Pennsylvania. Enormous deposits of hematite, recently discovered in the Provinces of Labrador and Quebec, Canada, and at Cerro Bolivar Mountain, Venezuela, are important sources of the ore.

Hematite is the chief source of the iron of commerce and industry. In the United States about 82 per cent of the iron ore mined annually is hematite. Relatively small amounts of hematite are used in paints and as a polishing powder, usually called *rouge*. See also page 455.

ILMENITE (*Menaccanite, Titanic Iron Ore*), $FeTiO_3$.

Hexagonal, trigonal rhombohedral class—$\bar{3}$. Crystals are tabular or rhombohedral in habit and resemble those of hematite. Occasionally rhombohedrons of the second and third orders are present. Generally in compact or granular masses; also in thin plates or disseminated grains, or as pebbles or sand.

No cleavage, but basal and rhombohedral partings. Conchoidal to uneven fracture. Hardness, 5 to 6. Specific gravity, 4.3 to 5.5. Iron to brownish black in color. Black to brownish-red streak. Metallic to submetallic luster. Opaque; thin plates are brown in transmitted light. Slightly magnetic, greatly increased by heating.

$FeTiO_3$. Fe 36.8, Ti 31.6, O 31.6 per cent. Magnesium or manganese may replace some of the iron. Infusible. Yields a blue or violet solution after fusion with sodium carbonate and subsequent boiling with hydrochloric acid and tin foil.

As an accessory mineral it is common in many igneous and metamorphic rocks, such as granite, syenite, diorite, diabase, gneiss, and mica schist. Also found in large quantities in black sand; thus at Pablo Beach, Florida, and elsewhere along the Atlantic coast; and Idaho. Common associates are hematite, magnetite, apatite, serpentine, sphene, rutile, and quartz. Some localities are Kragerö, Snarum, and elsewhere, Norway; various places in Sweden; the Saint Gotthard district and Binnenthal, Switzerland; India; Allard Lake, Province of Quebec, Canada; Orange County, New York; Magnet Cove, Arkansas. Large deposits of ilmenite, associated with magnetite, are mined at Tahawus, Essex County, New York; also in Colorado, Minnesota, Rhode Island, and Wyoming.

Ilmenite is an important source of the metal and the oxide TiO_2, which is used as a pigment in paint, paper, rubber, ceramics, plastics, textiles, linoleum, printing ink, cosmetics, and soap. Also see page 473.

Spinel Group

The members of this group—spinel, magnetite, franklinite, and chromite—crystallize in the hexoctahedral class of the cubic system. They are important minerals. Chemically, they had long been assumed to be aluminates and ferrites of magnesium, iron, zinc, manganese, and chromium. Now, however, on the basis of their crystal structures they are considered as double oxides. Thus, the formula of spinel, which was formerly written as $Mg(AlO_2)_2$, is now given as $MgAl_2O_4$ or $MgO.Al_2O_3$.

SPINEL, $MgAl_2O_4$.

Cubic, hexoctahedral class—$4/m\ \bar{3}\ 2/m$. Octahedral crystals, frequently in combination with the rhombic dodecahedron. Contact twins are common, twinned parallel to a face of the octahedron (spinel law). Generally in disseminated or loose crystals or in rounded grains.

Imperfect octahedral cleavage. Hardness, 7.5 to 8. Specific gravity, 3.5 to 4.5. Vitreous to nearly dull in luster. $n = 1.718$ to 1.8, depending upon the composition. All colors, but chiefly red, blue, green, brown, and black. White streak. Transparent to opaque. May become luminescent.

$MgAl_2O_4$. Magnesium may be partially replaced by iron, zinc, or manganese; the aluminum by ferric iron and chromium. Infusible. When pure, MgO 28.2, Al_2O_3 71.8 per cent. The varieties of spinel may be classified as follows:

1. *Gem Spinels.*
   a. *Ruby spinel.* Deep red, transparent. Most popular gem variety.
   b. *Balas ruby.* Rose red to pink.

c. *Rubicelle.* Yellow to orange red.
d. *Almandine.*[1] Violet and purple.
e. *Sapphirine.* Blue spinel.
f. *Chlorospinel.* Iron-bearing, grass-green.

2. *Pleonaste.* An iron-magnesium spinel. Also called ceylonite. Dark green, brown, or black. Usually opaque or nearly so.
3. *Picotite.* Chrome spinel. Black, yellow, or greenish brown. Translucent to nearly opaque.
4. *Gahnite.* Zinc spinel. Commonly in fairly large crystals. Various shades of green, also brown or black. Translucent to opaque. Specific gravity, 4.55.
5. *Hercynite.* Iron spinel. Black in color. Gray-green streak.

The names of the gem varieties of spinel are misleading and cause much confusion. Their use should be discontinued and gem spinels designated in terms of color, thus, red spinel, pink spinel, blue spinel, and so forth. Gem spinels are now made synthetically in very attractive colors and sold under various names.

Spinel is a common metamorphic mineral occurring usually in granular limestones, gneiss, and serpentine. It is also an accessory constituent of basic igneous rocks. Gem spinels are frequently found in placer deposits, especially in Ceylon, Burma, Thailand, and Madagascar. The common associates are calcite, chondrodite, corundum, graphite, and olivine. Important localities are Åker, Sweden; Orange and St. Lawrence counties, New York; Franklin, New Jersey; Bolton, Massachusetts; Macon County, North Carolina.

Synthetic spinel is an important refractory. Transparent and colored spinels (natural and synthetic) are used as gems (see page 435).

MAGNETITE (*Magnetic Iron Ore, Lodestone*), **$FeFe_2O_4$.**

Cubic, hexoctahedral class—$4/m\ \overline{3}\ 2/m$. Octahedral and rhombic dodecahedral crystals are very common, often very perfect and with bright surfaces. Striated faces are, however, not infrequently observed. Twinned according to the spinel law, yielding contact and polysynthetic twins. Crystals are sometimes highly modified and may be greatly distorted (Fig. 547). Usually occurs in coarse- to fine-grained masses, in lamellar to compact aggregates, as disseminated grains, or as loose grains or sand; more rarely dendritic, especially in mica.

Octahedral parting. Conchoidal to uneven fracture. Hardness, 5.5 to 6.5. Specific gravity, 5.2. Metallic, submetallic to dull luster. Iron black in color. Black streak. Opaque. Strongly magnetic (Fig. 548).

$FeFe_2O_4$. Often written Fe_3O_4 or $FeO.Fe_2O_3$. Fe 72.4, O 27.6 per

[1] Should not be confused with almandite.

Fig. 547. Magnetite crystals—octahedron, rhombic dodecahedron, tetragonal trisoctahedron, striated.

cent. May contain magnesium, nickel, manganese, phosphorus, or titanium. Fuses with difficulty. Alters to limonite and hematite (martite). Magnetite occurs as a pseudomorph after pyrite, hematite, and siderite.

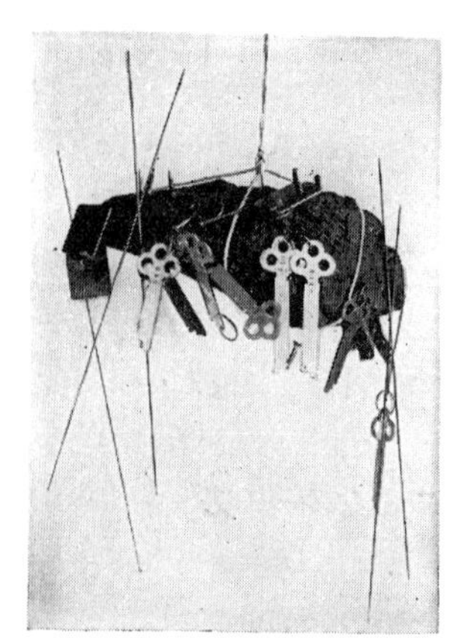

Fig. 548. Magnetite: variety, lodestone. Magnet Cove, Arkansas.

Magnetite occurs rather widespread, being found principally as (1) a primary constituent of basic igneous rocks, such as diabase, gabbro, nepheline syenite, and basalt; (2) as a metamorphic mineral; and (3) as a constituent of certain river, lake, and sea sands, called *black sands*. The common associates are chlorite, hornblende, pyroxene, feldspar, quartz, pyrite, chalcopyrite, epidote, chromite, garnet, corundum, and ilmenite. Large deposits are found in Norway and Sweden; the Ural Mountains; Brazil; Warren, Essex, and Clinton counties, New York; Cornwall, Pennsylvania; Oxford, New Jersey. Black sands are rather widespread in Alaska, California, Idaho, Montana, Colorado, Oregon, and Washington. They sometimes carry small amounts of platinum. Magnetite from Magnet Cove, Arkansas, is usually very strongly magnetic. It acts as a natural magnet and is termed *lodestone* (Fig. 548).

Magnetite is an important iron ore. Mixed with cement magnetite is used as ballast in ships. Also see page 455.

Fig. 549. Franklinite (octahedron and rhombic dodecahedron) with calcite. Franklin, New Jersey.

FRANKLINITE $(Zn,Mn)Fe_2O_4$.

Cubic, hexoctahedral class—$4/m\ \bar{3}\ 2/m$. The octahedron is rather common, sometimes with the rhombic dodecahedron (Fig. 549) and with rounded edges. Occurs usually in compact and granular masses or as rounded grains.

Imperfect octahedral cleavage. Conchoidal fracture. Hardness, 5.5 to 6.5. Specific gravity, 5 to 5.2. Metallic or dull luster. Iron black in color. Brown, reddish, or black streak. Often slightly magnetic. Opaque.

$(Zn,Mn)Fe_2O_4$. The composition varies greatly, ZnO 17 to 25 per cent, MnO 10 to 12 per cent, and Fe_2O_3 about 60 per cent. When heated becomes strongly magnetic. Infusible.

Franklinite occurs extensively in the metamorphic area about Franklin and Sterling Hill, Sussex County, New Jersey, where it is associated with willemite, zincite, rhodonite, and calcite. Also found in cubical crystals at Eibach, Hesse-Nassau, Germany.

Franklinite is a source of zinc which, by heating the mineral, is easily obtained either as spelter or zinc oxide. The residue contains about 12 per cent of manganese and 40 per cent of iron and is used as spiegeleisen in the manufacture of steel. See pages 463 and 476.

CHROMITE (*Chrome Iron, Chromic Iron Ore*), $Fe(Cr,Fe)_2O_4$.

Cubic, hexoctahedral class—$4/m\,\bar{3}\,2/m$. Rarely in octahedral crystals. Usually in fine granular, compact masses, or as disseminated grains.

Indistinct, octahedral cleavage. Uneven to conchoidal fracture. Hardness, 5.5. Specific gravity, 4.2 to 4.8. Pitchy submetallic to metallic luster. Iron black to brownish black in color. Dark-brown to grayish streak. Opaque. Sometimes slightly magnetic.

$Fe(Cr,Fe)_2O_4$. Composition varies. Magnesium, aluminum, and manganese may be present. Average composition, Cr_2O_3 52 to 58, Fe_2O_3 25 to 40, Al_2O_3 5 to 15, MgO 5 to 10 per cent.

Chromite occurs usually in veins and irregular masses in basic magnesium rocks, especially serpentine. It is often the result of magmatic segregation. The common associates are serpentine, talc, chrome garnet, zaratite, and corundum. It occurs at Franckenstein, Silesia; New Zealand; Rhodesia; New Caledonia; Greece; Asia Minor; India; U.S.S.R.; Philippine Islands; Cuba; Texas; Lancaster County, and elsewhere in Pennsylvania; Baltimore County, Maryland; Shasta and other counties in California; also in North Carolina, Oregon, Washington, and Wyoming. Also found in platinum placers and in black sands.

Chromite is used in the manufacture of refractory chrome bricks and furnace linings; for making special grades of steels, such as ferrochrome used for cutting tools, projectiles, and armor plate; for stainless steel, rustless iron, and chrome plating; also for the production of pigments, dyes, and mordants, and in tanning. See also page 450.

Hausmannite, $MnMn_2O_4$.

Tetragonal, ditetragonal bipyramidal class—$4/m\ 2/m\ 2/m$. Crystals are acute pyramidal and often form cyclic twins. Found generally in granular to compact masses.

Perfect basal cleavage. Hardness, 5 to 5.5. Specific gravity, 4.7 to 4.8. Brownish black to black in color. Chestnut-brown streak. Greasy metallic luster. Opaque.

$MnMn_2O_4$. Often written Mn_3O_4. May contain zinc and iron. Soluble in hydrochloric acid with an evolution of chlorine.

A comparatively rare mineral. The common associates are pyrolusite, psilomelane, magnetite, barite, and hematite. Occurs at Ilfeld and Ilmenau, Germany; Pajsberg and Långban, Sweden; Minas Gerais, Brazil; Batesville, Arkansas.

Chrysoberyl, $BeAl_2O_4$.

Orthorhombic, bipyramidal class—$2/m\ 2/m\ 2/m$. Crystals are tabular, also heart-shaped and pseudohexagonal twins; frequently striated (Figs. 550 to 552). Usually disseminated. Also as crystal fragments and loose or rounded grains.

Fig. 550.

Fig. 551. Chrysoberyl (twin). Haddam, Connecticut.

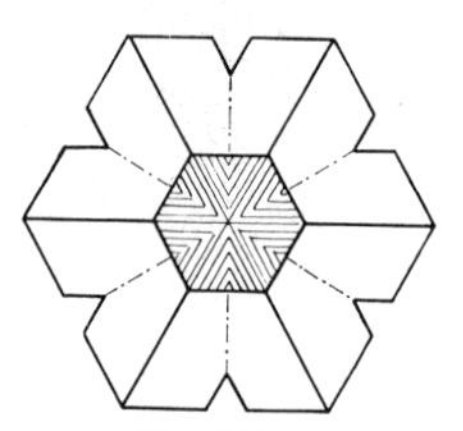

Fig. 552.

Distinct prismatic cleavage. Conchoidal fracture. Hardness, 8.5. Specific gravity, 3.6 to 3.8. Vitreous to greasy luster. α 1.747, β 1.748, γ 1.756, (+); indices and $2V$ variable; $r > v$ strong. Greenish white, greenish yellow, and asparagus to emerald green in color; often red in transmitted light. Transparent to translucent. Some varieties have a bluish opalescence or chatoyancy.

$BeAl_2O_4$. BeO 19.8, Al_2O_3 80.2 per cent. May contain some iron and chromium. Infusible. Insoluble in acids.

There are three varieties:

Ordinary Chrysoberyl. Usually green color.

Alexandrite. Emerald-green color in daylight, but columbine red in artificial light; with tungsten light, intermediate between red and green. Artificial gem corundum exhibiting these properties is often sold as alexandrite. See page 434.

Cat's-eye, or Cymophane. A chatoyant, opalescent, yellow-green variety. Has a silky luster and fibrous structure. When cut cabochon, light appears concentrated in a line or band across the stone, suggesting the appearance of a cat's eye.

Chrysoberyl is usually found in pegmatites, gneiss, mica schist, or granite. Common associates are beryl, tourmaline, garnet, apatite, and sillimanite. It occurs in the Ural Mountains; Haddam, Connecticut; Norway and Stoneham, Maine; Greenfield, New York; as rounded pebbles in the gem placers of Ceylon, Tasmania, and Brazil.

Transparent varieties are highly prized as gems.

Rutile Group

This group contains the three common oxides of titanium, tin, and manganese which crystallize in the tetragonal system.

RUTILE, TiO_2.

Tetragonal, ditetragonal bipyramidal class—$4/m\ 2/m\ 2/m$. Crystals are common. Usually prismatic or thick columnar, consisting of the

Fig. 553. Rutile. Georgia.

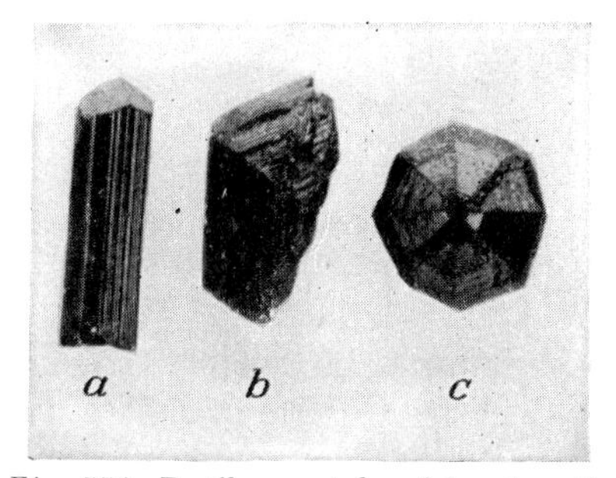

Fig. 554. Rutile crystals—(*a*) prismatic and striated, (*b*) knee-shaped, (*c*) rosette (eightling).

prisms and bipyramids of the first and second orders (Fig. 553). Prism faces frequently striated vertically (Fig. 554*a*). Knee-shaped twins often observed, the twinning plane being parallel to a face of the bipyramid of the second order (Fig. 554*b*). Also trillings, sixlings, and eightlings (rosettes) according to this law (Fig. 554*c*). Also in compact, granular masses. Needle-like crystals of rutile occur frequently as inclusions in quartz.

Distinct prismatic and pyramidal cleavages. Hardness, 6 to 6.5. Specific gravity, 4.2 to 4.3. Metallic adamantine luster. Very high indices of refraction and extremely strong double refraction; ω 2.616, ϵ 2.903, (+). Very strong dispersion. Opaque to transparent. Red-brown, blood-red, and black in color. Streak, yellow or pale brown.

TiO_2. Ti 60, O 40 per cent. TiO_2 occurs in two other modifications, *anatase* or *octahedrite* (tetragonal) and *brookite* (orthorhombic), which are not very common. Usually contains considerable iron, columbium, tantalum, and tin. Occurs pseudomorphous after hematite, brookite, and anatase. Leucoxene is a fine-grained yellowish-white to brown alteration product of various titanium minerals, chiefly rutile.

Rutile is the most common titanium mineral and occurs in gneiss, mica schist, slate, granite, granular limestone, and dolomite. Commonly associated with quartz, hematite, and feldspar. Found at Arendal and Kragerö, Norway; the Ural Mountains; Binnenthal and Saint Gotthard district, Switzerland; Nelson County, Virginia; Graves Mountain, Georgia; Magnet Cove, Arkansas; Keystone, South Dakota; Oaxaca, Mexico. Occurs also in secondary deposits; thus, at Pablo Beach, Florida, in quartz, ilmenite, and zircon sand.

Used in coloring porcelain yellow and artificial teeth bluish white; also in special grades of steel and copper-bearing alloys; as a mordant in dyeing leather and in carbons for arc lights. Also see page 473.

Rutile is now made synthetically in various colors. Because of its high indices of refraction and strong dispersion very attractive gems are cut. They are sold as *titania*.

CASSITERITE (*Tin Stone*), **SnO_2.**

Tetragonal, ditetragonal bipyramidal class—$4/m\ 2/m\ 2/m$. Crystals are usually short prismatic, showing the prisms and bipyramids of the first and second orders. Knee-shaped twins are common, the bipyramid of the second order being the twinning plane. Frequently in disseminated granular or reniform masses; also in grains and pebbles. Concentric and fibrous radial structure is frequently observed.

Hardness, 6 to 7. Specific gravity, 6.8 to 7. Adamantine to submetallic luster. High indices of refraction, ω 1.997, ϵ 2.093, (+). Reddish brown, brown, black; also yellow or white. Streak, white to pale brown.

Three varieties may be distinguished:

Ordinary Cassiterite, or Tin Stone. Crystals and compact masses.

Wood Tin. Botryoidal and reniform masses of varying colors, with concentric structure and commonly with a radial fibrous structure.

Stream Tin. Angular and rounded grains or pebbles in sands and gravels of streams.

SnO_2. Sn 78.6, O 21.4 per cent. Generally contains iron; also manganese, tantalum, and columbium. Infusible and insoluble in acids. For a rapid test for cassiterite, see page 237.

Cassiterite is commonly associated with quartz, topaz, fluorite, apatite, and tourmaline. It occurs usually in veins cutting granites and rhyolites, which have generally been greatly altered as the result of pneumatolytic action. Granitic rocks altered in this way are called *greisen*, while non-granitic rocks are termed *zwitter*. On account of its great resistance to weathering, cassiterite is also found extensively in secondary deposits. The Malay Peninsula, the islands of Banca and Billiton near Borneo, Bolivia, China, Nigeria, and Siam are the chief producers of cassiterite. Other localities are Cornwall, England; Altenberg, Saxony; Australia; Tasmania; Brazil; Buck Creek, Alaska; Black Hills, South Dakota; Gaffney, South Carolina; King's Mountain, North Carolina; El Paso, Texas.

Cassiterite is the only source of tin of commerce and industry. It is used extensively in the manufacture of tin plate or sheet tin, solder, bronze, tin amalgam, gun metal, type metal, speculum metal, britannia metals, and pewter. Sodium stannate is used in calico printing. The artificial oxide is used as a polishing powder. Also see page 472.

PYROLUSITE (*Black Oxide of Manganese*), MnO_2.

Tetragonal, ditetragonal bipyramidal class—$4/m\ 2/m\ 2/m$. Prismatic and needle-like crystals, rare; frequently pseudomorphous after manganite; generally compact, radially fibrous, columnar, stalactitic, dendritic, or powdery crusts (Fig. 555). When in crystals it is called *polianite*, hardness, 6 to 6.5, not common.

Fig. 555. Pyrolusite. Ilfeld, Thuringia, Germany.

Hardness, 1 to 2.5; soils the fingers. Specific gravity, 4.8. Black or dark steel-gray in color. Black or bluish-black streak. Metallic to dull luster. Opaque.

MnO_2. Mn 63.2, O 36.8 per cent. Usually contains small amounts of barium, water, and silica.

Pyrolusite is a secondary mineral resulting from the decomposition of manganite, rhodochrosite, and various manganiferous iron ores. Usually found with manganite, psilomelane, hematite, or limonite. The term *wad* is frequently applied as a field term to substances whose chief constituents are earthy hydrous manganese oxides.

Occurs extensively in Thuringia and in the Harz Mountains, Germany; Bohemia; France; Brazil; U.S.S.R.; Hungary; Ghana; Mexico; and Cuba. The principal localities in the United States are the Crimora district, Augusta County, Virginia; Cave Spring and Cartersville, Georgia; Batesville, Arkansas; Livermore, Alameda County, California; Butte, Montana; Brandon, Vermont.

Pyrolusite is used in the manufacture of chlorine, oxygen, ferromanganese, manganese bronze, spiegeleisen, and in dry batteries; as a coloring agent in calico printing and dyeing, glass, pottery, bricks, and paints; also as a decolorizer of green glass. Spiegeleisen is of great importance in the metallurgy of iron and steel. Also see page 462.

COLUMBITE (*Tantalite*), $(Fe,Mn)(Cb,Ta)_2O_6$.

Orthorhombic, bipyramidal class—$2/m\ 2/m\ 2/m$. Short prismatic or thick tabular crystals, often resembling those of wolframite. Also massive and disseminated.

Brachypinacoidal cleavage. Conchoidal to uneven fracture, often with iridescent tarnish. Hardness, 6. Specific gravity varies with increasing amount of tantalum oxide from 5.3 to 7.8. Brown to iron black in color. Brownish, reddish, or black streak. Greasy, submetallic to dull luster.

$(Fe,Mn)(Cb,Ta)_2O_6$. Composition varies greatly. Frequently contains tin and tungsten. When tantalum predominates, it is called *tantalite*. Columbite and tantalite grade into one another. Depending upon whether iron or manganese predominates, the terms *ferro-* or *manganocolumbite* or *ferro-* or *manganotantalite* are used. Infusible. Not attacked by acids.

Columbite and tantalite occur in granite pegmatites, or in alluvial deposits resulting from the disintegration and deposition of such rocks. Associates are beryl, tourmaline, spodumene, lepidolite, cryolite, quartz, feldspar, mica, wolframite, and cassiterite. They occur at Ivigtut, southern Greenland; Bodenmais, Bavaria; Miask, Ural Mountains; Pilbarra district, Western Australia; Nigeria; Federation of Malaya; Mozambique; Belgian Congo; Uganda; Madagascar; French Equatorial Africa; Southern Rhodesia; Union of South Africa; South-West Africa; northern Brazil; Standish, Maine; Branchville, Connecticut; Mitchell County, North Carolina; the Black Hills, South Dakota; Amelia County, Virginia; New Hampshire; Idaho.

An important source of columbium and tantalum. Tantalum was first used for electric-light filaments but has long been replaced by tungsten. It is now used in various electronic tubes, acid-resistant apparatus, tool steels, and as wire and plates in surgery. Columbium is used as an alloy in various types of steel, especially to improve the welding properties of stainless steel. See page 451.

URANINITE (*Pitchblende*), UO_2.

Cubic, hexoctahedral class—$4/m\ \bar{3}\ 2/m$. Crystals generally show the octahedron and rhombic dodecahedron but are rare. Commonly in compact botryoidal, reniform, curved lamellar, or granular masses. Often apparently amorphous.

Conchoidal to uneven fracture. Hardness, 3 to 6. Specific gravity, 6 to 10.6; crystals, 9 to 10.6. Pitchy to submetallic luster on fresh fracture surfaces, otherwise dull. Brown to black in color. Dark-green, brown, or black streak. Nonmagnetic.

UO_2 when pure. Composition is very complex and varies greatly, with varying percentages of lead, the rare earths thorium, cerium, yttrium, lanthanum, and erbium, and the gases nitrogen, argon, and helium. May also contain radium and be strongly radioactive. This element was discovered in uraninite from Jachymov, Czechoslovakia. *Cleveite* is a variety from near Arendal, Norway, and contains thorium, argon, and helium. *Nivenite* is characterized by about 10 per cent of the earths of the yttrium groups. It occurs in Llano County, Texas. *Bröggerite* occurs on the Island of Moss, near Oslo, Norway, and contains considerable thorium. The name *gummite* is often used for fine-grained yellow to orange-red alteration products of uraninite consisting chiefly of hydrated lead uranyl oxides.

As a primary constituent of pegmatites and granites, associated with allanite, thorite, and fergusonite, it is found in the Arendal and Moss districts, Norway; Sweden; Branchville, Connecticut; Mitchell County, North Carolina; Llano County, Texas; the Black Hills, South Dakota. With lead, silver, bismuth, and tin minerals it occurs at Katanga district, Belgian Congo; Jachymov and Příbram, Czechoslovakia; Johanngeorgenstadt, Saxony; Cornwall, England; Southern Rhodesia; Australia; LaBine Point, Great Bear Lake, Northwest Territory, Blind River district, Ontario, and Beaverlodge, Saskatchewan, Canada; Colorado Plateau (Colorado, Arizona, Utah, and New Mexico).

Uraninite is an important source of uranium and radium compounds. Uranium is used for atomic bombs, nuclear reactors, and in the manufacture of special grades of steels; its compounds for coloring glass, as pigments for porcelain painting, and in photography. As is well known, radium compounds possess important chemical, physical, and medicinal properties. See page 474.

B. Hydrated Oxides

Only the most important hydroxides will be described. These minerals are generally of secondary origin.

OPAL, $SiO_2.nH_2O$.

Amorphous. Usually compact, in veins or irregular masses, sometimes with botryoidal, reniform, stalactitic, or earthy structure.

Conchoidal fracture. Hardness, 5.5 to 6.5; earthy varieties may seem as low as 1. Specific gravity, 1.95 to 2.3. Vitreous, dull, or greasy luster. Index of refraction varies from 1.44 to 1.46. Transparent to opaque. Streak, white. Color varies greatly; colorless, white, yellow, brown, red, green, gray, blue, and so forth. Often a beautiful play of colors may be observed, which should not be confused with the fire caused by dispersion. It is due to fine cracks filled with material possessing a slightly different index of refraction than the original substance and perhaps also to an unequal distribution of the water content. Some opaque opals show an opalescence, especially after immersion in water. Luminescence is sometimes observed.

$SiO_2.nH_2O$. The amount of water present may vary from 1 to 21 per cent but is usually between 3 and 13 per cent. Opals are dried and hardened gelatinous silica. Yields water when heated in a closed tube. Infusible. Soluble in hot caustic potash or soda.

The principal varieties of opal include

Precious Opal. Yellowish white, dark gray, or bluish, with an excellent play of colors. Those with the lighter colors are called *white opals,* while the dark-gray, blue, and black opals are designated as *black opals.*

Fire Opal. Orange yellow to red in color. Semitransparent to transparent. May show a play of colors.

Common Opal. Translucent to opaque and of many colors. When milk white, yellowish, bluish, or greenish it is called *milk opal.* With a resinous luster and wax, honey or other yellow in color, it is *resin opal.* Wood petrified by opaline material is called *wood opal. Opal jasper* is red, reddish brown, or yellow-brown in color, with a resinous luster, and resembles jasper.

Fig. 556. Opal: variety, geyserite. Yellowstone Park.

Hyalite. Colorless and transparent masses of irregular outline. Looks like drops of melted glass. Sometimes luminescent.

Siliceous Sinter, Geyserite. These are opaline deposits from hot springs and geysers. May be porous, compact, fibrous, stalactitic, or botryoidal (Fig. 556) with a development like cauliflower; grayish, whitish, or brownish in color; sometimes with a pearly luster.

Diatomite, Diatomaceous Earth, Tripolite. Porous, earthy, and chalklike deposits of the siliceous remains of diatoms, radiolaria, and so forth. Light in weight.

Opal is commonly the result of the decomposition of silicate rocks by hot waters and is hence frequently found in cracks and cavities in igneous and sedimentary rocks. *Common opal* occurs rather widely distributed. *Precious opal* is found near Czerwenitz, Rumania; Queretaro and elsewhere in Mexico; Humboldt County, Nevada; Latah County, Idaho; Honduras; New South Wales, especially at White Cliffs, and at Lightning Ridge as black opal; Queensland; and South Australia.

Siliceous sinter, or *geyserite*, occurs abundantly in the Yellowstone Park, Iceland, and New Zealand. *Diatomite* is found in extensive deposits in California, Nevada, New Mexico, Oregon, and Washington.

Precious and fire opals are used for gem purposes; wood opal for ornamental purposes. Diatomite is used in the filtering and refining of sugar, fruit juices, and drugs; as a filler in paints, fertilizers, and insecticides; as a nonconductor of heat; and in polishing powders and scouring soaps.

MANGANITE, MnO(OH).

Monoclinic, prismatic class—$2/m$. Pseudo-orthorhombic, commonly in deeply striated prismatic crystals, arranged in groups or bundles (Fig. 557). Frequently twinned. Also in radial fibrous and columnar masses, more rarely granular and stalactitic.

Fig. 557. Manganite. Ilmenau, Thuringia, Germany.

Perfect clinopinacoidal cleavage. Uneven fracture. Hardness, 4. Specific gravity, 4.3. When fresh, manganite possesses a submetallic luster, an iron-black color, and a reddish-brown to brownish-black streak. If more or less decomposed, it is steel gray in color with a black streak and metallic luster.

MnO(OH). MnO 80.7, H_2O 10.2, O 9.1 per cent. Soluble in concentrated hydrochloric acid with an evolution of chlorine. Occurs as a pseudomorph after calcite. Alters easily to pyrolusite.

Commonly associated with hematite, barite, calcite, siderite, pyrolusite, and other manganese minerals. Excellent crystals occur at Ilfeld, Harz Mountains; Ilmenau, Thuringia; Långban, Sweden; Marquette County, Michigan; Douglas County, Colorado; Shenandoah County, Virginia; Alameda County, California; Sierra County, New Mexico; Nova Scotia; New Brunswick; Cornwall, England.

With pyrolusite it is used extensively in the preparation of oxygen and chlorine. An ore of manganese. See also page 462.

GOETHITE-LIMONITE (*Brown Hematite, Yellow Iron Ore*), $HFeO_2$.

Crystalline to amorphous. Found in crystals, but more commonly in compact, porous, or earthy masses. Often stalactitic, botryoidal, or mammillary. Radial fibrous structure and black varnish-like surfaces are quite characteristic. Also concretionary.

Hardness, 1 to 5.5. Specific gravity, 3.4 to 4. May be yellowish, brown, or black in color. Streak always yellow-brown. Conchoidal to earthy fracture.

$HFeO_2$. Fe_2O_3 89.9, H_2O 10.1 per cent. Crystals and the fibrous varieties, which are distinctly crystalline, have this composition. They are properly designated as **goethite,** although they have long been called **limonite.** Amorphous and earthy varieties, properly called limonite, are mixtures of iron oxides, with variable water content, and may contain silica, clay, manganese oxide, and organic matter. Common as a pseudomorph after iron minerals, especially pyrite, marcasite, and siderite.

Fig. 558. Stalactitic goethite. White Marsh, Pennsylvania.

Fig. 559. Goethite with varnish-like surface. Salisbury, Connecticut.

The important varieties are as follows:

Crystals. Orthorhombic, bipyramidal class—$2/m\ 2/m\ 2/m$. Vertically striated prisms, or flattened parallel to brachypinacoid. Perfect brachypinacoidal cleavage.

Compact. This includes the massive, stalactitic (Fig. 558), botryoidal, and other varieties, which often possess a radial fibrous structure and smooth varnish-like surfaces (Fig. 559).

Bog Iron Ore. Found in marshy and swampy places. More or less loose and porous in texture and may contain organic remains.

Ocherous Limonite. Here are placed the earthy, yellow, or brownish varieties, which may be quite impure on account of the admixture of clay and sand. Often called *yellow ocher.*

Goethite and limonite are the usual decomposition products of iron minerals, resulting from the action of water, carbon dioxide, humus acid, and oxygen. They are hence found very extensively, usually in association with such minerals as pyrite, hematite, magnetite, and siderite and also with many of the more strictly rock-forming minerals containing iron in small quantities, as the amphiboles and pyroxenes. *Residual goethite* and *limonite* may be the result of the decomposition of veins containing iron disulfide, or of the weathering of iron-bearing rocks. These minerals are usually associated with slates, schists, or limestones. They occur extensively in the United States in a belt extending from Vermont to Alabama, the principal mines being in Alabama, Virginia, West Virginia, Tennessee, and Georgia. They are also found in Texas, Iowa, Wisconsin, Minnesota, and Oregon. Very common as the yellow coloring matter of clays and soils and the brownish rusty stain on rocks.

Goethite and limonite are minor iron ores in the United States (see page 455). Also used as yellow ocher, burnt umber, and sienna in paints.

Diaspore, $HAlO_2$. Orthorhombic, bipyramidal class—$2/m\ 2/m\ 2/m$. Thin platy or acicular crystals, often striated; not common. Usually as thin scaly masses; also disseminated.

Perfect brachypinacoidal cleavage. Brittle. Hardness, 6.5 to 7. Specific gravity, 3.3 to 3.5. Colorless, pale yellow, violet-blue, and brown. Pearly on cleavage surfaces, otherwise vitreous. Excellent trichroism. α 1.702, β 1.722, γ 1.750, (+); $2V = 84°$.

$HAlO_2$. Al_2O_3 85, H_2O 15 per cent. May contain iron and manganese.

Commonly found with corundum or emery, dolomite, magnetite, spinel, chlorite, in metamorphic limestones, chloritic schists, and altered igneous rocks with alunite, and extensively in bauxite and aluminous clays. Occurs at Campolongo, Switzerland; Schemnitz, Czechoslovakia; Ural Mountains; Grecian Archipelago; Chester, Massachusetts; Unionville, Pennsylvania; and Macon County, North Carolina. See also occurrences of bauxite, below.

BAUXITE.

Commonly shows a pisolitic or oölitic structure with rounded, concretionary grains embedded in an amorphous or clay-like mass (Fig. 560).

Fig. 560. Pisolitic bauxite. Linwood, Georgia.

Hardness, 1 to 3. Specific gravity, 2.55. White, brown, yellow, or reddish. Argillaceous odor. Variable streak. Dull to earthy luster.

Bauxite is a mixture of hydrated aluminum oxide minerals, chiefly gibbsite, $Al(OH)_3$, boehmite, $AlO(OH)$, and diaspore; Al_2O_3 varying from 40 to 70 per cent. Ferric oxide, water, silica, and titanium oxide are usually present in varying amounts.

Bauxite is generally considered a rock. It is a decomposition production of feldspathic rocks, such as granites, syenites, gneisses, and so forth, the structure of the original rocks being sometimes well preserved. It is one of the principal constituents of *laterite*, which is quite abundant in tropical regions. Bauxite is also found in nodules, grains, and pockets of irregular shape in limestones and dolomites, probably the result of deposition from hot solutions.

The most important deposits of bauxite in the United States are found in Pulaski and Saline counties, Arkansas, the town of Bauxite being the chief center (Fig. 726, page 439); also in a belt extending from Jacksonville, Alabama, to Adamsville, Georgia; Tennessee; Virginia; in the departments of Var and Herault, southeastern France; Hesse-Nassau, Germany; British and Dutch Guiana (Surinam); Jugoslavia; Hungary; Jamaica; French West Africa; U.S.S.R.

Bauxite is the chief source of aluminum. It is also used in the manufacture of aluminum compounds, bauxite brick, and the artificial abrasives called *alundum*, *aloxite*, *exolon*, and *lionite*, and in the cement, steel, ferroalloy, and oil-refining industries. See also page 437.

Microlite, $(Ca,Na)_2Ta_2O_6(O,OH,F)$. Cubic, hexoctahedral class—$4/m\ \bar{3}\ 2/m$. Usually small octahedral crystals, sometimes highly modified. Good cleavage. Subconchoidal fracture. Pale yellow to brown, also hyacinth-red, olive-buff, or green. Resinous luster. Translucent to opaque. Streak, pale yellow to dark brown. Hardness, 5.5. Specific gravity increases with tantalum content from 4.2 to 6.4. May contain columbium and other rare elements. Occurs in pegmatites with columbite, tantalite, and other rare minerals. Microlite is found in Taos County, New Mexico; Gunnison County, Colorado; Riverside and San Diego counties, California.

Brucite, $Mg(OH)_2$.

Hexagonal, ditrigonal scalenohedral class—$\bar{3}\ 2/m$. Crystals are generally broad tabular. Commonly as foliated masses; sometimes fibrous and scaly. Fibers are elastic.

Hardness, 2.5. Specific gravity, 2.4. Pearly, waxy, or vitreous luster. Transparent to translucent. White, gray-blue, or green. White streak. Looks like gypsum or talc. ω 1.559, ϵ 1.580, (+).

$Mg(OH)_2$. MgO 69, H_2O 31 per cent. When considerable manganese or iron replaces magnesium, manganobrucite and ferrobrucite result. Zinc may be present in small amounts.

Found with serpentine, in metamorphic limestones, and chloritic and dolomitic schists. Occurs at Predazzo, Tirol; Hoboken, New Jersey; Brewster, New York; Lancaster County, Pennsylvania; Crestmore, California.

Used in the manufacture of refractory materials.

Psilomelane Group (*Black Hematite*).

Occurs usually in botryoidal, reniform, or stalactitic masses, having smooth surfaces (Fig. 561).

Hardness, 6 to 6.5, although some varieties are softer. Specific gravity, 4.3 to 5.5. Steel-gray to black in color. Black to brownish-black streak. Dull or submetallic luster. Opaque.

X-ray and chemical studies indicate that the material classed as psilomelane includes different species, all of which have more or less similar properties. These include the following:

Cryptomelane, KR_8O_{16}. R = manganese chiefly, also zinc, barium, and cobalt. Monoclinic, pseudotetragonal. Most commonly in fine-grained dense masses with conchoidal fracture, less commonly botryoidal, rarely coarse cleavage. Probably the most common manganese mineral except pyrolusite.

Fig. 561. Psilomelane. Ironwood, Michigan.

Psilomelane, $BaR_9O_{18}.2H_2O$. R = manganese chiefly, also cobalt and copper. Orthorhombic. The water is essential. Commonly botryoidal, sometimes with concentric banding. Next to cryptomelane in abundance.

Coronadite, PbR_8O_{16}?, and **hollandite, BaR_8O_{16}?**, are much less common. Isostructural with cryptomelane.

These psilomelane-type minerals are always secondary and are associated with other manganese minerals, limonite and barite.

Found at Ilfeld and Ilmenau, Germany; Cornwall, England; Brandon, Vermont; Batesville, Arkansas; Blue Ridge region, Virginia; Cartersville, Georgia. Also Soviet Russia, India, Africa, and Brazil.

Important ores of manganese. See page 462.

HALIDES

The following are the four most important halogen minerals:

HALITE	NaCl	Cubic
Cerargyrite	AgCl	Cubic
FLUORITE	CaF_2	Cubic
CRYOLITE	Na_3AlF_6	Monoclinic

The internal structures of halite and fluorite are discussed on pages 162 and 174.

HALITE (*Common Salt, Rock Salt*), NaCl.

Cubic, hexoctahedral class—$4/m\ \bar{3}\ 2m$. Crystals are generally cubes, sometimes in combination with the octahedron; also skeletal or hopper-shaped. Usually in cleavable, granular, or fibrous masses (Fig. 562); as an efflorescence in arid regions.

Excellent cubical cleavage. Hardness, 2 to 2.5. Specific gravity, 2.1 to 2.3. Colorless or white; when impure, often reddish, blue, gray, greenish, or black. The color may be unevenly distributed. Easily soluble in water, 1 part in 2.8 parts of water. Saline taste. Vitreous luster. $n = 1.544$. Transparent to translucent.

NaCl. Na 39.3, Cl 60.7 per cent. Sometimes very pure. May contain varying amounts of the chlorides and sulfates of calcium and magnesium, also admixtures of gypsum, anhydrite, organic matter, clay, and occluded liquids and gases. Colors the flame intensely yellow.

Halite occurs very widely distributed. There are four methods of occurrence: (1) *deposits*, often of great thickness and extent; (2) *in solution;* (3) *efflorescence;* (4) *sublimation product.*

Fig. 562. Halite. Cleavage cube, Stassfurt, Germany; granular, Retsof, New York.

Deposits. Here salt is generally associated with gypsum, anhydrite, clay, or dolomite and is found in sedimentary rocks of all ages. Some of these deposits extend over large areas and may be of great thickness. Thus, the aggregate thickness of the salt layers in central New York is over 300 feet; near Detroit, Michigan, 400 feet; Stassfurt, Germany, over 1,200 feet; Avery Island, Louisiana, several thousand feet.

Many explanations have been offered for the formation of extensive salt deposits, of which the *bar theory* of Ochsenius is perhaps in the larger number of cases the most satisfactory. This theory assumes that a portion of the ocean has been cut off from the main body of water by a bar, which rises almost to the surface. Evaporation within this bay would, on account of the shallowness of the water, be greatest on or near the bar. This would cause the water to become more dense, and a portion would settle to the bottom behind the bar, causing the water of the bay to become strongly saline. In due time, the concentration of this saline solution would be sufficient to cause the deposition of the various salts in order of their solubility. Calcium sulfate, being one of the least soluble, is generally deposited first, followed by rock salt. As the evaporation continues, more water would flow into the bay from the open ocean, thus furnishing a constant supply. If the bar emerges and cuts off the bay entirely, continued evaporation would cause the deposition not only of calcium sulfate and rock salt but also of the more soluble magnesium and potassium compounds, many of which are very complex. The salt deposits at Stassfurt, Germany, which cover an area of about 100 square miles, illustrate the order in which deposition will take place. These are underlain by clay and gypsum and contain over 30 different minerals. Of these minerals, aside from halite, carnallite ($KMgCl_3.6H_2O$), sylvite (KCl), polyhalite ($K_2Ca_2Mg(SO_4)_4.2H_2O$), and kainite ($KMg(SO_4)Cl.3H_2O$) are the most important and in commerce and industry are frequently known as *potash salts.* Similar deposits also occur in the Hannover, Werre, Unstrut, and Mecklenburg districts of Germany. There are also important deposits in Alsace, France; Saskatchewan, Canada; the Carlsbad area, New Mexico; and western Texas. Also see page 470.

In the United States, rock salt has been mined at Livonia, New York; Detroit, Michigan (page 470); Avery Island, Louisiana; Hutchinson, Kansas; and in Sevier County, Utah. Much salt is also produced by the evaporation of the brine obtained from wells that have been sunk to subsurface salt deposits. In California, from along the southeast shore of San Francisco Bay, large quantities of salt are obtained by the solar evaporation of sea water. The salt so obtained is called *solar salt.*

Along the Gulf coast of Louisiana and Texas, there are many occurrences of rock salt in more or less vertical, pipe-like masses, called *salt domes* or *plugs.* These domes were probably produced by earth forces, which caused the salt in plastic form to be pushed up from subsurface beds of rock salt. Gypsum, anhydrite, sulfur, and petroleum are commonly associated with these occurrences.

In Solution. Common salt occurs abundantly in solution in the ocean, salt lakes, saline springs, and wells. In many localities salt is usually produced by the evaporation of these saline solutions.

Efflorescence. Earthy crusts of salt are frequently found in arid regions: in the steppes near the Caspian Sea and in Africa and Chile.

Sublimation Product. Near volcanoes, salt is sometimes found as the result of sublimation.

Salt is used extensively for household and dairying purposes and in meat and fish packing. About 70 per cent of the annual production is used in the chemical industry to produce sodium and its compounds, chlorine, and bleaches, in various metallurgical processes, to glaze pottery, and to melt snow and ice on streets and highways. Sodium carbonate or soda ash is used in large quantities in glass- and soapmaking; sodium bicarbonate for cooking and baking and in medicine; and sodium cyanide in the cyanide process for the extraction of gold. Michigan, New York, Ohio, Louisiana, Texas, Kansas, California, West Virginia, and Utah produce enormous quantities of salt annually. Of these, the first five furnish about 87 per cent of the total production in the United States. See page 471.

Sylvite, KCl. Cubic, hexoctahedral class—$4/m\ \bar{3}\ 2/m$. Crystals are generally a combination of the cube and octahedron. Usually in granular and compact masses.

Perfect cubical cleavage. Hardness, 2. Specific gravity, 1.9 to 2. Colorless or white; may be bluish, yellowish, or red. Transparent to translucent. $n = 1.490$. When impure may deliquesce. Disagreeable bitter salty taste.

KCl. K 52.4, Cl 47.6 per cent. Sometimes almost pure. May contain chlorides of sodium and magnesium. Colors flame violet. Easily soluble in water.

Sylvite occurs with other potash minerals in large quantities in the salt deposits of the Stassfurt and other potash areas of Germany; at Kalusz, Galicia; Province of Saskatchewan, Canada; Carlsbad area, New Mexico; western Texas; and eastern Utah. See page 468.

Sylvite is an important source of potash for fertilizers and the chemical industry.

Cerargyrite (*Horn Silver*), AgCl.

Cubic, hexoctahedral class—$4/m\ \bar{3}\ 2/m$. Crystals are rare and poorly developed. Generally found as a waxy crust or coating, also stalactitic and dendritic.

No cleavage. Highly sectile, cutting easily, and yielding shiny surfaces. Resembles wax. Very soft. Hardness, 1 to 1.5. Specific gravity, 5.5. Pearly gray, yellowish, greenish, or white in color; on exposure to light turns violet, brown, or black. Transparent to translucent. $n = 2.071$. When rubbed becomes shiny. Waxy or resinous luster.

AgCl. Ag 75.3, Cl 24.7 per cent. Bromine may replace chlorine and the compound AgBr is called bromyrite; iodine may also be present. May contain mercury, ferric oxide, or other impurities. Fuses easily on charcoal and yields a globule of silver.

Found as an alteration product in the upper levels of silver deposits. The usual associates are the various silver minerals, also galena, limonite, calcite, barite, and cerussite. It has been observed in Saxony, Norway, Mexico, Peru, Chile; also at Broken Hill, New South Wales; near Leadville, Colorado; Comstock Lode, Nevada; Poorman's Lode, Idaho; Lake Valley, New Mexico; Cobalt, Ontario.

An important ore of silver.

FLUORITE (*Fluor Spar*), CaF_2.

Cubic, hexoctahedral class—$4/m\ \bar{3}\ 2/m$. Excellent crystals are common. The usual form is the cube (Fig. 563), either alone or in combination with the tetrahexahedron or hexoctahedron. Penetration cubes twinned according to the spinel law are frequently observed (Fig. 564). Also in cleavable, granular, and fibrous masses. The internal structure is discussed on page 173.

Excellent octahedral cleavage (Fig. 319, page 104). Hardness, 4. Specific gravity, 3 to 3.2. Usually greenish, yellowish, or bluish in color; also various shades of red or brown, white, and colorless. Sometimes multicolored. Transparent to nearly opaque. Vitreous luster. $n = 1.434$. Frequently strongly fluorescent and phosphorescent when heated or exposed to various types of radiation (see page 111).

CaF_2. Ca 51.1, F 48.9 per cent. Usually quite pure; but cerium and yttrium may replace calcium in appreciable amounts.

Fluorite is found in veins in limestones and dolomites, less frequently in granitic rocks and sandstones. It is also a common gangue mineral with ores of lead, silver, copper, and especially tin. The common associates are galena, sphalerite, cassiterite, calcite, quartz, barite, pyrite, chalcopyrite, topaz, tourmaline, and apatite. Excellent crystals occur

Fig. 563. Fluorite. Cumberland, England.

Fig. 564. Fluorite (penetration cubes). Durham, Weardale, England.

at Cumberland, Cornwall, and Derbyshire, England. Large quantities are mined annually in Hardin County, Illinois, and in Crittenden and Livingston counties, Kentucky. Smaller amounts have been obtained from Colorado, Nevada, Montana, Utah, and New Mexico; Canada, Germany, Italy, and Spain. Fluorite is a common mineral and occurs widely distributed.

Fluorite is used as a flux in the manufacture of open-hearth steel, iron and steel enamelware, opalescent glass, cyanamide, hydrofluoric acid, and in the electrolytic refining of antimony and lead. Fluorite is also used for vases, paper weights, dishes, and similar articles. See also page 454.

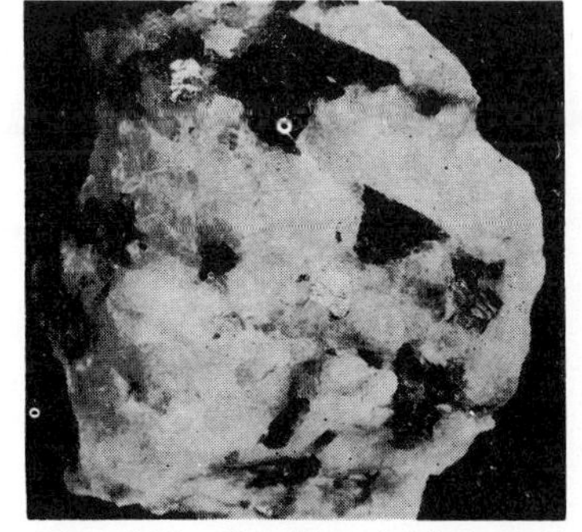

Fig. 565. Cryolite (white) and siderite. Ivigtut, Greenland.

CRYOLITE (*Ice Stone*), Na_3AlF_6.

Monoclinic, prismatic class—$2/m$. Crystals are pseudocubical in habit. Usually observed in compact, granular, or cleavable masses (Fig. 565).

Basal and prismatic partings, three directions nearly at right angles. Uneven fracture. Hardness, 2.5 to 3. Specific gravity, 2.9 to 3. Colorless to snow-white, more rarely reddish, brownish, or black. Pearly luster on the basal pinacoid, elsewhere vitreous to greasy. Often resembles snow ice or paraffin. Transparent to translucent. $\beta = 1.338$, (+); $2V = 43°$; $r < v$.

Na_3AlF_6. Na 32.8, Al 12.8, F 54.4 per cent. Usually quite pure. Fuses easily and imparts a yellow color to the flame.

The only important occurrence of cryolite is at Ivigtut on the southern coast of Greenland, where it is found in veins in granite and is associated with siderite, chalcopyrite, galena, pyrite, fluorite, sphalerite, columbite, cassiterite, and molybdenite. Found also at Miask in the Ilmen Mountains, Siberia, and in the Pikes Peak district, Colorado.

Used principally as a bath in the manufacture of aluminum from bauxite by the electrolytic process; thus, at Niagara Falls, New York; also in glasses, enamels, abrasives, and insecticides. Large quantities of cryolite are now produced synthetically. See also page 437.

NITRATES, CARBONATES, AND BORATES

Some of the minerals classified in these groups occur in large quantities and are of great economic importance.

A. Nitrates

Soda Niter	$NaNO_3$	Hexagonal

B. Carbonates

Calcite Group

CALCITE	$CaCO_3$	Hexagonal
DOLOMITE	$CaMg(CO_3)_2$	Hexagonal
MAGNESITE	$MgCO_3$	Hexagonal
SMITHSONITE	$ZnCO_3$	Hexagonal
RHODOCHROSITE	$MnCO_3$	Hexagonal
SIDERITE	$FeCO_3$	Hexagonal

Aragonite Group

ARAGONITE	$CaCO_3$	Orthorhombic
STRONTIANITE	$SrCO_3$	Orthorhombic
WITHERITE	$BaCO_3$	Orthorhombic
CERUSSITE	$PbCO_3$	Orthorhombic

Malachite Group

MALACHITE	$Cu_2(OH)_2CO_3$	Monoclinic
AZURITE	$Cu_3(OH)_2(CO_3)_2$	Monoclinic

C. Borates

COLEMANITE	$Ca_2B_6O_{11}.5H_2O$	Monoclinic
KERNITE	$Na_2B_4O_7.4H_2O$	Monoclinic

A. Nitrates

Soda niter, or Chile saltpeter, is the only nitrate occurring in nature which is of great commercial importance.

SODA NITER (*Chile Saltpeter*), $NaNO_3$.

Hexagonal, ditrigonal scalenohedral class—$\bar{3}\ 2/m$. Crystals resemble those of calcite but are rare. Generally in crystalline aggregates or grains, also in crusts or deposits of great extent.

Perfect rhombohedral cleavage. Conchoidal fracture. Hardness, 1.5 to 2. Specific gravity, 2.2 to 2.3. Vitreous luster. Colorless, white, yellowish, gray, or reddish brown. Transparent to nearly opaque. Strong double refraction, ω 1.587, ϵ 1.336, (−). Cooling and saline taste.

$NaNO_3$. Na_2O 36.5, N_2O_5 63.5 per cent. Usually contains some sodium chloride and sodium sulfate. Easily soluble in water. Absorbs moisture. Colors flame intensely yellow. Mixed with rock salt, guano, gypsum, clay, and sand, it occurs in extensive deposits, 6 to 12 feet thick, in the provinces of Tarapaca and Antofagasta in northern Chile and in Bolivia. The crude material is called *caliche* and must contain about 50 per cent sodium nitrate to be considered high grade. Smaller quantities also occur in San Bernardino and Inyo counties, California; Humboldt County, Nevada; New Mexico, Utah, and Texas.

Soda niter is a very important commercial mineral. It is used extensively as a fertilizer and in the manufacture of nitric acid and potassium nitrate. It is also a source of iodine, which is present in small amounts as lautarite ($Ca(IO_3)_2$). Chile furnished 95 per cent of the world's sodium nitrate until it became possible to produce it commercially in large quantities by air-reduction methods. Also see page 465.

Niter (*Saltpeter*), KNO_3. Orthorhombic, bipyramidal class—$2/m\ 2/m\ 2/m$. Hair and needle-like crystals and aggregates, or as crusts.

Conchoidal fracture. Brittle. Hardness, 2. Specific gravity, 2.1. White or gray. Vitreous luster. α 1.332, β 1.504, γ 1.504; (−); $2V = 7°$, $r < v$.

KNO_3. K_2O 46.5, N_2O_5 53.5 per cent. Easily soluble in water. Nonhygroscopic. Occurs as an efflorescence in arid regions, in Spain, Italy, northern Africa, India, Egypt, Arabia; in limestone caves in Ceylon, Brazil, Kentucky, Tennessee, Mississippi, California, New Mexico; also with soda niter in Chile.

Of minor importance commercially.

B. Carbonates

Some of the most widely distributed minerals are carbonates. Several of them are of great importance commercially. $CaCO_3$ is dimorphous with modifications in the hexagonal and orthorhombic systems, known as calcite and aragonite, respectively.

Calcite Group

This group contains six members, of which calcite is the most common and important. These minerals possess a perfect rhombohedral cleavage.

CALCITE (*Calcspar*), $CaCO_3$.

Hexagonal, ditrigonal scalenohedral class—$\bar{3}\ 2/m$. Commonly in good crystals; often very complex. The habit varies greatly and may be obtuse

Fig. 566. Calcite (scalenohedron). Joplin, Missouri.

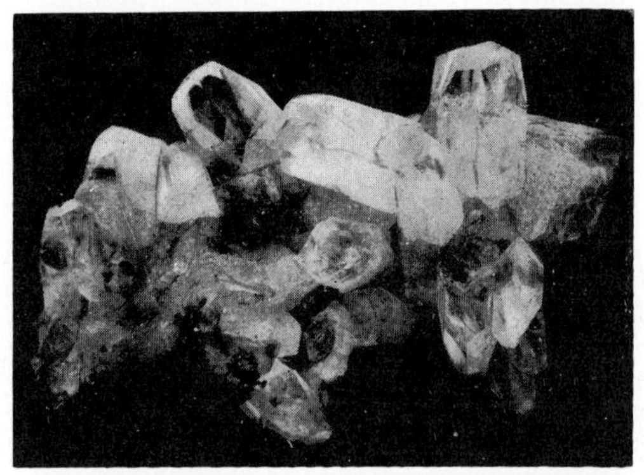

Fig. 567. Calcite. Cumberland, England.

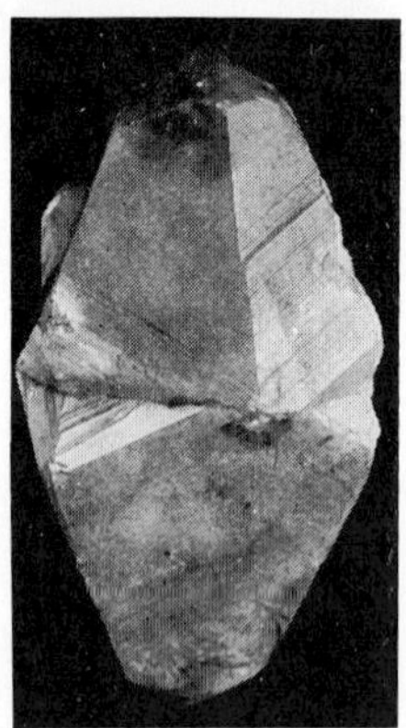

Fig. 568. Calcite (twinned parallel to the base). Guanajuato, Mexico.

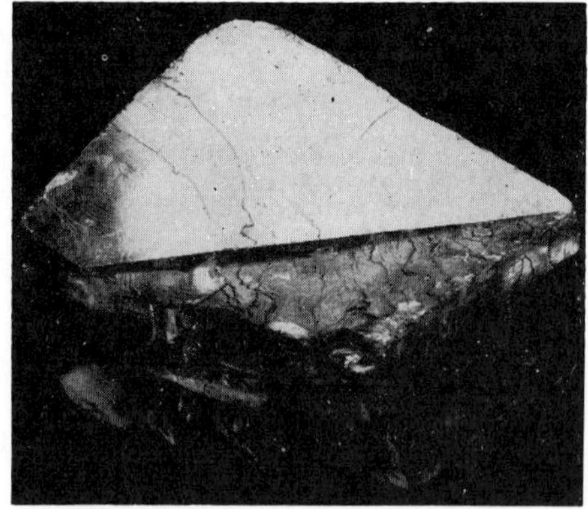

Fig. 569. Calcite (twinned parallel to $01\bar{1}2$). Joplin, Missouri.

or acute rhombohedral, tabular, long prismatic, or scalenohedral (Figs. 566 and 567). Over 300 forms and more than 1,000 combinations have been observed. Twins are relatively common. The two most important laws involve twinning parallel to (1) the basal pinacoid (Fig. 568) and (2) the negative rhombohedron $\{01\bar{1}2\}$ (Fig. 569). Calcite also occurs in granular, lamellar, fibrous, compact, porous, or earthy masses; less frequently it is oölitic, pisolitic, or stalactitic.

The highly perfect rhombohedral cleavage (105°) is very characteristic. Hardness, 3. Specific gravity, 2.72. Vitreous to earthy luster. Commonly colorless, white, or yellowish but may be any color. Transparent to opaque. Transparent varieties show strong double refraction (Fig. 570); ω 1.658, ϵ 1.486, (−). Sometimes becomes luminescent.

$CaCO_3$. CaO 56, CO_2 44 per cent. Sometimes very pure. May contain varying amounts of magnesium, iron, or manganese replacing the calcium. Often mixed with limonite, hematite, organic matter, sand, or clay. Easily soluble with a brisk effervescence in cold dilute acids. This test serves to distinguish calcite from dolomite, which does not effervesce freely in cold dilute acid. Calcite may be distinguished from aragonite by *Meigen's test*, which consists of boiling the powdered minerals in a solution of cobalt nitrate. When calcite is treated in this way, the powder remains unchanged or turns a pale yellow, while aragonite assumes a lilac-red color. See page 235.

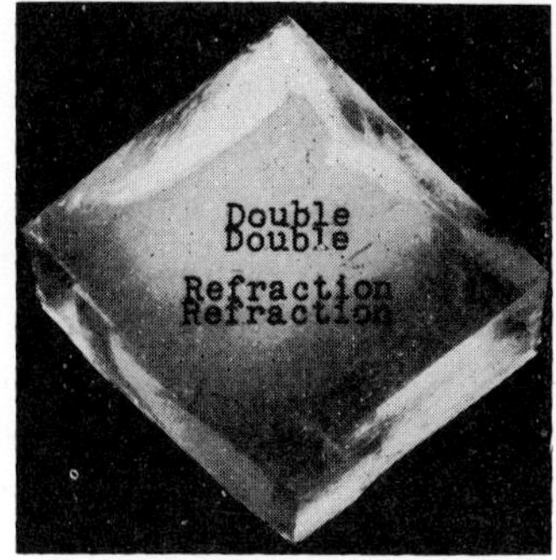

Fig. 570. Calcite: variety, Iceland spar, showing double refraction. Big Timber, Montana.

The different varieties of calcite may be grouped as follows: (1) *ordinary calcites*, (2) *limestones*, (3) *marbles*, (4) *chalk and marl*, and (5) *spring, stream, and cave deposits.*

Ordinary Calcite. These include crystals and cleavable, fibrous, and lamellar masses.

Dog-tooth Spar. Scalenohedral crystals, often in beautiful aggregates (Fig. 566).

Iceland Spar. Colorless and transparent, showing strong double refraction (Fig. 570).

Satin Spar. A fibrous variety with a silky luster. This term is also more frequently applied to fibrous gypsum (Fig. 592, page 345).

Limestones. Calcite is the chief constituent of limestone rocks, which occur so widely distributed. They are massive and may be dull and compact, coarse or fine granular, or composed of fragmental material.

Compact Limestones. These may be nearly white, yellow, bluish gray, reddish, or black in color.

Magnesian or Dolomitic Limestones. As the name indicates, these limestones contain varying percentages of magnesium carbonate and are mechanical mixtures of calcite and dolomite.

Lithographic Limestones. An even-grained, compact limestone, suitable for lithographic purposes. That from Solenhofen, Bavaria, is buff or drab in color.

Hydraulic Limestones. These are impure limestones, containing 10 to 14 per cent of clayey impurities. They are used extensively in the manufacture of cement.

Bituminous Limestones. Owing to the presence of much organic matter, these limestones yield the characteristic odor of bitumen when struck a blow with a hammer.

Fig. 571. Calcite: variety, coquina. Anastasia Island, Florida.

Coquina. This is a mass of shell remains (Fig. 571). Found along the coast of Florida, near St. Augustine.

Oölitic Limestones. These are composed of small, spherical concretions, resembling fish roe.

Pisolitic Limestones. The concretions are larger and about the size of a pea.

Marbles. These possess a fine-to-coarse crystalline structure and are generally metamorphosed limestones (Fig. 5, page 6). Commercially, however, any calcareous rock capable of taking a polish and suitable for decorative and structural purposes is termed a marble.

Chalk and Marl. These are soft, earthy varieties.

Chalk. Soft, white or grayish, earthy masses, consisting principally of the remains of Foraminifera. Found in large deposits at Dover, England.

Marl. A soft, calcareous deposit mixed with clay and sand. Often contains shell or organic remains. It is used in the manufacture of cement.

Spring, Stream, and Cave Deposits. These are due largely to the escape of carbon dioxide, which causes the soluble calcium bicarbonate ($CaH_2(CO_3)_2$) to pass over to the more insoluble normal carbonate ($CaCO_3$) and be deposited. It is thought that certain algae aid in this process.

Travertine, Calcareous Sinter, or Calcareous Tufa. These occur around springs and in stream beds and are usually porous and often contain twigs, leaves, and other organic remains.

Stalactites. Icicle-like forms suspended from the roofs of caves.

Stalagmites. Formed on the floors of caves, usually conical in shape.

Onyx Marble. Compact deposits with a crystalline structure, often banded, translucent, and of colors suitable for decorative purposes. Often called *cave onyx* or *Mexican onyx* (Fig. 572).

Calcite occurs very widely distributed. As limestone, marble, chalk, and marl it is found in large deposits, often of great thickness and extending over wide areas. It is also abundant as deposits around springs and in streams, and in cracks and cavities in igneous and sedimentary rocks. Often observed as an associate of metalliferous ore deposits. Excellent crystals are very common. A few of the most noted localities are Eskifiord, Iceland; Derbyshire, Cumberland, Devonshire, Durham, Lancashire, England; Andreasberg, Germany; Kapnik, Rumania; Guanajuato, Mexico; Joplin, Missouri; Rossie, St. Lawrence County, New York; Lake Superior copper district. Large and commercially important deposits of calcite marble occur in Vermont, Tennessee, Georgia, Alabama, and Colorado. The leading limestone-producing states are Indiana, Pennsylvania, Ohio, New York, Illinois, and Michigan.

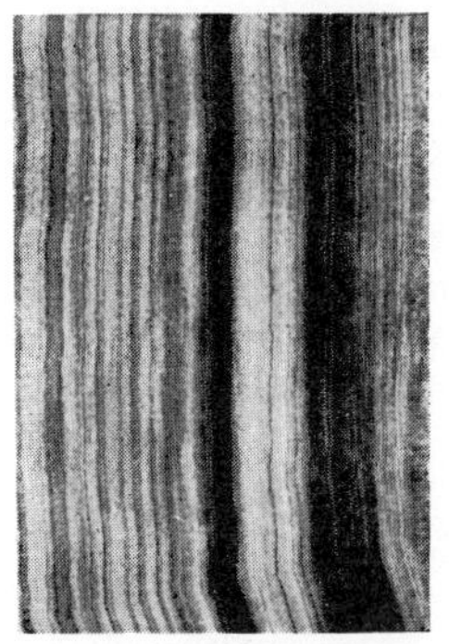

Fig. 572. Calcite: variety, Mexican onyx. Lehi City, Utah.

The different varieties of calcite are commercially of great value. Iceland spar is used in optical instruments; limestone for building purposes, quicklime, fertilizer, cement, flux in various metallurgical processes, railroad ballast, macadam, in lithography, and concrete; marble for building, ornamental, monumental, and statuary purposes, and as a source of carbon dioxide; chalk for whiting, crayon, scouring and polishing preparations, and as an adulterant; marl for cement. See also page 445.

DOLOMITE (*Pearl Spar*), $CaMg(CO_3)_2$.

Hexagonal, trigonal rhombohedral class—$\bar{3}$. Rhombohedral crystals are common. The faces are frequently curved, forming saddle-shaped

Fig. 573. Dolomite. Joplin, Missouri.

crystals (Fig. 573). Also in fine- to coarse-grained, cleavable, or compact masses.

Perfect rhombohedral cleavage. Hardness, 3.5 to 4. Specific gravity, 2.9. White, reddish, yellow, brown, or black; rarely colorless.

Vitreous to pearly luster. Indices of refraction for pure dolomite are ω 1.679, ϵ 1.500, (−); for dolomite containing manganese and iron, called *ankerite*, they may be ω 1.716, ϵ 1.526, (−). Transparent to translucent.

$CaMg(CO_3)_2$. CaO 30.4, MgO 21.7, CO_2 47.9 per cent. In the crystals of dolomite, the carbonates of calcium and magnesium are usually present in the proportion of 1 : 1; in massive varieties, this ratio varies greatly, but $CaCO_3$ generally predominates. In many instances, dolomite is believed to have been formed by the action of soluble magnesium salts upon calcium carbonate, either before or after emergence from the sea.

$$2CaCO_3 + MgCl_2 = CaMg(CO_3)_2 + CaCl_2$$

Fragments of dolomite are but slightly acted upon by cold dilute acid; the powder effervesces briskly with hot dilute acids.

Dolomite occurs abundantly in many ore deposits and in cavities of various igneous and sedimentary rocks. Thus, at Joplin, Missouri; Lockport, New York; Austria; Switzerland; Freiberg, Saxony. The compact granular variety occurs in deposits of great thickness and extent. Thus, some of the mountain ranges of central Europe, especially southern Tyrol, are principally dolomite. These dolomites grade into dolomitic and magnesian limestones. The term *marble* includes metamorphosed dolomites (see page 205). Dolomitic marbles of commercial importance occur in New York, Maryland, and Massachusetts.

Dolomite is used for building, statuary, monumental, and ornamental purposes; as a source of magnesium and its compounds; and as refractory material. See also page 461.

MAGNESITE, $MgCO_3$.

Hexagonal, ditrigonal scalenohedral class—$\bar{3}\ 2/m$. Rarely in rhombohedral crystals; usually in cleavable, granular, compact, or earthy masses with the appearance of unglazed porcelain. Also coarsely crystalline, resembling coarse dolomite or marble in texture.

Crystals have a rhombohedral cleavage. Conchoidal fracture is conspicuous on massive varieties. Brittle. Hardness, 3.5 to 4.5. Specific gravity, 2.9 to 3.1. Colorless, white, yellow, brown, or blackish. Vitreous to dull luster. ω 1.700, ϵ 1.509, higher when iron is present, (−). Transparent to opaque.

$MgCO_3$. MgO 47.6, CO_2 52.4 per cent. Iron, manganese, or calcium may be present. Powdered magnesite is soluble in hot dilute acids.

Magnesite is commonly the result of the alteration and carbonation of magnesium minerals. Thus, olivine may alter to magnesite, serpentine, limonite, and opal. It is found in veins in talcose and chloritic schists and in serpentine. It occurs in Moravia and Styria, Austria; Silesia; Zillerthal, Tirol; Ural Mountains; Greece; and very extensively in

Santa Clara, Sonoma, Napa, Kern, Fresno, and San Benito counties, California; Stevens County, Washington; Nye County, Nevada; also in New Mexico; Quebec and Yukon, Canada.

Magnesite is used chiefly in the manufacture of refractory bricks, crucibles, furnace hearths, oxychloride or Sorel cement, and magnesium sulfite for the digestion and whitening of wood-pulp paper; as a source of carbon dioxide and magnesium compounds; when mixed with asbestos it serves as a boiler and steam-pipe covering; calcined magnesite is used for flooring, tiling, wainscoting, and sanitary finishes. See also page 460.

SMITHSONITE (*Calamine, Dry Bone*), $ZnCO_3$.

Hexagonal, ditrigonal scalenohedral class—$\bar{3}$ $2/m$. Crystals are usually small and rough or curved. Generally found in reniform, botryoidal, stalactitic, or compact granular masses. *Dry bone* is a term given to cellular and porous varieties.

Rhombohedral cleavage, observed on crystals. Uneven to splintery fracture. Hardness, 5. Specific gravity, 4.1 to 4.5. Color is commonly gray or brown; also white, yellow, blue, green, and pink. Greenish smithsonite is called *bonamite.* Translucent to opaque. Vitreous to pearly luster. ω 1.849, ϵ 1.621, $(-)$.

$ZnCO_3$. ZnO 64.8, CO_2 35.2 per cent. Iron, copper, manganese, calcium, and magnesium may be present. *Turkey fat* is yellow smithsonite containing greenockite (CdS). Common as a pseudomorph after calcite, especially at Mineral Point, Wisconsin.

Smithsonite is a secondary mineral and occurs extensively in the upper levels in limestones and dolomites. It is often the result of the action of carbonated waters on other zinc minerals. The common associates are sphalerite, hemimorphite, galena, limonite, and calcite. Sometimes it is mixed with sand and clay. Occurs at Broken Hill, New South Wales; Laurium, Greece; Altenberg, near Aachen, Germany; Sardinia, Italy; Broken Hill Mine, Rhodesia; Tsumeb, South-West Africa; Scotland; Kelly, New Mexico; also extensively in Missouri, Arkansas, Iowa, Wisconsin, and Virginia, where it is mined as zinc ore. The term *calamine* is sometimes applied to smithsonite, but it refers more properly to hemimorphite ($Zn_4Si_2O_7(OH)_2.H_2O$) (page 375). These two minerals often occur in intimate association.

Chiefly used as an ore of zinc; green, blue, and yellowish varieties are sometimes polished for gem and ornamental purposes. See page 476.

RHODOCHROSITE, $MnCO_3$.

Hexagonal, ditrigonal scalenohedral class—$\bar{3}$ $2/m$. Crystals are rhombohedral in habit, small, and quite rare. Generally in cleavable, granular, and botryoidal masses; also in crusts.

Perfect rhombohedral cleavage. Uneven fracture. Hardness, 3.5 to 4.5. Specific gravity, 3.3 to 3.6. Usually rose red or pink in color; also gray, dark brown, and, more rarely, colorless. Vitreous to pearly luster. ω 1.816, ϵ 1.597, (−). Translucent.

$MnCO_3$. MnO 61.7, CO_2 38.3 per cent. Calcium, iron, zinc, and magnesium are often present, replacing the manganese. Occurs as a pseudomorph after calcite and fluorite.

Usually found with iron, lead, gold, silver, and copper ores, and other manganese minerals. Most common associates are galena, sphalerite, pyrite, rhodonite, and psilomelane; thus, at Hucha, Spain; Freiberg, Saxony; Kapnik, Rumania; Franklin, New Jersey; Alicante, Colorado; Butte, Montana; Austin, Nevada; Park City and elsewhere, Utah.

Rhodochrosite is not a very common mineral. It is sometimes used as a source of manganese and its compounds. See page 462.

SIDERITE (*Spathic Iron, Chalybite*), **$FeCO_3$.**

Hexagonal, ditrigonal scalenohedral class—$\bar{3}$ $2/m$. Distorted and curved rhombohedral crystals (saddle-shaped) are quite common. Usually found in cleavable, granular, botryoidal, or fibrous masses.

Perfect rhombohedral cleavage. Conchoidal fracture. Hardness, 3.5 to 4.5. Specific gravity, 3.7 to 3.9. Vitreous to pearly luster. ω 1.875, ϵ 1.633, (−). Usually brownish to nearly black in color; also gray, green, and white. Translucent to nearly opaque. Streak, white or yellowish. May be iridescent.

$FeCO_3$. FeO 62.1, CO_2 37.9 (Fe 48.2) per cent. Usually contains $MgCO_3$, $CaCO_3$, or $MnCO_3$. Manganiferous varieties are termed *oligonite*. When mixed with clay, sand, and organic matter, it is often called *clay ironstone* or *blackband*. Occurs as a pseudomorph after calcite, aragonite, dolomite, barite, and fluorite. It alters to limonite, hematite, and magnetite.

Siderite occurs commonly with sulfide ore deposits, also in beds and as concretions in limestones and shales. The usual associates are pyrite, chalcopyrite, galena, tetrahedrite, and cryolite. It is an important gangue mineral in the silver-lead deposits in Idaho. It occurs with ore deposits in the Harz Mountains; Příbram, Bohemia; Cornwall, England; Freiberg, Saxony; with cryolite and chalcopyrite in southern Greenland; in beds and as concretions in Westphalia, Germany; southern Wales, Silesia; Roxbury, Connecticut; St. Lawrence County, New York; in the coal measures in eastern Ohio, Kentucky, western Pennsylvania, and elsewhere.

A minor ore of iron. If it contains considerable manganese, it is used for spiegeleisen.

Aragonite Group

The members of this isomorphous group crystallize in the orthorhombic system. The prism angles of these minerals approximate 120°, so that crystals frequently have a pseudohexagonal development.

ARAGONITE, $CaCO_3$.

Orthorhombic, bipyramidal class—$2/m\ 2/m\ 2/m$. Crystals are quite common and show great diversity in development. They may be (1) domatic or chisel-like, (2) acute pyramidal or spear-shaped, and (3) prismatic and pseudohexagonal, consisting of a prism and striated base. The prism angle is 116°16′. This pseudohexagonal symmetry is often accentuated by twinning parallel to a face of the unit prism (Fig. 574).

Fig. 574. Aragonite (trillings). Girgenti, Sicily.

Fig. 575. Aragonite: variety, flos ferri. Styria, Austria.

Contact, cyclic, and penetration twins are common. Also occurs in radial, branching, columnar, and fibrous aggregates; oölitic, globular, stalactitic, and in crusts.

Imperfect brachypinacoidal and prismatic cleavages. Conchoidal fracture. Hardness, 3.5 to 4. Specific gravity, 2.9 to 3. Most commonly colorless, white, or yellow; also reddish, bluish, or black. Greasy luster on fracture surfaces, elsewhere vitreous. α 1.530, β 1.681, γ 1.685, $(-)$; $2V = 18°$; $r < v$. Transparent to translucent. May show luminescence.

$CaCO_3$. CaO 56, CO_2 44 per cent. May contain some lead, strontium, and zinc. Effervesces easily with acids but not so easily as calcite. Massive varieties are easily distinguished from calcite by Meigen's test (see page 235). Occurs as a pseudomorph after gypsum and calcite, but calcite pseudomorphs after aragonite are more abundant. At about 400°C., aragonite changes to calcite. Aragonite is usually deposited from hot solutions, while calcite is formed from cold solutions. It may also be formed at ordinary temperatures through the action of organic agencies or by precipitation from saline waters containing sulfates or small amounts of the carbonates of strontium, magnesium, or lead.

Aragonite is found (1) in cracks and cavities, often associated with the zeolites; (2) in ore deposits, especially iron ore; the coralloidal variety occurring with siderite, as at Hüttenberg, Carinthia, is termed *flos ferri* (Fig. 575); (3) disseminated in clay, associated with gypsum, sulfur, and celestite; (4) as a deposit from hot springs and geysers, sometimes pisolitic and in crusts; (5) it constitutes the pearly layer of many shells and pearls. Aragonite is not nearly so common as calcite. Excellent crystals are found at Herrengrund, Hungary; Bilin, Karlsbad, and Horschenz, Bohemia; Aragon, Spain; Girgenti, Sicily; Alton Moor, England; other varieties at Hoboken, New Jersey; Lockport, New York; Warsaw, Illinois; Organ Mountains, New Mexico; Bisbee, Arizona; Fort Collins and Leadville, Colorado; Kern County, California.

Aragonite is of no importance commercially.

STRONTIANITE, $SrCO_3$.

Orthorhombic, bipyramidal class—$2/m\ 2/m\ 2/m$. Crystals are usually spear-shaped or acicular and arranged in radial aggregates. Forms and twinning are similar to those of aragonite. Pseudohexagonal with a prism angle of 117°19′. Also granular and compact, sometimes with a divergent fibrous structure (Fig. 576).

Fig. 576. Strontianite. Dreisteinfurt, Westphalia, Germany.

Prismatic cleavage. Conchoidal fracture. Hardness, 3.5 to 4. Specific gravity, 3.6 to 3.8. Colorless, white, gray, yellow, and green. Vitreous luster, greasy on fracture surfaces. α 1.520, β 1.667, γ 1.669, (−); $2V = 7°$; $r < v$. Transparent to translucent. May fluoresce and phosphoresce.

$SrCO_3$. SrO 70.1, CO_2 29.9 per cent. Usually contains some calcium and barium. Occurs as a pseudomorph after celestite.

Occurs in ore deposits, commonly with barite, celestite, and galena. Important localities are Strontian, Argyllshire, Scotland; Hamm, Westphalia, Germany; Schoharie, New York; near Austin, Texas; Skagit County, Washington; San Bernardino and Plumase counties, California. With celestite in the cap rock of salt domes in Texas and Louisiana.

Strontianite is a source of strontium compounds, some of which are used extensively. The oxides and hydroxide are of importance in the precipitation of sugar from molasses; the nitrate, carbonate, and oxalate are used for red fire; and the iodide, bromide, and lactate in medicine. See page 471.

WITHERITE, $BaCO_3$.

Orthorhombic, bipyramidal class—$2/m\ 2/m\ 2/m$. Usually in pseudohexagonal bipyramids, resembling quartz (Fig. 577). These are penetration trillings with the twinning plane parallel to the unit prism. The prism angle is 117°48′. Parallel groups not uncommon. Also in compact, botryoidal, reniform, or globular masses; sometimes with a lamellar or radial fibrous structure.

Fig. 577. Witherite (trillings). Northumberland, England.

Distinct pinacoidal cleavage. Uneven fracture. Hardness, 3.5. Specific gravity, 4.2 to 4.35. Colorless, grayish, white, or yellowish. Vitreous luster, on fracture surfaces somewhat greasy. α 1.529, β 1.676, γ 1.677, (−); $2V = 16°$; $r > v$. Translucent to transparent. May fluoresce and phosphoresce.

$BaCO_3$. BaO 77.7, CO_2 22.3 per cent. Usually quite pure.

Occurs with deposits of galena in northwestern England; thus at Fallowfield, Northumberland; Durfton, Westmoreland; Alston Moor, Cumberland; with barite at Freiberg, Saxony; Siberia; Lexington, Kentucky; El Portal, California; Rosiclare, Illinois; Yuma County, Arizona; Thunder Bay district, Lake Superior.

Witherite is used to adulterate white lead, in the extracting of sugar from sugar beets, and in ceramics, glass, and drilling muds.

CERUSSITE (*White Lead Ore*), $PbCO_3$.

Orthorhombic, bipyramidal class—$2/m\ 2/m\ 2/m$. Crystals are generally tabular, prismatic, or pyramidal in habit; frequently arranged in clusters or star-shaped groups. Often very complex. Pronounced pseudohexagonal symmetry, the prism angle being 117°14′. Twins are very common and similar to those of aragonite. Also in granular, fibrous, and compact masses, interlaced bundles (Fig. 578); and stalactitic.

Hardness, 3 to 3.5. Specific gravity, 6.4 to 6.6. Generally colorless, white, or gray. Very brittle. Adamantine luster, sometimes silky. High indices of refraction, α 1.804, β 2.076, γ 2.078, (−); $2V = 8°$; $r > v$. Transparent to almost opaque. Fluoresces.

$PbCO_3$. PbO 83.5, CO_2 16.5 per cent. At times, contains some strontium and zinc. Occurs as a pseudomorph after galena and anglesite.

Fig. 578. Cerussite. Leadville, Colorado.

Found usually in the upper levels of galena deposits, from which it has resulted by the action of carbonated waters. Common associates are galena, pyromorphite, anglesite, malachite, and limonite. Occurs at Broken Hill, New South Wales; Leadhills, Scotland; Tsumeb, South-West Africa, various places in Mexico; Leadville, Colorado; Pima and Yuma counties, Arizona; Park City, Utah; Coeur d'Alene district, Idaho; New Mexico; Montana; Nevada; California.

An important ore of lead and silver.

Malachite Group

This group includes two basic carbonates of copper, which are of great importance commercially.

MALACHITE (*Green Carbonate of Copper*), $Cu_2(OH)_2CO_3$.

Monoclinic, prismatic class—$2/m$. Crystals are usually acicular, very slender, and without good terminations; often arranged in groups or tufts. Commonly in reniform, botryoidal, and stalactitic masses with smooth surfaces and a banded or radial fibrous structure (Fig. 579); also earthy and in velvety crusts.

Fig. 579. Malachite (polished). Rhodesia, Africa.

Conchoidal to splintery fracture. Hardness, 3.5 to 4. Specific gravity, 3.9 to 4.1. Bright emerald green, grass green, to nearly black in color. Translucent to opaque. Silky, adamantine, or dull luster. α 1.655, β 1.875, γ 1.909, $(-)$; $2V = 43°$; $r < v$. Light-green streak.

$Cu_2(OH)_2CO_3$. CuO 71.9 (Cu 57.4), CO_2 19.9, H_2O 8.2 per cent. Masses may contain the oxides of iron and manganese, clay, and sand. Occurs commonly as a pseudomorph after cuprite, azurite, and native copper.

Malachite is a common alteration product of copper minerals, resulting from the action of carbonate waters and, hence, is found in smaller or larger quantities in the upper levels of all copper mines. Common associates are azurite, cuprite, native copper, chalcocite, chalcopyrite, and bornite. Occurs in large quantities in the Ural Mountains; at Chessy, France, as pseudomorphs after cuprite; Cornwall, England; Rhodesia; Tsumeb, South-West Africa; Belgian Congo; Australia; Chile; Bisbee and Clifton districts, Arizona; Park City, Utah; Nevada; New Mexico; as a coating on native copper in the Lake Superior copper district.

An important ore of copper, especially in Africa. Also used in jewelry and for ornamental purposes, such as table tops and vases. *Malachite matrix* is a term given to polished specimens with admixtures of gangue material.

AZURITE (*Chessylite, Blue Carbonate of Copper*), $\mathbf{Cu_3(OH)_2(CO_3)_2}$.

Monoclinic, prismatic class—$2/m$. Short prismatic or tabular crystals, often very complex, and arranged in spherical aggregates. Commonly found in reniform or botryoidal masses, with a velvety, radial fibrous structure; also earthy and in crusts.

Domatic cleavage. Hardness, 3.5 to 4. Specific gravity, 3.7 to 3.8. Vitreous to adamantine luster. α 1.730, β 1.758, γ 1.838, (+); $2V = 68°$; $r > v$. Light azure to deep blue in color. Streak, light blue. Translucent to opaque.

$Cu_3(OH)_2(CO_3)_2$. CuO 69.2 (Cu 55.3), CO_2 25.6, H_2O 5.2 per cent. Occurs as a pseudomorph after cuprite and tetrahedrite. Alters to malachite.

Origin and occurrences are the same as for malachite; not so common as malachite. Excellent crystals occur at Chessy, France; in the Ural Mountains; Chile; Tsumeb, South-West Africa; Australia; the Bisbee and Clifton copper districts, Arizona; Kelly, New Mexico; also in Utah and California.

Used as an ore of copper. When intimately mixed with malachite, it is sometimes polished for gem purposes and sold as *azurmalachite*.

C. Borates

The two borate minerals, which are described, occur in large quantities.

Colemanite, $Ca_2B_6O_{11}.5H_2O$.

Monoclinic, prismatic class—$2/m$. Crystals are usually short prismatic and resemble datolite, often highly modified. Also in compact, granular, and cleavable masses, which look like chalk or porcelain.

Highly perfect, clinopinacoidal cleavage. Uneven to subconchoidal fracture. Hardness, 4 to 4.5. Specific gravity, 2.4. Vitreous to dull luster. α 1.586, β 1.592, γ 1.614, (+); $2V = 56°$; $r > v$. Colorless to white. Transparent to opaque.

$Ca_2B_6O_{11}.5H_2O$. CaO 27.2, B_2O_3 50.9, H_2O 21.9 per cent. Easily soluble in hot hydrochloric acid. Boracic acid separates on cooling. Insoluble in water. Treated with sodium carbonate or sulfate it yields borax ($Na_2B_4O_7.10H_2O$).

Commonly associated with halite, thenardite, trona, gypsum, celestite, kernite, and ulexite. As a lake deposit it occurs extensively in San Bernardino, Inyo, Los Angeles, Kern, and Ventura counties, California, and Clark, Esmeralda, and Mineral counties, Nevada.

Formerly an important source of borax (see kernite, below).

Kernite (*Rasorite*), $Na_2B_4O_7.4H_2O$.

Monoclinic, prismatic class—$2/m$. Large crystals; usually as cleavage masses, resembling cleavage gypsum (selenite).

Perfect basal and orthopinacoidal cleavages. Breaks easily into fibers or long thin laths. Hardness, 2.5 to 3. Specific gravity, 1.9. Colorless to white. Transparent. Vitreous to pearly luster. α 1.454, β 1.472, γ 1.488, (−); $2V = 80°$; $r > v$.

$Na_2B_4O_7.4H_2O$. Na_2O 22.7, B_2O_3 51.0, H_2O 26.3 per cent. Slowly soluble in water; the solution yields borax ($Na_2B_4O_7.10H_2O$) on evaporation.

Occurs in very large deposits at Kramer, Kern County, California, associated with borax, ulexite, and colemanite; and Salta, Argentina.

The chief source of borax, which is used extensively in the manufacture of soap, enamels, glass, washing powders, ointments, and lotions; also in welding, soldering, assaying, and blowpiping, as an antiseptic, and as a preservative for meat and fish. See page 443.

SULFATES, CHROMATES, MOLYBDATES, AND TUNGSTATES

The minerals belonging to this division may be conveniently arranged as follows:

ANHYDRITE	$CaSO_4$	Orthorhombic
	BARITE GROUP	
CELESTITE	$SrSO_4$	Orthorhombic
BARITE	$BaSO_4$	Orthorhombic
ANGLESITE	$PbSO_4$	Orthorhombic
	———	
Brochantite	$Cu_4(OH)_6SO_4$	Monoclinic
Alunite	$KAl_3(OH)_6(SO_4)_2$	Hexagonal
Chalcanthite	$CuSO_4.5H_2O$	Triclinic
Melanterite	$FeSO_4.7H_2O$	Monoclinic
Epsomite	$MgSO_4.7H_2O$	Orthorhombic
GYPSUM	$CaSO_4.2H_2O$	Monoclinic
Crocoite	$PbCrO_4$	Monoclinic

WOLFRAMITE GROUP

Ferberite	$FeWO_4$	Monoclinic
WOLFRAMITE	$(Fe,Mn)WO_4$	Monoclinic
Huebnerite	$MnWO_4$	Monoclinic
SCHEELITE	$CaWO_4$	Tetragonal
Wulfenite	$PbMoO_4$	Tetragonal

Most of these minerals possess nonmetallic lusters.

ANHYDRITE, $CaSO_4$.

Orthorhombic, bipyramidal class—$2/m\ 2/m\ 2/m$. Crystals are prismatic or thick tabular in habit, but not common. Generally in granular, cleavable, fibrous, or contorted masses. When granular, may resemble marble or lumps of sugar (Fig. 6, page 6).

Pinacoidal cleavages in three directions at right angles, yielding cubical or rectangular fragments. Conchoidal fracture. Hardness, 3 to 3.5. Specific gravity, 2.7 to 3. Colorless, white, grayish, bluish, reddish, or black. Vitreous to pearly luster. α 1.570, β 1.575, γ 1.614, (+); $2V = 44°$; $r < v$. Transparent to translucent.

$CaSO_4$. CaO 41.2, SO_3 58.8 per cent. Often mixed with organic matter. Absorbs water and alters to gypsum ($CaSO_4.2H_2O$), causing an increase of 33 to 62 per cent of the original volume. This hydration is, no doubt, the cause of the many local disturbances in the rock strata commonly observed in regions where gypsum occurs; thus, in central New York, and on the Island of Put-in-Bay in Lake Erie. Occurs sometimes as a pseudomorph after gypsum.

Found commonly with limestones and shales associated with halite and gypsum. Some of the principal localities are the Stassfurt salt district, Germany; Hall, Tirol; Bex, Switzerland; Nova Scotia; New Brunswick; Lockport, New York; Detroit, Michigan; Ellsworth County, Kansas. With gypsum, halite, and potash salts in the Carlsbad district, New Mexico; in the cap rock of salt domes in Louisiana and Texas.

Anhydrite has been of little use commercially; now potential source of sulfur. A siliceous variety is sometimes cut and polished for ornamental purposes.

Barite Group

CELESTITE, $SrSO_4$.

Orthorhombic, bipyramidal class—$2/m\ 2/m\ 2/m$. Tabular or prismatic crystals are common (Figs. 580 to 582). Also in cleavable, granular, or fibrous masses.

Perfect basal and prismatic cleavages. Uneven fracture. Hardness, 3 to 3.5. Specific gravity, 3.9 to 4. Vitreous to pearly luster. α 1.622,

β 1.624, γ 1.631, (+); $2V = 51°$; $r < v$. Generally possesses a faint blue tinge but may be white, yellow, and, more rarely, green or reddish. Transparent to translucent. May fluoresce.

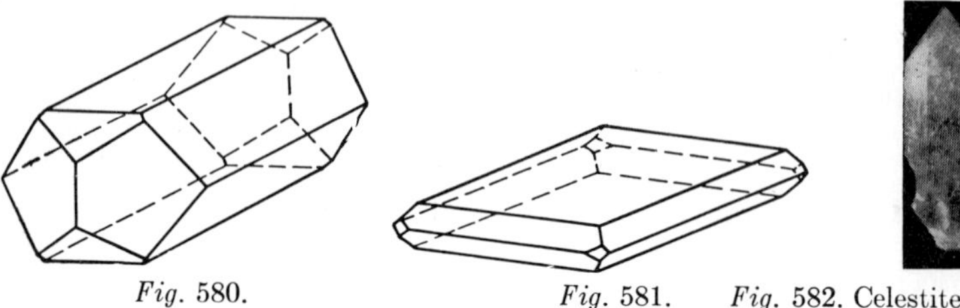

Fig. 580. *Fig.* 581. *Fig.* 582. Celestite (tabular). Woolmith Quarry, Monroe County, Michigan.

$SrSO_4$. SrO 56.4, SO_3 43.6 per cent. Usually very pure but may contain small amounts of calcium and barium. Imparts a red color to the flame. More soluble in water than barite.

Celestite is usually associated with sulfur, gypsum, halite, aragonite, anhydrite, and, occasionally, galena and sphalerite. There are two principal types of occurrences:

Disseminated as crystals or irregular particles in shales, limestones, and dolomites. By the action of circulating water the celestite is dissolved and these rocks become more or less porous. They are often called *gashed, acicular,* or *vermicular* limestones and dolomites. Such rocks occur near Syracuse, New York; and at various places in Michigan and northern Ohio.

In cracks and *cavities* in rocks of varying ages but principally of sedimentary origin. Most of the best known localities for the occurrence of celestite are of this type. It is found in association with sulfur, gypsum, and aragonite in the Girgenti sulfur district of Sicily; also at Maybee, Michigan; with halite at Bex, Switzerland; excellent crystals, some over 18 inches in length, are found on the Island of Put-in-Bay, Lake Erie; Mineral County, West Virginia; Kingston, Canada; numerous deposits in Arizona, California, Texas, Washington; also Brown County, Kansas; with fluorite at Clay Center, Ottawa County, Ohio.

Used in the manufacture of strontium compounds. See page 471.

BARITE (*Heavy Spar, Barytes*), $BaSO_4$.

Orthorhombic, bipyramidal class—$2/m\ 2/m\ 2/m$. Tabular and prismatic crystals are very common, usually well developed (Figs. 583 to 586); often complex. Tabular crystals may be arranged in crested divergent groups (Fig. 587). Also in cleavable, granular, fibrous, or reniform masses; sometimes lamellar, nodular, or earthy; also rosette aggregates of tabular crystals, called *desert roses.*

Perfect basal and prismatic cleavages. Uneven fracture. Hardness, 3 to 3.5. Specific gravity, 4.3 to 4.7. Colorless, white, yellow, blue, brown, or red. Transparent to opaque. Vitreous to pearly luster. α 1.636, β 1.637, γ 1.648, (+); $2V = 37°30'$; $r < v$. May fluoresce and phosphoresce.

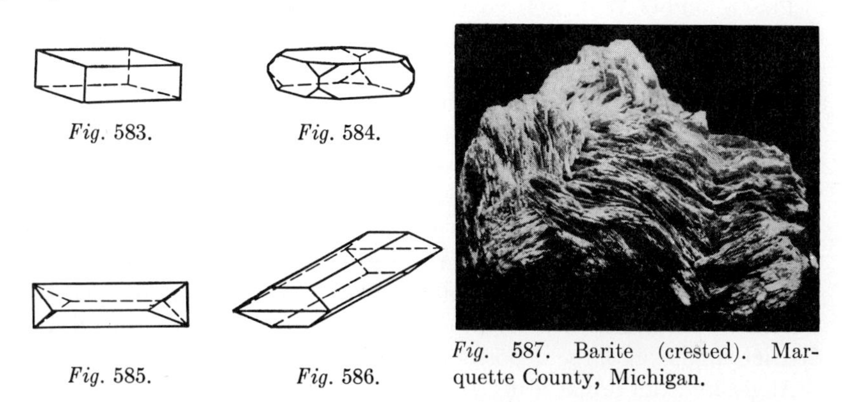

Fig. 583. *Fig.* 584. *Fig.* 585. *Fig.* 586.

Fig. 587. Barite (crested). Marquette County, Michigan.

$BaSO_4$. BaO 65.7, SO_3 34.3 per cent. May contain varying amounts of the oxides of strontium, calcium, and lead; also silica, clay, or organic matter. Colors the flame green.

Barite is a common and widely distributed mineral. It occurs in metalliferous veins associated with galena, sphalerite, fluorite, chalcopyrite, and the various manganese and iron minerals. This type of occurrence furnishes most of the finest crystals of barite. Thus, at Cornwall, Cumberland, and Derbyshire, England; Kapnik, Rumania; Herrengrund, Hungary; Bohemia; Marquette County, Michigan; DeKalb, New York; Fort Wallace, New Mexico. Also in pockets and lenticular deposits in limestones and associated with calcite and celestite. Deposits of this character are mined at Cartersville, Georgia; also in Missouri, Tennessee, Kentucky, Virginia, California, and North and South Carolina, Arkansas, Nevada; desert roses, central Oklahoma and Salina, Kansas.

The largest use of barite is to produce heavy muds or sludges used in oil well drilling; also in the manufacture of paint, glass, insecticides, leather, and glazed paper. It is the principal source of the various barium compounds. Prepared $BaSO_4$ is used in medical radiology. See also page 441.

ANGLESITE, $PbSO_4$.

Orthorhombic, bipyramidal class—$2/m\ 2/m\ 2/m$. Crystals are frequently highly modified and may be prismatic, tabular, or pyramidal in habit. Massive varieties are compact, granular, or nodular.

Distinct basal and prismatic cleavages. Conchoidal fracture. Brittle. Hardness, 3 to 3.5. Specific gravity, 6.1 to 6.4. Colorless, white, yellow, brown, green, or blue. Adamantine to greasy luster. High indices of refraction, α 1.877, β 1.882, γ 1.894, (+); $2V$ varies from 60 to 75°; $r < v$. Transparent to opaque. May fluoresce yellow.

$PbSO_4$. PbO 73.6, SO_3 26.4 per cent. Usually quite pure. Fuses easily in a candle flame. Occurs as a pseudomorph after galena. Alters to cerussite.

Anglesite is a common oxidation product of lead minerals, especially galena. It is commonly found in cracks and cavities with galena and cerussite. Other associates are sphalerite, smithsonite, hemimorphite, and limonite. Excellent crystals are found at Monte Poni, Sardinia; Clausthal, Harz Mountains, Germany; Anglesea, England; Leadhills, Scotland; Tsumeb, South-West Africa; Broken Hill, New South Wales; Phoenixville, Pennsylvania; Tintic district, Utah; various places in Colorado, Missouri, Wisconsin, Arizona, California; and Coeur d'Alene district, Idaho; in large deposits in Mexico and Australia.

Anglesite is an ore of lead.

Brochantite, $Cu_4(OH)_6SO_4$.

Monoclinic, prismatic class—$2m$; pseudo-orthorhombic. Short prismatic and acicular crystals with vertical striations. Also tabular, reniform with fibrous structure, and as drusy crusts.

Perfect orthopinacoidal cleavage. Hardness, 3.5 to 4. Specific gravity, 3.8 to 3.9. Emerald to blackish green in color. Light-green streak. Transparent to translucent. Vitreous to pearly luster. α 1.728, β 1.771, γ 1.800, (−); $2V = 77°$; $r < v$.

$Cu_4(OH)_6SO_4$ or $CuSO_4.3Cu(OH)_2$. CuO 70.3, SO_3 17.7, H_2O 12.0 per cent. Loses water at 300°C.

A secondary copper mineral, commonly associated with malachite, azurite, cuprite, chalcopyrite, and limonite. Occurs in Rumania; the Ural Mountains; Bolivia; Chile; Sonora, Mexico; in various copper districts of Arizona; Chaffee County, Colorado; the Tintic district, Utah; New Mexico; Idaho.

Of minor importance as a copper mineral.

Antlerite, $Cu_3(OH)_4SO_4$, has properties much like those of brochantite. It occurs in large quantities at Chuquicamata, Chile. It has been mistaken for brochantite.

Alunite (*Alum Stone*), **$KAl_3(OH)_6(SO_4)_2$.**

Hexagonal, ditrigonal pyramidal class—$3m$. Crystals are generally small rhombohedrons resembling cubes, often with curved surfaces; more rarely tabular. Commonly compact, granular, fibrous, or earthy.

Perfect basal cleavage. Conchoidal, splintery, or earthy fracture. Hardness, 3.5 to 4; sometimes harder due to admixtures of quartz and feldspar. Tough. White streak. Specific gravity, 2.6 to 2.8. Colorless, white, yellowish, or reddish. Pearly luster on cleavage surfaces, otherwise vitreous. ω 1.572, ϵ 1.592 (+). Transparent to translucent. Pyroelectric.

$KAl_3(OH)_6(SO_4)_2$. K_2O 11.4, Al_2O_3 37.0, SO_3 38.6, H_2O 13.0 per cent. May contain some sodium. Insoluble in hydrochloric acid and water.

Alunite occurs in irregular deposits and in veins in altered feldspathic rocks, such as rhyolites, trachytes, and andesites. Common associates are kaolin, pyrite, opal, and quartz. Occurs in Czechoslovakia, Greece, Italy, France, Mexico, and Japan. In the United States, it is found at Silverton and Cripple Creek, Colorado; Mariposa County, California; Morenci, Arizona; in large quantities with gold in the Goldfield district, Nevada; and Marysvale, Utah.

Alunite is a source of alum and potassium sulfate, which are obtained by roasting and subsequent leaching. Some of the Hungarian varieties are so hard and tough as to be used for millstones. Alunite is also a minor source of aluminum. See page 468.

Chalcanthite (*Blue Vitriol, Blue Stone*), **$CuSO_4.5H_2O$.**

Triclinic, pinacoidal class—$\bar{1}$. Rarely as small, flat crystals. Generally in crusts with reniform, stalactitic, or fibrous structure.

Crystals possess imperfect basal and prismatic cleavages. Conchoidal fracture. Hardness, 2.5. Specific gravity, 2.1 to 2.3. Vitreous to dull luster. α 1.514, β 1.537, γ 1.543, (−); $2V = 56°$; $r < v$. Deep blue, sky blue, or greenish blue in color. White to light-blue streak. Translucent. Disagreeable metallic taste.

$CuSO_4.5H_2O$. CuO 31.8, SO_3 32.1, H_2O 36.1 per cent. May contain iron. Readily soluble in water, yielding a blue solution, especially when ammoniacal.

Chalcanthite is an alteration product of copper minerals, such as chalcopyrite, chalcocite, and bornite. Occurs in the mines of the Harz Mountains, Germany; also in Czechoslovakia; Falun, Sweden; Rio Tinto, Spain; Chessy, France; Cornwall, England; Wicklow, Ireland. It was formerly found in considerable quantities in the Bluestone Mine, near Reno, Nevada, and at Chuquicamata and Copiapo, Chile. Found also in the water of the copper mines of Arizona and Montana. The copper in such mine water is recovered by precipitation with scrap iron.

In Chile, chalcanthite is an ore of copper. The artificial compound is used in copperplating, in batteries, as a mordant and preservative of timber, and for spraying plants.

Melanterite (*Copperas*), $\mathbf{FeSO_4.7H_2O}$.

Monoclinic, prismatic class—$2/m$. Crystals are very rare. Usually as earthy, fibrous, or capillary crusts or efflorescences; also stalactitic.

Crystals have perfect basal and distinct prismatic cleavages. Conchoidal to earthy fracture. Hardness, 2. Specific gravity, 1.8 to 1.9. Various shades of green in color, often yellowish after exposure. Vitreous to dull luster. α 1.471, β 1.478, γ 1.486, (+); $2V = 86°$; $r > v$. Transparent to translucent. Sweet, astringent taste, somewhat metallic.

$FeSO_4.7H_2O$. FeO 25.9, SO_3 28.8, H_2O 45.3 per cent. Sometimes contains manganese, magnesium, copper, or zinc. Easily soluble in water. Loses water on exposure and crumbles to powder.

Decomposition product of iron sulfide minerals, especially pyrite, marcasite, chalcopyrite, and pyrrhotite. Some localities are the Harz Mountains, Germany; Bodenmais, Bavaria; Falun, Sweden; Rio Tinto, Spain. In the United States, it is generally found as an efflorescence with the sulfides of iron.

Melanterite does not occur abundantly enough in nature to be of commercial importance. The artificial compound is used in large quantities as a mordant in dyeing, as a disinfectant, and in the manufacture of inks, bluing, and pigments.

Epsomite (*Epsom Salt*), $\mathbf{MgSO_4.7H_2O}$.

Orthorhombic, bisphenoidal class—222. Occasionally in nearly square prismatic crystals. Commonly as granular, fibrous, or earthy masses, or in crusts.

Perfect brachypinacoidal cleavage. Hardness, 2 to 2.5. Specific gravity, 1.7 to 1.8. Colorless or white. Transparent to translucent. Bitter salty taste. α 1.433, β 1.455, γ 1.461, (−); $2V = 52°$; $r < v$.

$MgSO_4.7H_2O$. MgO 16.3, SO_3 32.5, H_2O 51.2 per cent. May contain some iron, manganese, nickel, zinc, or copper. Loses water on exposure to air. Soluble in water.

Epsomite is a common constituent of ocean, salt lake, and spring waters. Thus, it occurs in the springs at Epsom, England; Saidschitz and elsewhere, Bohemia; Ofen, Hungary. As an alteration product of kieserite, it is found in the salt deposits of Stassfurt, Germany. It may be the result of the action of sulfuric acid from decomposing sulfides, on serpentine, talc, magnesite, or other magnesium rocks. At Montmartre, Paris, it occurs with gypsum. It is also found in limestone caves in Kentucky, Tennessee, and Indiana, and in crusts on the alkali plains of Utah, Nevada, New Mexico, and California. It occurs with mirabilite in Albany County, Wyoming, and near Oroville, Washington.

Epsomite is used in medicine, as a fertilizer in place of gypsum, and as a coating for cotton cloth.

GYPSUM (*Selenite, Satin Spar, Alabaster*), $CaSO_4.2H_2O$.

Monoclinic, prismatic class—$2/m$. Crystals are usually simple and either tabular or prismatic in habit. Sometimes twinned parallel to the orthopinacoid yielding contact (swallow-tailed) and penetration twins (Figs. 588 to 590). Very common in cleavable, columnar (Fig. 591), granular, fibrous (Fig. 592), foliated, or earthy masses.

Fig. 588. Gypsum crystals—tabular, contact and penetration twins.

Fig. 589.

Fig. 590.

There are three cleavages parallel to (1) clinopinacoid, (2) positive unit hemipyramid, and (3) orthopinacoid, yielding very thin and smooth folia, and fibrous and conchoidal surfaces, respectively. Hardness, 2. Specific gravity, 2.2 to 2.4. Vitreous to pearly or silky luster. α 1.521 β 1.523, γ 1.530, (+); $2V = 58°$; $r > v$. Colorless, white, gray, yellow, brown, reddish, or black. Transparent to opaque.

Fig. 591. Gypsum (columnar or "pencil rock"). Grand Rapids, Michigan.

Fig. 592. Gypsum: variety, satin spar. Montmartre, Paris, France.

$CaSO_4.2H_2O$. CaO 32.6, SO_3 46.5, H_2O 20.9 per cent. Often mixed with clay, sand, or organic matter. Yields water when heated and becomes white and opaque. Soluble in 380 to 460 parts of water, depending upon temperature and pressure.

There are five varieties of gypsum.

Selenite. This includes crystals and cleavable masses and is usually colorless and transparent.

Satin Spar. A fibrous variety with a pronounced silky luster (Fig. 592). Sometimes used in cheap jewelry.

Alabaster. A massive and usually fine-grained variety. Sometimes used for statuary and decorative purposes.

Rock Gypsum. A compact scaly or granular variety, often very impure. It is frequently ground and used as a fertilizer under the name of *land plaster.*

Gypsite. An impure earthy or sandy variety occurring abundantly in Kansas, Arizona, New Mexico, and Oklahoma.

Gypsum is a common mineral and often occurs in extensive deposits of great thickness. It is usually found with limestones and shales and in connection with salt deposits. Deposits of this character are frequently of great commercial importance. Some of the best known and most extensively worked occurrences are in central and western New York; Alabaster and Grand Rapids, Michigan; Fort Dodge, Iowa; Blue Rapids, Gypsum City, and Medicine Lodge, Kansas; Plaster City, California (page 446); also various places in Oklahoma, Texas, Oregon, South Dakota, and Wyoming. Large deposits occur also at Hillsboro, Albert County, New Brunswick; and in Nova Scotia. Excellent transparent crystals are found at Ellsworth and Canfield in Trumbull County, and also in Mahoning County, Ohio; very large crystals in Wayne County, Utah. New York, Michigan, Iowa, Kansas, Ohio, California, and Texas are the chief producers of gypsum.

Gypsum may be formed by deposition from solution or by the hydration of anhydrite; in volcanic regions by the action of sulfurous vapors upon limestone; and in metalliferous veins by the action of sulfuric acid resulting from the oxidation of metallic sulfides. The common associates are halite, celestite, sulfur, aragonite, dolomite, calcite, pyrite, and quartz.

Ground rock gypsum is used to a limited extent as a fertilizer and is called *land plaster.* It is also used as a disinfectant, flux in glass and porcelain manufacture, retarder in cement, and filler in fertilizers. Alabaster is used for statues, vases, pedestals, lamps, and bric-a-brac. Satin spar and a small amount of selenite are used in cheap jewelry and microscopy, respectively. It is also used as an adulterant of foods, medicines, and paints. When gypsum is calcined at 190° to 200°C. so as to drive off 1½ molecules of water, it forms *plaster of paris,* which has the property of *setting* or becoming hard after being mixed with water. Plaster of paris is used in very large quantities in wall plasters, wall board, "rock" lath, stucco, whitewash, crayons, casts, and in many other ways. See also page 445.

Crocoite, $PbCrO_4$.

Monoclinic, prismatic class—$2/m$. Commonly in prismatic or acicular crystals, often highly modified and striated. Also columnar, granular, or in crusts.

Distinct prismatic cleavage. Conchoidal to uneven fracture. Hardness, 2.5 to 3. Specific gravity, 5.9 to 6.1. Various shades of red, resembling potassium bichromate in color. Orange-yellow streak. Adamantine to greasy luster. Very high indices of refraction, α 2.29, β 2.36, γ 2.66 (all for lithium light), (+); $2V = 57°$; $r > v$, very strong. Translucent.

$PbCrO_4$. PbO 68.9, CrO_3 31.1 per cent. Usually quite pure; may contain sulfur.

An alteration product of galena and usually associated with galena, pyromorphite, cerussite, pyrite, vanadinite, wulfenite, and limonite. Found in excellent crystals near Dundas, Tasmania; Siberia; Rumania; Maricopa and Pinal counties, Arizona; and also Inyo and Riverside counties, California.

Not a common mineral and of no commercial importance.

Wolframite Group

The three tungsten minerals in this group—ferberite, wolframite, and huebnerite—have submetallic to greasy or resinous lusters, and are heavy, with specific gravities varying from 6.7 to 7.5. Chemically they form an isomorphous series between $FeWO_4$, ferberite, and $MnWO_4$, huebnerite, as end members. Wolframite has an intermediate composition, (Fe,Mn)-WO_4. These minerals are often grouped together as wolframite and called "black ore." They may contain columbium, tantalum, and calcium. Another important source of tungsten is the mineral scheelite, but it does not belong to this group.

Ferberite, $FeWO_4$.

Monoclinic, prismatic class—$2/m$. Crystals are usually tabular and in crested aggregates. Also in compact and granular masses.

Perfect clinopinacoidal cleavage. Uneven fracture. Hardness, 5. Specific gravity, 7.5. Brown to black in color and streak. Opaque.

$FeWO_4$. FeO 23.7, WO_3 76.3 per cent. Usually contains manganese and passes over into wolframite.

Occurs with quartz, hematite, limonite, molybdenite, pyrite, scheelite, wolframite, and sylvanite. The principal occurrences are in Boulder County, Colorado.

Uses are the same as for wolframite.

WOLFRAMITE, (Fe,Mn)WO_4.

Monoclinic, prismatic class—$2/m$. Crystals are thick tabular or short columnar and often quite large (Fig. 593). Commonly in bladed, curved lamellar, or granular masses.

Perfect clinopinacoidal cleavage. Uneven fracture. Hardness, 5 to 5.5. Specific gravity, 7.1 to 7.5. Dark gray, reddish brown, brownish black, or iron black in color. Streak varies from dark red-brown for manganiferous varieties to black for those containing much iron. Greasy, submetallic luster. Opaque. Sometimes slightly magnetic.

$(Fe,Mn)WO_4$. Wolframite is intermediate between ferberite and huebnerite, with a composition of not less than 20 per cent of one of its constituents and not over 80 per cent of the other. Occurs as a pseudomorph after scheelite.

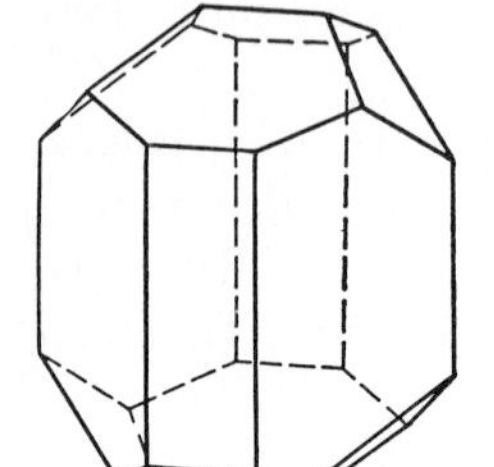

Fig. 593.

Occurs with quartz, lithium mica, fluorite, cassiterite, apatite, scheelite, molybdenite, huebnerite, ferberite, galena, and sphalerite. Some localities are Cornwall, England; in Saxony; Zinnwald, Bohemia; Siberia; New South Wales; Burma; the Malay States; Hunan and Kiangsi provinces, China; the Black Hills, South Dakota; Monroe and Trumbull, Connecticut.

Wolframite is a source of tungsten and its compounds. Tungsten is used in the manufacture of high-speed tool steels and as the filament in electric incandescent lamps; sodium tungstate as a mordant and to render cloth noninflammable; tungstic oxide to color glass; and calcium tungstate in X-ray apparatus. See page 474.

Huebnerite, $MnWO_4$.

Monoclinic, prismatic class—$2/m$. Generally in long fibrous, bladed (Fig. 594), or stalky crystals without good terminations. Also in compact, lamellar, or cleavable masses.

Fig. 594. Huebnerite in quartz. Pima County, Arizona.

Clinopinacoidal cleavage. Hardness, 5 to 5.5. Specific gravity, 6.7 to 7.3. Brownish, red, brownish black, pale yellow, or nearly black in color; in transmitted light, pale ruby-red to yellow. Submetallic to resinous luster. Translucent to opaque. Streak, yellow to yellow-brown.

$MnWO_4$. MnO 23.4, WO_3 76.6 per cent. Usually contains iron and grades into wolframite.

Occurs in quartz veins with wolframite, fluorite, pyrite, scheelite, galena, tetrahedrite, and muscovite. Thus, in Lemhi County, Idaho; White Pine County, Nevada; Arivaca, Pima County, Arizona; Ouray and San Juan counties, Colorado; Peru and New South Wales.

An ore of tungsten.

SCHEELITE, $CaWO_4$.

Tetragonal, tetragonal bipyramidal class—$4/m$. Crystals are generally small and pyramidal in habit (Figs. 595 and 596); rarely tabular; sometimes with third-order forms. More often as crystalline crusts on quartz, or in reniform, disseminated, or granular masses.

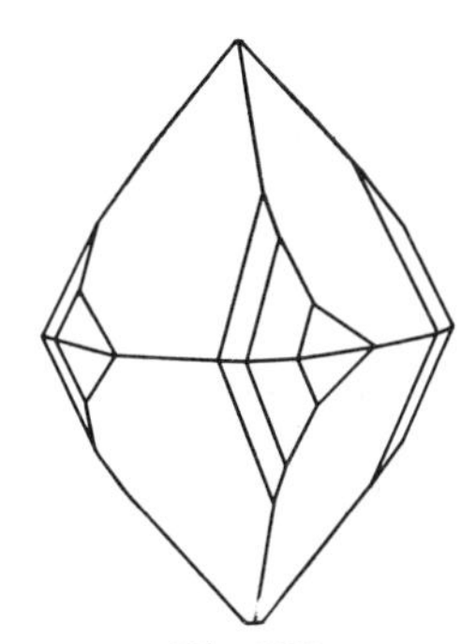

Fig. 595.

Fig. 596. Scheelite on quartz. Zinnwald, Bohemia.

Distinct pyramidal cleavage. Conchoidal to uneven fracture. Hardness, 4.5 to 5. Specific gravity, 5.9 to 6.1. White, yellow, brown, green, or reddish. Adamantine to greasy luster. ω 1.920, ϵ 1.936, (+). White streak. Transparent to opaque. Usually fluoresces. Thermoluminescent.

$CaWO_4$. CaO 19.4, WO_3 80.6 per cent. Usually contains some molybdenum. Occurs as a pseudomorph after wolframite.

Usually found with quartz, cassiterite, fluorite, topaz, molybdenite, wolframite, and apatite. Occurs in Cornwall and Cumberland, England; Schlaggenwald and Zinnwald, Bohemia; New South Wales; New Zealand; Tasmania; British Columbia, Nova Scotia, Quebec, Canada; Monroe and Trumbull, Connecticut; San Bernardino and Kern counties, California; Cochise, Pinal, and Santa Cruz counties, Arizona; Jardine, Montana; White Pine and Humboldt counties, Nevada; New Mexico; also Utah and Colorado.

An important source of tungsten and its compounds. See page 474.

Wulfenite, $PbMoO_4$.

Tetragonal, tetragonal pyramidal class—4. Usually in square and thin tabular crystals (Fig. 597). Also pyramidal or short columnar. Sometimes with third-order forms. Hemimorphic development very rare. Also in coarse to fine granular masses.

Hardness, 3. Specific gravity, 6.3 to 7. Resinous to adamantine luster. ω 2.40, ϵ 2.28 (lithium), (−). Various shades of yellow, red, or

Fig. 597. Wulfenite. Bleiberg, Carinthia, Austria.

green; also gray or white. Yellowish-white streak. Transparent to translucent.

$PbMoO_4$. PbO 60.8, MoO_3 39.2 per cent. May contain some tungsten, calcium, vanadium, or chromium. Occurs as a pseudomorph after galena.

Wulfenite is a secondary mineral, usually the result of the decomposition of lead minerals. It is commonly associated with galena, pyromorphite, and vanadinite. Occurs at Bleiberg, Carinthia, Austria; Přibram, Bohemia; Saxony; Mexico; Phoenixville, Pennsylvania; various places in Yuma, Maricopa, and Pinal counties, Arizona; Searchlight, Nevada; also in Southampton, Massachusetts; Wisconsin, New Mexico, Utah, and California.

A source of molybdenum and its compounds. See page 463.

PHOSPHATES, ARSENATES, AND VANADATES

Of the many minerals belonging to this division which have been recorded in the literature, the following are the most important.

Monazite	**$(Ce,La)PO_4$**	Monoclinic
Amblygonite	**$LiAl(F,OH)PO_4$**	Triclinic
	Apatite Group	
APATITE	**$Ca_5F(PO_4)_3$**	Hexagonal
Pyromorphite	**$Pb_5Cl(PO_4)_3$**	Hexagonal
Vanadinite	**$Pb_5Cl(VO_4)_3$**	Hexagonal
Wavellite	**$Al_3(OH)_3(PO_4)_2.5H_2O$**	Orthorhombic
Turquois	**$CuAl_6(OH)_2(PO_4)_4.4H_2O$**	Triclinic
Carnotite	**$K_2(UO_2)_2(VO_4)_2.3H_2O$**	Orthorhombic

Monazite, $(Ce,La)PO_4$.

Monoclinic, prismatic class—$2m$. Crystals are thick tabular or square prismatic, usually small and not common. Generally found as angular disseminated masses and as rolled grains in sand.

Perfect basal cleavage. Conchoidal fracture. Hardness, 5 to 5.5. Specific gravity, 4.6 to 5.4. Brownish gray, yellow, or reddish in color. White streak. Resinous luster. α 1.800, β 1.801, γ 1.849, (+); $2V = 11°$; $r < v$; optical constants vary. Translucent to opaque.

$(Ce,La)PO_4$. May contain 1 to 15 per cent of ThO_2. Some of the yttrium rare earths may also be present.

Occurs disseminated in granites and gneisses; thus, at Arendal, Norway;

Miask, Ural Mountains; Binnenthal, Switzerland; Amelia Court House, Virginia. The most important occurrence of monazite is as sand, extensive deposits of which are found in the western part of North and South Carolina and Georgia; Florida; Idaho; Montana; California; Rio Arriba County, New Mexico; in the provinces of Bahia, Minas Gerais, Rio de Janeiro, and São Paulo, Brazil; Travancore, India; Australia; Union of South Africa; also in the Ural Mountains. Common associates are magnetite, zircon, garnet, ilmenite, rutile, thorite, gold, chromite, and sometimes the diamond.

Monazite is the chief source of thorium, which is important in atomic fission, and of the compounds of the rare earths used in electrodes, optical glass, refractories, and the textile industry. Most of the world's supply of monazite is obtained from Brazil and India. See page 449.

Triphylite, $Li(Fe,Mn)PO_4$. Orthorhombic, bipyramidal class—$2/m\ 2/m\ 2/m$. Crystals are rare but may be large. Usually as compact, coarse granular, or cleavable masses. Perfect basal cleavage. Hardness, 4 to 5. Specific gravity, 3.4 to 3.6. Greenish gray to blue; when manganiferous, pink to brown. Gray to white streak. Greasy luster. Translucent. α 1.688, β 1.688, γ 1.692, (+); $2V = 0°$.

A pegmatite mineral, associated with spodumene, tourmaline, and beryl. Occurs at Bodenmais and Rabenstein, Bavaria; Keyto, Finland; South-West Africa; Grafton, New Hampshire; Huntington, Massachusetts; Peru, Maine; Black Hills, South Dakota.

Amblygonite, $LiAl(F,OH)PO_4$.

Triclinic, pinacoidal class—$\bar{1}$. Large poorly developed crystals. Usually as cleavable, columnar, or compact masses.

Basal, prismatic, and domatic cleavages. Conchoidal fracture. Brittle. Hardness, 6. Specific gravity, 3 to 3.1. Pearly to vitreous luster. White, green, blue, gray, yellow, or brownish in color. White streak. Translucent. Looks like feldspar. α 1.591, β 1.605, γ 1.612, (−); $2V = 55°$; $r > v$. Optical constants vary.

$LiAl(F,OH)PO_4$. Composition varies. May contain sodium. Colors flame red.

Amblygonite is a pegmatite mineral. Common associates are lepidolite, spodumene, tourmaline, quartz, apatite. Occurs at Arendal, Norway; Penig, Saxony; Brazil; South-West Africa; Hebron and Paris, Maine; Branchville, Connecticut; in large quantities at the Etta Mine, Black Hills, South Dakota, and Pala, San Diego, Riverside, and San Bernardino counties, California.

A source of lithium and its compounds. See page 458.

APATITE, $Ca_5F(PO_4)_3$.

Hexagonal, hexagonal bipyramidal class—$6/m$. Prismatic and thick tabular crystals are common, often well developed and highly modified

(Figs. 598 and 599). Sometimes large. The edges may be rounded and have a fused appearance. At times forms of the third order are to be observed. Also in compact, fibrous, nodular, reniform, oölitic, or earthy masses.

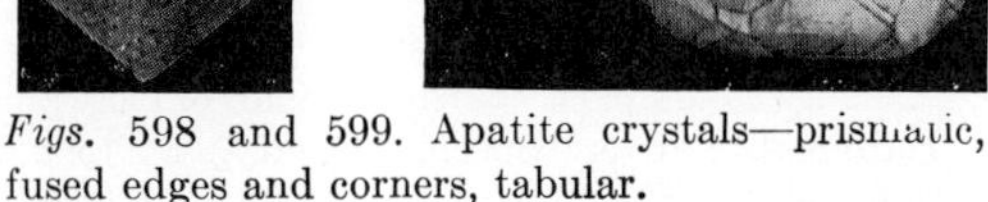

Figs. 598 and 599. Apatite crystals—prismatic, fused edges and corners, tabular.

Fig. 600. Apatite in calcite. Franklin, New Jersey.

Imperfect basal cleavage. Conchoidal fracture. Hardness, 5. Specific gravity, 3.1 to 3.2. Sometimes colorless and transparent but usually translucent to opaque and variously colored, brown, green, gray, yellow, red, blue, purple, or white. Sometimes unevenly colored. Vitreous to greasy luster. ω 1.646, ϵ 1.642, varying with composition (−). May become luminescent.

Apatite is essentially an orthophosphate of calcium containing fluorine, chlorine, or hydroxyl in varying amounts. Hence, the following formulas have been assigned to it: $Ca_5F(PO_4)_3$, $Ca_5Cl(PO_4)_3$, and $Ca_5(Cl,F,OH)$-$(PO_4)_3$. Fluorine usually predominates, *fluorapatite* being more common than *chlorapatite*. CO_3OH in appreciable amounts replaces PO_4. Magnesium, manganese, strontium, cerium, and iron may also be present. Fuses with difficulty. Easily soluble in acids. May phosphoresce when heated.

There are three important varieties:

Ordinary Apatite. This includes crystallized, cleavable, and granular varieties.

Phosphate Rock. Collophane. An impure massive variety, containing 15 to 40 per cent of P_2O_5. Color is gray, white, brown, or black. The hardness varies from 2 to 5. It occurs in beds, or as nodules and concretions.

Guano. Animal excrement, chiefly of birds, rich in phosphoric acid. Gray to brown in color, and porous, granular, or compact in structure.

Apatite is a common accessory constituent of many igneous rocks. It is an associate of metalliferous ore deposits, especially those of magnetite and cassiterite. It occurs also in granular limestones and, in fact, is present in small quantities in nearly all types of rocks. Common associates are calcite (Fig. 600), cassiterite, quartz, fluorite, wolframite, and magnetite. Some important localities are Ehrenfriedersdorf, Saxony; Schlaggenwald, Bohemia; Saint Gotthard, Switzerland; Knappenwand, Tirol; Japan; U.S.S.R.; Renfrew County, Ontario; Ottawa County, Quebec; Norwich and Bolton, Massachusetts; St. Lawrence and Jefferson counties, New York; Chester County, Pennsylvania; Franklin, New Jersey; Auburn, Maine.

Phosphate rock occurs in extensive deposits in Florida, Tennessee, Wyoming, Idaho, Utah, and Montana.

Phosphate rock is used in enormous quantities in the manufacture of fertilizers, its phosphoric acid content being rendered available by treating with sulfuric acid. Apatite is also used to some extent as a source of phosphorus and of phosphoric acid (H_3PO_4). Well-developed, transparent crystals of good color are used for gem purposes. Also see page 466.

Pyromorphite, $Pb_5Cl(PO_4)_3$.

Hexagonal, hexagonal bipyramidal class—$6/m$. Crystals are usually small, rounded, or barrel-shaped. Often hollow and skeletal or in parallel groups. Sometimes they resemble those of apatite. Occurs also in botryoidal and reniform aggregates, disseminated, and in crusts.

Conchoidal to uneven fracture. Hardness, 3.5 to 4. Specific gravity, 6.7 to 7.1. Usually some shade of green, but may be yellow, gray, brown, orange, or white. White to pale-yellow streak. Greasy to adamantine luster. ω 2.058, ϵ 2.048, (−). May be optically anomalous. Translucent to opaque.

$Pb_5Cl(PO_4)_3$. PbO 82.2, P_2O_5 15.7, Cl 2.6 per cent. May contain calcium, fluorine, or arsenic. Occurs as a pseudomorph after galena and cerussite.

Pyromorphite is generally a secondary mineral formed from the decomposition of lead ores. Common associates are galena, cerussite, barite, and limonite. It occurs in the Freiberg district, Saxony; Clausthal, Harz Mountains; Ems, Hesse-Nassau, Germany; Ural Mountains; Broken Hill, New South Wales; Cornwall and Cumberland, England; Leadhills, Scotland; Phoenixville, Pennsylvania; Sierro and Grant counties, New Mexico; Leadville, Colorado; Lubec and Lenox, Maine; Coeur d'Alene, Idaho.

A minor source of lead.

Vanadinite, $Pb_5Cl(VO_4)_3$.

Hexagonal, hexagonal bipyramidal class—$6/m$. Crystals are usually prismatic, often skeletal and resembling those of pyromorphite. Occurs also compact, fibrous, globular, and in crusts.

Uneven to conchoidal fracture. Hardness, 3. Specific gravity, 6.7 to 7.2. Yellow, brown, or red in color. White to pale-yellow streak. Translucent to opaque. Resinous luster. ω 2.416, ϵ 2.350, (−).

$Pb_5Cl(VO_4)_3$. PbO 78.7, V_2O_5 19.4, Cl 2.5 per cent. May contain phosphorus or arsenic. *Endlichite* is a light-yellow variety containing arsenic. ω 2.25, ϵ 2.20, (−). Fuses easily. Readily soluble in nitric acid.

Occurs associated with lead minerals but never in large quantities. Some localities are Zimapan, Mexico; the Ural Mountains; Abenab and Tsumeb, South-West Africa; various places in Yuma, Maricopa, Pinal, and Yavapai counties, Arizona; San Bernardino and Riverside counties, California; Kelley, New Mexico.

It is a source of vanadium and its compounds. See page 475.

Vivianite, $Fe_3(PO_4)_2.8H_2O$. Monoclinic, prismatic class—$2/m$. Crystals are prismatic; also reniform and globular aggregates with radial, fibrous structure; often earthy and then called *blue iron-earth*.

Clinopinacoidal cleavage. Sectile. Thin laminae are flexible. Hardness, 1.5 to 2. Specific gravity, 2.6 to 2.7. Vitreous luster, pearly on cleavage surfaces. Colorless and transparent when unaltered, otherwise blue or green and translucent or opaque. Colorless or bluish-white streak which changes to indigo-blue or brown. α 1.579, β 1.602, γ 1.629, (+); $2V = 83°$; $r < v$. Strongly pleochroic.

$Fe_3(PO_4)_2.8H_2O$. FeO 43.0, P_2O_5 28.3, H_2O 28.7 per cent. Small amounts of calcium, magnesium, and manganese may be present. Fuses easily. Colors flame bluish green. Yields magnetic globule on charcoal. Soluble in hydrochloric acid.

Occurs as a secondary mineral with pyrite, pyrrhotite, limonite in copper and tin deposits. Also found in bones, shells, roots, and ferruginous clays. Important localities are Cornwall and Devonshire, England; Bodenmais, Germany; Llallagua, Bolivia; Allentown, New Jersey; Leadville, Colorado; in green sand, New Castle County, Delaware; in phosphate rock, Plant City, Florida.

Erythrite (*Cobalt Bloom*), $Co_3(AsO_4)_2.8H_2O$. Monoclinic, prismatic class—$2/m$. Very small, vertically striated, acicular crystals, often in spherical or stellate groups; also globular, reniform, and earthy masses, and as a coating.

Clinopinacoidal cleavage. Sectile and flexible in thin laminae. Hardness, 1.5 to 2.5. Specific gravity, 3 to 3.2. Pearly luster on cleavages, otherwise adamantine to vitreous. Crimson to peach-red, greenish gray when decomposed. Streak, pale red; dry powder is lavender-blue. Transparent to translucent. α 1.626, β 1.661, γ 1.699, (+); $2V = 90°$; $r > v$.

$Co_3(AsO_4)_2.8H_2O$. Co 37.5, As_2O_5 38.4, H_2O 24.1 per cent. Yields water in closed tube and turns blue. Acid solutions are red.

Erythrite is a decomposition product of the arsenides of cobalt. Found with cobaltite, smaltite, and chloanthite in the Freiberg district, Saxony, and rather abundantly at Cobalt, Ontario; also in Nevada, Arizona, Idaho, and California. Principal use is as a guide in locating cobalt and silver minerals.

Annabergite (*Nickel Bloom*), $Ni_3(AsO_4)_2.8H_2O$. Monoclinic, prismatic class—$2/m$. Crystals are rare; usually as earthy, somewhat crystalline crusts and masses. Very soft. Specific gravity, 3 to 3.1. Apple-green color. α 1.622, β 1.658, γ 1.687, (−);

$2V = 84°$; $r > v$. Decomposition product of nickel and arsenic minerals, such as niccolite and chloanthite. Occurs in Freiberg, Saxony, and at Cobalt, Ontario; also in Nevada and Colorado.

Wavellite, $Al_3(OH)_3(PO_4)_2.5H_2O$.

Orthorhombic, bipyramidal class—$2/m\ 2/m\ 2/m$. Good crystals are very rare. Usually in crystalline crusts, or hemispherical or globular masses made up of concentric layers and possessing a radial fibrous structure (Fig. 601).

Fig. 601. Wavellite. Arkansas.

Conchoidal to uneven fracture. Hardness, 3.5 to 4. Specific gravity, 2.3 to 2.5. May be colorless but is usually gray, yellow, green, blue, or black. Vitreous luster. α 1.525, β 1.534, γ 1.552, (+); $2V = 72°$; $r > v$. Translucent.

$Al_3(OH)_3(PO_4)_2.5H_2O$. Al_2O_3 37.11, P_2O_5 34.47, H_2O 28.42 per cent. The water of crystallization may vary. Some varieties contain fluorine and iron. Infusible. Soluble in hydrochloric acid.

Wavellite is a secondary mineral formed by the action of circulating waters, containing phosphoric acid, upon rocks and minerals rich in aluminum. It is, hence, found on the surfaces of such rocks, or lining the cracks and cavities in the same. Some localities are Devonshire and Cornwall, England; Czerhovic, Bohemia; Kapnik, Rumania; Llallagua, Bolivia; Chester and York counties, Pennsylvania; Montgomery and Garland counties, Arkansas; Silver Hill, South Carolina. In phosphate rock deposits, Marion County, Florida.

Of no commercial importance.

Turquois, $CuAl_6(OH)_8(PO_4)_4.4H_2O$.

Triclinic, pinacoidal class—$\bar{1}$. Crystals are tabular but very rare. Usually apparently amorphous, in reniform, botryoidal, or stalactitic masses and in veins; also as crusts, coatings, and disseminated grains, or rolled and rounded pebbles.

Conchoidal fracture. Hardness, 5.5 to 6. Specific gravity, 2.6 to 2.8. Various shades of blue or green. Darker blue in artificial light. Translucent to opaque. Waxy to dull luster. α 1.61, β 1.62, γ 1.65, (+); $2V = 40°$; $r < v$. White or slightly greenish streak.

$CuAl_6(OH)_8(PO_4)_4.4H_2O$. CuO 9.78, Al_2O_3 37.60, P_2O_5 34.90, H_2O 17.72 per cent. May contain iron. Infusible. Soluble in acids after ignition.

Turquois is a secondary mineral and is often associated with limonite, quartz, feldspar, or kaolin. It occurs in trachyte near Nishapur in the Province of Khorassan, Persia; Jordansmühl, Silesia; crystals, Campbell County, Virginia; near Mineral Park, Mohave County, and elsewhere, Arizona; Texas; Los Cerrillos and elsewhere, New Mexico; San Bernardino County, California; Nye County, Nevada; Colorado.

Used as a gem mineral. Color fades in time and is destroyed by heat.

Turquois matrix consists of turquois in associated rock, which is usually limonitic.

Bone or *fossil turquois,* often called *odontolite,* is ivory, fossil bones or teeth, colored blue either naturally or artificially.

Carnotite, $K_2(UO_2)_2(VO_4)_2.3H_2O$.

Orthorhombic. Crystals are small, tabular, and with a rhombic outline. Usually observed in scaly aggregates, incrustations, or as a crystalline powder.

Perfect basal cleavage. Earthy fracture. Hardness, 1 to 2. Canary to lemon yellow in color. Resinous to dull luster. α 1.750, β 1.925, γ 1.950, (−); $2V$ varies from 39 to 44°; $r < v$. Transparent to translucent.

A vanadate of potassium and uranium, containing small amounts of radium. Composition varies.

Occurs as a powdery incrustation in loosely cohering masses or as an impregnation in sand or sandstone. Common associates are malachite, azurite, biotite, and magnetite. Occurs in San Miguel, Rio Blanco, and Montrose counties, Colorado; San Juan County, Utah; Maricopa County, Arizona; New Mexico; Mauch Chunk, Pennsylvania; Radium Hill, South Australia; Katanga, Belgian Congo.

An important source of uranium and radium. See page 474.

SILICATES

This division contains a very large number of minerals, some of which are exceedingly common. For example, the members of the groups known as the feldspars, pyroxenes, amphiboles, and micas are abundant and important as rock minerals. The feldspars alone make up 60 per cent of the igneous rocks.

For the most part, the chemical composition of these minerals is complex. In contrast to such groups as the carbonates or sulfates in which the acid radical has the definite composition CO_3 or SO_4, the silicate radical may vary greatly. The silicate minerals listed on pages 361 and 362 have the radicals SiO_3, SiO_4, Si_3O_8, Si_3O_{10}, Si_4O_{11}, and so forth. The silicates have been interpreted as salts of various hypothetical silicic acids, all of which were derived from orthosilicic acid (H_4SiO_4). By the loss of a molecule of water, metasilicic acid (H_2SiO_3) was assumed to be formed. By the loss of water from several molecules of these acids, more complex acids were derived. This method of interpreting the composition of the silicates has been discarded. The terms metasilicate and orthosilicate are still sometimes used for compositions with radicals SiO_3 and SiO_4, respectively. The current interpretation has been made possible through the comprehensive knowledge of the crystal structures of these compounds.

Structures of the Silicates. The structures of a large number of silicates have been investigated by X-ray methods. The results have shown that invariably the silicon atom is surrounded by four oxygen atoms. These oxygen atoms may be arranged symmetrically at equal distances, occurring at the corners of a regular tetrahedron, or at unequal distances, forming a slightly distorted tetrahedron. The Si–O distance never departs more than a few per cent from a value of 1.62 Å. This SiO_4 tetrahedron apparently is the fundamental unit of all silicates. It may occur either singly or in groups formed by the sharing of one or more of the oxygen atoms by adjacent tetrahedrons.

The orthosilicates have independent SiO_4 groups (Figs. 602 and 603), joined together through the positive atoms or ions. Each $(SiO_4)^{-4}$ ion requires four positive metal valences, such as Mg_2SiO_4 or $ZrSiO_4$. Among the minerals with this type of structure are olivine, zircon, garnet, and topaz. In Fig. 602 the relative sizes of the silicon and oxygen atoms are ignored, and the symbols ● and ○, respectively, merely indicate the centers of the atoms. Actually the oxygen atoms are about five times as large as those of silicon, and the single silicon atom occupies the space at the center of four oxygen atoms arranged tetrahedrally. This is shown in Fig. 603, where only the four oxygen atoms are visible, the silicon atom being hidden at the center.

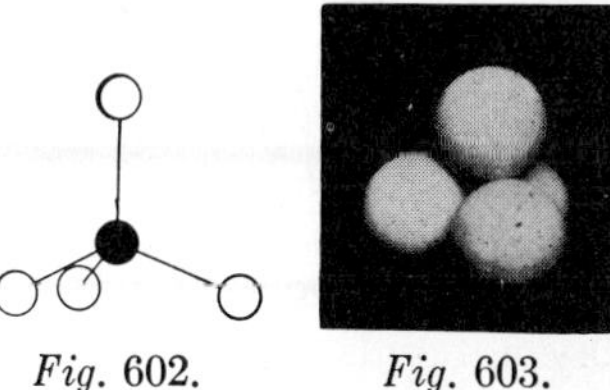

Fig. 602. *Fig.* 603.

Two SiO_4 tetrahedrons may be linked together, with one oxygen atom held in common, resulting in a Si_2O_7 group (Figs. 604 and 605). Independent groups of this kind have been found in hemimorphite and vesuvianite. Three SiO_4 groups may be joined by shared oxygen atoms to form a triangular ring, with the composition Si_3O_9; four groups may form a square ring, Si_4O_{12}; and six may form a hexagonal ring, with the composition Si_6O_{18} (Fig. 606). Such groups have been reported for the minerals benitoite, neptunite, and beryl, respectively.

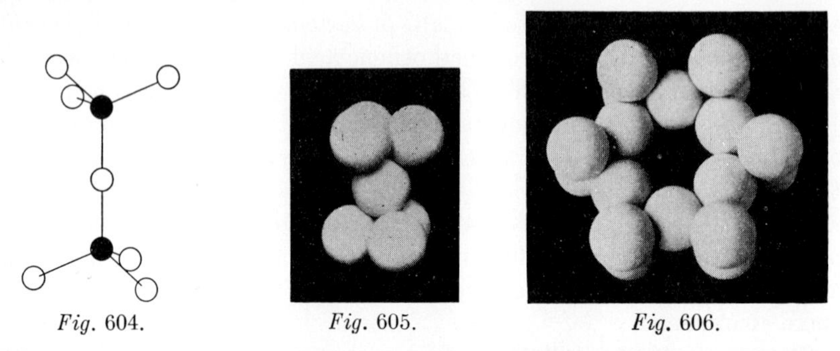

Fig. 604. *Fig.* 605. *Fig.* 606.

The two important mineral groups, the pyroxenes and the amphiboles, have structures in which the SiO_4 tetrahedrons are linked into long chains. In the pyroxenes the chain is single (Fig. 607), and the silicon and oxygen are present in the ratio of 1 : 3, giving the formula SiO_3. In the amphiboles the chain is double, corresponding to a single chain reflected across a plane of symmetry (Fig. 608). The silicon to oxygen ratio in the double chain is 4 : 11, that is, Si_4O_{11}. In a few cases there is a partial substitution of aluminum for silicon, giving $(Si,Al)_4O_{11}$.

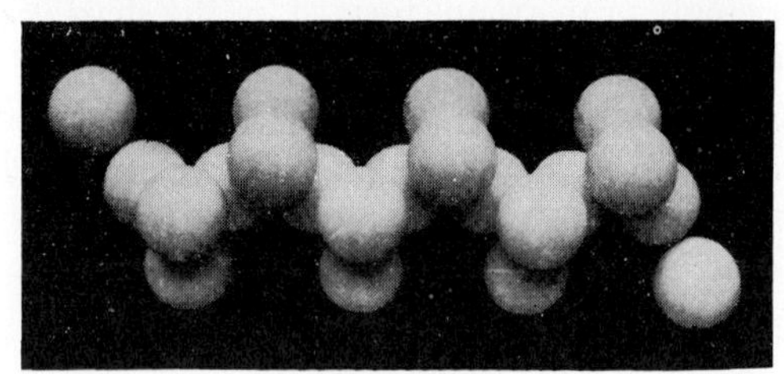

Fig. 607.

Several important mineral groups, such as the micas, chlorites, and clay minerals, have structures in which the SiO_4 tetrahedrons are linked together to form continuous sheets. Three oxygen atoms of each tetrahedron are shared, resulting in a Si to O ratio of 2 : 5 (4 : 10). This composition may be varied by the partial substitution of Al for Si, giving $(Si,Al)_4O_{10}$. These minerals usually have conspicuous basal cleavages. The sheet structure represents an extension of the double chain structure (Fig. 608) and these minerals frequently have a pseudohexagonal appearance (Figs. 671 and 672). The crystal system is usually monoclinic or triclinic, for the successive layers are slightly offset.

A further possibility is a structure in which all oxygen atoms are shared by adjacent SiO_4 tetrahedrons. This results in a three-dimensional framework of tetrahedrons, in which the Si : O ratio is 1 : 2. The various forms of silicon dioxide (SiO_2) (quartz, cristobalite, and tridymite) have this arrangement. These minerals, of course, are not silicates, but oxides.[1] The positive tetravalent silicon is completely balanced by the two negative divalent oxygen atoms, and no additional positive metallic

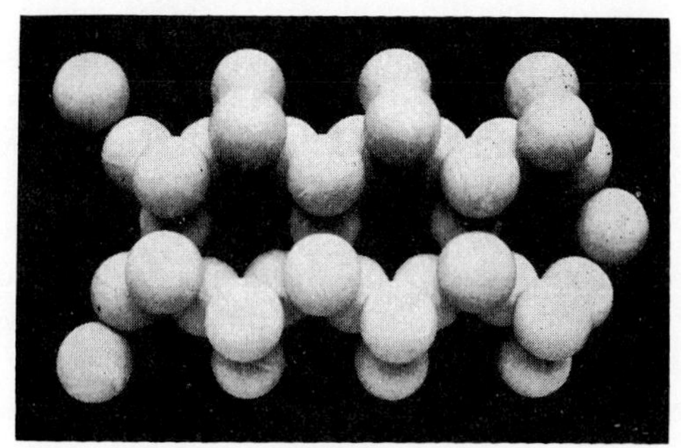

Fig. 608.

ions are needed. A silicate with a three-dimensional structure has at least one-fourth of the silicon atoms replaced by aluminum. The substitution of Al^{+3} for Si^{+4} requires additional metallic ions in order to balance the valences. The feldspars and the zeolites are characterized by this type of structure. In these compounds silicon and aluminum are present in such amounts that the ratio of these elements to oxygen is 1 : 2. This is readily seen in the following formulas:

Feldspars	Orthoclase	$KAlSi_3O_8$
	Anorthite	$CaAl_2Si_2O_8$
Zeolite	Analcime	$NaAlSi_2O_6.H_2O$

The various silicate structures and their characteristic Si : O ratios are summarized in Table 39.

TABLE 39

Structure	Ratio	Example
Single tetrahedron	1:4	Mg_2SiO_4
Double tetrahedron	2:7	$Zn_4(OH)_2Si_2O_7.H_2O$
Rings	3:9, 4:12, 6:18	$Be_3Al_2Si_6O_{18}$
Single chain	1:3 = 4:12	$Ca_2Mg_2Si_4O_{12}$
Double chain	4:11	$Ca_2Mg_5(OH)_2(Si_4O_{11})_2$
Sheet	2:5 = 4:10	$Al_4(OH)_8Si_4O_{10}$
Three dimensional	1:2 = 4:8	$KAlSi_3O_8$

[1] Because of this close relationship of the various forms of SiO_2 to the silicates, quartz is sometimes grouped with the silicates. See p. 298.

Some of the silicate minerals have mixed structures. Vesuvianite, for example, has both SiO_4 and Si_2O_7 groups, its formula being $Ca_{10}Al_4$-$(Mg,Fe)_2(OH)_4(SiO_4)_5(Si_2O_7)_2$. Likewise, in addition to the silicate radical, other radicals, as CO_3, SO_4, OH, F, and Cl, may be present. The mineral topaz, for example, has the formula $Al_2(F,OH)_2SiO_4$.

Composition of the Silicates. The silicates show wide variation in composition because of the different Si : O ratios which are possible. They may also have variable compositions because of extensive isomorphous replacement. In this case, similarity in ionic size is a controlling factor. Thus Fe^{+2} (radius 0.83 Å.) or Mn^{+2} (0.91) may replace Mg (0.78); Fe^{+3} (0.67) may replace Al^{+3} (0.57). There may also be dual replacements involving change in valence, as Ca^{+2} (1.06) for Na^{+1} (0.98) with simultaneous replacement of Al^{+3} (0.57) for Si^{+4} (0.39). Such a replacement occurs in the minerals albite and anorthite (see page 409). As previously indicated, this type of replacement is necessary in the three-dimensional silicate structures, and it may occur in the chain and sheet structures.

Silicate Formulas. Various methods are used for expressing the chemical composition of the silicates. Molecular structural formulas, similar to those used by the organic chemist, are unsatisfactory, because in silicates a molecule does not form the structural unit. Empirical formulas, giving the total number of atoms present, are frequently used. Another common method of expressing the composition is one in which the constituents are given as a series of oxides. Thus the formula of the mineral staurolite may be written either $H_2FeAl_4Si_2O_{12}$ or $FeO.2Al_2O_3$-$2SiO_2.H_2O$. Neither of these methods gives any indication of the structural arrangement. Since the structure of staurolite has been interpreted as consisting of alternate layers of $Fe(OH)_2$ and $2Al_2OSiO_4$, the formula may also be written $Fe(OH)_2.2Al_2OSiO_4$.

In many cases the empirical formula does not reveal the Si : O ratio, according to which the silicate structures are classified. Thus the members of the trimorphous series—andalusite, sillimanite, and kyanite—all have independent SiO_4 groups, although the formula has usually been written Al_2SiO_5. As the fifth oxygen atom is linked to aluminum instead of silicon, the composition should properly be expressed as Al_2OSiO_4. Moreover, many of the silicates contain an OH group, and in an empirical formula the oxygen of this group is added to the oxygen from the silicate radical. Thus talc has the empirical formula $H_2Mg_3Si_4O_{12}$. The formula $Mg_3(OH)_2Si_4O_{10}$ is preferable, for it reveals the silicon-oxygen ratio of 2 : 5, characteristic of the sheet structure which is present in talc.

Silicate Minerals. The following minerals include the most abundant and important silicates, arranged in the order of their structure as given in Table 39, page 359.

Mineral	Formula	Crystal system
WILLEMITE	Zn_2SiO_4	Hexagonal
OLIVINE	$(Mg,Fe)_2SiO_4$	Orthorhombic
GARNETS	$M_3''M_2'''(SiO_4)_3$	Cubic
ZIRCON	$ZrSiO_4$	Tetragonal

ANDALUSITE GROUP

Mineral	Formula	Crystal system
ANDALUSITE	Al_2OSiO_4	Orthorhombic
KYANITE	Al_2OSiO_4	Triclinic
Sillimanite	Al_2OSiO_4	Orthorhombic

Mineral	Formula	Crystal system
STAUROLITE	$Fe(OH)_2.2Al_2OSiO_4$	Orthorhombic
TOPAZ	$Al_2(F,OH)_2SiO_4$	Orthorhombic
Chondrodite	$Mg(F,OH)_2.2Mg_2SiO_4$	Monoclinic
Datolite	$CaB(OH)SiO_4$	Monoclinic
SPHENE	$CaTiOSiO_4$	Monoclinic
HEMIMORPHITE	$Zn_4(OH)_2Si_2O_7.H_2O$	Orthorhombic

EPIDOTE GROUP

Mineral	Formula	Crystal system
EPIDOTE	$Ca_2(Al,Fe)_3O(OH)SiO_4Si_2O_7$	Monoclinic
Allanite	$(Ca,Ce,La)_2(Al,Fe)_3O(OH)SiO_4Si_2O_7$	Monoclinic

Mineral	Formula	Crystal system
VESUVIANITE	$Ca_{10}Al_4(Mg,Fe)_2(OH)_4(SiO_4)_5(Si_2O_7)_2$	Tetragonal
Prehnite	$Ca_2Al_2(OH)_2Si_3O_{10}$	Orthorhombic
BERYL	$Be_3Al_2Si_6O_{18}$	Hexagonal
Cordierite	$Mg_2Al_3(AlSi_5O_{18})$	Orthorhombic
TOURMALINE	$M_7Al_6(OH,F)_4(BO_3)_3Si_6O_{18}$	Hexagonal
CHRYSOCOLLA	$CuSiO_3.nH_2O$	Amorphous?

PYROXENE GROUP

Mineral	Formula	Crystal system
ENSTATITE	$(Mg,Fe)_2Si_2O_6$	Orthorhombic
DIOPSIDE	$CaMgSi_2O_6$	Monoclinic
AUGITE	$Ca(Mg,Fe,Al)(Al,Si)_2O_6$	Monoclinic
Aegirite	$NaFeSi_2O_6$	Monoclinic
SPODUMENE	$LiAlSi_2O_6$	Monoclinic

Mineral	Formula	Crystal system
RHODONITE	$MnSiO_3$	Triclinic
Wollastonite	$CaSiO_3$	Triclinic
Pectolite	$HNaCa_2(SiO_3)_3$	Triclinic

AMPHIBOLE GROUP

Mineral	Formula	Crystal system
Tremolite	$Ca_2Mg_5(OH)_2Si_8O_{22}$	Monoclinic
Actinolite	$Ca_2(Mg,Fe)_5(OH)_2Si_8O_{22}$	Monoclinic
HORNBLENDE	$Ca_2(Mg,Fe)_5(OH)_2(Al,Si)_8O_{22}$	Monoclinic
Glaucophane	$Na_2Mg_3Al_2(OH)_2Si_8O_{22}$	Monoclinic

Mineral	Formula	Crystal system
APOPHYLLITE	$KCa_4F(Si_4O_{10})_2.8H_2O$	Tetragonal
TALC	$Mg_3(OH)_2Si_4O_{10}$	Monoclinic

MICA GROUP		
MUSCOVITE	$KAl_2(OH,F)_2AlSi_3O_{10}$	Monoclinic
PHLOGOPITE	$KMg_3(F,OH)_2AlSi_3O_{10}$	Monoclinic
BIOTITE	$K(Mg,Fe)_3(OH,F)_2AlSi_3O_{10}$	Monoclinic
Lepidolite	$K_2Li_3Al_3(F,OH)_4(AlSi_3O_{10})_2$	Monoclinic
CHLORITE	$Mg_5Al(OH)_8AlSi_3O_{10}$	Monoclinic
KAOLINITE	$Al_4(OH)_8Si_4O_{10}$	Monoclinic
SERPENTINE	$Mg_6(OH)_8Si_4O_{10}$	Monoclinic
Garnierite	$(Ni,Mg)_6(OH)_8Si_4O_{10}$	Monoclinic
Sepiolite	$Mg_4(OH)_2Si_6O_{15}.6H_2O$	Monoclinic
FELDSPAR GROUP		
ORTHOCLASE	$KAlSi_3O_8$	Monoclinic
MICROCLINE	$KAlSi_3O_8$	Triclinic
ALBITE	$NaAlSi_3O_8(Ab)$	Triclinic
LABRADORITE	$Ab_{50}An_{50}$ to $Ab_{30}An_{70}$	Triclinic
Anorthite	$CaAl_2Si_2O_8(An)$	Triclinic
FELDSPATHOID GROUP		
NEPHELINE	$Na(AlSiO_4)$	Hexagonal
Cancrinite	$Na_3CaCO_3(AlSiO_4)_3.nH_2O$	Hexagonal
Sodalite	$Na_4Cl(AlSiO_4)_3$	Cubic
Lazurite	$Na_5S(AlSiO_4)_3$	Cubic
LEUCITE	$K(AlSi_2O_6)$	Pseudocubic
SCAPOLITE	$nNa_4Cl(AlSi_3O_8)_3 +$ $mCa_4CO_3(Al_2Si_2O_8)_3$	Tetragonal
ZEOLITE GROUP		
Natrolite	$Na_2Al_2Si_3O_{10}.2H_2O$	Orthorhombic
ANALCIME	$NaAlSi_2O_6.H_2O$	Cubic
STILBITE	$(Ca,Na_2)Al_2Si_7O_{18}.7H_2O$	Monoclinic
CHABAZITE	$CaAl_2Si_4O_{12}.6H_2O$	Hexagonal

WILLEMITE, Zn_2SiO_4.

Hexagonal, trigonal rhombohedral class—$\bar{3}$. Crystals are either slender or thick prismatic in habit but generally quite small. *Troostite*, a variety containing manganese, is commonly found in larger crystals. Occurs also in compact or granular masses and in disseminated grains.

Basal cleavage. Uneven fracture. Hardness, 5 to 6. Specific gravity, 3.9 to 4.3. Greasy vitreous luster. ω 1.691, ϵ 1.719, (+). Commonly yellow, green, brown, or reddish; more rarely blue, black, white, or colorless. Transparent to opaque. Often shows luminescence.

Zn_2SiO_4. ZnO 73, SiO_2 27 per cent. Manganese and iron may be present. Fuses with difficulty. Gelatinizes with hydrochloric acid. Sometimes pseudomorphous after hemimorphite.

The usual associates are franklinite, zincite, rhodonite, and calcite. The most important locality is Franklin and vicinity, Sussex County, New Jersey, where it can be found in large quantities. Found also at Altenberg, Belgium; Musartut, Greenland; Mindouli, French Congo; Northern Rhodesia; South-West Africa; Merritt Mine, Socorro County, New Mexico; and Clifton, Arizona.

Willemite is an ore of zinc. Used as a detector in radio apparatus. See page 476.

OLIVINE (*Chrysolite, Peridot*), $\mathbf{(Mg,Fe)_2SiO_4}$.

Orthorhombic, bipyramidal class—$2/m\ 2/m\ 2/m$. Crystals are prismatic or thick tabular. Occurs generally in rounded, disseminated, glassy grains, granular aggregates, or in rounded loose pebbles.

Pinacoidal cleavages. Conchoidal fracture. Hardness, 6.5 to 7. Specific gravity, 3.2 to 3.6. Vitreous luster. α 1.653 to 1.681, β 1.670 to 1.706, γ 1.689 to 1.718. Optically positive when FeO content is less than 13 per cent, otherwise negative. $2V$ is large; $r < v$. The specific gravity and the indices increase with the iron content. Commonly various shades of green, also yellowish, brown, reddish, grayish, or colorless. Transparent to translucent.

$(Mg,Fe)_2SiO_4$. The composition varies between that of *forsterite* (Mg_2SiO_4) and *fayalite* (Fe_2SiO_4). Titanium, nickel, and calcium may be present in small amounts. Infusible. Easily decomposed and gelatinizes with acids. Alters to serpentine, magnetite, limonite, magnesite, opal, and garnierite.

Olivine is a constituent of many basic igneous rocks, such as basalt, dunite, gabbro, and peridotite. Found also in crystalline limestones and dolomites. The common associates are augite, enstatite, spinel, plagioclase, chromite, pyrope, corundum, talc, and magnetite. Occurs in Egypt; on Mount Vesuvius; in Burma; Norway; Arizona; Vermont; New Hampshire; Virginia; Pennsylvania; North Carolina; Oregon; New Mexico; Canada; Brazil. Olivine also occurs in meteorites and blast-furnace slags.

Peridot is a transparent green variety used for gem purposes. Olivine is used as a refractory.

Garnet Group

This group embraces minerals possessing the general formula $M_3''M_2'''(SiO_4)_3$, in which M'' may be calcium, magnesium, manganese, or ferrous iron, and M''' aluminum, ferric iron, or chromium. Sometimes titanium may replace a portion of the silicon. Six varieties depending upon composition have been distinguished:

Grossularite	$Ca_3Al_2(SiO_4)_3$
Pyrope	$Mg_3Al_2(SiO_4)_3$
Spessartite	$Mn_3Al_2(SiO_4)_3$
Almandite	$Fe_3Al_2(SiO_4)_3$
Uvarovite	$Ca_3Cr_2(SiO_4)_3$
Andradite	$Ca_3Fe_2(SiO_4)_3$

These varieties grade over into one another, the composition of a given specimen being usually rather complex.

Cubic, hexoctahedral class—$4/m\ \bar{3}\ 2/m$. Crystals are usually rhombic dodecahedrons or tetragonal trisoctahedrons, often in combination (Figs. 609 to 612). The hexoctahedron is quite frequently observed. Other

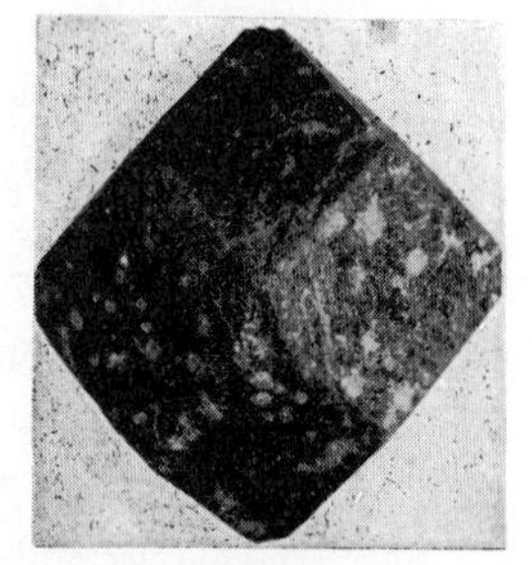

Fig. 609. Garnet (rhombic dodecahedron). Salida, Colorado.

Fig. 610.

Fig. 611.

forms are rare. Generally well crystallized but occurs also as rounded disseminated glassy grains and in compact granular aggregates.

Indistinct dodecahedral parting. Conchoidal to uneven fracture. Hardness, 6.5 to 7.5. Specific gravity, 3.4 to 4.3; varying with the composition. Commonly red, brown, yellow, green, or black; less frequently

Fig. 612. Rhombic dodecahedral crystals of garnet.

white or colorless. Light-colored garnets are generally transparent to translucent; dark-colored varieties translucent to opaque. Vitreous to resinous luster. The index of refraction varies from 1.70 to 1.94, and the dispersion from 0.024 to 0.028; some varieties may be optically anomalous. *Demantoid* has an unusually high dispersion of 0.057.

$M_3''M_2'''(SiO_4)_3$. Composition varies greatly, as indicated above. The chemical properties of the six varieties differ materially. They generally fuse easily to a brownish or black glass, which is sometimes magnetic. With the exception of uvarovite, all varieties gelatinize with acids after fusion. Garnets alter readily; epidote, mica, chlorite, serpentine, hornblende, scapolite, orthoclase, calcite, and limonite have been observed occurring as pseudomorphs after garnet. Large chlorite pseudomorphs after garnet occur at Spurr Mountain Mine, Lake Superior region.

Garnet is a very common mineral. It occurs in crystalline schists, as a contact metamorphic mineral, as a constituent of many eruptive rocks, with various ores, and in secondary deposits.

Grossularite (*Hessonite, Cinnamon Stone*). Calcium-aluminum garnet. Calcium may be partially replaced by ferrous iron, and aluminum by ferric iron. Specific gravity varies from 3.5 to 3.7. White, various shades of yellow, cinnamon brown, rose red; also green and colorless. The index of refraction varies from 1.735 to 1.763. It occurs in crystalline limestones and dolomites with wollastonite, vesuvianite, diopside, and scapolite. Some localities are Ceylon; Mussa Alp, Piedmont; Wilui River, Siberia; Morelos, Mexico; Monzoni, Tirol; Rumford, Maine; Warren, New Hampshire. Green, massive grossularite, often mottled with white, from Buffelsfontein, Transvaal, is called *South African* or *Transvaal jade*. Yellow, green, and orange grossularites are used for gem purposes.

Pyrope. Magnesium-aluminum garnet. Calcium and ferrous iron may partially replace magnesium. Specific gravity, 3.5 to 3.8. Deep red to almost black. The index of refraction varies from 1.705 to 1.749. When clear and transparent is often called *precious garnet* and used as a gem. Commonly known as *Cape ruby* or *Arizona ruby*. Found usually in basic igneous rocks, such as peridotite or serpentine. Frequently an associate of the diamond. Rarely found in good crystals, usually in irregular particles or rounded grains. Important localities are Teplitz, Aussig, and Bilin, Bohemia; Kimberley and other diamondiferous localities in South Africa; various places in southern Utah, Arizona, New Mexico, Madagascar, Ceylon, and Brazil.

Spessartite. Manganese-aluminum garnet. May contain ferrous and ferric iron. Specific gravity, 4.1 to 4.3. Brownish to hyacinth red. $n = 1.794$ to 1.814. Occurs in granitic rocks with topaz, tourmaline, quartz, and orthoclase. Occurs in Tirol; Piedmont; Ceylon; Haddam, Connecticut; Amelia Court House, Virginia; Bethel, Maine; Salem, North Carolina.

Almandite (*Carbuncle*). Iron-aluminum garnet. May contain magnesium and ferric iron. Specific gravity, 3.9 to 4.2. Deep red to brownish red or black in color. The index of refraction varies from 1.766 to

1.83. Transparent red varieties are known as precious garnets and used as gems; translucent varieties are called *common garnets.* Commonly found in mica and other schists, associated with staurolite, kyanite, andalusite, and tourmaline. Occurs in India; Ceylon; Minas Novas, Brazil; Bodö, Norway; Tirol; Uruguay; Australia; Salida, Colorado; Fort Wrangel, Alaska; Benewah County, Idaho; Charlemont, Massachusetts; Gore Mountain, Warren and Essex counties, New York. *Rhodolite* is a pale-violet variety, $n = 1.76$, between pyrope and almandite, occurring in Macon and Jackson counties, North Carolina.

Uvarovite. Calcium-chromium garnet. Emerald green in color. Specific gravity, 3.4 to 3.5. $n = 1.838$. Crystals are usually small. Not a common variety. Found with chromite in serpentine or in crystalline limestones and gneiss. Some localities are the Ural Mountains; western Transvaal, Union of South Africa; Oxford, Canada; New Idria, California.

Andradite. Calcium-iron garnet. The composition varies greatly. The color may be brownish red, brown, grayish black, black, also various shades of yellow or green. Specific gravity, 3.7 to 3.8. The index of refraction varies from 1.865 to 1.95. *Topazolite* is yellowish or greenish and often resembles topaz. *Demantoid* is a grass-green variety. *Melanite* is black; $n = 1.94$. These garnets occur in syenite, serpentine, chloritic schists, and crystalline limestones. Common associates are feldspar, nepheline, leucite, epidote, and magnetite. Found at Dobschau, Czechoslovakia; Tirol; the Island of Elba; Arendal, Norway; the Ural Mountains; Franklin, New Jersey; Magnet Cove, Arkansas; Henderson, North Carolina.

Pyrope and almandite furnish most of the garnets used as gems. Almandite and andradite are often called common garnets. Garnet is an important abrasive. Garnet paper and cloth are used extensively for smoothing wood and glass surfaces and for finishing leather and rubber articles.

ZIRCON (*Hyacinth, Jargon*), $ZrSiO_4$.

Tetragonal, ditetragonal bipyramidal class—$4/m\ 2/m\ 2/m$. Usually in simple, well-developed crystals, consisting of the prism and bipyramid of the first order (Fig. 613); more complex crystals sometimes observed (Fig. 614). Also as rounded or angular lumps or grains in sands and gravels.

Hardness, 7.5. Specific gravity, 4.65 to 4.71. Adamantine luster. High indices of refraction, ω 1.93, ϵ 1.99, (+). Transparent to opaque. High dispersion, 0.048. Some crystals are optically biaxial. Commonly, brown or grayish; also red, yellow, blue, and colorless. Streak, uncolored. Clear, transparent zircons are used as gems.

The gem varieties are as follows:

Hyacinth and *jacinth* are the terms applied to the clear, transparent yellow, orange, red, and brown varieties.

Jargon includes most of the other colors.

Matara or *matura diamond* is the name given to zircon from Matara, Ceylon, either naturally colorless or made so by subjecting colored stones to heat-treatment. As these terms are misleading, they should not be used. These colorless stones should be called *white zircon.*

Blue zircon of gem quality has become very popular in recent years. These stones are obtained from the Mongka district, Indo-China. The attractive blue color is the result of heat-treatment.

The variability in the character of zircon is noteworthy. Three different types of the mineral are now recognized. These types, called *high, intermediate,* and *low zircons,* differ in specific gravity, hardness, optical

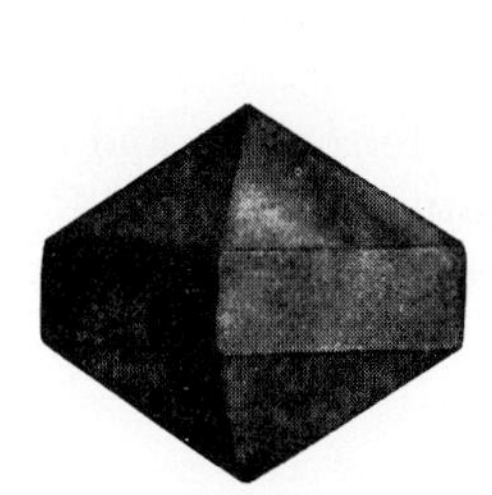

Fig. 613.

Fig. 614.

properties, and behavior on heating. Some specimens are composed of all three types.

High zircon, also called *normal zircon,* occurs with a uniform tetragonal crystal structure; hence, well-developed crystals are common (Figs. 613 and 614). The various physical and optical properties given above apply to this type.

Low zircon occurs as rolled pebbles and is without crystal form. It is usually amorphous, or nearly so, and hence isotropic. However, it may be slightly doubly refractive and even biaxial. Its specific gravity varies from 3.94 to 4.4. The hardness is 6 to 6.5. The indices of refraction are lower than for the high type, namely, 1.78 to 1.84. In color the low type may be green or greenish brown. It is composed of amorphous silica (SiO_2) and amorphous or microcrystalline zirconium oxide (ZrO_2). This type is rare.

Intermediate zircon has properties which lie between those of the low and high types. Thus, the specific gravity varies from 4.1 to 4.65. The index of refraction is approximately 1.85. On heating to 1450°C. this type is converted to high zircon with slight changes in specific gravity, index of refraction, and double refraction.

Zircon ($ZrSiO_4$) is considered a silicate. It was formerly often interpreted as an oxide of zirconium and silicon. Iron, hafnium, thorium, uranium, and the rare earths may be present. The varieties which contain uranium have a very characteristic absorption spectrum, consisting of a number of sharp, narrow bands throughout the spectrum. Figure 450 (page 175) shows the unit cell of zircon.

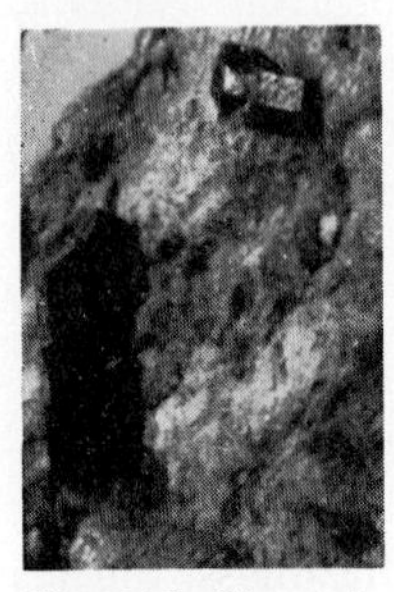

Fig. 615. Zircon in syenite. Miask, Ural Mountains.

Occurs disseminated in the more acid igneous rocks, especially granites and syenites; also found in gneiss, schist, and crystalline limestone. Occurs in southeastern Norway; Miask, Ural Mountains (Fig. 615); Australia; Madagascar; French West Africa; India; Wichita Mountains, Oklahoma; Litchfield, Maine. Common in the sands and gravels of Ceylon, also in Henderson, Iredell, and Buncombe counties, North Carolina, and at Pablo Beach, Florida.

Zircon is a source of ZrO_2, which is used in ferroalloys and as a refractory for lining and patching high-temperature furnaces. It is also a source of metallic zirconium and hafnium; see page 477. Zircon is used as a gemstone; see pages 366–367.

Andalusite Group

The compound Al_2OSiO_4 is trimorphous and occurs in nature as the three minerals andalusite, kyanite, and sillimanite. The first and third minerals crystallize in the orthorhombic system, while the second is triclinic. Upon heating, the composition of these minerals is changed to $3Al_2O_3.2SiO_2$ (mullite) with liberation of silica. Kyanite alters at the lowest temperature (1350 to 1370°C.), sillimanite at the highest (about 1545°C.), while the change in andalusite takes place at about 1390°C.

ANDALUSITE, Al_2OSiO_4.

Orthorhombic, bipyramidal class—$2/m\ 2/m\ 2/m$. Occurs usually in large, rough, and nearly square prismatic crystals (Figs. 616 and 617). *Chiastolite* is a variety with a regular internal arrangement of dark organic matter, best seen in polished cross sections (Fig. 618). Found also in fibrous, columnar, and granular masses, and in rounded pebbles.

Prismatic cleavage. Uneven fracture. Hardness, 7 to 7.5; owing to alteration, may be softer on the surface. Specific gravity, 3.1 to 3.2. Gray, greenish, reddish, or bluish in color. Transparent to opaque. Vitreous to dull luster. α 1.634, β 1.639, γ 1.643, $(-)$; $2V = 85°$.

Al_2OSiO_4. Often impure; usually contains some iron and manganese,

Al_2O_3 63.2, SiO_2 36.8 per cent. Infusible. Insoluble in acids. Alters to kyanite, sericite, and kaolinite.

Occurs in metamorphic rocks, especially in schists and slates. Commonly associated with kyanite, sillimanite, mica, garnet, cordierite, and

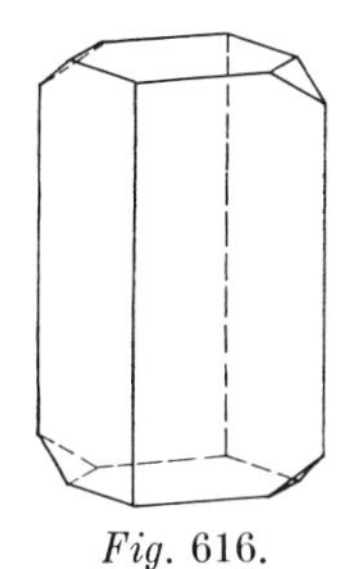

Fig. 616.

Fig. 617. Andalusite. Andalusia, Spain.

tourmaline. Some localities are Andalusia, Spain; Tirol; Kazakhston, Soviet Russia; in transparent crystals in Minas Gerais, Brazil; Ceylon; Australia; Westford, Lancaster, and Sterling, Massachusetts; Litchfield and Washington, Connecticut; Standish, Maine; in large quantities in

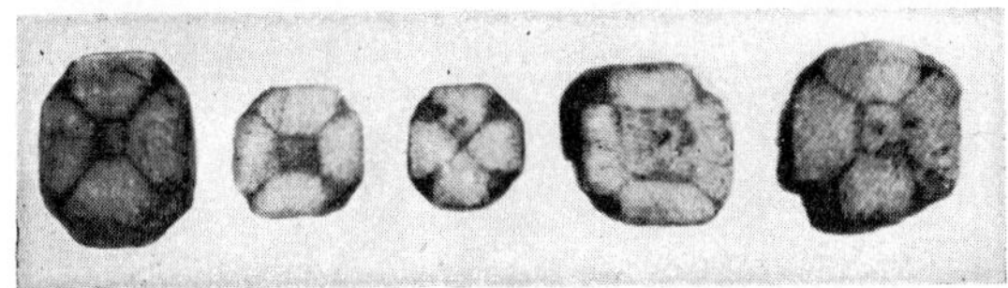

Fig. 618. Andalusite: variety, chiastolite. Lancaster, Massachusetts.

Mono County, California; and in sands containing up to 90 per cent of andalusite in the Zeerust and Marico districts, western Transvaal, Union of South Africa.

Formerly an important mineral used, after conversion to mullite, in the manufacture of spark-plug and chemical porcelain and in refractories; transparent varieties are sometimes used for gem purposes. See also page 437.

KYANITE (*Cyanite, Disthene*), Al_2OSiO_4.

Triclinic, pinacoidal class—$\bar{1}$. Generally in long, broad crystals without distinct terminations; or in coarse-bladed, columnar, or fibrous masses (Fig. 619). Crystals are sometimes curved and arrange radially.

Macro- and brachypinacoidal cleavages. Hardness varies greatly with direction, 4 to 5 parallel to the long direction of the blades, 6 to 7 across them. Specific gravity, 3.5 to 3.7. Generally some shade of blue in color, also grayish, white,

Fig. 619. Kyanite (bladed). Litchfield, Connecticut.

green brownish, or colorless. The edges are usually lighter in color than the central portions of the blades; that is, the color is distributed in streaks or spots. Vitreous luster. α 1.712, β 1.720, γ 1.728, $(-); 2V = 82°$; $r > v$. Transparent to translucent. May become luminescent.

Al_2OSiO_4. Chemical composition and behavior similar to that of andalusite and sillimanite. Kyanite is, however, more resistive to the action of acids.

Kyanite is a metamorphic mineral and is commonly found in gneisses and mica schists, especially paragonite schist. Usual associates are staurolite, garnet, corundum, rutile, and lazulite. Some localities are the Saint Gotthard district, Switzerland; Tirol; Sweden; Brazil; Western Australia; Kenya, East Africa; Chesterfield, Massachusetts; Litchfield and Washington, Connecticut; Chester and Delaware counties, Pennsylvania; Gaston, Rutherford, and Yancey counties, North Carolina; South Carolina; Georgia; Prince Edward County, Virginia. The principal commercial deposits of kyanite occur in India at Lapsa Buru, in the state of Kharsawan, about 100 miles west of Calcutta.

Used in ceramic and metallurgical industries, and sometimes for gem purposes (Fig. 725, page 438).

Sillimanite (*Fibrolite*), **Al_2OSiO_4.**

Orthorhombic, bipyramidal class—$2/m\ 2/m\ 2/m$. Usually in long, thin, needle-like crystals; or in radiating fibrous or columnar masses. Crystals are often bent, striated, interlaced, poorly terminated, and without sharp edges.

Macropinacoidal cleavage. Uneven fracture. Hardness, 6 to 7. Specific gravity, 3.2 to 3.3. Gray, brown, yellowish, or greenish in color. Vitreous or silky luster. α 1.659, β 1,660, γ 1.680, $(+); 2V = 20°; r > v$. Transparent to translucent.

Al_2OSiO_4. Chemical composition and behavior are the same as for andalusite.

Occurs as an accessory constituent of gneisses, quartzites, mica schists, and other metamorphic rocks. It is sometimes associated with andalusite, zircon, or corundum. Found at Bodenmais, Bavaria; Freiberg, Saxony; Minas Gerais, Brazil; Assam, India; Mogok, Burma; Ceylon; Worcester, Massachusetts; Montana; Idaho; Front Range, Colorado; Norwich and Willimantic, Connecticut; Westchester and Monroe counties, New York; Chester, Pennsylvania.

Dumortierite, $Al_8B(OH)Si_3O_{19}$. Orthorhombic, prismatic class? Distinct crystals are rare. Usually as fibrous or columnar aggregates, often arranged radially. Distinct macropinacoidal cleavage. Hardness, 7. Specific gravity, 3.2 to 3.4. Vitreous to dull luster. Blue, pink, lavender, green, or white in color. α 1.678, β 1.686, γ 1.689, (−); $2V = 30$ to 52°; $r < v$. Strongly pleochroic.

$Al_8B(OH)Si_3O_{19}$. Loses B_2O_3 and H_2O on heating to high temperatures and passes over to mullite, $3Al_2O_3.2SiO_2$.

Most commonly found in schists, gneisses, and pegmatites. Occurs in commercial quantities in sericite schist near Oreana, Pershing County, Nevada; also near Quartzsite, Arizona, associated with andalusite, kyanite, and sillimanite, and in Imperial County, California, and Yuma County, Arizona; Brazil; South-West Africa; Vallenar, Province of Atacama, Chile.

Formerly important in the manufacture of spark-plug insulators and laboratory porcelain.

STAUROLITE, $Fe(OH)_2.2Al_2OSiO_4$.

Orthorhombic, bipyramidal class—$2/m$ $2/m$ $2/m$. Generally in well-developed prismatic crystals, consisting of the unit prism, basal and brachypinacoids, and a macrodome. Penetration twins according to two laws are common, yielding *cross-* or *plus-shaped* and *X-shaped twins* (Fig. 620).

Fig. 620. Staurolite crystals—simple and plus- and X-shaped twins.

Brachypinacoidal cleavage. Conchoidal to uneven fracture. Hardness, 7 to 7.5. Specific gravity, 3.4 to 3.8. Usually reddish brown in color; also brownish black, yellowish brown, or gray when altered. Colorless streak when fresh. Vitreous to dull luster. α 1.736, β 1.741, γ 1.746, (+); $2V = 88°$; $r > v$. Commonly translucent to opaque, rarely transparent.

Fig. 621. Staurolite in schist. Little Falls, Minnesota.

Fig. 622. Staurolite (dark) in paragonite schist. Tessin, Switzerland.

$Fe(OH)_2.2Al_2OSiO_4$. Composition varies greatly. May contain magnesium, manganese, and zinc. Often quite impure. Infusible. Insoluble in acids.

Occurs generally in metamorphic rocks, especially gneiss, mica schists, and slates (Fig. 621). The common associates are kyanite, garnet, tourmaline, and sillimanite. In the Saint Gotthard district, Switzerland, it occurs with kyanite in paragonite (soda mica) schist (Fig. 622); also in Tirol; France; South-West Africa; Brazil; Fannin and Cherokee counties, Georgia; Henry and Patrick counties, Virginia; Ducktown, Tennessee; Grantham, New Hampshire; Windham, Maine; Chesterfield, Massachusetts; North Carolina; Litchfield, Connecticut.

Clear and transparent crystals and plus-shaped twins are sometimes used for gem purposes.

TOPAZ, $Al_2(F,OH)_2SiO_4$.

Orthorhombic, bipyramidal class—$2/m$ $2/m$ $2/m$. Generally in highly modified, prismatic crystals; often developed on one end only (Figs. 623 to 625). Often vertically striated. Occurs also in granular to compact masses and in rolled fragments.

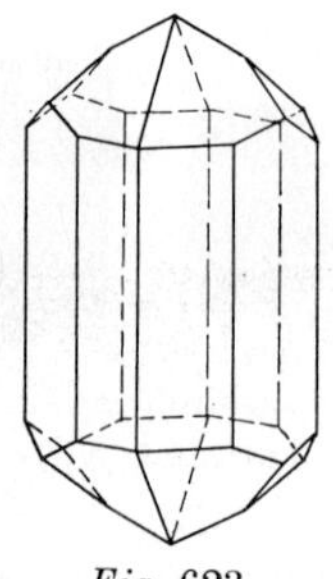

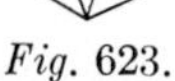

Fig. 623.

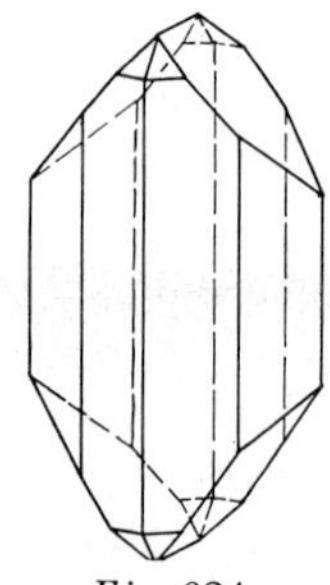

Fig. 624.

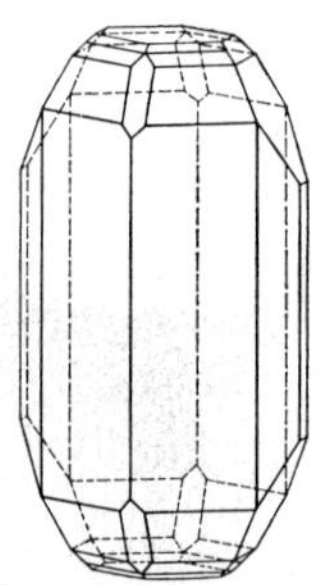

Fig. 625.

Very perfect basal cleavage. Conchoidal to uneven fracture. Hardness, 8. Specific gravity, 3.4 to 3.6. Colorless, wine yellow, grayish, violet, reddish, or bluish in color. Some colored varieties fade on exposure to sunlight. Transparent to opaque. Vitreous luster. α 1.619, β 1.620, γ 1.627, variable, (+); $2V$ varies from 49 to 66°; $r > v$.

$Al_2(F,OH)_2SiO_4$. The percentages of fluorine and hydroxyl vary greatly. Often contains many microscopic liquid inclusions. Infusible. On heating yellow Brazilian topaz to temperatures between 300 and 450°C. the color changes to a beautiful rose or pink. Slightly acted upon by sulfuric acid. Sometimes alters to muscovite and kaolinite.

Topaz is a characteristic mineral of the pneumatolytic process of formation and is hence generally associated with cassiterite, tourmaline, quartz, fluorite, apatite, beryl, mica, scheelite, wolframite, and zircon. It occurs in crevices, cavities, and pegmatite dikes in highly acid igneous rocks such as granites and rhyolites, also in gneisses and schists. Excellent crystals are found at Schneckenstein and elsewhere in Saxony; the Ural Mountains; Sweden; Japan; Australia; Mexico; Thomas Range, Utah; Nathrop and Devils Head, Colorado; San Diego County, California; Chesterfield, South Carolina; and various places in Connecticut, New Hampshire, and Maine. Frequently found in the sands and gravel of the streams of Ceylon, Brazil, and the Ural Mountains.

Clear and transparent crystals are used for gem purposes. The yellow variety from Brazil is often called *precious topaz.* Much yellow quartz (citrine), colored naturally or artificially, is erroneously called topaz, especially in the jewelry trade.

Chondrodite, $Mg(F,OH)_2.2Mg_2SiO_4$.

Monoclinic, prismatic class—$2/m$. Occurs in small, highly modified, pseudo-orthorhombic crystals, also in grains or lumps and in granular aggregates.

Basal cleavage. Uneven to conchoidal cleavage. Hardness, 6 to 6.5. Specific gravity, 3.1 to 3.3. Brown, yellow, or red in color. Vitreous to resinous luster. The optical properties vary greatly; the mean index is about 1.63. Translucent to opaque.

$Mg(F,OH)_2.2Mg_2SiO_4$. Some of the magnesium may be replaced by bivalent iron and manganese. Infusible. Gelatinizes with hydrochloric acid. Alters to serpentine and brucite.

Chondrodite is a typical contact metamorphic mineral. It occurs commonly in crystalline limestones and dolomites, associated with spinel, vesuvianite, magnetite, pyroxenes, and phlogopite. Some important localities are Pargas, Finland; Mount Vesuvius; Burma; Sparta, New Jersey; Tilly Foster Mine, near Brewster, and in Orange County, New York.

Chondrodite belongs to the humite group of minerals. The compositions of the various members show increasing amounts of Mg_2SiO_4:

Norbergite	$Mg(F,OH)_2.Mg_2SiO_4$
Chondrodite	$Mg(F,OH)_2.2Mg_2SiO_4$
Humite	$Mg(F,OH)_2.3Mg_2SiO_4$
Clinohumite	$Mg(F,OH)_2.4Mg_2SiO_4$

Although the members do not crystallize in the same system, very interesting crystallographic relationships exist. Chondrodite is the most important member.

Datolite, $CaB(OH)SiO_4$.

Monoclinic, prismatic class—$2/m$. Usually prismatic, pyramidal, or tabular crystals, often highly modified (Figs. 626 and 627). Also in compact, dull, or granular masses resembling Wedgwood ware or unglazed porcelain.

Conchoidal to uneven fracture. Hardness, 5 to 5.5. Specific gravity, 2.9 to 3. Colorless, white, or greenish but often with yellowish, reddish, or brownish streaks and spots. Transparent to translucent, rarely opaque. Vitreous to dull luster. α 1.626, β 1.654, γ 1.670, (−); $2V$ = 74°; $r > v$.

$CaB(OH)SiO_4$. CaO 35.0, B_2O_3 21.8, SiO_2 37.6, H_2O 5.6 per cent. Crystals are usually very pure. Gelatinizes with hydrochloric acid.

Datolite is a secondary mineral and is generally found in cracks and cavities in basic igneous rocks, such as diorite, diabase, basalt, gabbro, and serpentine. The common associates are native copper, apophyllite, prehnite, calcite, epidote, magnetite, and the zeolites. Some localities

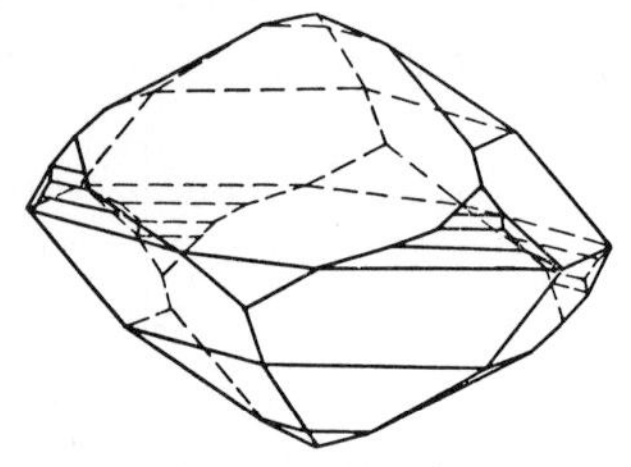

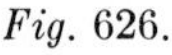

Fig. 626.

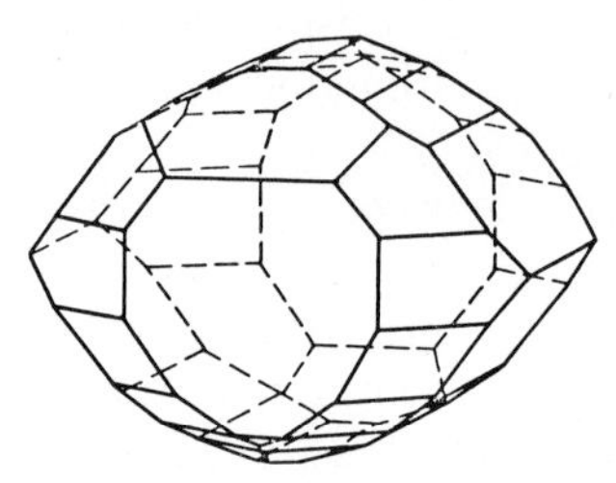

Fig. 627.

are the Kilpatrick Hills, Scotland; Arendal, Norway; the Harz Mountains, Germany; Tirol; Bohemia; Italy; Bergen Hill, New Jersey; Westfield and elsewhere, Massachusetts; Hartford, Connecticut; in the Lake Superior copper district excellent crystals and compact porcelain-like masses with inclusions of native copper.

The massive varieties are sometimes used for gem purposes.

SPHENE (*Titanite*) $CaTiOSiO_4$.

Monoclinic, prismatic class—$2/m$. The crystal habit varies greatly. Disseminated crystals are generally wedge- or envelope-shaped, while attached crystals are apt to be tabular or prismatic (Figs. 628 to 630). Occurs also in compact or lamellar masses and in disseminated grains.

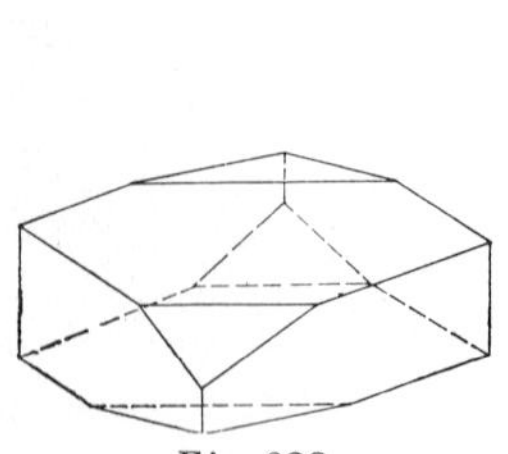

Fig. 628.

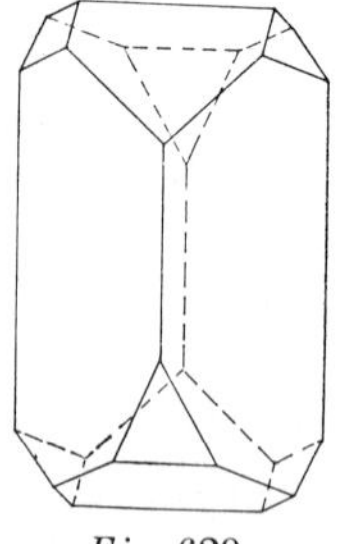

Fig. 629.

Fig. 630. Sphene. Arendal, Norway.

Prismatic cleavage. Conchoidal fracture. Hardness, 5 to 5.5. Specific gravity, 3.4 to 3.6. Yellow, green, brown, reddish brown, red, or black in color. Vitreous luster, inclining to adamantine. Transparent to opaque. α 1.900, β 1.907, γ 2.034, (+); $2V$ is about 27°; $r > v$ marked.

$CaTiOSiO_4$. May contain iron, aluminum, manganese, cerium, and yttrium. Fuses with intumescence on the edges to a dark-colored glass. Only partially decomposed by hydrochloric acid, completely by sulfuric and hydrofluoric acids. Alters to rutile, leucoxene, brookite, or ilmenite.

Sphene occurs disseminated as an important accessory constituent of many igneous rocks, especially in hornblende granite, syenite, nepheline syenite, trachyte, phonolite, and diorite; also in crystalline schists and granular limestones. It is found attached in cracks and cavities in granite, gneiss, and various schists. The common associates are the amphiboles, pyroxenes, apatite, zircon, scapolite, chlorite, feldspars, quartz, and various iron minerals. Some localities are Laacher See, Rhenish Prussia; many places in Switzerland and Tirol, especially Saint Gotthard, Tavetsch, and Zillerthal; Arendal, Norway; Ala, Piedmont; the Ural Mountains; Grenville, Quebec, and Eganville, Renfrew County, Ontario, Canada; Sanford, Maine; Bolton and Lee, Massachusetts; various places in Lewis, Orange, and other counties, New York; Franklin, New Jersey; Magnet Cove, Arkansas.

The clear, green, yellow, or brownish varieties are used for gem purposes. They are very brilliant, possess an excellent adamantine luster, but are comparatively soft.

HEMIMORPHITE (*Calamine*), $Zn_4(OH)_2Si_2O_7.H_2O$.

Orthorhombic, pyramidal class—*mm*2. Crystals are usually thin tabular or pyramidal in habit, sometimes showing a pronounced hemi-

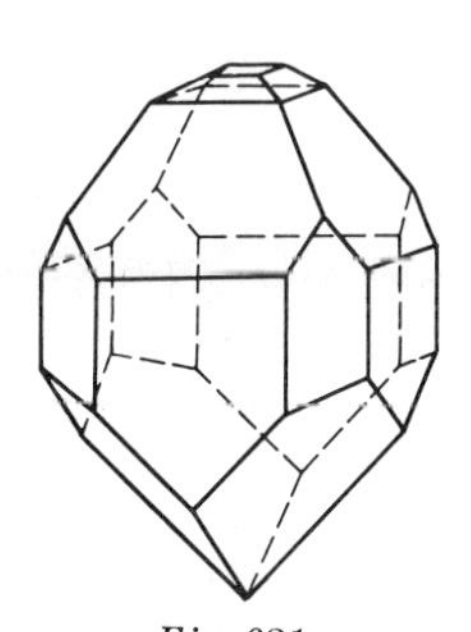

Fig. 631.

Fig. 632. Hemimorphite. Chihuahua, Mexico.

morphic development (Fig. 631). Often arranged in sheaf-like or crested groups (Fig. 632). More commonly in fibrous, globular, granular, or porous and earthy masses.

Prismatic cleavage. Uneven to conchoidal fracture. Hardness, 4.5 to 5. Specific gravity, 3.4 to 3.5. Colorless, white, brown, green, or bluish.

Transparent to opaque. Vitreous to dull luster. α 1.614, β 1.617, γ 1.636, (+); $2V = 46°$; $r > v$.

$Zn_4(OH)_2Si_2O_7.H_2O$. ZnO 67.5, SiO_2 25.0, H_2O 7.5 per cent. May contain small amounts of iron, lead, or aluminum. Fuses with difficulty. Gelatinizes easily with acids. Occurs as a pseudomorph after calcite, galena, dolomite, fluorite, and pyromorphite.

Hemimorphite is a secondary mineral, formed by the action of silica-bearing water upon other zinc ores, and is usually found in limestones associated with smithsonite, sphalerite, galena, cerussite, and anglesite. It is often intimately mixed with smithsonite. Some localities are Aachen, Germany; Raibel and Bleiberg, Carinthia, Austria; Silesia; Cumberland and Derbyshire, England; Sardinia; Mexico; Sussex County, New Jersey; Phoenixville and Friedensville, Pennsylvania; Granby and elsewhere, Missouri; Pulaski and Wythe counties, Virginia; Colorado; Utah; Tennessee; Montana; New Mexico; Arkansas.

Hemimorphite is an important ore of zinc. See page 476.

Epidote Group

Under this heading two rather complex but isomorphous silicates of calcium and aluminum will be described.

EPIDOTE, $Ca_2(Al,Fe)_3O(OH)SiO_4Si_2O_7$.

Monoclinic, prismatic class—$2/m$. Excellent prismatic and highly modified crystals are rather common; usually elongated and deeply

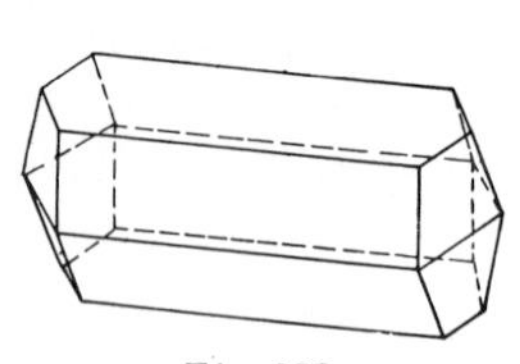

Fig. 633.

Fig. 634. Epidote. Untersulzbachthal, Tirol.

striated parallel to the b axis and terminated at one end only (Figs. 633 and 634). Occurs also in divergent or parallel fibrous and columnar aggregates, coarse- to fine-granular masses, or in rounded or angular grains.

Basal cleavage. Uneven fracture. Hardness, 6 to 7. Specific gravity, 3.3 to 3.5. Yellowish to blackish green in color; more rarely red (*piedmontite*—manganese variety) or colorless. Crystals are usually darker in color than massive varieties. Vitreous to resinous luster. α

1.716 to 1.733, β 1.719 to 1.763, γ 1.723 to 1.780, $(-)$; $2V$ is large; $r > v$. Transparent to opaque. Strongly pleochroic.

$Ca_2(Al,Fe)_3O(OH)SiO_4Si_2O_7$. The percentages of the oxides of calcium, iron, aluminum, and silicon vary considerably; manganese may also be present. *Clinozoisite* contains little or no iron. *Zoisite* is an orthorhombic modification of clinozoisite. Yields water when strongly ignited and gelatinizes with hydrochloric acid after ignition. Occurs as a pseudomorph after scapolite, garnet, augite, and hornblende.

Epidote is a typical metamorphic and hydrothermal mineral. It is found in gneiss, schists of various kinds, and in crystalline limestones; often occurs very extensively, forming epidote rocks, called epidosite. It is commonly associated with the zeolites. It is also a common alteration product of minerals high in calcium and aluminum, such as feldspar, pyroxene, amphibole, scapolite, chlorite, and biotite. Important localities are Zillerthal and Untersulzbachthal, Tirol; Traversella, Piedmont; the Island of Elba; Dauphiné, France; Arendal, Norway; the Ural Mountains; Prince of Wales Island, Alaska; Haddam, Connecticut; various places in New York, New Jersey, and Colorado; with native copper in the Lake Superior copper district.

The clear and transparent dark-green crystals are sometimes used for gem purposes.

Allanite (*Orthite*), $\mathbf{(Ca,Ce,La)_2(Al,Fe)_3O(OH)SiO_4Si_2O_7}$.

Monoclinic, prismatic class—$2/m$. Crystals are tabular or prismatic but rare. Usually in massive, granular, or bladed aggregates; also as disseminated grains.

Uneven to conchoidal fracture. Hardness, 5.5 to 6. Specific gravity, 3.5 to 4.2. Pitch black in color, sometimes brownish or grayish; often coated with a yellowish or brownish alteration product. Greenish-gray to brown streak. Pitchy submetallic luster. Opaque. α 1.727, β 1.739, γ 1.751; $2V$ = medium large; $r > v$.

$(Ca,Ce,La)_2(Al,Fe)_3O(OH)SiO_4Si_2O_7$. Very similar to epidote, with cerium replacing some calcium. Composition varies greatly; lanthanum and other rare earths, sodium, manganese, beryllium, magnesium, and water may be present. Fuses easily with intumescence to a black magnetic glass. Gelatinizes with hydrochloric acid but not if previously ignited.

Allanite occurs in small quantities in igneous rocks, such as granites, syenites, diorites, and pegmatites; also in gneiss, mica and amphibolite schists, and crystalline limestones. Commonly associated with epidote, magnetite, quartz, and feldspar. Occurs in Greenland; Falun, Sweden; Miask, Ural Mountains; Madagascar; Edenville, New York; Haddam, Connecticut; Franklin, New Jersey; Madison and Iredell counties, North Carolina; Barringer Hill, Texas; and Amherst County, Virginia.

A source of cerium. See page 449.

VESUVIANITE (*Idocrase*), $Ca_{10}Al_4(Mg,Fe)_2(OH)_4(SiO_4)_5(Si_2O_7)_2$.

Tetragonal, ditetragonal bipyramidal class—$4/m\ 2/m\ 2/m$. Crystals are generally short prismatic (Figs. 635 and 636), rarely pyramidal or acicular. Occurs also in compact and granular masses and in aggregates with parallel (Fig. 637) or divergent striations or furrows.

Uneven fracture. Hardness, 6.5. Specific gravity, 3.3 to 3.5. Occurs in many shades of yellow, green, and brown; more rarely blue, red, or nearly black. *Californite* is a compact green variety with colorless or

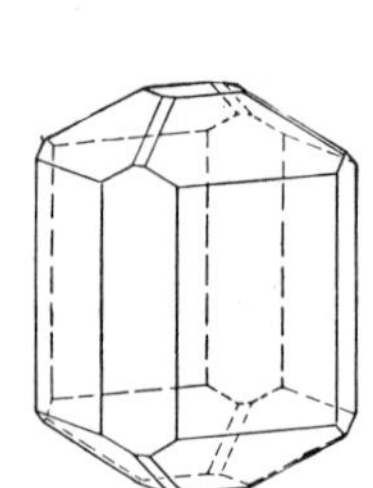

Fig. 635.

Fig. 636. Vesuvianite. (Left) Wilui River, Siberia; (right) Achmatovsk, Soviet Russia.

Fig. 637. Vesuvianite. Egg, Norway.

white streaks, resembling jade. Vitreous greasy luster. ω 1.705 to 1.736, ϵ 1.701 to 1.732, (−, often +); sometimes abnormally biaxial. Commonly translucent.

$Ca_{10}Al_4(Mg,Fe)_2(OH)_4(SiO_4)_5(Si_2O_7)_2$. The composition is complex and variable. May contain titanium, boron, fluorine, iron, magnesium, manganese, sodium, potassium, and beryllium. Fuses with intumescence to a greenish or brownish glass. After ignition, it decomposes easily with acids.

Vesuvianite is a typical contact metamorphic mineral. It is found commonly in crystalline limestones, gneisses, and schists, associated with garnet, tourmaline, chondrodite, wollastonite, epidote, and the pyroxenes. Important localities are Monzoni, Tirol; Ala Valley, Piedmont; Mount Vesuvius; Eger, Bohemia; Egg, Norway; Wilui River, Siberia; Morelos, Mexico; Rumford, Maine; Amity, New York; various places in California, Ontario, and Quebec.

Clear and transparent brown and green varieties are used for gem purposes.

Prehnite, $Ca_2Al_2(OH)_2Si_3O_{10}$.

Orthorhombic, pyramidal class—*mm*2. Single crystals are rare. Commonly tabular parallel to basal pinacoid, prismatic, or pyramidal, and as reniform or globular masses, often with a cock's-comb structure.

Basal cleavage. Uneven fracture. Hardness, 6 to 6.5. Specific gravity, 2.8 to 3. Light or yellowish green, white, or colorless. Transparent to translucent. Vitreous luster; on basal pinacoid pearly. White streak. α 1.615, β 1.625, γ 1.645, (+); 2*V* large; $r > v$. Often optically anomalous.

$Ca_2Al_2(OH)_2Si_3O_{10}$. CaO 27.1, Al_2O_3 24.8, SiO_2 43.7, H_2O 4.4 per cent. Iron may replace some aluminum. Fuses easily with intumescence; at higher temperature yields water. Decomposed by acids after fusion.

Prehnite is a secondary mineral, found in veins and cavities in basic igneous rocks, such as basalt, diabase, and gabbro; more rarely in granite. Common associates are zeolites, datolite, native copper, pectolite, calcite, epidote. It occurs in the Lake Superior copper district; Paterson and Bergen Hill, New Jersey; Somerville, Massachusetts; Farmington, Connecticut.

BERYL, $Be_3Al_2Si_6O_{18}$.

Hexagonal, dihexagonal bipyramidal class—6/*m* 2/*m* 2/*m*. Crystals are usually long prismatic and very simple (Fig. 638). Rarely tabular.

Fig. 638. Beryl. Auburn, Maine.

Fig. 639.

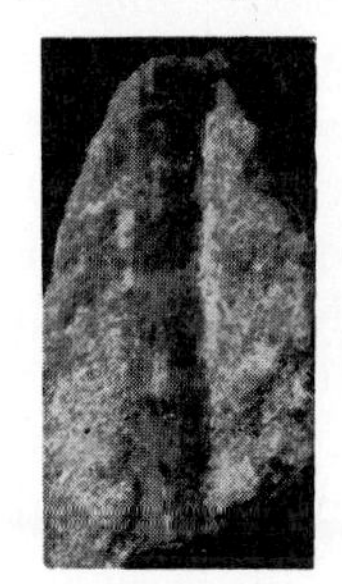

Fig. 640. Beryl in quartz. Acworth, New Hampshire.

Sometimes highly modified, showing prisms and bipyramids of the first and second orders and other forms (Fig. 639). Crystals are frequently striated vertically and may be very large. Occurs also in columnar, granular, and compact masses and in rounded grains.

Indistinct basal cleavage. Conchoidal to uneven fracture. Hardness, 7.5 to 8; is sometimes substituted for topaz in the scale of hardness. Specific gravity, 2.6 to 2.8. Various shades of green, blue, yellow, and reddish in color; sometimes mottled. Vitreous luster. Transparent to translucent. May become luminescent. Indices of refraction vary from

ω 1.568, ϵ 1.564, (−), for varieties low in alkalies, to ω 1.602, ϵ 1.595, (−), for those high in alkalies. Due to strain may be optically anomalous.

There are five important varieties of beryl:

Emerald. Emerald green in color. Transparent. Highly prized as a precious stone.

Aquamarine. Usually blue to sea green in color. Transparent. Used as a gem, but not so valuable as the emerald.

Yellow or Golden Beryl. Beautiful golden yellow in color. Transparent. An attractive gem stone.

Morganite. Pale pink to rose red in color. Transparent. Used as a gem. The color of many cut morganites has been improved by heat-treatment.

Common Beryl. Generally green, yellowish, or grayish white in color. Often mottled. Crystals are sometimes extremely large, being measured in feet and weighing several tons; thus, at Grafton, New Hampshire, and Keystone, South Dakota.

$Be_3Al_2Si_6O_{18}$. BeO 14, Al_2O_3 19, SiO_2 67 per cent. Beryllium may be partially replaced by varying amounts of calcium, iron, potassium, lithium, sodium, and cesium. A small amount of water is present. Fuses with great difficulty, turning white and cloudy. Insoluble in acids. Alters to mica and kaolin.

Commonly found in granitic pegmatites; also in gneiss, mica schist, clay slate, limestone, or in secondary deposits. The common associates are quartz (Fig. 640), feldspar, mica, topaz, tourmaline, cassiterite, chrysoberyl, garnet, zircon, and corundum. Emeralds of good quality occur in limestone at Muzo and Chivon, near Bogotá, Colombia; in altered dolomitic marble near Bom Jesus dos Meiras, Bahia, Brazil; in the district of Sverdlousk, Ural Mountains; Tirol; Upper Egypt; Poona, Western Australia; Alexander County, North Carolina; Chaffee County, Colorado. Morganite is found on the Island of Madagascar and in San Diego County, California. Aquamarine and other gem beryls occur on the Island of Elba; Ireland; Mursinka, Ural Mountains; Mitchell County, North Carolina; in secondary deposits in Brazil, Ceylon, and India. Common beryl occurs in very large crystals at Grafton and Acworth, New Hampshire; Royalston, Massachusetts; Paris and Stoneham, Maine; Haddam and Litchfield, Connecticut; Pennsylvania; the Black Hills, South Dakota; Taos County, New Mexico.

Used for gem purposes and as a source of beryllium and its compounds. Emeralds of good quality are produced synthetically. See also page 442.

Cordierite (*Iolite, Dichroite*), $Mg_2Al_3(AlSi_5O_{18})$.

Orthorhombic, bipyramidal class—$2/m\ 2/m\ 2/m$. Crystals are short prismatic and pseudohexagonal. Penetration trillings rather common. Frequently as irregular and rounded grains or masses, resembling quartz.

Distinct brachypinacoidal cleavage. Lamellar parting parallel to basal pinacoid. Conchoidal to uneven fracture. Hardness, 7 to 7.5. Specific gravity, 2.6 to 2.75. Vitreous to greasy luster. Transparent to translucent. Light to dark smoky blue, dark blue, and violet in color; also gray, colorless, green, and yellow. White streak. Optical properties vary greatly with the iron and alkali content; α 1.534 to 1.592, β 1.538 to 1.597, γ 1.540 to 1.599; usually optically negative; $2V = 40°$ to large; $r < v$. Strongly pleochroic, except in thin sections.

$Mg_2Al_3(AlSi_5O_{18})$. Composition varies; may contain iron and small amounts of calcium, manganese, the alkalies, and water. Alters readily to mica and chlorite (pinite), talc, and various intermediate substances.

Cordierite occurs in gneiss (*cordierite gneiss*), schists, granite, pegmatites, contact metamorphic zones, and in secondary deposits. Common associates are garnet, mica, quartz, andalusite, sillimanite, staurolite, chalcopyrite, and spinel. Occurs at Bodenmais and Vilshofen, Bavaria; Laacher See, Rhenish Prussia; Falun, Sweden; Finland; Ceylon; Madagascar; Great Slave Lake, Northwest Territory, Canada; Bancroft, Ontario; Collins Hill, Connecticut; Wyoming; New Hampshire.

Transparent varieties from Ceylon are used for gem purposes.

TOURMALINE, $M_7Al_6(OH,F)_4(BO_3)_3Si_6O_{18}$.

Hexagonal, ditrigonal pyramidal class—$3m$. Commonly in short to long prismatic crystals with vertical striations. Well-developed crystals

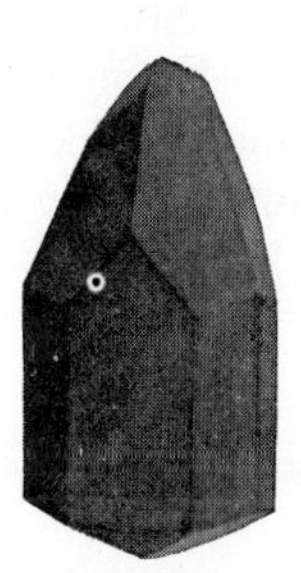

Fig. 641.

Fig. 642.

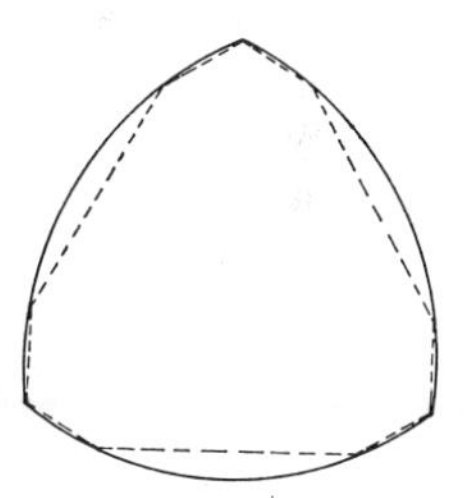

Fig. 643.

have rhombohedral-like terminations and possess pronounced hemimorphism (Figs. 641 and 642). Crystals show a characteristic spherical triangular outline in cross section (Figs. 643 and 644). Occurs also in compact and disseminated masses and in radially divergent aggregates, called *tourmaline suns;* also in loose crystals in secondary deposits.

Conchoidal to uneven fracture. Hardness, 7 to 7.5. Specific gravity, 2.9 to 3.2. Usually pitch black or brown in color; also gray, yellow, green, or red, and, more rarely, colorless or white. The reddish varieties are frequently called *rubellite;* the black, *schorl* or *schorlite;* the dark blue, *indicolite;* and the green, *Brazilian emerald.* Zonal distribution of color is often very marked, especially in crystals of the lighter colors (Fig. 644). Vitreous to resinous luster. ω 1.636 to 1.698, ϵ 1.613 to 1.658, (−). Tourmalines rich in iron have the higher indices. Transparent to opaque. Strongly dichroic. May often be pyroelectric and piezoelectric. May become luminescent.

$M_7Al_6(OH,F)_4(BO_3)_3Si_6O_{18}$. A very complex silicate. M represents varying amounts of lithium, sodium, potassium, iron, magnesium, manga-

Fig. 644. Tourmaline showing zonal distribution of color and spherical triangular outline. San Diego County, California.

Fig. 645. Tourmaline in quartz. Auburn, Maine.

Fig. 646. Tourmaline in albite. Mesa Grande, California.

nese, and calcium. The varieties are usually classified according to composition as alkali (*elbaite*), iron (*schorlite*), and magnesium (*dravite*) tourmalines. *Rubellite* is a lithium tourmaline, commonly associated with lepidolite. Fusibility varies greatly. Insoluble in acids but gelatinizes after fusion or strong ignition. Alters to muscovite, biotite, or chlorite.

Tourmaline is a very characteristic mineral of pegmatite dikes associated with intrusions of granite. It is the result of pneumatolytic and

Fig. 647. Tourmaline: variety, rubellite, in lepidolite. San Diego County, California.

hydrothermal action, as is evidenced by the presence of fluorine, hydroxyl, and boron. It is also rather common in metamorphic rocks, such as gneisses, schists, and in crystalline limestones and dolomites. Some of the common associates are quartz (Fig. 645), feldspar (Fig. 646), beryl, topaz, fluorite, lepidolite (Fig. 647), apatite, muscovite, and cassiterite. Excellent crystals occur on the Island of Elba; in the Ural Mountains; Burma; Ceylon; South-West Africa; Tasmania; Bolivia; St. Gotthard, Switzerland;

Madagascar; Minas Gerais, Brazil; Paris, Auburn, and Rumford, Maine; Haddam Neck, Connecticut; Gouverneur and elsewhere in St. Lawrence County, New York; Mesa Grande, Pala, and elsewhere in San Diego County, California.

Stones of good colors are used for gem purposes. On account of its strong absorption of light, it has been used in the making of tourmaline tongs, a simple instrument for the production of polarized light. Properly oriented sections of tourmaline are used for frequency control in short-wave radio apparatus and in pressure gauges.

CHRYSOCOLLA, $CuSiO_3.nH_2O$.

Crystals are small, acicular, and very rare; system not determined. Usually cryptocrystalline in compact, reniform, or earthy masses; also as incrustations and stains, and in veins. May have an enamel-like appearance and resemble opal.

Conchoidal fracture. Hardness, 2 to 4. Specific gravity, 2 to 2.2. Usually various shades of green or blue; when impure, brown to black. Translucent to opaque. Vitreous, greasy, or dull luster. The index of refraction varies from 1.575 to 1.635.

$CuSiO_3.nH_2O$. Variable composition. Frequently quite impure. Infusible. Decomposed by acids but does not gelatinize. Forms pseudomorphs after atacamite, azurite, and cerussite.

Chrysocolla is a secondary mineral, formed by the alteration of various copper ores, such as chalcopyrite, cuprite, and tetrahedrite. Generally found in the zone of oxidation of copper ore deposits. It is commonly associated with malachite, native copper, azurite, and limonite. Some localities are Cornwall, England; Belgian Congo; Northern Rhodesia; the Ural Mountains; the Clifton and Bisbee copper districts, Arizona; Wyoming; Nevada; New Mexico; Lake Superior copper district; in fact, all important copper localities.

It is an ore of copper. It is sometimes cut and polished for gem purposes. At times, it is substituted for turquois.

Pyroxene Group

The members of the pyroxene group are important rock minerals They consist of silicates of calcium, magnesium, iron, aluminum, sodium and lithium, corresponding to the general formulas $M_2''Si_2O_6$ and $M'M'''.Si_2O_6$. Although these minerals crystallize in both the orthorhombic and monoclinic systems, they are characterized by prism angles and cleavages of about 87 and 93°. The orthorhombic pyroxenes generally contain no calcium and little or no aluminum. The monoclinic members usually have considerable calcium and may, or may not, contain aluminum and the alkalies.

As stated on page 358, the pyroxenes have structures containing chains of linked SiO_4 tetrahedrons (Fig. 607). The pyroxenes are rather closely related, chemically and crystallographically, to the minerals of the amphibole group. This relationship is discussed on page 390.

The following important pyroxenes will be described:

Enstatite, Bronzite, Hypersthene	$(Mg,Fe)_2Si_2O_6$	Orthorhombic
Diopside	$CaMgSi_2O_6$	Monoclinic
Augite	$Ca(Mg,Fe,Al)(Al,Si)_2O_6$	Monoclinic
Aegirite	$NaFeSi_2O_6$	Monoclinic
Spodumene	$LiAlSi_2O_6$	Monoclinic

In addition to the above, the following minerals were formerly classified as pyroxenes:

Rhodonite	$MnSiO_3$	Triclinic
Wollastonite	$CaSiO_3$	Triclinic
Pectolite	$HNaCa_2(SiO_3)_3$	Triclinic

These minerals, however, differ from the pyroxenes in optical and crystallographic properties as well as in structure. See pages 388 and 389.

ENSTATITE (*Bronzite, Hypersthene*), **$(Mg,Fe)_2Si_2O_6$.**

Orthorhombic, bipyramidal class—$2/m\ 2/m\ 2/m$. Rarely found in distinct crystals, usually in fibrous, lamellar, columnar, or compact masses. Hypersthene occurs frequently in cleavable aggregates.

Prismatic cleavage and pinacoidal parting. Hardness, 5 to 6. Specific gravity, 3.1 to 3.5. Translucent to opaque.

Enstatite. Grayish white, greenish, or brownish in color. Vitreous to pearly luster. Contains less than 5 per cent of ferrous oxide.

Bronzite. Darker in color than enstatite, usually brown, yellowish, or green. Pronounced pinacoidal parting, producing fibrous or irregular wavy surfaces with a chatoyant bronzy luster. Contains 5 to 14 per cent of ferrous oxide.

Hypersthene. Black, brownish black, or green in color. Pearly to metalloidal luster. Often shows a copper-red iridescence on the macropinacoid. Contains more than 14 per cent of ferrous oxide.

The optical properties for these varieties vary with the iron content: α 1.650 to 1.715, β 1.653 to 1.728, γ 1.658 to 1.731; $2V = 31$ to 90°. Enstatite and bronzite are optically positive, $r < v$; hypersthene is negative, $r > v$.

These minerals occur commonly in basic igneous rocks such as pyroxenite, peridotite, norite, andesite, gabbro, basalt, and meteorites. The most frequent associates are olivine, spinel, serpentine, talc, labradorite, hornblende, pyrrhotite, and magnetite. Some localities are Norway; Styria, Austria; Bavaria; Kimberley, South Africa; St. Paul's Island off the coast of Labrador; Laacher See, Rhenish Prussia; Greenland; Scotland; along the Hudson River and in the Adirondack Mountains, New York; also in Texas, Maryland, and North Carolina.

Hypersthene showing an iridescence and metalloidal luster is sometimes used in jewelry.

DIOPSIDE, $CaMgSi_2O_6$.

Monoclinic, prismatic class—$2/m$. Crystals are generally short and thick and nearly square or octagonal in cross section, the faces of the unit prism intersecting at angles of 87 and 93°. Striations parallel to the basal pinacoid are frequently observed on the faces of the vertical zone. Common forms are the three pinacoids, unit prism, positive and negative hemipyramids, and the negative hemiorthodome (Figs. 648 to 650).

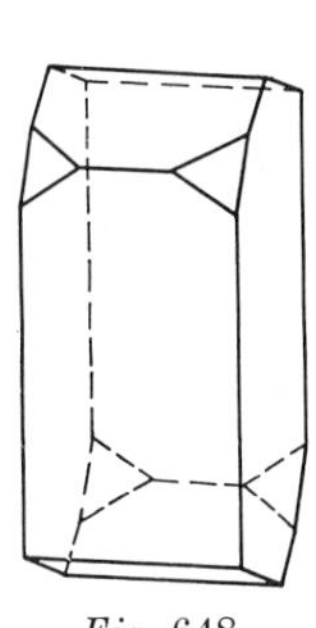

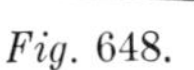

Fig. 648.

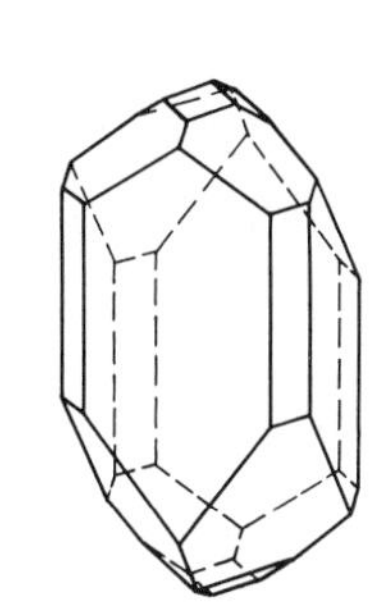

Fig. 649.

Fig. 650. Diopside with zonal distribution of color. Ala, Italy.

Occurs also in compact, broad columnar, granular, lamellar, or fibrous masses.

Prismatic cleavage and basal parting are conspicuous. Hardness, 5 to 6. Specific gravity, 3.2 to 3.3. Uneven to conchoidal fracture. Vitreous, resinous, or dull luster; sometimes inclining to pearly on the basal parting. α 1.673, β 1.680, γ 1.702, (+); $2V = 59°$; $r > v$. Generally light to dark green in color; also colorless, gray, yellow, and, rarely, blue. Zonal distribution of color not uncommon (Fig. 650). White to greenish streak. Transparent to opaque. May become luminescent.

$CaMgSi_2O_6$. Usually contains up to 5 per cent of FeO. Aluminum, chromium, or manganese may also be present. More or less fusible to a dark-colored or green glass. Not acted upon by the common acids. Alters to serpentine, talc, chlorite, and limonite. *Diallage* is a thin-foliated, or lamellar variety, containing 8 to 16 per cent of iron oxide, and greenish or brownish in color. In *hedenbergite* the magnesium has been largely or entirely replaced by iron; the color is black or greenish black.

Occurs in diorite, gabbro, basalt, pyroxenite, and peridotite; also in crystalline schists and as a contact mineral in limestone and dolomite. Common associates are vesuvianite, tremolite, garnet, scapolite, spinel, apatite, sphene, phlogopite, the amphiboles, tourmaline, and the feldspars. Found at various places in Tirol; Zermatt, Switzerland; Pargas, Finland; Sweden; Ural Mountains; Lanark and Hastings counties, Ontario; Lewis and St. Lawrence counties, New York; Litchfield County, Connecticut.

Clear and transparent varieties are sometimes used for gem purposes.

AUGITE, Ca(Mg,Fe,Al)(Al,Si)$_2$O$_6$.

Monoclinic, prismatic class—$2/m$. Crystals are short, prismatic, or thick columnar with a prism angle of 87°, often yielding a pseudotetragonal outline. The most usual combination consists of the orthopinacoid (*a*), clinopinacoid (*b*), unit prism (*m*), negative unit hemipyramid (*o*), and

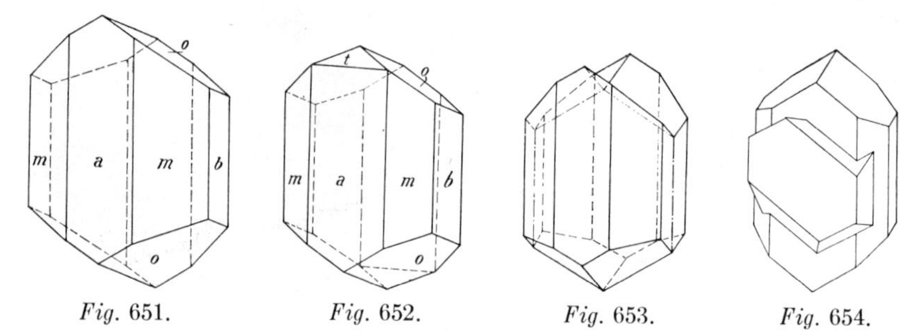

Fig. 651. *Fig.* 652. *Fig.* 653. *Fig.* 654.

positive hemiorthodome (*t*) (Figs. 651 and 652). Sometimes occurs as contact twins, twinned parallel to the orthopinacoid (Fig. 653), or as penetration twins in which the clinohemipyramid is the twinning plane (Fig. 654). It is also observed in compact and disseminated grains and granular aggregates; rarely fibrous.

Prismatic cleavage. Conchoidal to uneven fracture. Hardness, 5 to 6. Specific gravity, 3.2 to 3.6; varying with the composition. Commonly black or greenish black in color, also leek green. Grayish-green streak. Usually opaque but may be translucent. Vitreous to dull. α 1.698, β 1.704, γ 1.723, variable, (+); $2V = 60°$; $r > v$.

Ca(Mg,Fe,Al)(Al,Si)$_2$O$_6$. Sodium, manganese, and titanium are sometimes present. Fuses, and often forms a magnetic glass. Slightly acted upon by acids. Alters to a fibrous hornblende having the form of augite, termed *uralite,* and also to serpentine.

Augite is a common rock mineral and often occurs in disseminated crystals as an essential or accessory constituent of andesite, basalt, diabase, gabbro, tuff, and volcanic sand and ash. Also occurs in crystalline schists and limestones and is commonly the result of contact metamorphism. Some notable localities are Fassathal, Tirol; Mount Vesuvius; Mount Etna; Kaiserstuhl, Baden; Teplitz, Bohemia; Norway; Finland; Thetford, Vermont; Amherst County, Virginia.

Aegirite (*Aegirine, Acmite*), **$NaFeSi_2O_6$.**

Monoclinic, prismatic class—$2/m$. Long prismatic crystals, often bladed parallel to the orthopinacoid, vertically striated, with acute terminal faces. Also as hair-like crystals and fine fibrous aggregates.

Distinct prismatic cleavages at 87 and 93°. Parting parallel to the orthopinacoid. Uneven fracture. Hardness, 6 to 6.5. Specific gravity, 3.4 to 3.55. Vitreous to resinous luster. Translucent to opaque. Green, brown, and black in color. Yellow-gray to dark-green streak. α 1.742 to 1.776, β 1.768 to 1.819, γ 1.787 to 1.836 (−); $2V = 69$ to 81°; $r > v$. Strongly pleochroic.

$NaFeSi_2O_6$. Na_2O 13.4, Fe_2O_3 34.6, SiO_2 52.0 per cent. May contain calcium, aluminum, magnesium; also titanium, vanadium, and the rare-earth elements. Fuses easily, coloring the flame yellow.

Aegirite is not common. It occurs in alkali rocks, such as nepheline syenite, soda granite, soda aplite, and phonolite. Common associates are soda orthoclase, soda amphiboles, feldspathoids, and rare zirconium minerals. Occurs at Aeker and Langesundfiord, southern Norway; Kola Peninsula, Soviet Russia; southern Greenland; Magnet Cove, Arkansas; Bear Paw Mountains and Libby, Montana.

SPODUMENE (*Hiddenite, Kunzite*), **$LiAlSi_2O_6$.**

Monoclinic, prismatic class—$2/m$. Long, columnar crystals with the unit prism predominating; also tabular, and frequently with vertical striations and furrows (Fig. 655). Often very large, several crystals from the Etta Mine, near Keystone, South Dakota, having measured 36, 40, 42, and 47 feet in length and 2½ to 6 feet in width; each weighed over 30 tons (Fig. 733, page 459). Occurs more commonly in cleavable masses and broad columnar aggregates.

Fig. 655. Spodumene. Norwich, Massachusetts.

Perfect prismatic cleavage; also very easy parting parallel to the orthopinacoid. Uneven to splintery fracture. Hardness, 6 to 7. Specific gravity, 3.1 to 3.2. White, grayish, green, pink, and purple. Vitreous to pearly luster. α 1.660, β 1.666, γ 1.676, (+); $2V$ is about 58°; $r < v$. Transparent to opaque. *Hiddenite* is a clear-yellow to emerald-green variety from Stony Point, Alexander County, North Carolina. A transparent lilac-pink variety from Pala, San Diego County, California, is called *kunzite*. This variety phosphoresces with an orange-pink light when exposed to electric discharges, X rays, ultraviolet light, or to radium emanations.

$LiAlSi_2O_6$. Li_2O 8.0, Al_2O_3 27.4, SiO_2 64.6 per cent. May contain sodium, potassium, iron, chromium, or calcium. Fuses easily, turns white, intumesces, and colors the flame purple-red. Insoluble in acids. Alters to albite, muscovite, and quartz.

Occurs in pegmatites with tourmaline, beryl, garnet, lepidolite, feldspar, mica, and quartz as the principal associates. Some localities are Sweden; Tirol; Ireland; Madagascar; Belgian Congo; Brazil; Quebec and Manitoba, Canada; Windham, Maine; Sterling, Chester, and Goshen, Massachusetts; Branchville, Connecticut; Alexander and Cleveland counties, North Carolina; Etta Mine, Pennington County, and elsewhere in South Dakota; Pala, San Diego County, California; Kings Mountain district, North Carolina.

Important source of lithium. The Kings Mountain district, North Carolina, and the Etta Mine and elsewhere in the Black Hills, South Dakota, are principal producers. For uses see page 458. Hiddenite and kunzite are used for gem purposes.

Jadeite (*Jade*), $NaAlSi_2O_6$. Monoclinic, prismatic class—$2/m$. Occurs generally as compact, microcrystalline, fibrous, or granular masses. Fibers have cleavages at about 87 and 93°. Tough. Splintery fracture. Hardness, 6.5 to 7. Specific gravity, 3.3 to 3.5; heavier than nephrite. The color is white or greenish white to emerald green, more rarely, brown, orange, red, or black. The mean index of refraction is 1.66. Occurs in upper Burma, Yünnan in southern China, Tibet, Mexico, South America; Gem Mine, San Benito County, California.

Jadeite has long been highly prized in China for the manufacture of ornaments and utensils, many being of exquisite design and great beauty. It was also used by prehistoric man for weapons and tools.

Jadeite and nephrite (page 392) are included in the general term *jade*.

RHODONITE (*Fowlerite*), $MnSiO_3$.

Triclinic, pinacoidal class—$\bar{1}$. Crystals are usually tabular or prismatic, comparatively large and with rounded edges, but not very common. Occurs generally in fine-grained, cleavable, or compact masses; also in disseminated grains.

Prismatic and basal cleavages. Conchoidal to uneven fracture. Hardness, 5 to 6. Specific gravity, 3.4 to 3.7. Rose red, pink, yellowish, greenish, or brownish in color; often black externally. Vitreous to pearly luster. α 1.724, β 1.728, γ 1.737, (+); $2V$ about 70°; $r < v$. Optical properties vary. Transparent to opaque.

$MnSiO_3$. MnO 54.1, SiO_2 45.9 per cent. Commonly contains some calcium and iron. *Fowlerite* is a zinciferous variety obtained from the

Franklin district, New Jersey; α 1.726, β 1.730, γ 1.737, (+); $2V$ is large. Fuses easily to a brownish or black glass. Slightly acted upon by acids, although varieties containing an admixture of calcite will effervesce.

Occurs with calcite, rhodochrosite, tetrahedrite, franklinite, willemite, zincite, quartz, and iron ores. Some localities are the Harz Mountains, Germany; Rumania; Italy; Sweden; near Sverdlosk in the Ural Mountains; Peru; Brazil; Mexico; Broken Hill, New South Wales; San Juan Mountains, Colorado; Cummington, Massachusetts; Franklin, New Jersey; Butte, Montana.

Sometimes used for gem and ornamental purposes.

Wollastonite (*Tabular Spar*), $CaSiO_3$.

Triclinic. Crystals are usually elongated parallel to the *b* axis and tabular in habit. Most commonly observed in cleavable, fibrous, granular, and compact masses. The fibers may have a parallel or divergent structure.

Basal and macropinacoidal cleavages. Uneven fracture. Hardness, 4 to 5. Specific gravity, 2.8 to 2.9. Usually white, colorless, or gray; also yellowish, reddish, or brownish. Vitreous to silky luster. α 1.620, β 1.632, γ 1.634, (−); $2V = 39°$; $r > v$. Transparent to translucent.

$CaSiO_3$. CaO 48.3, SiO_2 51.7 per cent. Magnesium may be present; often mixed with calcite and hence effervesces with acid. Fusible on the thin edges. Decomposes with hydrochloric acid with separation of silica.

Wollastonite is a typical contact metamorphic mineral and is generally associated with garnet, diopside, vesuvianite, tremolite, graphite, epidote, quartz, and calcite. It is found in granular limestone near granite contacts. Some localities are the Island of Elba; Norway; Mount Vesuvius; Rumania; Mexico; Grenville, Quebec; North Burgess and elsewhere, Ontario; Essex, Lewis, and Warren counties, New York; Riverside County, California.

Used in ceramic ware and as a filler in paint.

Fig. 656. Pectolite. Paterson, New Jersey.

Pectolite, $HNaCa_2(SiO_3)_3$.

Triclinic. Generally consists of aggregates of divergent fibers or acicular crystals, sometimes of considerable length and with sharp ends (Fig. 656).

Basal and macropinacoidal cleavages. Uneven fracture. Hardness, 4 to 5. Specific gravity, 2.7 to 2.8. Colorless, white, or grayish white.

Translucent to opaque. Vitreous, pearly to silky luster. α 1.595, β 1.606, γ 1.634, (+); $2V = 60°$; $r > v$.

$HNaCa_2(SiO_3)_3$. CaO 33.8, Na_2O 9.3, SiO_2 54.2, H_2O 2.7 per cent. Manganese, magnesium, and iron may be present. Yields water in a closed tube. Decomposed by hydrochloric acid with the separation of silica. Sometimes phosphoresces when crushed in the dark.

Occurs in fissures and cavities in basic igneous and metamorphic rocks. Commonly associated with the zeolites, datolite, prehnite, and calcite. Some localities are Fassathal and Monzoni, Tirol; Scotland; Thunder Bay, Ontario; Bergen Hill, Paterson and vicinity, New Jersey; Magnet Cove, Arkansas; Isle Royale, Michigan.

Amphibole Group

The members of the amphibole group are closely related to the pyroxenes, being important rock minerals and silicates of magnesium, calcium, aluminum, iron, sodium, and potassium. The amphiboles and pyroxenes together make up about 17 per cent of the igneous rocks. The amphiboles differ from the pyroxenes in having double chains of linked SiO_4 tetrahedrons, with the Si : O ratio of 4 : 11, that is, Si_4O_{11} (Fig. 608, page 359).

TABLE 40

	Pyroxenes	Amphiboles
Crystals	Short prismatic, complex, commonly four- or eight-sided	Long prismatic, simple, commonly six-sided
Prism angles	87 and 93°, pseudotetragonal	56 and 124°, pseudohexagonal
Cleavages	Prismatic, nearly 90°, bladed	Prismatic, nearly 120°, more distinct
Structure	Single chains (SiO_3)	Double chains (Si_4O_{11})
Masses	Lamellar or granular	Columnar or fibrous
Specific gravity	Higher	
Chemical composition	Anhydrous, alter to amphibole	Yield water on heating. Magnesium and the alkalies are more prominent
Occurrence	Formed at higher temperatures. Common in more basic rocks	Common in metamorphic and the more acid rocks

Also the amphiboles yield a small amount of water on heating. This indicates that the amphiboles are formed under hydrous and the pyroxenes under anhydrous conditions. Like the pyroxenes, these minerals crystallize in the orthorhombic and monoclinic systems. Only the following monoclinic amphiboles are sufficiently important to warrant description:

Tremolite	$Ca_2Mg_5(OH)_2Si_8O_{22}$
Actinolite	$Ca_2(Mg,Fe)_5(OH)_2Si_8O_{22}$
Hornblende	$Ca_2(Mg,Fe)_5(OH)_2(Al,Si)_8O_{22}$
Glaucophane	$Na_2Mg_3Al_2(OH)_2Si_8O_{22}$

The principal differences between the members of the pyroxene and amphibole groups are shown in Table 40.

Tremolite, $Ca_2Mg_5(OH)_2Si_8O_{22}$.

Monoclinic, prismatic class—$2/m$. Crystals are bladed, either long or short, but generally without terminal faces (Fig. 657). Occurs also in fibrous, radiating, and asbestiform aggregates and in compact columnar or granular masses.

Perfect prismatic cleavage, at angles of 56 and 124°. Hardness, 5 to 6. Specific gravity, 2.9 to 3.1. Generally white, gray, greenish, or yellowish in color. *Hexagonite* is an amethystine to lavender variety, due to a small

Fig. 657. Tremolite. Haliburton, Ontario.

amount of manganese. Vitreous to silky luster. α 1.609, β 1.623, γ 1.635, variable, (−); $2V$ is about 85°; $r < v$. Transparent to opaque.

$Ca_2Mg_5(OH_2)Si_8O_{22}$. Contains little or no iron. Not acted upon by acids. Fuses with difficulty. Alters to talc.

Tremolite is often a contact metamorphic mineral and occurs in granular limestones and dolomites and in schists. Found in the Saint Gotthard district, Switzerland; Tirol; Piedmont, Italy; South-West Africa; Lee, Massachusetts; Easton, Pennsylvania; Edenville, Orange County, and Edwards, St. Lawrence County, New York; Pontiac County, Quebec; Renfrew and Lanark counties, Ontario.

Asbestos. Under this term are included fibrous varieties of tremolite, actinolite, and other nonaluminous amphiboles. The fibers are sometimes long, parallel, flexible, and easily separated by the fingers. Amphibole asbestos is commonly called *long-fibered asbestos*, while serpentine asbestos (see page 403) is termed *short-fibered.* The heat-resisting property of the amphibole asbestos is about the same as that of the chrysotile asbestos, but the nonconductivity of heat and strength of fiber are less.

It is also not so suitable for spinning as the short-fibered asbestos. Hence, serpentine or chrysotile asbestos gives the better results. Amphibole asbestos occurs at Sall Mountain, Georgia, and in Lewis County, Idaho. For the uses of asbestos, see page 404.

Actinolite, $Ca_2(Mg,Fe)_5(OH)_2Si_8O_{22}$.

Monoclinic, prismatic class—$2/m$. Long- or short-bladed crystals, but generally without terminal faces (Fig. 658). Occurs usually in divergent or irregular columnar, fibrous, or asbestiform aggregates; also in compact granular masses. *Nephrite* is a compact, tough variety and is known as *jade*.

Fig. 658. Actinolite (dark) in talc. Greiner, Tirol.

Perfect prismatic cleavage, at angles of about 56 and 124°. Hardness, 5 to 6. Specific gravity, 2.9 to 3.2. Usually green in color. Vitreous to silky luster. α 1.611, β 1.627, γ 1.636, $(-)$; $2V = 78°$; $r < v$. Transparent to opaque.

$Ca_2(Mg,Fe)_5(OH)_2Si_8O_{22}$. Usually contains considerable iron and small amounts of aluminum and sodium. Fuses to a gray enamel. Slightly acted upon by acids. Alters to talc, chlorite, epidote, or to an aggregate of serpentine and calcite.

Actinolite occurs in crystalline schists; sometimes in such quantities that the rock may be termed *actinolite schist.* It is often the result of contact metamorphism. Some localities are Greiner, Zillerthal, Tirol; Norway; Zöblitz, Saxony; Iyo, Japan; Brome County, Quebec; Bare Hills, Maryland; Franklin, New Jersey; Delaware and Chester counties, Pennsylvania; Lee and Chester, Massachusetts; Windham, Vermont.

Nephrite and jadeite (page 388) are included in the term *jade.* Nephrite is the more common variety. It has a splintery fracture and is commonly bright to dark green, owing to the presence of ferrous iron. Old ornaments of nephrite often have a superficial brownish to reddish color, because of the oxidation of the iron. Nephrite may also be white, yellowish, reddish, or bluish, frequently irregularly distributed. Appropriately colored nephrite is often called *mutton fat* and *spinach jade.* Nephrite occurs in various parts of China, Turkestan, Siberia, New Zealand, and Alaska; at Lander, Wyoming, and near Porterville, California.

HORNBLENDE, $Ca_2(Mg,Fe)_5(OH)_2(Al,Si)_8O_{22}$.

Monoclinc, prismatic class—$2/m$. Prismatic crystals with a pseudohexagonal outline and rhombohedral-like terminations are common. The prism angles are 56 and 124°. The common forms are the unit prism (m), clinopinacoid (b), orthopinacoid (a), clinodome (d), and positive hemibipyramid (q) (Figs. 659, 660, 661, 663, and 664). Sometimes twinned parallel to orthopinacoid (Fig. 662). Occurs also in bladed, fibrous, columnar, granular, or compact masses.

Perfect prismatic cleavage, better developed than in augite. Hardness, 5 to 6. Specific gravity, 2.9 to 3.3. Usually dark green, brown, or black in color; grayish-green to grayish-brown streak. Vitreous to silky luster. May be transparent but generally only translucent to opaque. The optical constants vary: (a) *common hornblende*, green to black in color;

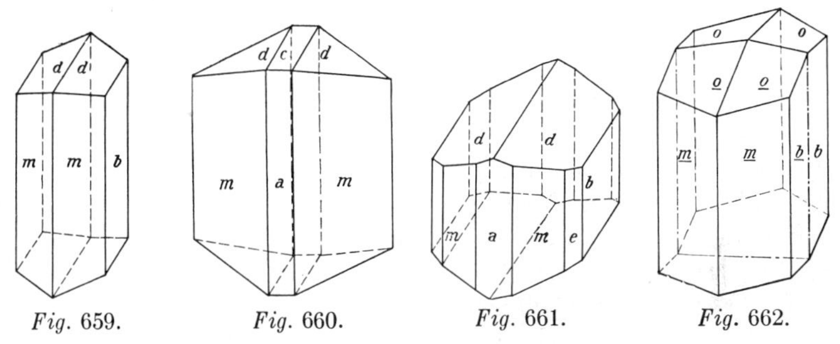

Fig. 659. *Fig.* 660. *Fig.* 661. *Fig.* 662.

α 1.661, β 1.673, γ 1.683, $(-)$; $2V$ is about 84°; $r < v$; (b) *basaltic hornblende*, brownish black to black in color; α 1.677, β 1.695, γ 1.708, $(-)$; $2V$ is large; $r < v$.

$Ca_2(Mg,Fe)_5(OH)_2(Al,Si)_8O_{22}$. The composition is similar to that of augite (see page 386) but the presence of the hydroxyl group in hornblende distinguishes it from augite. Some varieties contain small amounts of the alkalies and titanium. Alters to chlorite, epidote, calcite, siderite, limonite, and quartz. *Uralite* is augite altered to hornblende with the

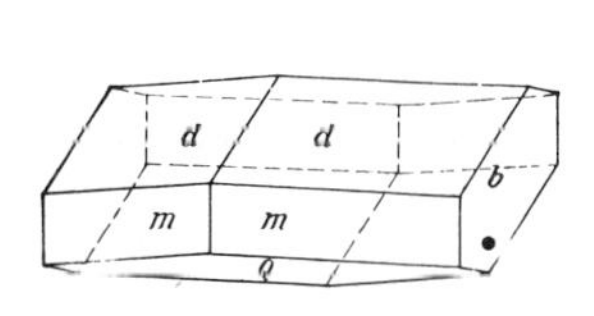

Fig. 663.

Fig. 664. Hornblende. Bilin, Bohemia.

form of the original mineral but with the cleavage of hornblende. Augite commonly alters in this way, and the process is termed *uralitization.*

Hornblende is commonly associated with quartz, feldspar, pyroxenes, chlorite, and calcite. It is an essential or accessory constituent of many plutonic rocks such as granite, syenite, diorite, gabbro, and peridotite; also of basalt, hornblende schist, andesite, and crystalline limestones.

Some of the more important localities are Mount Vesuvius; Bilin, Bohemia; Pargas, Finland; Renfrew County, Ontario; Russel, Pierrepont, and DeKalb, New York; Hawley, Massachusetts; Franconia, New Hampshire; Franklin, New Jersey.

Glaucophane, $Na_2Mg_3Al_2(OH)_2Si_8O_{22}$.

Monoclinic, prismatic class—$2/m$. Prismatic crystals, indistinctly terminated; usually as fibrous or granular aggregates or masses.

Perfect prismatic cleavages at 56 and 124°. Uneven to conchoidal fracture. Hardness, 6 to 6.5. Specific gravity, 3 to 3.15. Vitreous to pearly luster. Translucent to opaque. Blue to bluish black, also gray. Grayish-blue streak. Strongly pleochroic. α 1.621 to 1.655, β 1.638 to 1.664, γ 1.639 to 1.668, (−); $2V = 0$ to 45°; $r < v$.

$Na_2Mg_3Al_2(OH)_2Si_8O_{22}$. Calcium, iron, and manganese may be present. Fuses easily.

Occurs in metamorphic rocks, such as mica and glaucophane schists, gneiss, and crystalline limestone. Associates are quartz, muscovite, garnet, epidote, pyroxene, and rutile. Found on the islands of Syra and Thermia, Greece; Zermatt, Switzerland; Italy; Japan; New Caledonia; and the Coast Ranges, California. Not very common.

APOPHYLLITE, $KCa_4F(Si_4O_{10})_2.8H_2O$.

Tetragonal, ditetragonal bipyramidal class—$4/m\ 2/m\ 2/m$. Crystals may be (1) long and square prismatic (Fig. 666), (2) pseudocubical (Fig. 667), (3) pyramidal (Fig. 668), or (4) thin tabular (Fig. 665). The most general combination consists of the prism of the second order (a), unit bipyramid of the first order (o), and the basal pinacoid (c). The prism faces are often brilliant and striated vertically; those of the basal pinacoid are dull or rough, while the bipyramidal faces may be uneven. Occurs also massive and in granular and lamellar aggregates.

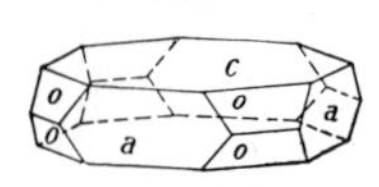

Fig. 665.

Perfect basal cleavage. Uneven fracture. Hardness, 4.5 to 5. Spe-

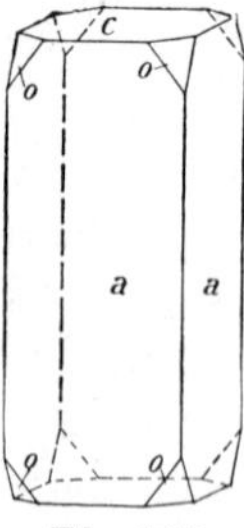

Fig. 666.

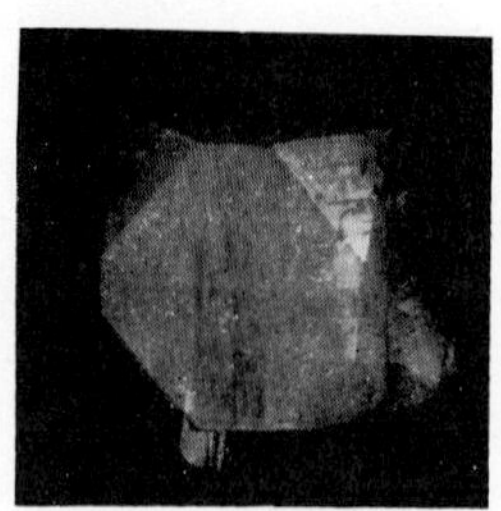
Fig. 667. Apophyllite. Paterson, New Jersey.

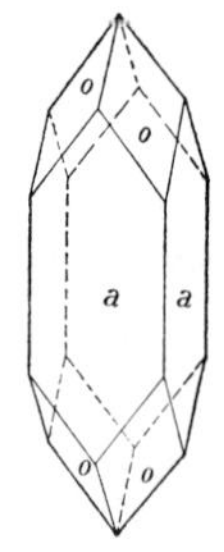

Fig. 668.

cific gravity, 2.3 to 2.4. Generally colorless or white, also green, yellow, or reddish. Vitreous to pearly luster, with *fish-eye* opalescence on basal pinacoid. Usually transparent, rarely nearly opaque. Anomalous optical properties; ω 1.535 or 1.537, ϵ 1.537 or 1.535, $(\pm)$.

$KCa_4F(Si_4O_{10})_2.8H_2O$. The composition is somewhat variable. Potassium may be partially replaced by sodium, and fluorine by the hydroxyl (OH) group. Because it contains water apophyllite was often classified as a zeolite (page 418), but its structure differs materially from that of the zeolites. Exfoliates and fuses easily to a white enamel, coloring the flame violet. Decomposed by hydrochloric acid with a separation of silica. Alters to calcite, pectolite, and kaolin.

Occurs as a secondary mineral in cracks and cavities in basic igneous rocks, also in granite and gneiss. Common associates are natrolite, analcime, datolite, prehnite, pectolite, native copper, and calcite. Found in the Harz Mountains, Germany; Freiberg, Saxony; Tirol; Sweden; Iceland; Greenland; Nova Scotia; Bergen Hill, New Jersey; Table Mountain, Colorado; the Lake Superior copper district; New Almaden, California.

TALC, $Mg_3(OH)_2Si_4O_{10}$.

Monoclinic, prismatic class—$2/m$. Crystals are tabular or scaly but indistinctly developed. Occurs usually as foliated or compact masses and globular or stellate groups; also fibrous or granular.

Perfect basal cleavage. Laminae are flexible but inelastic. Compact varieties have an uneven fracture. Hardness, 1 to 2.5. Specific gravity, 2.6 to 2.8. Commonly green, white, or gray in color; also yellowish, reddish, and brown. Pearly to greasy luster. α 1.539, β 1.589, γ 1.589, $(-)$; $2V$ varies from 6 to 30°; $r > v$. Greasy or soapy feel. Opaque to transparent.

There are several varieties of talc:

Foliated Talc. Consists of easily separable but inelastic scales or plates. Soapy or greasy feel. Hardness 1; easily impressed by the fingernail. Light green to white in color.

Steatite or Soapstone. Massive, often impure. Coarse to fine granular, also schistose. Gray to greenish in color. Hardness, 1.5 to 2.5. Occurs in large deposits.

French Chalk. Soft, compact, whitish masses. Marks cloth easily.

$Mg_3(OH)_2Si_4O_{10}$. SiO_2 63.5, MgO 31.7, H_2O 4.8 per cent. May contain iron, aluminum, and nickel. Fuses with great difficulty. Yields water when strongly ignited. Unattacked by acids. Occurs as a pseudomorph after pyroxenes, hornblende, tremolite, enstatite, spinel, quartz, dolomite, and many other minerals.

Talc is usually considered an alteration product of nonaluminous magnesium minerals, such as the pyroxenes, amphiboles, and olivine.

Commonly found in metamorphic rocks, especially chlorite schists; also with serpentine and magnesite. Occurs frequently as talc or talcose schist containing doubly terminated crystals of magnetite, dolomite, apatite, tourmaline, pyrite, and actinolite. Foliated talc is found at Greiner, Tirol; various places in Switzerland, Italy, France, and Germany; Grafton and elsewhere, New Hampshire; St. Lawrence County, New York. The most important producing locality in the United States for talc is in St. Lawrence County, New York, where it occurs with limestone and has been derived from tremolite and enstatite. Vermont is also an important producer of talc. Albemarle and Nelson counties, Virginia; Montgomery and Northampton counties, Pennsylvania; and Phillipsburg, New Jersey, also produce large quantities. Other important localities are in North Carolina; Georgia; Maryland; Rhode Island; Massachusetts; and California.

Talc and soapstone, cut into slabs or other shapes, are used for washtubs, laboratory tables and tanks, electrical switchboards, mantels, hearthstones, firebricks, foot warmers, slate pencils, and as crayon for marking iron, glass, and fabrics. Ground talc is used in toilet powders and soaps, for dressing skins and leather, in waterproof cement, in ceramic products, as a lubricant, nonconductor of heat, and as "mineral pulp" for filler in paint, paper, and roofing material. Over 40 industries use talc or soapstone in some form. See page 461.

Mica Group

Although the members of the mica group vary greatly from the chemical standpoint, they have, nevertheless, many characteristics in common. Crystals are apparently hexagonal or orthorhombic in development, but they all belong to the monoclinic system. The prism angles approximate 60° and 120°. Twins are not uncommon. The micas possess an excellent basal cleavage, which is sometimes considered the most perfect cleavage observed on minerals. Cleavage laminae are elastic. As stated on page 358, the micas have structures based on sheets of linked $(Si,Al)O_4$ tetrahedrons. This structure accounts for the characteristic basal cleavage. When a blow is struck with a blunt point upon a cleavage surface, a six-rayed *percussion figure* is produced.

The micas are silicates of varying compositions of aluminum and potassium, containing hydroxyl, magnesium, iron, sodium, lithium, and fluorine. The silica content varies between 33 and 55 per cent. All the micas yield water when heated in a closed tube. They fuse with difficulty. They are important rock-forming minerals, being essential constituents of many igneous and metamorphic rocks. Some sedimentary rocks often contain considerable quantities of mica.

The compositions of the micas are often very complex and, accordingly, difficult to interpret. The formulas for muscovite, phlogopite, and biotite are well established on the basis of both chemical and X-ray data. The composition of lepidolite is quite variable; hence, only an approximate formula can be given.

Muscovite	$KAl_2(OH,F)_2AlSi_3O_{10}$
Phlogopite	$KMg_3(F,OH)_2AlSi_3O_{10}$
Biotite	$K(Mg,Fe)_3(OH,F)_2AlSi_3O_{10}$
Lepidolite	$K_2Li_3Al_3(F,OH)_4(AlSi_3O_{10})_2$

The minerals of the chlorite group, as well as serpentine, talc, and kaolinite, are closely related to the micas, both in chemical and physical properties. Their structures are all based on layers of linked SiO_4 tetrahedrons, with the composition Si_4O_{10} or $(Si,Al)_4O_{10}$. Kaolinite has single layers with the apex oxygen atoms all on one side, forming part of $Al(O,OH)_6$ groups; serpentine has single layers with $Mg(O,OH)_6$ groups. Talc has double layers, with the apex oxygen atoms on the inside, forming part of $Mg(O,OH)_6$ groups. Muscovite also has double layers, with $Al(O,OH)_6$ groups in between, alternating with layers containing K ions. Chlorite has double layers like talc, alternating with additional layers of $Mg(O,OH)_6$.

In the text, the more compact formulas $Mg_5Al(OH)_8AlSi_3O_{10}$ and $Al_4(OH)_8Si_4O_{10}$ will be used for chlorite and kaolinite, respectively.

MUSCOVITE (*White Mica, Potash Mica, Isinglass*), $KAl_2(OH,F)_2AlSi_3O_{10}$.

Monoclinic, prismatic class—$2/m$. Crystals are usually tabular and possess a rhombic or hexagonal outline (Figs. 669 and 670). Tapering

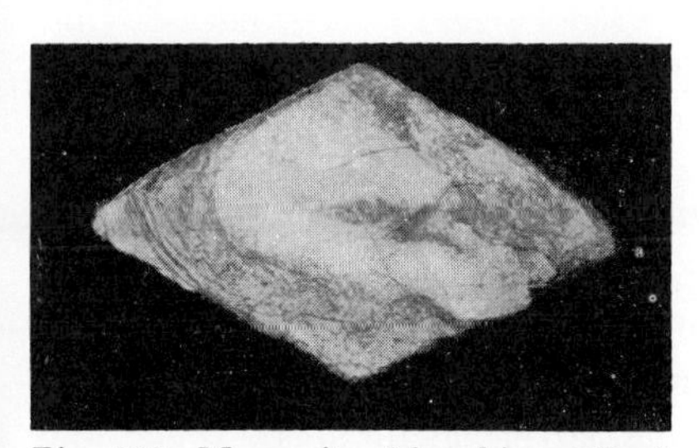

Fig. 669. Muscovite (rhombic outline). Buckfield, Maine.

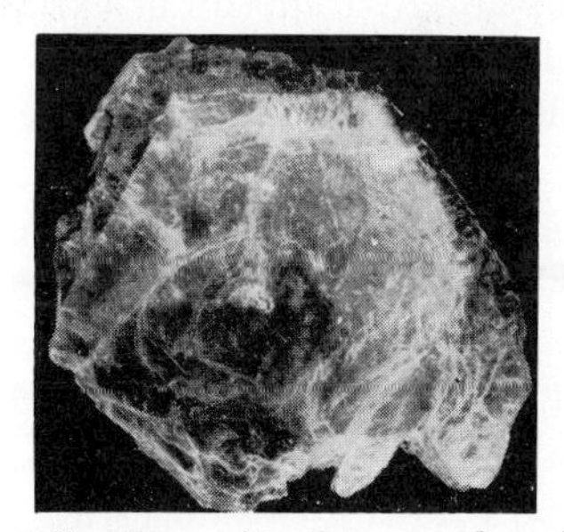

Fig. 670. Muscovite (hexagonal outline) bordered with lepidolite. Auburn, Maine.

pyramidal habits are also observed. Crystals are often large and rough, measuring at times several feet in diameter. Large crystals may show distinct partings perpendicular to the cleavage and are then called *ruled, ribbon,* or *A mica.* The term *wedge mica* is applied to crystals which are thicker at one end than at the other. Usually occurs in scaly, foliated, and plumose aggregates.

Highly perfect basal cleavage, permitting very thin, transparent, and elastic leaves to be split. Hardness, 2 to 3. Specific gravity, 2.8 to 3.1. Colorless, yellowish, brownish, or reddish (*ruby mica*). Transparent to translucent. Pearly to vitreous luster. α 1.552 to 1.574, β 1.581 to 1.611, γ 1.587 to 1.616, $(-)$; $2V$ is about 40°; $r > v$.

$KAl_2(OH,F)_2AlSi_3O_{10}$. Frequently contains small amounts of calcium, lithium, magnesium, iron, and sodium. *Fuchsite* contains small amounts of chromium, while *roscoelite* has considerable vanadium replacing the aluminum (see page 475). *Paragonite* contains sodium replacing potassium. Fuses with difficulty to a grayish or yellowish glass. Not attacked by common acids. *Sericite* is a variety consisting of fine scaly aggregates with a silky luster. It often results from the hydrothermal alteration of feldspars.

Muscovite is generally considered the most common mica. It occurs in granites and syenites and especially in pegmatites where pneumatolytic action has been effective. It is also common in metamorphic rocks, such as gneisses and schists, and in some limestones and fragmental rocks. The usual associates are feldspar, quartz, tourmaline, beryl, spodumene, garnet, apatite, and fluorite. Deposits of muscovite of commercial value occur in North Carolina, New Hampshire, South Dakota, Idaho, New Mexico, Colorado, Virginia, South Carolina, Georgia, and Alabama. Some of the principal producing localities are in Mitchell, Yancey, Macon, Jackson, Haywood, and Ashe counties, North Carolina; Custer County, South Dakota; Grafton and Cheshire counties, New Hampshire. Deposits of excellent muscovite also occur in Ottawa and Berthier counties, Quebec.

Sheet mica is used principally in the manufacture of electrical apparatus and machinery such as dynamos, motors, transformers, condensers, switchboards, lamp sockets, and for flexible mica-covered insulating cloth and tape. Clear and transparent sheets are used for windows in coal, gas, and oil stoves, gas-lamp chimneys, and lamp shades. Scrap mica, that is, material too small to be cut into sheets, is ground in large quantities and used in the manufacture of wallpaper, lubricants, fancy paints, rubber goods, electrical insulators, coverings for steam pipes, and roofing papers.

Micanite—built-up mica—is prepared by cementing with shellac or resins successive layers of small, thin sheets of mica and subjecting the mass to heat and pressure.

The United States consumes about 75 per cent of the world's production of mica; a minor amount is of domestic origin, the remainder being imported from Canada, India, Brazil, and Madagascar.

PHLOGOPITE (*Magnesium Mica, Amber Mica, Bronze Mica*), **$KMg_3(F,OH)_2AlSi_3O_{10}$.**

Monoclinic, prismatic class—$2/m$. Crystals usually resemble those of biotite in form and habit and are sometimes large and coarse (Fig. 671). They may be hexagonal or rhombic in outline. Commonly found in disseminated scales, plates, or aggregates.

Fig. 671. Phlogopite. Perth, Lanark County, Ontario.

Highly perfect basal cleavage. Thin laminae are tough and elastic. Specific gravity, 2.8 to 3. Pearly to submetallic luster. The indices of refraction vary from 1.540 to 1.606, (−); $2V$ varies from 0 to 10°; $r < v$. Color may be silvery gray, yellow, brown, green, copper or bronze red. Thin leaves are transparent. Often shows asterism.

$KMg_3(F,OH)_2AlSi_3O_{10}$. Usually contains small amounts of iron and sodium. Whitens and fuses on thin edges. Slightly acted upon by hydrochloric acid but readily decomposed by hot concentrated sulfuric acid. In synthetic phlogopite, which is produced in small crystals, fluorine replaces the hydroxyl (OH).

Phlogopite occurs in crystalline magnesium limestones, dolomites, schists, serpentine, peridotite, and leucite basalt. Important localities are Pargas, Finland; Åker, Sweden; Fassathal, Tirol; St. Lawrence and Jefferson counties, New York; Morris and Warren counties, New Jersey; Sydenham and Burgess, Ontario, where crystals measuring 7 feet across the cleavage plane have been found; various localities in Quebec; Ceylon; Madagascar.

It is used chiefly as an insulator in electrical apparatus. For use on commutators, phlogopite is preferred to muscovite, as it has more nearly the same hardness as the copper of the commutator segments.

BIOTITE (*Magnesium-iron Mica, Black Mica*), **$K(Mg,Fe)_3(OH,F)_2AlSi_3O_{10}$.**

Monoclinic, prismatic class—$2/m$. Crystals are usually tabular with an hexagonal or rhombic habit; sometimes striated horizontally. Crystals are rare. Generally found in plates, lamellar masses, or disseminated scales.

Highly perfect basal cleavage. Hardness, 2.5 to 3. Specific gravity, 2.7 to 3.2. Dark brown or black in color; more rarely, light brown, or greenish. The indices of refraction vary generally from 1.541 to 1.680,

(−); $2V$ varies from 0 to 25°; $r < v$. White to greenish streak. Transparent to opaque. Sometimes shows asterism.

$K(Mg,Fe)_3(OH,F)_2AlSi_3O_{10}$. The composition varies greatly. May contain titanium, manganese, and sodium. *Lepidomelane* contains large amounts of iron and but little magnesium. Fuses with difficulty. Only slightly attacked by hydrochloric acid; completely decomposed by hot concentrated sulfuric acid. Alters to chlorite, or to epidote, sphene, quartz, and iron oxide.

Biotite is an extremely common mica, being an important constituent of many intrusive igneous and metamorphic rocks, such as granite, syenite, diorite, porphyry, gneiss, and mica schist. It is often associated with muscovite.

Biotite is of little use commercially.

Lepidolite (*Lithium Mica*), $\mathbf{K_2Li_3Al_3(F,OH)_4(AlSi_3O_{10})_2}$.

Monoclinic, prismatic class—$2/m$. Crystals are short prismatic but very rare. Usually in scaly, granular masses, often resembling granular limestone, and in tabular, cleavable plates.

Perfect basal cleavage. Hardness, 2 to 4. Specific gravity, 2.8 to 2.9. Rose red or lilac in color, also white, gray, greenish, or brown. Pearly luster. The indices of refraction vary from 1.530 to 1.605, (−); $2V$ varies from 0 to 40°; $r > v$. Translucent.

$K_2Li_3Al_3(F,OH)_4(AlSi_3O_{10})_2$. Some varieties contain rubidium and cesium. Colors the flame red and fuses to a white glass. After fusion easily acted upon by acids.

Occurs commonly in pegmatites, also in granites and gneisses. It is usually the result of pneumatolytic action. The common associates are tourmaline (especially rubellite) (Fig. 647, page 382), spodumene, amblygonite, cassiterite, muscovite, albite, and topaz. Some localities are Rozena, Moravia; the Island of Elba; Paris, Hebron, Auburn, and Rumford, Maine; Chesterfield, Massachusetts; San Diego County, California; Colorado; New Mexico; Black Hills, South Dakota.

An important source of lithium compounds.

Vermiculite. This term includes a group of micaceous minerals which are formed by the hydration and oxidation of biotite, phlogopite, and chlorite. These minerals have variable compositions. When heated they exfoliate, owing to the formation of steam between the layers. This causes the volume to increase, often as much as sixteen times. Large deposits occur near Libby, Montana; also in Colorado, Wyoming, Georgia, North Carolina, Union of South Africa, and Western Australia. After heat-treatment vermiculite minerals are used as heat and sound insulators, oil absorbents, refractories, and soil conditioners.

CHLORITE (*Prochlorite, Clinochlorite*), $Mg_5Al(OH)_8AlSi_3O_{10}$.

The general term *chlorite* is applied to a number of minerals which are closely related to the micas.

Monoclinic, prismatic class—$2/m$. Crystals are tabular and six-sided, resembling those of mica. Commonly in foliated, scaly, granular, or earthy masses. Often as a scaly or dusty coating on, or disseminated through, quartz, sphene, and adularia.

Perfect basal cleavage. Laminae are flexible but inelastic. Slightly soapy feel. Hardness, 1 to 2.5. Specific gravity, 2.6 to 3.5. Grass green, brownish green, or blackish green in color. The indices of refraction vary from 1.562 to 1.650, (±); $2V$ varies from 0 to 50°; $r < v$. Translucent to opaque, very thin laminae may be transparent. Streak, greenish.

$Mg_5Al(OH)_8AlSi_3O_{10}$. The minerals included in this description are silicates of aluminum or trivalent iron with magnesium, bivalent iron, or manganese. They are more basic than the micas and are free from the alkalies. The composition varies greatly. They yield water when heated in a closed tube.

These minerals are of secondary origin and are usually the result of the decomposition of pyroxenes, amphiboles, garnet, biotite, and vesuvianite. Very common in schists and serpentine. Often associated with garnet, diopside, talc, epidote, magnesite, magnetite, and apatite. Very widespread. Some principal localities are the Ural Mountains; various places in Tirol; Zermatt, Switzerland; Saxony; Chester and Unionville, Pennsylvania; Brewster, New York; Utah; Texas.

KAOLINITE (*Kaolin, China Clay*), $Al_4(OH)_8Si_4O_{10}$.

Monoclinic, domatic class—m. Rarely in small scales with a hexagonal or rhombic outline. Generally in compact, friable, mealy, or clay-like masses.

Scales possess a basal cleavage. Earthy fracture. Hardness, 1 to 2.5. Specific gravity, 2.2 to 2.6. Compact masses are dull, scales pearly. α 1.561, β 1.565, γ 1.567, (−); $2V$ is variable; $r > v$. White, yellowish, reddish, bluish, greenish, or brownish in color. Greasy feel. White to yellowish streak. Opaque to translucent. Usually adheres to the tongue and becomes plastic when moistened. Argillaceous odor when breathed upon.

$Al_4(OH)_8Si_4O_{10}$. Al_2O_3 39.5, SiO_2 46.5, H_2O 14.0 per cent. May contain some iron. Yields water on ignition. Infusible. Partially decomposed by hydrochloric acid. Occurs as a pseudomorph after many minerals.

Optical and X-ray data indicate that there are three distinct minerals possessing the composition $Al_4(OH)_8Si_4O_{10}$, namely, kaolinite, dickite, and nacrite. In physical characteristics they resemble one another very closely. Kaolinite is the most common.

Kaolinite, dickite, and nacrite are always secondary minerals resulting from the action of postvolcanic, pneumatolytic, and hydrothermal processes upon rocks containing feldspar, nepheline, topaz, beryl, augite, scapolite, and other aluminous minerals. Kaolinite may also result from ordinary weathering. Occurs in irregular deposits in kaolinized pegmatites, granites, porphyries, and gneisses. Also in secondary deposits, the result of transportation and deposition under water. These occurrences are often very pure. It is an important constituent of clay and soil. Common associates are feldspar, quartz, corundum, and diaspore. Some localities are Saint Yrieix, near Limoges, France; Cornwall and Devonshire, England; Meissen, Saxony. In the United States, kaolin is mined at Newcastle and Wilmington, Delaware; also in Florida, North Carolina, Pennsylvania, Vermont, California, and Maryland.

Kaolinite is used in large quantities as a filler in paper and rubber, in the manufacture of chinaware, porcelain, tiles, and refractory materials.

Clay Minerals. In addition to kaolinite, there are other minerals included under the general term *clay*. Among these are halloysite, montmorillonite, beidellite, and illite, which are complex hydrous silicates of aluminum, and may contain calcium, magnesium, and sodium. They all have sheet structures, and occur in extremely fine grains. They are plastic when wet and can be molded, and become very hard when fired. Some clays swell in water, and others show the property of base-exchange (see page 418). The clays are the basic materials for many ceramic products.

The term *ceramics* originally referred to products made from clay, such as pottery, brick, and tile. Porcelain, or chinaware, contains feldspar in addition to the clay, as do the glazes used both on porcelain and metal (porcelain enamel). The term ceramics as now used includes also glass, cement, and refractory materials. Cement consists of varying proportions of CaO, Al_2O_3, and SiO_2. The major constituent of cement is limestone ($CaCO_3$), but clay or shale is also an essential component. Clays are likewise used for refractory bricks and linings. Other important refractory materials are quartz, magnesite, bauxite, and chromite.

SERPENTINE, $Mg_6(OH)_8Si_4O_{10}$.

Monoclinic, optically. Never in crystals except as pseudomorphs. Usually compact, columnar, fibrous, or lamellar. Massive varieties often have a microscopically fine fibrous or foliated structure.

Conchoidal to splintery fracture. Hardness, 2.5 to 4. Specific gravity, 2.5 to 2.8. Various shades of green; also yellowish, grayish, reddish, brownish, or black. Often spotted, clouded, or multicolored. Dull resinous, greasy, or waxy luster. The indices of refraction vary from 1.49 to 1.57, ($\pm$); $2V$ is variable, sometimes large. Smooth to greasy feel.

Fig. 672. Serpentine: variety, asbestos. Near Globe, Arizona.

Fig. 673. Serpentine: variety, asbestos (light). Thetford–Black Lake district, Quebec, Canada.

The name serpentine is applied to two varieties: *antigorite,* which is platy in character, and *chrysotile,* which is distinctly fibrous. Massive varieties may be either one of these or a mixture of both.

There are five types of serpentine:

Antigorite. Platy or foliated masses. Dark green in color. Translucent.

Chrysotile, Fibrous Serpentine, Asbestos. Consists of delicate, fine, parallel fibers, which can be easily separated (Fig. 672). Fibers are flexible and adapted for spinning. Silky to silky-metallic luster. Various shades of green in color; also white, yellowish or brownish. Usually found in veins with the fibers perpendicular to the walls of the veins (Fig. 673). Sometimes called *short-fibered asbestos.*

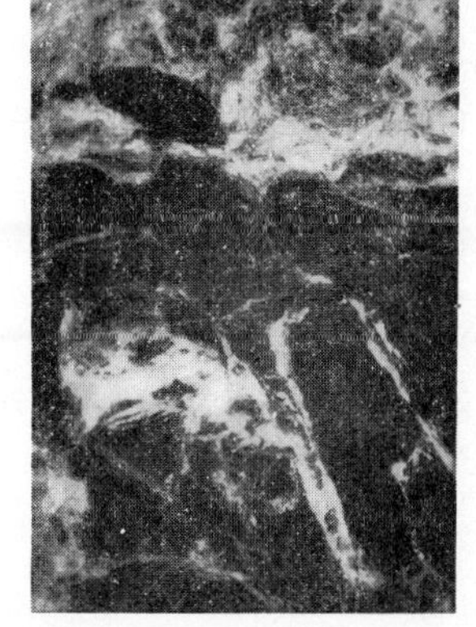

Fig. 674. Serpentine: variety, verd antique. Roxbury, Vermont.

Common Serpentine. Compact, massive. Generally dark in color, often multicolored. Sometimes impure. Very abundant.

Precious Serpentine. Massive, more or less homogeneous. Various shades of green in color, sometimes yellowish. Translucent.

Verd Antique. Massive greenish serpentine mixed irregularly with calcite, dolomite, magnesite, or talc. Has a mottled or veined appearance (Fig. 674). Takes an excellent polish and is used extensively for ornamental purposes. It is sometimes called *serpentine marble.*

The platy character of antigorite is due to the sheet structure, as expressed by the Si_4O_{10} composition; the fibers of chrysotile, as shown by the electron microscope, have a rolled sheet structure.

$Mg_6(OH)_8Si_4O_{10}$. May contain iron, nickel, manganese, aluminum, and chromium. Yields water when ignited. Splinters fuse with difficulty. Decomposed by acids with a separation of silica. May alter to brucite, magnesite, and hydromagnesite. Serpentine is a secondary mineral resulting from the alteration of magnesium minerals and rocks, such as olivine, enstatite, hornblende, tremolite, augite, chondrodite, and peridotite. Olivine is the most common source of serpentine. Common associates are magnesite, calcite, magnetite, chromite, garnierite, pyrope, platinum, and talc.

Serpentine occurs in many localities, some of which are Sweden; Silesia; Chester County and Easton, Pennsylvania, where it is mined; Milford, Connecticut; Hoboken and Montville, New Jersey; Syracuse, New York; Vermont; northern New York; Washington. Asbestos is not found in large quantities in the United States. Most of the asbestos of commerce is obtained from the mines in the Thetford–Black Lake district, Quebec; next in importance are Rhodesia, the Union of South Africa, Soviet Russia, and the Island of Cyprus.

Polished massive serpentine and verd antique are used for ornamental and interior decorative purposes. Translucent yellowish serpentine is sometimes cut and polished for gem purposes. Asbestos is used extensively in the manufacture of nonconductors of heat and in noncombustible materials such as cloth, boards, felt, rope, paper, paint, cement, theater curtains, shingles, and brake linings.

Garnierite, $(Ni,Mg)_6(OH)_8Si_4O_{10}$.

Probably monoclinic. Never found in crystals. Occurs commonly as rounded, pea-shaped masses with varnish-like surfaces; also compact, reniform, or earthy.

Conchoidal or earthy fracture. Hardness, 2 to 3. Specific gravity 2.3 to 2.8. Pale, apple, or emerald green in color. Dull to greasy luster. $n = 1.59$. Greasy feel. Frequently adheres to the tongue. Streak, white to greenish.

$(Ni,Mg)_6(OH)_8Si_4O_{10}$. Garnierite is closely related to chrysotile (serpentine) in which nickel has partially replaced magnesium. Composition varies greatly. Infusible, decrepitates, and becomes magnetic. Yields water on ignition. Attacked by acids.

An alteration of olivine and serpentine rocks. Usually associated with olivine, serpentine, chromite, and talc. Occurs in serpentine at Nouméa,

New Caledonia; also found in the Transvaal, South Africa; Madagascar; Brazil; Philippine Islands; Webster, North Carolina; Riddle, Douglas County, Oregon.

A source of nickel. See page 464.

Sepiolite (*Meerschaum*), $Mg_4(OH)_2Si_6O_{15}.6H_2O$.

Monoclinic. Occurs only in compact nodular, earthly, or clayey masses.

Conchoidal to uneven fracture. Hardness, 2 to 2.5. Impressed by the fingernail. Specific gravity, 1 to 2. On account of its porosity it may float on water. Adheres to the tongue. Usually white, yellowish, or grayish in color. Dull luster. α 1.519, β 1.52, γ 1.529, (−).

$Mg_4(OH)_2Si_6O_{15}.6H_2O$. Yields water when strongly ignited. Fuses with difficulty on thin edges to a white glass; some varieties first turn black. Gelatinizes with hydrochloric acid.

An alteration product of serpentine, magnesite, or impure opal containing considerable magnesium. It is found principally in nodular masses in serpentine or in secondary deposits on the plains of Eskisehir, Turkey. Occurs in smaller quantities in Spain; the Grecian Archipelago; Morocco; Moravia; Utah; California; New Mexico; Pennsylvania.

Meerschaum is easily carved and worked on the lathe, takes an excellent polish, and has been used extensively for pipe bowls.

Feldspar Group

The feldspars constitute the most abundant group of minerals. They are very important rock minerals and, according to Clarke, make up about 60 per cent of the igneous rocks. Their chemical compositions are very similar and may be expressed, in general, by the formulas $M'AlSi_3O_8$ or $M''Al_2Si_2O_8$, in which the metal may be potassium, sodium, calcium, or, more rarely, barium. The feldspars crystallize in the monoclinic and triclinic systems, but many of their physical properties are strikingly similar. The prism angles are about 120°. Hardness, 6. Specific gravity, 2.55 to 2.75. The color is usually white or gray but may also be reddish, yellow, or greenish. All feldspars possess good cleavages in two directions, that is, parallel to the basal and clino- or brachypinacoids. In the case of orthoclase, these cleavages make an angle of 90°, but in the case of the triclinic members they are inclined, the angles differing slightly from 90° (see Table 41, page 409).

The feldspars are important economic minerals. About 460,000 long tons are produced annually in the United States, most of the output being consumed in the ceramic and glass industries. The chief producing states are North Carolina, South Dakota, Colorado, New Hampshire, Maine, Connecticut, Georgia, Arizona, Virginia, and California.

The following feldspars will be described:

Orthoclase	$KAlSi_3O_8$	Monoclinic
Microcline	$KAlSi_3O_8$	Triclinic
	PLAGIOCLASES	
Albite	$NaAlSi_3O_8(Ab)$	Triclinic
Labradorite	$Ab_{50}An_{50}$ to $Ab_{30}An_{70}$	Triclinic
Anorthite	$CaAl_2Si_2O_8(An)$	Triclinic

Igneous rocks are commonly classified according to the kind of feldspar they contain.

ORTHOCLASE (*Potash Feldspar, Feldspar*), **$KAlSi_3O_8$.**

Monoclinic, prismatic class—$2/m$. Well-developed crystals are common, the habit being usually prismatic parallel to the *c* axis (Fig. 675), tabular parallel to the clinopinacoid, or square columnar and elongated

Fig. 675. Orthoclase. Lincoln County, Nevada.

Fig. 676. Orthoclase: variety, sanidine. Fort Bayard, New Mexico.

Figs. 677 and 678. Orthoclase (left and right Carlsbad twins). Fort Bayard, New Mexico.

parallel to the *a* axis (Fig. 676). In the latter case, the basal and clinopinacoids are about equally developed. The unit prism, negative hemi-orthodomes, a clinodome, and the basal and clinopinacoids are the forms most frequently observed. Crystals are sometimes highly modified and may be quite large. Twinning is frequently observed according to three laws.

Carlsbad Law. The orthopinacoid acts as the twinning plane, or the crystallographic *c* axis may be considered the twinning axis. Irregular contact and penetration twins are common (Figs. 677 and 678).

Baveno Law. The clinodome $(\infty a : b : 2c)$ is the twinning plane. Nearly square or columnar contact twins are most common (Fig. 679).

Manebach Law. This law yields contact twins with the basal pinacoid acting as the twinning and composition plane (Fig. 680). This law is not so common as the first two.

Aside from occurring in crystals, orthoclase is found in cleavable, compact, or granular masses and in irregular disseminated grains. Some massive orthoclase resembles jasper or flint.

Perfect basal and good clinopinacoidal cleavages, making an angle of 90°. Conchoidal to uneven fracture. Hardness, 6. Specific gravity, 2.5 to 2.6. Usually colorless, white, gray, or reddish, or yellowish; more rarely greenish. Transparent to opaque. Vitreous to pearly luster. α 1.518, β 1.524, γ 1.526, (−); $2V$ varies from 0 to 70°; ($r > v$). Some varieties may become luminescent.

Fig. 679.

Fig. 680.

There are three important varieties:

Adularia. This variety occurs usually in white or colorless crystals, which may be transparent or slightly cloudy. It frequently possesses an excellent opalescence. It is then termed *moonstone* and is used for gem purposes (see page 411). Adularia is a low-temperature hydrothermal feldspar formed below 400°C., and is usually found in cracks and veins in gneiss and mica schist.

Sanidine. Occurs in glassy, transparent, or translucent crystals and is sometimes called *glassy feldspar*. Generally colorless, white, or gray. Tabular and square habits and Carlsbad twins are very common. Sanidine is a high-temperature potassium feldspar, formed above 950°C. It is characteristic of eruptive rocks, especially rhyolite, trachyte, and phonolite (Fig. 681). $2V$ is very small.

Fig. 681. Orthoclase: variety, sanidine, in trachyte. Drachenfels, Rhine Valley.

Ordinary or Common Orthoclase. Generally more or less dull in color, yellowish, flesh red, dark red, or greenish. Occurs in well-developed crystals. Very common in granite, syenite, and gneiss.

$KAlSi_3O_8$. K_2O 16.9, Al_2O_3 18.4, SiO_2 64.7 per cent. Often contains considerable sodium or barium. Fuses with difficulty. Insoluble in acids. Alters to kaolinite and muscovite (sericite). Occurs as a pseudomorph after analcime and leucite.

Orthoclase is a very common mineral. It is especially characteristic of such plutonic rocks as granite and syenite. It is also an important constituent of certain eruptive and metamorphic rocks, for example, rhyolite, trachyte, phonolite, porphyry, gneiss, and various schists. Not infrequently, it occurs in some sandstones and conglomerates. The most common associates of orthoclase are muscovite, biotite, quartz, tourmaline, the other feldspars, feldspathoids, hornblende, apatite, zircon, and beryl. It occurs widely distributed and is frequently considered the most abundant of the silicate minerals. A few localities for excellent crystals are the Saint Gotthard district, Switzerland; Mount Vesuvius; Karlsbad, Bohemia; Striegau, Silesia; Norway; Ceylon; Perth, Quebec; Bedford, Ontario; Paris, Maine; Acworth, New Hampshire; Haddam, Connecticut; St. Lawrence County, New York; Mount Antero, Chaffee County, Colorado. Massive varieties are found at Bedford, Ontario; Georgetown and Brunswick, Maine; Crown Point and elsewhere, New York; Mitchell and Yancey counties, North Carolina; also in Pennsylvania, Maryland, Virginia, Minnesota, and Massachusetts.

The feldspar of commerce, which is often called orthoclase, is in reality microcline or an intergrowth of microcline and albite; see page 412. Moonstone and transparent yellow orthoclase are used as gems.

MICROCLINE, $KAlSi_3O_8$.

Triclinic, pinacoidal class—$\bar{1}$. Crystals resemble very closely those of orthoclase in habit (Fig. 682), angles, crystal forms, and twinning. The

Fig. 682. Microcline: variety, Amazon stone. Pikes Peak, Colorado.

Fig. 683. Microcline showing rectangular cleavage.

Fig. 684. Microcline with quartz (graphic granite). Bedford, New York. (*After Bastin.*)

angle between the basal and brachypinacoids is nearly 90°, being about 90°30′ (Fig. 683). Crystals are frequently large, and although apparently simple individuals, they are, in reality, usually polysynthetic twins according to the albite and pericline laws (see page 411), so characteristic of albite and other triclinic feldspars. Accordingly, basal sections of microcline show under the microscope a characteristic grating or gridiron structure. Also occurs in cleavable and compact granular masses.

Basal and brachypinacoidal cleavages. Uneven fracture. Hardness, 6. Specific gravity, 2.54 and 2.57. Vitreous luster, inclining to pearly on the basal pinacoid. White, yellowish, gray, green, or red in color. Green varieties—often bright verdigris green—are called *amazonite* or *Amazon stone.* Transparent to translucent. α 1.522, β 1.526, γ 1.530, $(-)$; $2V$ varies from 77 to 84°; $r > v$.

$KAlSi_3O_8$. Usually contains some sodium and is then called *soda microcline.* In *anorthoclase* sodium predominates over potassium.

Orthoclase and microcline are dimorphous. Orthoclase is the high-temperature modification and is characteristic of igneous rocks. Microcline forms at lower temperatures, 400 to 750°C. It is the main feldspar in pegmatites and may occur in granites. Quartz and muscovite are typical associates. Intergrowths with quartz, called *graphic granite* (Fig. 684), and the other feldspars are common. Some localities are Striegau, Silesia; Arendal, Norway; the Ural Mountains; Greenland; the Pikes Peak district, Colorado; North Carolina; South Dakota; Virginia; Wyoming; Maine; Connecticut.

The feldspar of commerce is principally microcline. It is used in the manufacture of glass, porcelain, china, enamelware; as a bond in the production of abrasive wheels; also in artificial teeth, scouring soaps and powders, and paint fillers. Amazon stone is cut and polished for gem and ornamental purposes.

Plagioclase Feldspars

These feldspars are sometimes called the *soda-lime* feldspars. They crystallize in the triclinic system, forming an isomorphous series with albite ($NaAlSi_3O_8$) and anorthite ($CaAl_2Si_2O_8$) as the end members. The chemical compositions of the various members of the series vary within the limits indicated in the tabulation at the top of page 410.

Five to fifteen per cent of $KAlSi_3O_8$ may be present in the various members of the series, especially in the *acid plagioclases,* that is, in the members in which the albite molecule predominates.

There are two modifications of the plagioclase feldspars depending upon the temperature of formation. The high-temperature modification occurs as phenocrysts in extrusive rocks, the low-temperature modification in plutonic igneous and metamorphic rocks.

The plagioclase feldspars possess good cleavages parallel to the basal and brachypinacoids, which are inclined to each other at angles of about 86°. This inclined or oblique cleavage serves to differentiate these from orthoclase, which possesses a rectangular cleavage. Twinning according

$NaAlSi_3O_8$(Ab)

Ab per cent	An per cent	
100	0	Albite (0–10)
90	10	
80	20	Oligoclase (10–30)
70	30	
60	40	Andesine (30–50)
50	50	
40	60	Labradorite (50–70)
30	70	
20	80	Bytownite (70–90)
10	90	
0	100	Anorthite (90–100)

$CaAl_2Si_2O_8$(An)

to the albite law (see below) is very characteristic for this group. The twinning laws for orthoclase may also be observed.

Table 41 shows clearly the progressive changes in the physical and chemical properties of the various members of this group.

TABLE 41

Name	Per cent $NaAlSi_3O_8$	Al_2O_3	SiO_2	Na_2O	CaO	Specific gravity	Extinction angles: Basal Pinacoids	Extinction angles: Brachy- Pinacoids	Cleavage angles
Albite	95	20.4	67.3	11.2	1.1	2.61	+3½°	+18°	86°26′
Oligoclase	80	23.1	63.3	9.3	4.3	2.64	+1°	+6°	86°18′
Andesine	60	26.6	58.1	6.9	8.4	2.67	−4°	−8°	86°10′
Labradorite	40	30.0	53.0	4.6	12.4	2.70	−10°	−23°	86°03′
Bytownite	20	33.4	48.0	2.3	16.3	2.72	−23°	−34°	85°56′
Anorthite	5	35.8	44.4	0.6	19.2	2.75	−37°	−37½°	85°48′

The intermediate members are important constituents of many igneous rocks and more common than either albite or anorthite. They are rarely well crystallized but can usually be recognized by the striations on the basal pinacoid, due to multiple twinning according to the albite law. Only albite, labradorite, and anorthite will be described.

ALBITE (*Soda Feldspar*), **$NaAlSi_3O_8$(Ab).**

Triclinic, pinacoidal class—$\bar{1}$. Crystals are usually small and often similar in development to those of orthoclase (Figs. 685 and 686). They may also be tabular and elongated parallel to the *b* axis (Fig. 689). Twins are very common, single individuals being rare. There are two important laws.

Fig. 685.

Fig. 686.

Fig. 687.

Fig. 688.

Albite Law. This involves the brachypinacoid acting as the twinning plane and yields simple contact and repeated twins (Figs. 687 and 688). The polysynthetic twins according to this law show striations on the basal pinacoid which extend parallel to the edge between the basal and brachypinacoids.

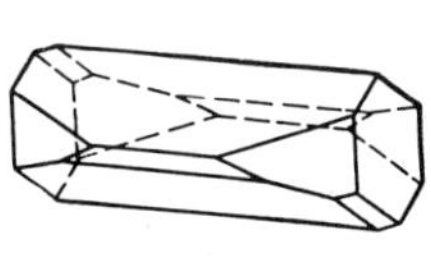

Fig. 689.

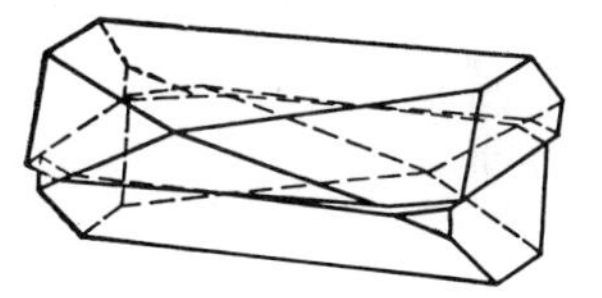

Fig. 690.

Pericline Law. The *b* axis acts as the twinning axis (Fig. 690). Contact and polysynthetic twins are observed, the latter being characterized by striations on the brachypinacoid.

Albite also occurs in lamellar and granular masses, the laminae being often curved and divergent.

Perfect basal and brachypinacoidal cleavages, *inclined* at 86°26′. Uneven fracture. Hardness, 6. Specific gravity, 2.6. Usually colorless or gray; rarely colored. Transparent to translucent. α 1.525, β 1.529, γ 1.536, (+); $2V = 74°; r < v$. Some varieties show a bluish opalescence and are called *moonstone* (see page 408).

$NaAlSi_3O_8$. Generally contains some potassium and calcium. Fuses to a colorless or white glass. Colors the flame yellow. Not acted upon by acids.

As a rock mineral, albite is not so abundant as the other plagioclases. It occurs, nevertheless, in many gneisses and other crystalline schists, also in acid igneous rocks, such as granite, syenite, trachyte, and other eruptive rocks; more rarely in limestone and dolomite. Frequently found in pegmatite veins, sometimes as the platy variety *cleavelandite*. Some of the associates of albite are chlorite, sphene, adularia, axinite, beryl, tourmaline, quartz, chrysoberyl, and apatite. It occurs often intergrown with microcline and is then known as *perthite* (Fig. 691). *Peristerite* is a variety showing a play of colors.

Fig. 691. Perthitic intergrowth of microcline and albite. Georgetown, Maine. (*After Bastin.*)

Fig. 692. Albite. Amelia Court House, Virginia.

Some important localities are the Saint Gotthard district, Switzerland; various places in Tirol; Rauris, Salzburg; Dauphiné, France; the Ural Mountains; Paris, Maine; Haddam and Branchville, Connecticut; Chesterfield, Massachusetts; Pikes Peak, Colorado; Amelia Court House, Virginia (Fig. 692).

Sunstone or *aventurine oligoclase* is reddish in color with bright-yellow or red reflections from included thin scales of hematite.

LABRADORITE (*Lime-soda Feldspar*), $Ab_{50}An_{50}$ **to** $Ab_{30}An_{70}$.

Triclinic, pinacoidal class—$\bar{1}$. Well-developed crystals are rare. In habit they are usually tabular parallel to the brachypinacoid. The twinning is the same as for albite. Generally observed in cleavable or granular masses.

Perfect basal and brachypinacoidal cleavages, making an angle of 86°3′. Uneven fracture. Hardness, 6. Specific gravity, 2.7. Gray brown, or greenish in color. Often shows a beautiful play of yellowish, bluish, greenish, or reddish colors on the brachypinacoid. This *labradorescence* is due to a fine lamellar structure or to microscopic inclusions or to both. Translucent. α 1.559, β 1.563, γ 1.568, (+); $2V = 79°$; for a composition of $Ab_{40}An_{60}$.

$Ab_{50}An_{50}$ to $Ab_{30}An_{70}$. Fuses to a colorless or white glass. Colors the flame yellow. Decomposed with difficulty by hydrochloric acid.

Occurs in basic igneous rocks, such as gabbro, norite, basalt, diabase, and andesite. Found on Mount Etna; in Rumania; Sweden; Greenland; varieties showing an excellent play of colors are common on the coast of Labrador, also on the Isle of St. Paul; in the Adirondack Mountains, New York; the Wichita Mountains, Arkansas; and elsewhere.

Varieties showing a good play of colors are used for ornamental and decorative purposes. They are sometimes termed *Labrador spar.*

Anorthite (*Lime Feldspar*), **$CaAl_2Si_2O_8$(An)**.

Triclinic, pinacoidal class—$\bar{1}$. Crystals are usually prismatic parallel to the *c* axis or tabular parallel to the basal pinacoid; often very complex. Twins occur according to the laws common on albite. Also observed in cleavable, compact, and lamellar masses.

Perfect basal and brachypinacoidal cleavages, inclined at an angle of 85°48′. Conchoidal to uneven fracture. Hardness, 6. Specific gravity, 2.7 to 2.8. Commonly white, colorless, or grayish; more rarely bluish, yellowish, or reddish. Vitreous luster, inclining to pearly on the cleavages. Transparent to translucent. α 1.567, β 1.584, γ 1.588, (−); $2V = 77°$.

$CaAl_2Si_2O_8$. Usually contains small amounts of sodium and, at times, of potassium, magnesium, and iron. Fuses with difficulty to a colorless glass. Decomposed by hydrochloric acid with a separation of gelatinous silica.

Anorthite occurs as an important constituent of basic igneous rocks, such as gabbros and basalts; also as a contact mineral and in meteorites. Excellent crystals are found on Mount Vesuvius; the Island of Miyake, Japan; Iceland; the Monzoni district, Tirol; Rumania; the Ural Mountains; Franklin, New Jersey.

Feldspathoid Group

In this group are included several minerals which are closely related chemically to the feldspars, but which contain a lower percentage of silica, SiO_2. These minerals are called *feldspathoids*. They are important rock minerals and are formed from magmas which contain insufficient silica to produce the feldspars. The feldspathoids are never associated with primary quartz.

The most important of these minerals include the following:

Nepheline	$Na(AlSiO_4)$	Hexagonal
Cancrinite	$Na_3CaCO_3(AlSiO_4)_3.nH_2O$	Hexagonal
Sodalite	$Na_4Cl(AlSiO_4)_3$	Cubic
Lazurite	$Na_5S(AlSiO_4)_3$	Cubic
Leucite	$K(AlSi_2O_6)$	Pseudocubic

The mineral analcime (page 419) is sometimes classified as a feldspathoid and not as a zeolite.

NEPHELINE (*Nephelite*), $Na(AlSiO_4)$.

Hexagonal, hexagonal pyramidal class—6. Crystals are short prismatic or tabular. Commonly in compact masses or as disseminated grains.

Imperfect prismatic and basal cleavages. Conchoidal to uneven fracture. Hardness, 5 to 6. Specific gravity, 2.55 to 2.65. Colorless, white, yellowish, greenish, gray, or reddish. Greasy luster on cleavages, otherwise vitreous. ω 1.542, ϵ 1.538, (−). Transparent to opaque.

There are two varieties:

Nepheline Proper. This includes the light-colored, glassy occurrences showing in many instances a definite crystal outline. Common in the more recent eruptive rocks. Transparent to translucent.

Elaeolite. This is a massive or granular variety and rarely shows a definite outline. Gray or more highly colored—green, red, brown, or blue. Cloudy or opaque. Greasy luster. Common in the older plutonic rocks, such as syenites, phonolites, and basalts.

$Na(AlSiO_4)$. Composition varies greatly. May contain an excess of silica and some potassium, so that the formula may be written as $(Na,K)_8Al_8Si_9O_{34}$. Small amounts of calcium, lithium, and chlorine may also be present. Fuses easily to a colorless glass. Gelatinizes with hydrochloric acid, yielding on evaporation cubes of NaCl. Alters readily to hydronepheline, sodalite, muscovite, cancrinite, analcime, kaolinite, or garnet. Pseudomorphous after leucite.

Nepheline is commonly associated with feldspar, cancrinite, biotite, apatite, sodalite, corundum, and zircon; but not with primary quartz. Some localities are Mount Vesuvius; Katzenbuckel, Baden; Laacher See, Rhenish Prussia; southern Norway; the Ural Mountains; South Africa; Brazil; near Lakefield, Ontario, Canada; Litchfield, Maine; Cripple Creek, Colorado; Magnet Cove, Arkansas; Salem, Massachusetts.

Nepheline is an important constituent of nepheline syenite, which is mined in large quantities at Lakefield, Ontario, and is used as a substitute for feldspar in the manufacture of glass and ceramic products.

Cancrinite, $Na_3CaCO_3(AlSiO_4)_3.nH_2O$.

Hexagonal, hexagonal pyramidal class—6. Crystals are columnar or prismatic, but rare. Usually in compact, lamellar, columnar, or disseminated masses.

Perfect prismatic cleavage. Uneven fracture. Hardness, 5 to 6. Specific gravity, 2.45. Generally colored; lemon to brownish yellow, reddish, green; sometimes gray, white, or colorless. Pearly luster on cleavages, elsewhere vitreous to greasy. ω 1.524, ϵ 1.496, (−). Transparent to translucent.

$Na_3CaCO_3(AlSiO_4)_3.nH_2O$. Composition varies; $CaCO_3$ may be replaced by $CaSO_4$, $CaCl_2$, $NaCO_3$, $Na_2CO_3.3H_2O$. Fuses easily with intumescence to a white blebby glass. Upon ignition turns white and yields water. Effervesces with hydrochloric acid and gelatinizes on heating.

Commonly associated with sodalite, nepheline, biotite, feldspar, sphene, and apatite. May be a primary constituent of igneous rocks, although in most cases it is secondary, resulting from the alteration of nepheline. Occurs in nepheline syenites at Barkevik, Norway; Miask, Ural Mountains; Finland; Sweden; Rumania; Laacher See, Germany; Province of Quebec, Canada; Gunnison County, Colorado; Litchfield, Maine.

Cancrinite is of no importance commercially.

Sodalite, $Na_4Cl(AlSiO_4)_3$.

Cubic, hextetrahedral class—$\bar{4}\ 3m$. Crystals are not common; when observed, usually rhombic dodecahedrons. Generally in compact, cleavable, nodular, or disseminated masses.

Distinct dodecahedral cleavage. Uneven to conchoidal fracture. Hardness, 5 to 6. Specific gravity, 2.2 to 2.4. Vitreous luster on crystal faces, greasy on cleavages. $n = 1.483$. Usually blue in color; also white, green, reddish, or gray. Transparent to opaque. Colored varieties turn white when heated.

$Na_4Cl(AlSiO_4)_3$. Approximate composition: Al_2O_3 31.6, Na_2O 25.6, SiO_2 37.2, Cl 7.3 per cent. Fuses with intumescence to a colorless glass. Gelatinizes with hydrochloric acid.

Commonly associated with nepheline, cancrinite, leucite, feldspar, and zircon, but not with primary quartz. Occurs at Miask, Ural Mountains; Mount Vesuvius; Norway; Laacher See, Germany; Bolivia; provinces of Quebec, British Columbia, and Ontario, Canada; Litchfield, Maine; Montana.

Sodalite is of no importance commercially.

Lazurite (*Lapis Lazuli, Native Ultramarine*), $\mathbf{Na_5S(AlSiO_4)_3}$.

Cubic, hextetrahedral class—$\bar{4}\ 3m$. Crystals are rare, either dodecahedral or cubic in habit. Usually as irregular grains or in masses containing disseminated pyrite.

Uneven fracture. Hardness, 5 to 5.5. Specific gravity, 2.4 to 2.5. Vitreous to greasy luster. $n = 1.50$. Deep to azure blue in color, sometimes violet to greenish blue. Opaque to translucent.

$Na_5S(AlSiO_4)_3$. Composition varies, may contain Cl and SO_4. Fuses easily to a white blebby glass. Gelatinizes with hydrochloric acid, loses color, and evolves an odor of hydrogen sulfide.

Lazurite is a contact mineral and occurs in crystalline limestones. The principal localities are Persia; Turkestan; Afghanistan; the southern end of Lake Baikal, Siberia; Ovalle, Chile; Cascade Canyon, San Bernardino County, California.

Lazurite is highly valued for ornaments, mosaics, and vases. It was formerly used as a pigment in oil painting. Lazurite is also used for gem purposes.

LEUCITE, $\mathbf{K(AlSi_2O_6)}$.

Dimorphous, tetragonal and cubic. At ordinary temperatures, crystals are pseudocubic, in that they show what is apparently a tetragonal trisoctahedron; at times, also, the cube and rhombic dodecahedron. Optically, the crystals consist of tetragonal twin lamellae, which can sometimes be recognized by the striations on the faces. Heated to a temperature of about 600°C., the lamellae disappear and the crystals become isotropic and truly cubic. Generally found in well-developed and disseminated crystals (Fig. 693); also in rounded grains.

Fig. 693. Leucite (light) in basalt. Tavolato, near Rome, Italy.

Conchoidal fracture. Hardness, 5.5 to 6. Specific gravity, 2.5. White, gray, yellowish, or reddish in color. Vitreous to greasy luster. Translucent, rarely transparent. Usually weakly doubly refractive; the indices of refraction vary from 1.508 to 1.509.

$K(AlSi_2O_6)$. K_2O 21.5, Al_2O_3 23.5, SiO_2 55.0 per cent. Sodium, lithium, and rubidium may replace some of the potassium. Infusible. Alters to analcime, nepheline, orthoclase, and kaolin.

Leucite occurs usually in extrusive rocks. The principal associates are sanidine, augite, nepheline, and olivine. Some localities are Mount Vesuvius and the vicinity of Rome; Laacher See, Rhenish Prussia; Kaiserstuhl, Baden; Saxony; Brazil; Leucite Hills, Wyoming; Highwood Mountains, Montana; Magnet Cove, Arkansas.

At present, leucite is of no importance commercially.

SCAPOLITE (*Wernerite*), $n\mathbf{Na_4Cl(AlSi_3O_8)_3} + m\mathbf{Ca_4CO_3(Al_2Si_2O_8)_3}$.

Tetragonal, tetragonal bipyramidal class—$4m$. Commonly as thick, coarse, prismatic crystals, often large with dull and uneven faces. Crystals sometimes appear as though partially fused. The common forms are the prisms (m and a) and bipyramids (o and d) of the first and second orders; more rarely the bipyramid of the third order (s) is observed (Figs.

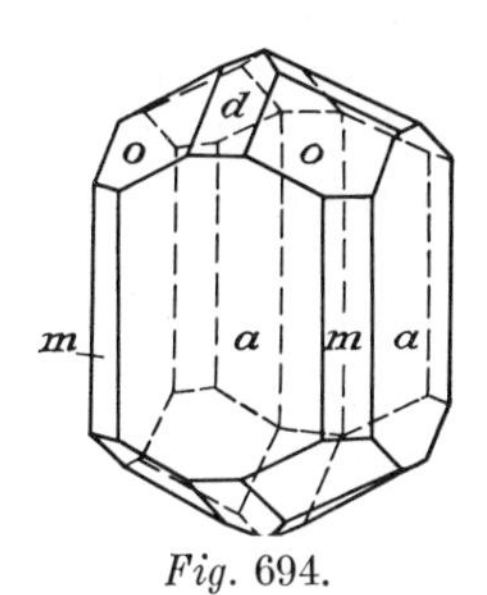

Fig. 694.

Fig. 695. Scapolite. Ottawa County, Quebec.

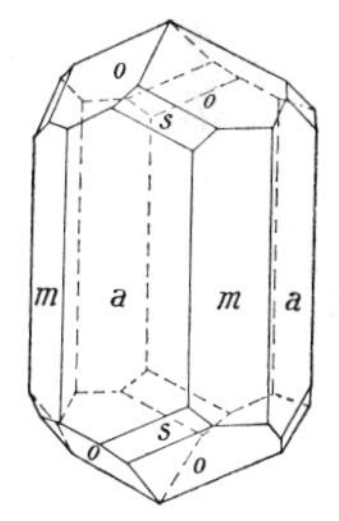

Fig. 696.

694 to 696). Occurs also in fibrous, coarse- to fine-granular, columnar, and compact masses.

Prismatic cleavage. Conchoidal fracture. Hardness, 5 to 6. Specific gravity, 2.6 to 2.8. Colorless, white, gray, greenish, bluish, or reddish. Vitreous to greasy luster. Translucent. May show luminescence. ω 1.550, ϵ 1.542, (−) for *marialite*; ω 1.607, ϵ 1.571, (−) for *meionite*.

The composition varies greatly between *marialite*, $Na_4Cl(AlSi_3O_8)_3$, and *meionite*, $Ca_4CO_3(Al_2Si_2O_8)_3$. In marialite, SO_4 and CO_3 may replace Cl; and in meionite, Cl and SO_4 the CO_3. Some scapolites are readily decomposed by hydrochloric acid. All are quite easily fusible with intumescence. The scapolites alter to kaolin, jade, epidote, muscovite, biotite, albite, and various zeolites.

Commonly the result of metamorphism and frequently found in granular limestones near the contact with igneous rocks; also in crystalline schists and volcanic ejectamenta. Typical associates are pyroxenes, amphiboles, apatite, garnet, sphene, zircon, and biotite. Some localities are Arendal, Norway; Pargas, Finland; Madagascar; Laacher See, Germany; Mount Vesuvius; Ripon and Grenville, Quebec, and various places in Ontario, Canada; Bolton, Massachusetts; various places in northern New York; Franklin, New Jersey.

Sometimes used as a gem.

Zeolite Group

The zeolites are secondary minerals, being hydrated silicates of aluminum, calcium, sodium, and potassium. The water of hydration is peculiar in that it is lost gradually and continuously upon heating, rather than at a definite temperature. The water thus lost is readily regained upon exposure to water vapor. Moreover, dehydration causes no change in the general crystalline structure, unless the water is almost completely removed. The zeolites also possess the property of base exchange. This refers to the easy substitution of various metals for the alkali element originally present. This property is the basis of the *zeolite process* to soften water; see Permutit, below. The zeolites have structures with a three-dimensional framework of linked $(Si,Al)O_4$ tetrahedrons, with (Si,Al) and O being present in the ratio of 1 : 2.

The zeolites are commonly found in good crystals, have comparatively low specific gravities, 2 to 2.4, and are rather soft, the hardness varying from 3.5 to 5.5. Although generally colorless and transparent or translucent, they may be light-colored, due to the presence of pigments. All zeolites are readily decomposed by hydrochloric acid, and on the evaporation of the acid may gelatinize. They result from the decomposition of such minerals as nepheline, leucite, sodalite, and the feldspars. They are rarely found disseminated but usually in cracks, crevices, or cavities in basic igneous rocks, such as basalt, diabase, and phonolites; less frequently in granite and mica schist. Their common associates are calcite, datolite, and pectolite.

Although the zeolite group is a large one, only the following zeolites will be discussed: natrolite, analcime, stilbite, and chabazite.

Natrolite (*Needle Zeolite*), $Na_2Al_2Si_3O_{10}.2H_2O$.

Orthorhombic, pyramidal class—*mm*2. Crystals are slender prismatic and nearly square in cross section; also acicular and arranged in radial or interlacing groups (Fig. 697). Occurs also in fibrous, granular, or compact masses.

Perfect prismatic cleavage. Hardness, 5 to 5.5. Specific gravity, 2.2 to 2.3. Colorless or white; also reddish, yellowish, or greenish. Transparent to translucent. Vitreous to silky luster. α 1.480, β 1.482, γ 1.493, (+); $2V = 63°$; $r < v$.

$Na_2Al_2Si_3O_{10}.2H_2O$. Na_2O 16.3, Al_2O_3 26.8, SiO_2 47.4, H_2O 9.5 per cent. May contain some calcium and potassium. Fuses easily to colorless glass. Gelatinizes with acids. Yields water in a closed tube.

Occurs in cracks and cavities in basic igneous rocks. Common associates are chabazite, analcime, apophyllite, stilbite, calcite, and datolite.

Some notable localities are Teplitz and Aussig, Bohemia; Puy de Dome, France; Fassathal, Tirol; Hohentwiel and Kaiserstuhl, Baden; Kimberley, South Africa; Nova Scotia; Bergen Hill, New Jersey; San Benito County, California; Lake Superior copper district.

Fig. 697. Natrolite. Paterson, New Jersey.

Permutit is the trade name given to a synthetic zeolite with the approximate composition $Na_2Al_2Si_2O_6.6H_2O$, which is similar to that of natrolite. The sodium in the permutit can be replaced by the calcium, magnesium, manganese, and iron in hard water. The original sodium permutit can then be regenerated by treatment with a strong solution of sodium chloride. Permutit is used to soften water and in sugar refining.

ANALCIME (*Analcite*), **$NaAlSi_2O_6.H_2O$.**

Cubic, hexoctahedral class—$4/m\ 3\ 2/m$. Generally in well-developed

Fig. 698. Analcime (tetragonal trisoctahedron). Lake Superior copper district.

Fig. 699.

tetragonal trisoctahedrons (Fig. 698); sometimes in combination with the cube (Fig. 699). Crystals are usually quite small, although some measuring a foot in diameter have been observed. Occurs also in compact, granular, or earthy masses.

Uneven to conchoidal fracture. Hardness, 5 to 5.5. Specific gravity, 2.2 to 2.4. Colorless or white; also yellowish, reddish, or greenish. Viterous luster. Transparent to nearly opaque. $n = 1.487$.

$NaAlSi_2O_6.H_2O$. Na_2O 14.1, Al_2O_3 23.2, SiO_2 54.5, H_2O 8.2 per cent. Potassium and calcium may be present. Chemically it is closely related to leucite and is sometimes considered a member of the feldspathoid group (see page 413). Fuses to a colorless glass. Decomposes with hydrochloric acid with the separation of silica.

Analcime is commonly a secondary mineral occurring with the other zeolites, calcite, datolite, native copper, magnetite, and prehnite, in basalt, diabase, granite, and gneiss; also as a primary constituent of feldspathoidal basalts. Some localities are the Cyclopean Islands, near Sicily; Tirol; Bohemia; Victoria, Australia; Iceland; various places in Nova Scotia; Bergen Hill, New Jersey; the Lake Superior copper district; Table Mountain, Colorado.

STILBITE (*Desmine*), $(Ca,Na_2)Al_2Si_7O_{18}.7H_2O$.

Monoclinic, prismatic class—$2/m$. Simple crystals are unknown; usually as tabular penetration twins. Very commonly several twin

Fig. 700. Stilbite. Viesch, Switzerland.

crystals are arranged nearly parallel, forming sheaf-like aggregates (Fig. 700). Occurs also in radial or globular aggregates.

Clinopinacoid cleavage. Uneven fracture. Hardness, 3 to 4. Specific gravity, 2.1 to 2.2. Vitreous to pearly luster. α 1.494, β 1.498, γ 1.500, $(-)$; $2V$ is about 33°; $v > r$. Transparent to translucent. Colorless or white, also brown, yellow, reddish.

$(Ca,Na_2)Al_2Si_7O_{18}.7H_2O$. Composition varies; may contain some potassium. Exfoliates, swells up, and fuses to a white glass. Decomposed by hydrochloric acid with a separation of silica.

Stilbite occurs with other zeolites, datolite, and calcite, in cavities in amygdaloidal basalts and related rocks; also in granites and crystalline schists and in ore deposits. Some localities are Deccan Trap area, India;

Tirol; Sweden; Iceland; Switzerland; Kilpatrick, Scotland; Nova Scotia; Bergen Hill, New Jersey; the Lake Superior copper district; Table Mountain, Colorado.

CHABAZITE, $CaAl_2Si_4O_{12}.6H_2O$.

Hexagonal, ditrigonal scalenohedral class—$\bar{3}\ 2/m$. Generally in cube-like rhombohedrons. Sometimes crystals are complex or twinned. Occurs also in compact masses.

Rhombohedral cleavage. Uneven fracture. Hardness, 4 to 5. Specific gravity, 2.1 to 2.2. Colorless, white, reddish, yellowish, or brown. Vitreous luster. Transparent to translucent. Anomalous optical properties; generally uniaxial, either positive or negative with indices of refraction from 1.478 to 1.482; sometimes biaxial, positive, with $2V$ small.

$CaAl_2Si_4O_{12}.6H_2O$. Composition varies considerably. May contain potassium and sodium, replacing some of the calcium. Fuses with intumescence to a nearly opaque, blebby glass. Decomposed by hydrochloric acid with a separation of silica. Associated with the other zeolites, it generally occurs in cavities in basalts, phonolite, and related rocks. Some localities are the Giant's Causeway, Ireland; Aussig, Bohemia; Idar-Oberstein, Germany; Faroe Islands; Greenland; Iceland; Nova Scotia; Bergen Hill, New Jersey; Somerville, Massachusetts; Goble Station, Oregon; Table Mountain, Colorado.

17 | Gemstones[1]

A considerable number of minerals occur with beautiful colors; some are transparent and exceedingly brilliant, while others possess a pleasing luster or sheen. Minerals of this character have, from the earliest times, been eagerly sought after for personal adornment and ornamentation. They have long been called *gems* and *precious stones*. In fact, it is well known that among primitive peoples many of these gem minerals were supposed to possess peculiar properties. Some were believed to bring good luck to the wearer, while others were thought to be useful in warding off or curing certain diseases.

Fig. 701. Max Bauer (1844-1917). Professor of mineralogy and petrography in the University of Marburg (1884–1917). Distinguished authority on gemstones.

Characteristics of Gems. The outstanding qualities of a gemstone are (1) *splendor* or *beauty*, (2) *durability*, (3) *rarity*, (4) *fashion*, and (5) *portability*. The beauty of a gem depends upon its transparency or clarity, brilliancy, color, luster, and fire. In most cases, these qualities are seen to best advantage when the stone is cut and polished. Red and blue diamonds, for example, embody all these qualities to a marked extent. Sometimes the beauty of a gem does not depend upon all, but only upon one or more, of the above properties. Thus, the beauty of the ruby is due to its excellent color, luster, and transparency. The ruby is, however, almost totally lacking in fire. The opal is attractive principally on account of its fascinating play of colors. In the case of

[1] For a more comprehensive discussion, consult E. H. Kraus and C. B. Slawson, "Gems and Gem Materials," 5th ed., McGraw-Hill Book Company, Inc., New York, 1947.

turquois, the beauty depends mainly upon a pleasing color. Water-white diamonds are exceptionally beautiful, but they are devoid of color, their splendor being due to their brilliancy, luster, and fire.

Many minerals may be pleasing to the eye but may not be very serviceable as gems because of their inferior hardness. They do not wear well, that is, they lack durability. In order to serve to advantage as a gem, a mineral must be hard. It must resist abrasion. When worn on the hand, a stone is subject to the action of the ever-present dust, which commonly contains finely divided quartz particles and, hence, is hard. The stone is also subject to sudden shocks and knocks. Soft stones, even though they may take a beautiful polish and possess other necessary gem properties, may become dull and worthless in a very short time. Stones of such inferior hardness serve fairly well in pins and brooches. A gem to be durable must, therefore, be hard, preferably harder than quartz. In fact, durability plays a prominent role in the classification of gems. Those which are generally classed as the distinctly precious stones—diamond, emerald, ruby, sapphire—all possess superior hardness, being decidedly harder than quartz. Opal and turquois are softer than quartz.

Fig. 702. George F. Kunz (1856–1932). Author of many publications on gemstones. (*Photograph by the Champlain Studios, Inc., New York City.*)

While durability is a fundamental quality of a gem, frequency of occurrence has much to do with determining the value of a mineral for gem purposes. Many minerals occur rather abundantly in nature, but only rarely are some of them found in such condition as to warrant their use as gems. Thus, the mineral beryl is fairly common. It occurs in large crystals, some of which weigh several tons, but the colors are then usually dull and the crystals are not transparent. The green transparent variety, called the emerald, is, however, quite rare and is accordingly very highly prized. There are other transparent varieties of beryl, such as golden beryl and aquamarine, but these are more frequently found and are not so valuable as the rarer emerald. Other things being equal, the rarer the stone the greater its value, for there are many people who will always desire that which is rare and exceptional and are willing to pay enormous prices in order to obtain those gems which others cannot afford.

Fashion and style exert a definite influence upon the favor with which a gem is received. Indeed, it frequently happens that, as the result of a change in fashion or style, an excellent gem mineral—excellent with respect to the various properties referred to above—is suddenly discarded for some new and perhaps inferior stone. During the last 50 years, many stones have thus come into favor, most of which are of bright color. Hence, the number of minerals which are to be counted as gems is subject to change, the tendency being toward an extension of the list.

One of the outstanding characteristics of gems is the ease with which they can be carried from place to place, that is, their portability. This is, of course, principally due to the fact that comparatively large sums of money are generally represented by relatively small volumes of the gemstones. For centuries gems have been considered a desirable form of investment, especially during periods of economic and political instability.

List of Gems. The minerals listed below are used as gems or ornamental stones. *They are all described in the text,* and in each case the page number is indicated. The special terms by which varieties of gem quality have been known are also given.

Important Gemstones

Diamond, 267	
Corundum, 299	(*Ruby, Sapphire, White Sapphire, Golden Sapphire, Oriental Emerald, Oriental Topaz, Oriental Amethyst*)
Beryl, 379	(*Emerald, Aquamarine, Yellow or Golden Beryl, Morganite*)
Topaz, 372	(*Precious Topaz*)
Garnet, 363 to 366	
Grossularite	(*Hessonite, Cinnamon Stone*)
Pyrope	(*Cape Ruby, Arizona Ruby*)
Spessartite	
Almandite	(*Carbuncle, Rhodolite*)
Uvarovite	
Andradite	(*Topazolite, Demantoid*)
Zircon, 366	(*Hyacinth, Jacinth, Jargon*)
Opal, 313	(*Precious Opal, White Opal, Black Opal, Fire Opal*)
Quartz, 293	(*Rock Crystal, Amethyst, Rose Quartz, Smoky Quartz, Cairngorm Stone, Topaz Quartz, Spanish Topaz, Citrine, Aventurine, Rutilated Quartz, Cat's-eye, Tiger's-eye, Chalcedony, Carnelian, Sard, Chrysoprase, Heliotrope, Bloodstone, Agate, Onyx*)
Jade, 388	(*Nephrite, Jadeite*)
Chrysoberyl, 308	(*Alexandrite, Cat's-eye, Cymophane*)
Tourmaline, 381	(*Rubellite, Indicolite, Brazilian Emerald*)
Olivine, 363	(*Peridot*)
Spinel, 304	(*Ruby Spinel, Rubicelle, Blue Spinel*)
Turquois, 355	
Feldspar, 405	
Orthoclase	(*Moonstone*)
Microcline	(*Amazon Stone, Amazonite*)
Albite	(*Moonstone*)
Labradorite	(*Labrador Spar*)
Lazurite, 416	(*Lapis Lazuli*)

Other Gems and Ornamental Stones

(Arranged alphabetically)

Andalusite, 368	
Apatite, 351	
Azurite, 337	(*Azurmalachite*)
Calcite, 326	(*Satin Spar, Onyx Marble, Mexican Marble*)
Chrysocolla, 383	
Cordierite, 380	(*Iolite, Disthene*)
Datolite, 373	
Epidote, 376	
Fluorite, 322	(*Blue-john*)
Gypsum, 345	(*Satin Spar*)
Hematite, 301	
Kyanite, 369	
Malachite and Azurite, 336	(*Malachite Matrix, Azurmalachite*)
Pyrite, 285	
Pyroxene, 383	
Hypersthene	
Diopside	
Spodumene	(*Hiddenite, Kunzite*)
Rhodonite, 388	
Rutile, 309	
Scapolite, 417	
Serpentine, 402	(*Precious Serpentine*)
Sphene, 374	(*Titanite*)
Staurolite, 371	
Vesuvianite, 378	(*Californite*)

Popular Names of Gems. Many of the names applied to gem minerals are of ancient origin and, hence, were in use long before mineralogy was developed as a science. Considerable ambiguity has arisen, therefore, by the simultaneous use of popular terms by jewelers and of scientific names by mineralogists. Indeed, many of the popular terms are intentionally misleading. Thus, yellow quartz or citrine is commonly called in the trade *Spanish*, *Brazilian*, or *Oriental topaz*. Popular names have frequently been based upon color; hence, it is not surprising to find the term *ruby* incorporated in several of the popular names given to gem stones of a red color: *ruby spinel*, *balas ruby*, and *rubicelle* for red spinel; *cape ruby* and *Arizona ruby* for pyrope garnet; and *rubellite* for red tourmaline. Popular names of this character suggest relations with more valuable stones which are not warranted by the facts. Obviously, all ambiguity and misconceptions would be avoided if only the scientific names of the mineralogist were used.

Methods of Identification. Rough and uncut gemstones can be readily determined by means of their physical properties in the same way as other minerals. This usually involves the use of a set of mineral tables, such as are found on pages 493 to 661. When the stones are cut and polished, the properties generally used for determination are color, index of refraction, dispersion, fracture or cleavage as revealed around the prongs of the setting, inclusions, and dichroism. The index of refraction can be easily and quickly determined by the use of a direct-reading refractometer (Figs. 351 to 354, pages 127 and 128). The diamondscope (Fig. 703) is very useful in examining unmounted or mounted cut gems for inclusions, cracks, other flaws, and the character of the cutting. The instrument is a binocular microscope with a substage which illuminates the stone uniformly from all sides. The stone is held with tongs which can be easily moved and rotated.

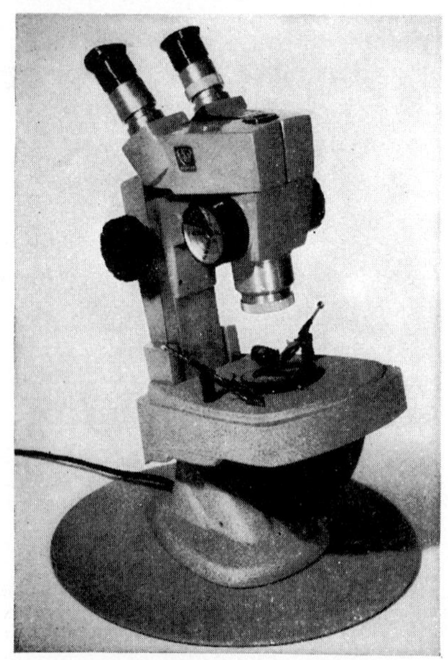

Fig. 703. Diamondscope. (*Courtesy of the Gemological Institute of America.*)

If it is necessary to determine the hardness of a gem, great care should be exercised not to injure a soft but otherwise perfectly good stone. Hardness pencils and the hardness wheel (Figs. 316 and 317, page 102) are well adapted for the accurate testing of the hardness of gems. When stones are unmounted, a determination of the specific gravity can often be made the basis of an accurate recognition of the gem under consideration (page 108).

Size and Weight of Gems. In the sale of gem minerals four units of weight are used, namely, (1) *carat,* (2) *gram,* (3) *pennyweight,* and (4) *grain.* In addition, some gemstones are sold in terms of size, as expressed in *millimeters* or *inches.* Of these units, only the carat needs to be defined and accordingly it will be discussed in some detail.

Carat. The carat now in use in the principal countries of the world is 200 milligrams or two-tenths of a gram, 0.200 gram. It is often called the *metric carat.* It was adopted as the standard in the United States in 1913. The value of a gemstone, per carat, generally increases rapidly with weight.

Originally grains or leguminous seeds were used as units of weight for gems, and naturally they were not of uniform size. Consequently down to comparatively recent times the weight of the carat varied greatly in different gem centers. Thus, for many years it was taken as 0.2053 gram in London, while in Florence it was 0.1972 gram, in Madras 0.2073,

Amsterdam 0.2057, and so on. In 1871 an attempt was made to establish as the standard the "international carat" of 0.205 gram. Later the metric carat was proposed, which is now the generally accepted standard.

Before the introduction of the metric carat, the weight of a gem was expressed by a series of fractions, such as 2 carats and ½, ¼, $\frac{1}{16}$, and $\frac{1}{64}$ carat. In the metric system this weight so clumsily expressed by the older method is simplified to 2.828 carats, the sum of the fractional parts of a carat being indicated by the more convenient decimals.

The weight of a diamond is often expressed in *points*. Thus, a stone weighing 65 points actually weighs 0.65 carat. That is, a *point* is 0.01 carat.

The application of the term "carat" as a unit of weight must not be confused with its use in indicating fineness or purity of the gold in which gems are mounted. In this latter connection a carat means one twenty-fourth part. Thus, pure gold is said to be 24 carats fine. The amount of baser metal alloyed with gold is indicated by a proportional decrease in the number of carats fineness. That is, 18-carat gold is 18 twenty-fourths gold and 6 twenty-fourths base metal, while 12-carat gold is 12 twenty-fourths, or half, gold. When used in this sense, the term is commonly spelled *karat* and abbreviated as K. Thus, an 18-carat ring may be stamped 18K.

The carat is the unit of weight for the diamond, natural and synthetic rubies and sapphires, emerald, aquamarine, tourmaline, zircon, spinel, precious opal, superior opal doublets, and precious garnets. Pearls are sometimes sold by the carat.

Gram. The following gem minerals are commonly sold by the gram: lapis lazuli, Spanish topaz, moonstone, amethyst, and superior grades of malachite.

Pennyweight. In some countries the minerals listed under gram are sold by the pennyweight (troy), which equals 24 grains, or 1.56 grams.

Grain. Pearls are commonly sold by the grain. A *pearl grain* is a twentieth of a gram; hence, four pearl grains equal one carat. The pearl grain (0.05 gram) is not the same as the troy grain (0.0648 gram).

Millimeter or *Inch.* Minerals such as amazonite, garnet, most of the varieties of quartz, malachite, Swiss lapis, and the cheaper grades of opal and opal doublets are sold according to size, as expressed in millimeters or inches.

Cutting of Gems. Although gem minerals are frequently found in nature in beautiful and well-developed crystals, they are rarely adapted for use as gems without suitable cutting and polishing. While crystals may show excellent reflections, the full optical splendor of such gem minerals is best brought out by cutting or grinding the specimen into symmetrical shapes, which will allow the stone to appear as brilliant as possible, show its best color, and exhibit the maximum amount of fire. This process of cutting involving the production of artificial faces or *facets*, as these plain surfaces are called, is of comparatively recent origin. Louis de Berquem has been generally credited with having discovered this process during the latter part of the fifteenth century, 1456 to 1476, although now it is believed that the process was in common use in Italy at an earlier date.

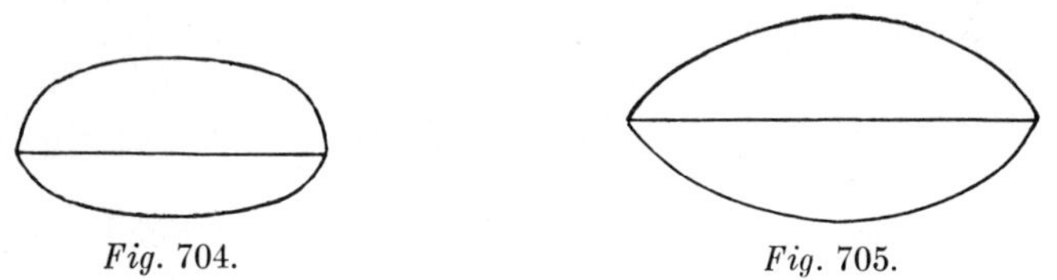

Fig. 704. *Fig.* 705.

The ancients contented themselves with simply polishing the natural crystal faces, or they ground the stone into certain rounded shapes. The *cabochon* cuts are, hence, the oldest of the various styles of cutting still in common use. The following types may be differentiated:

Double or Convex Cabochon. This involves generally circular, elliptical, or oval forms with two convex surfaces, the upper side being more convex than the lower (Fig. 704). When the convexity is the same above and below, the cut is sometimes called *lentil shape* (Fig. 705).

High Cabochon. This is somewhat similar to type 1, but the upper portion is very much higher and, hence, more convex than the underside (Fig. 706).

Simple or Plain Cabochon. In this cut, the upper side is convex as in types 1 and 2, but the underside is a flat surface. Stones with this style of cutting are mounted with the plain surface down (Fig. 707).

Hollow or Concavo-convex Cabochon, also called *Shell Cut.* In this style, the upper side is convex, but the under portion is hollowed out (Fig. 708).

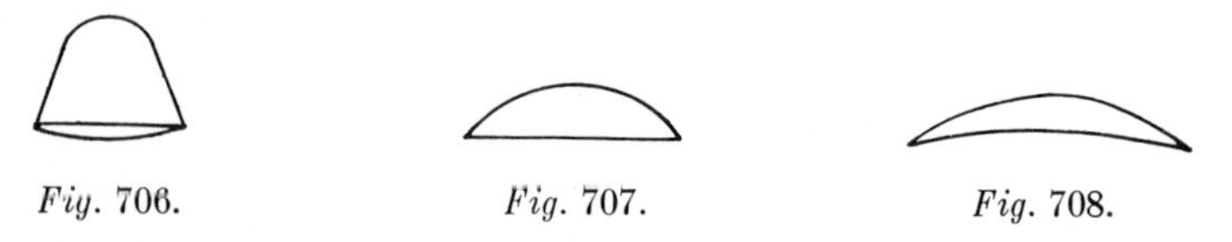

Fig. 706. *Fig.* 707. *Fig.* 708.

The cabochon cuts are used for stones exhibiting sheens, play of colors, opalescence, and asterism; thus, for tiger's-eye, opal, moonstone, and star rubies and sapphires. They are also used for many colored stones, for example, garnet, amethyst, turquois, and chrysocolla. The hollow cabochon cut is generally employed for transparent but deeply colored stones through which very little light could pass if cut in the other styles; for example, the almandite variety of garnet.

The principal style of cutting involving facets is the *brilliant cut.* Thus, in cutting the diamond, the octahedron, either natural or produced by

Fig. 709. Cleaving a diamond. (*Courtesy Harry Winston, Inc.*)

Fig. 710. Sawing the Jonker diamond. (*Courtesy Harry Winston, Inc.*)

cleavage, is made the basis, as shown in Figs. 709 and 711. The upper and lower portions are removed, usually by sawing (Fig. 710), in such a manner that when the stone is cut, the portion above the *girdle* G (Fig. 714) should be about 40 per cent as thick as that below the girdle. The upper portion of the stone is called the *crown*, *top*, or *bezel* (Fig. 712); the lower part, the *pavilion*, *back*, or *base* (Fig. 713). The uppermost facet T is the table, and C is the culet. Exclusive of the table and culet there are usually 56 facets, though in some cases the number is increased by groups of 8 to 64, 72, or even 80 facets. All the facets of a brilliant have definite names. The 58 facets of the usual brilliant include one table T, 8 star facets S, 4 bezel or top main facets B, 4 top corner facets TC, 16 top half (break or

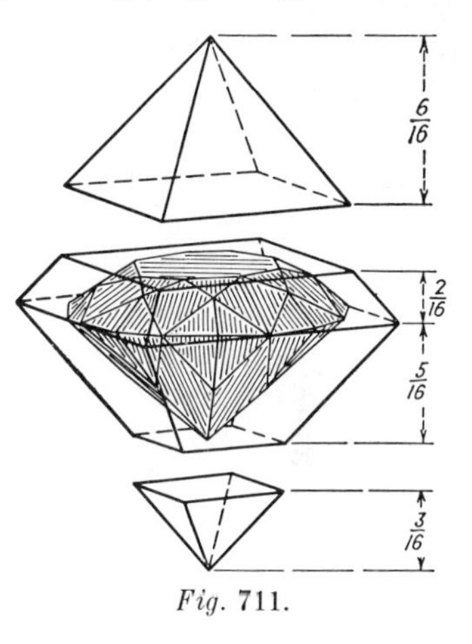

Fig. 711.

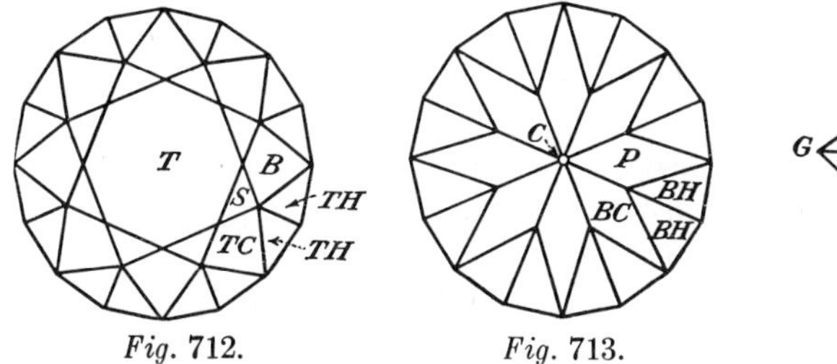

Fig. 712. *Fig.* 713.

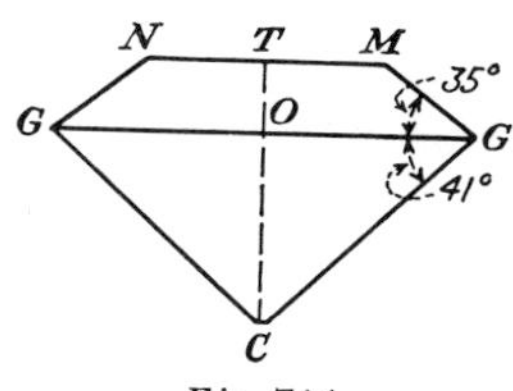

Fig. 714.

girdle) facets *TH*, 16 bottom half (break or girdle) facets *BH*, 4 bottom corner facets *BC*, 4 pavilion or bottom main facets *P*, and 1 culet *C*.

Since the four top corner facets *TC* may be of the same shape and size as the four bezel facets *B*, as is the case on the round brilliant, they also may be called bezel facets. Such stones are then said to have eight bezel facets. Similar conditions may apply to the bottom corner *BC* and the pavilion *P* facets. In such cases, stones are said to have eight pavilion facets.

The girdle of the stone is formed where the top half and the bottom half facets (*TH* and *BH*, Figs. 712 and 713) meet in a sharp edge. In order to retain as much as possible of the original weight of the uncut stone the experienced diamond cutter may leave a very small portion of the rough original surface of the diamond crystal at one or two points around the girdle. These are known as *naturals* and generally do not detract from the value of the stone if they are minute, because they are evidence of careful workmanship. However, if they are easily recognized the stone is said to have a *thick girdle*. At times the girdle is polished, or a series of small facets may even be placed around the entire circumference of the stone. For a given weight, stones with a polished or faceted girdle obviously have a smaller spread than those with knife-edge girdles.

The cutting of the diamond so as to exhibit the maximum brilliancy and fire is based upon long practical experience. Accordingly, it is common practice to cut stones so that the thickness *TC* (Fig. 714) from the table to the culet is about 60 per cent of the width or *spread GG* at the girdle. The distance *TO* of the table above the diameter through the girdle may vary from about one-third to slightly less than one-half of the distance *OC* that the culet is below it. The width of the table *NM* may be 40 to 60 per cent of the spread.

Under the foregoing conditions the angle that the main upper facets make with the plane through the girdle will be 35 to 37°, whereas the lower main facets will be inclined at about 41°. Depending upon the character of the stones to be cut, a variation of 5 to 7° may be observed in the inclination of the upper main facets, that is, from 30 to 37°. The permissible variation in the inclination of the lower main facets is much less.

Depending upon the character of the rough material, the outline of the cut stone varies, being circular, quadratic, oval, elliptical, or pear-shaped. While the diamond was formerly cut almost exclusively in this style, in recent years the *emerald cut* has become quite popular (Figs. 715 and 716), especially for stones of larger size. Usually stones with the emerald cut have 50 facets, including the table and culet.

The *rose* cut has 24 triangular facets with a flat base (Figs. 717 and 718). This style of cutting is one of the earliest involving facets but it is not employed much at present. At present various fancy cuts are used, such as *baguette, cut corner triangle, epaulet, half moon, hexagon, keystone, kite, lozenge, marquise, pentagon* or *bullet, square, trapeze,* and *triangle.* Figures 719 and 720 illustrate *step, trap,* or *cushion cuts,* which are frequently used for colored stones.

In cutting gems, the stone is held in some cement or mechanical holder and placed against a rapidly revolving metallic wheel or disk containing or covered with some abrasive, such as diamond dust, carborundum, or

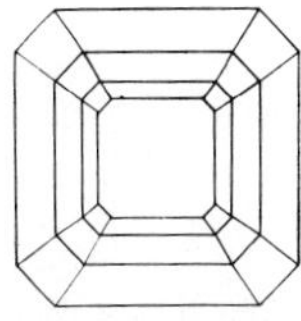
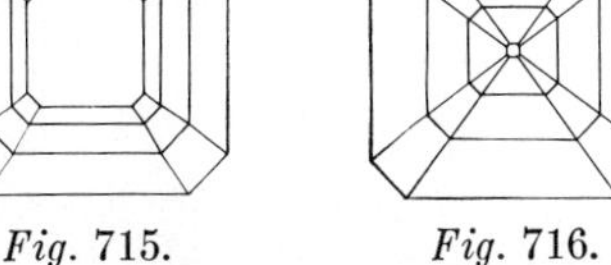
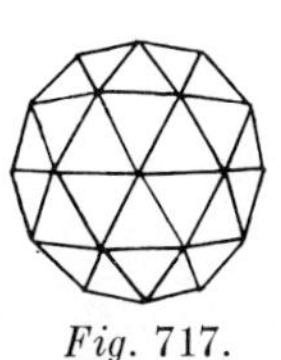
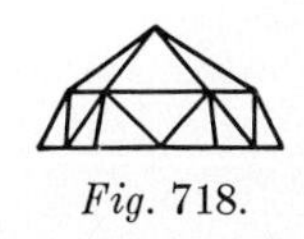

Fig. 715. *Fig.* 716. *Fig.* 717. *Fig.* 718.

emery. The position and inclination of the various facets are determined by the eye of the cutter, who obviously must exercise great judgment in order to cut stones to the best advantage. These cutters become very expert, and rarely does an experienced cutter exceed the permissible limits of variation in the angles between the different facets. After the facets have been produced, they are polished in much the same manner as they were cut, except that some polishing material, such as tripolite or rouge, instead of an abrasive, is used. Diamonds are usually cut and

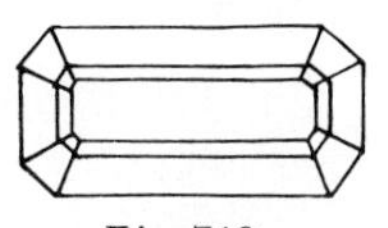
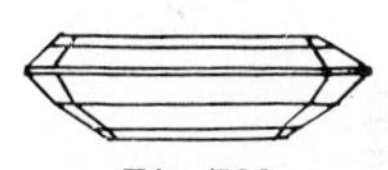
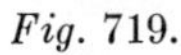

Fig. 719. *Fig.* 720.

polished by men who specialize on the diamond (Fig. 721), while a lapidist is one who cuts and polishes all other types of gems. Amsterdam, Antwerp, Paris, London, Idar-Oberstein (Germany), and New York are important gem-cutting centers. Gemstones are also cut in South Africa, Israel, Puerto Rico, and Brazil. In the United States and Canada there are many amateur and professional lapidists who are primarily interested in the cutting of gemstones other than the diamond. Improved mechanical devices and many small and efficient shops have been developed by these lapidists. In evaluating a cut gem the "4 C's" of gem value, namely, the *color, clarity, cutting,* and *caratweight* (size) of the gem, must be taken into consideration.

Synthetic Gems. A synthetic gem is one prepared in the laboratory and, in its chemical and physical properties, is identical with the corresponding natural gem. For many years, scientists have endeavored to produce the diamond in the laboratory. Prominent among the many earlier investigators who have worked on this problem are Moissan, Hannay, and Noble. These investigators believed that they had succeeded in producing small diamonds of microscopic size, but the evidence submitted by them was not incontrovertible. This is because their products could not be subjected to the accurate determination of their properties now possible by modern optical, chemical, and X-ray methods.

All the attempts to produce the diamond by the various methods which had been used were unsuccessful. However, on Feb. 15, 1955, the

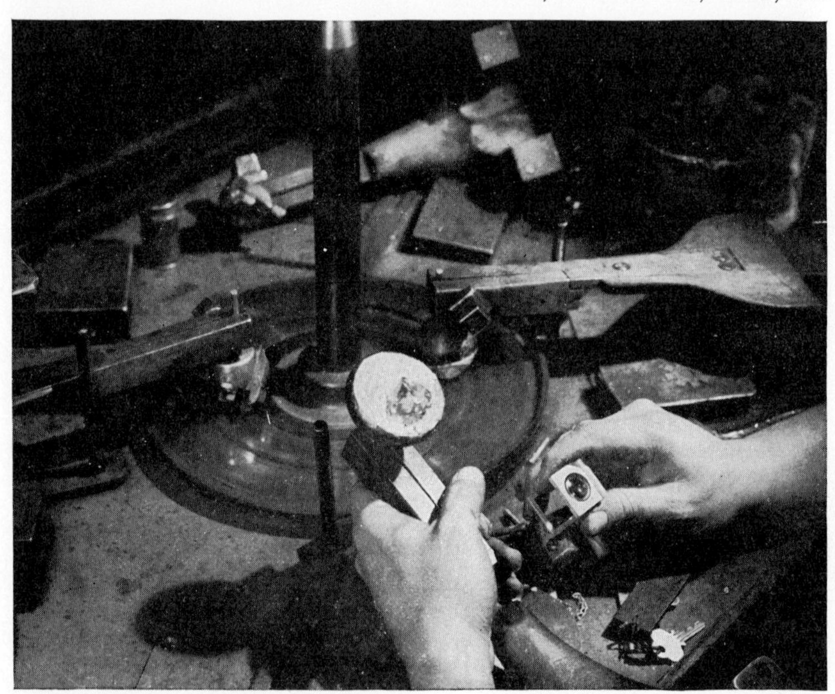

Fig. 721. Polishing one of the Jonker diamonds. (*Courtesy Harry Winston, Inc.*)

General Electric Company reported that in its laboratory at Schenectady, New York, a team of four research scientists, after four years of study, had succeeded in producing the diamond. This was accomplished by the use of pressures up to 1,500,000 pounds per square inch and temperatures up to 5000°F. The most modern methods were employed to identify positively the product as the diamond. Although these *synthetic or man-made* diamonds are small in size and not of gem quality, they have proved to be of value for some industrial purposes. They are now produced in quantity and at a cost to compete with natural industrial diamonds.

Since 1902 synthetic gems having the composition and physical properties of the various varieties of corundum, Al_2O_3, that is, synthetic rubies and sapphires, have been produced and are manufactured on a large scale. These synthetic gems differ from the natural stones only in certain details incidental to the process of production.

The apparatus for producing these synthetic rubies and sapphires (Figs. 722 and 723) was devised by Verneuil. It consists of a vertical blowpipe, burning a mixture of hydrogen and oxygen, entering from *H* and *O*, respectively. By means of suitable mechanism, very finely divided

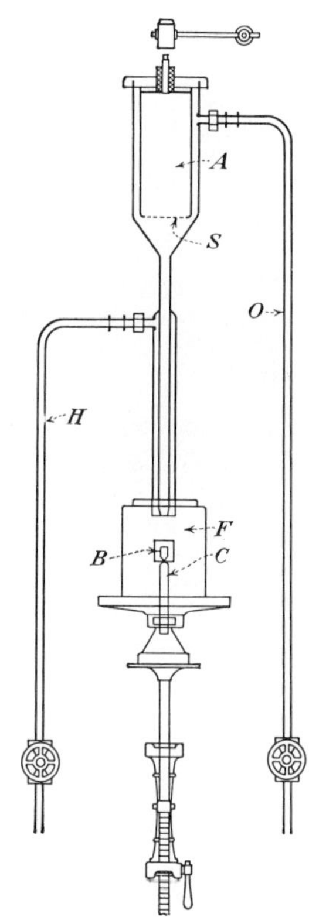

Figs. 722 and 723. Cross section and general view of apparatus for the manufacture of artificial rubies, sapphires, and spinels. (*Swiss Jewel Company, Locarno, Switzerland.*)

particles of aluminum oxide (Al_2O_3) in the receptacle *A* pass through a fine sieve *S*. These particles mix with the gases and fuse in the very hot flame (about 2100°C.) at *F*, which is directed against a small fire-clay support *C*. These fused particles collect on this clay support at first as a small drop, which slowly increases in size, as the process continues, until a fairly large and inverted conical, carrot- or pear-shaped, colorless mass *B*, called the *boule* or *birne*, is formed (Figs. 723 and 724). This process is commonly known as the *flame fusion method*. The boules are broad on top and very narrow below where supported on the fire-clay cone. When no pigmenting material is added to the aluminum oxide a colorless, transparent product, called *white sapphire*, is obtained. By the addition to the Al_2O_3 of a small amount of chromium oxide, boules of a red color are obtained. These correspond to the ruby. The addition of the oxides of iron and titanium gives the deep-blue color of the sapphire proper.

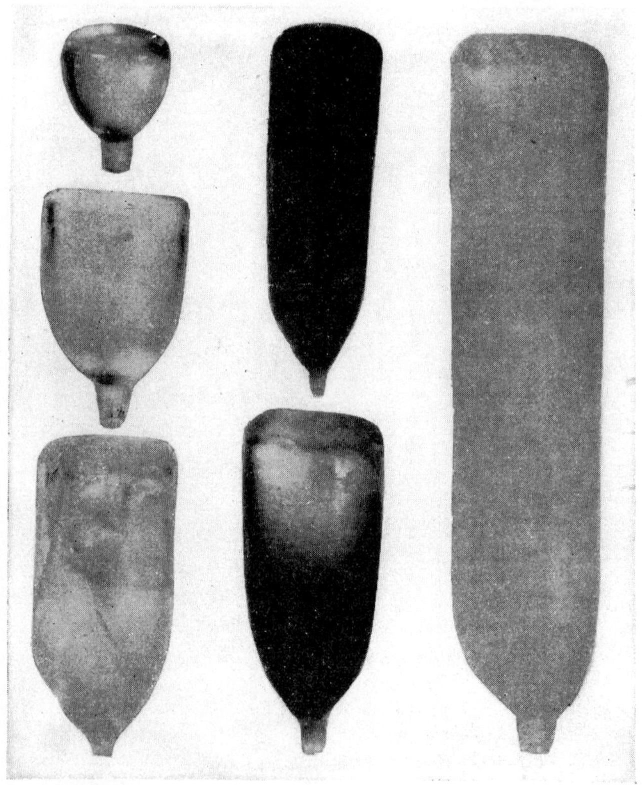

Fig. 724. Pear- and carrot-shaped *boules* or birnes of different colors varying in weight from 37 to 560 carats. Natural size.

Green sapphire is obtained when a mixture of vanadium and cobalt oxides is added. The so-called *artificial alexandrite* is produced by the addition of small percentages of vanadium compounds to the aluminum oxide. Yellow, orange, and violet synthetic sapphires are also produced.

In chemical composition and all physical properties, such as hardness, specific gravity, and indices of refraction, these synthetic gems are identical with those occurring in nature. Because of the presence of inclusions, tension cracks, and peculiar structure lines, cut synthetic gems can, in most instances, be easily distinguished from natural stones. In some cases, however, especially if the cut stones are about ½ carat or less in size, their synthetic character may be very difficult to determine.

Synthetic spinel in beautiful colors is also produced by this process and is sometimes sold as aquamarine or as the emerald. Synthetic spinels may have compositions in which the ratio between the oxides of magnesium and aluminum may vary from 1 : 1, as in normal spinel, to 1 : 5.

Cut synthetic rubies and sapphires can be obtained at varying prices up to $4 or $5 per carat, depending upon the quality of the stone. Not all these synthetics are sold as gems. Comparatively large quantities are used as *jewels* in the manufacture of watches and in delicate physical and electrical measuring instruments, such as balances, meters, and chronometers, where hard bearing surfaces are required; also for precision gauges, injector nozzles, and as thread guides in the textile industry. As white synthetic sapphire has excellent infrared, ultraviolet, and microwave transmission characteristics, as well as high temperature, abrasion, and chemical resistance, rods and disks up to 5 inches in diameter have many military, medical, and civilian applications.

The most important plants for the manufacture of synthetic rubies, sapphires, and spinels are located at Locarno and Monthey, Switzerland; Annecy and Jarrie, France; Freyung, West Germany; Bitterfeld, East Germany; Salford, England; and East Chicago. The total annual world production of these synthetics is approximately one billion carats.

In 1947 the Linde Air Products Company, a division of the Union Carbide and Carbon Company, announced the successful production of synthetic star rubies and sapphires. These synthetics are of very good color and show excellent stars (see asterism, page 100). A synthetic star ruby weighing 100.25 carats is in the American Museum of Natural History in New York. Synthetic star rubies and sapphires are also produced by the Wiedes Carbid-Werk at Freyung in Eastern Bavaria, Germany.

The Bell Telephone Laboratories in New York City succeeded in 1958 in producing synthetic sapphire crystals up to three-quarters of an inch square and one-quarter of an inch thick by a new hydrothermal process. Pressures of 20,000 to 50,000 pounds per square inch and temperatures of about 395°C. and above are used. At these pressures and temperatures Al_2O_3 can be dissolved in water. If a small amount of a chromate is added to the solution, synthetic ruby crystals are produced. The crystals obtained by this hydrothermal process are essentially free from strain, in contrast to those produced by the flame fusion method.

In 1930 Hermann Espig and Max Jaeger announced that synthetic emerald crystals, $Be_3Al_2Si_6O_{18}$, of good color had been produced at the plant of the I. G. Farbenindustrie, now known as the Veb. Elektrochemisches Kombinat, Bitterfeld, East Germany. For this synthetic product the term *igmerald* was suggested but it has not been widely used. The manufacture of synthetic emeralds has been discontinued by this German firm.

Also in 1930 Carroll F. Chatham of San Francisco, California, succeeded in producing synthetic beryl and later, in 1935, emerald crystals of appreciable size. These crystals possess the characteristic hexagonal forms of the natural emerald. Important aids in the identification of synthetic emeralds are cracks and characteristic wisp-like inclusions and the slightly lower specific gravity and indices of refraction.

The method of producing synthetic emeralds differs materially from that used to manufacture synthetic rubies, sapphires, and spinels. Although no details of the method employed have been revealed, it is assumed that it is a hydrothermal process involving slow crystallization. Chatham has achieved great success in producing synthetic emerald. His annual production is approximately 60,000 carats, of which about 20 per cent is of gem quality. The largest crystal produced by Chatham weighs 1,275 carats and is in the Mineralogical Museum of Harvard University; another of good quality weighing 1,014 carats is in the National Museum at Washington, D.C.

Although chrysoberyl ($BeAl_2O_4$) has been made synthetically with the color of alexandrite, it has not been marketed. This is because the product is inferior to synthetic sapphire or spinel, having an alexandrite color, and because of the higher cost of manufacture.

Since 1948, transparent, colorless, and colored synthetic rutile (TiO_2) has been made by the Linde Air Products Company and the Titanium Division of the National Lead Company. The Verneuil process, often called the *flame fusion method*, is used. Because of its high indices of refraction and strong dispersion synthetic rutile, frequently called *titania*, serves as an attractive gemstone. It is, however, relatively soft, 6.5 to 7. One-carat cut stones cost about $10.

18 Classification of Minerals According to Elements

In this chapter minerals are grouped under the element which is an important constituent and in the order in which they are described in the text. Following each list there is a discussion of some of the uses of minerals of economic importance, and where possible statistics of production are given. The numbers after the names of the minerals are page references to detailed descriptions.

ALUMINUM

CORUNDUM, 299	Al_2O_3	Hexagonal
SPINELS, 304	$MgAl_2O_4$	Cubic
Chrysoberyl, 308	$BeAl_2O_4$	Orthorhombic
BAUXITE, 317	Considered a rock	
CRYOLITE, 323	Na_3AlF_6	Monoclinic
ALUNITE, 342	$KAl_3(OH)_6(SO_4)_2$	Hexagonal
GARNETS, 363	$M_3''M_2'''(SiO_4)_3$	Cubic
ANDALUSITE, 368	Al_2OSiO_4	Orthorhombic
KYANITE, 369	Al_2OSiO_4	Triclinic
Sillimanite, 370	Al_2OSiO_4	Orthorhombic
Dumortierite, 370	$Al_8B(OH)Si_3O_{19}$	Orthorhombic
STAUROLITE, 371	$Fe(OH)_2.2Al_2OSiO_4$	Orthorhombic
TOPAZ, 372	$Al_2(F,OH)_2SiO_4$	Orthorhombic
BERYL, 379	$Be_3Al_2Si_6O_{18}$	Hexagonal
SPODUMENE, 387	$LiAlSi_2O_6$	Monoclinic
KAOLINITE, 401	$Al_4(OH)_8Si_4O_{10}$	Monoclinic
FELDSPAR, 405	$KAlSi_3O_8$, etc.	Monoclinic and triclinic
NEPHELINE, 414	$Na(AlSiO_4)$	Hexagonal
LEUCITE, 416	$K(AlSi_2O_6)$	Pseudocubic
SCAPOLITE, 417	$nNa_4Cl(Al,Si_3O_8)_3 + mCa_4CO_3(Al_2Si_2O_8)_3$	Tetragonal
ZEOLITES, 418	Hydrated silicates	Various systems

In addition to the above there are many phosphate and silicate minerals which contain aluminum as a minor constituent.

Aluminum is the most abundant metal in nature, and the minerals in which this element is an important constituent are exceedingly numerous. Only bauxite, cryolite, kyanite, andalusite, and dumortierite will be referred to in this discussion. Bauxite is used as a source of metallic aluminum and aluminum salts and in the manufacture of bauxite bricks and abrasives, such as *alundum*, *aloxite*, *exolon*, and *lionite*. These products, which are artificial Al_2O_3, are made by fusing bauxite in an electric furnace. The annual production of artificial abrasives made from bauxite

Fig. 725. Stockpile of Indian kyanite at plant of Chas. Taylor Sons Company, Cincinnati, Ohio.

amounts to over 245,000 short tons. Cryolite is used as a flux in the electrolytic method for the extraction of the metal from bauxite. Kyanite is used in the manufacture of furnace linings, chemical porcelains, insulators, refractories, and mill balls (Fig. 725). Upon heating, andalusite, kyanite, and dumortierite break down into $3Al_2O_3.2SiO_2$ (mullite), a compound which imparts great tensile strength, high dielectric properties, and low thermal expansion to material containing it. Synthetic mullite can be prepared by fusing mixtures of siliceous and aluminous materials.

In the manufacture of metallic aluminum the finely powdered crude ore (bauxite) is digested with a hot caustic solution that dissolves the alumina, while the impurities, mainly iron and silica, are left as a residue. From the filtrate containing sodium aluminate the aluminum is precipitated as the hydroxide. It is then filtered and ignited to the oxide. In the electrolysis, cryolite or an artificial sodium-aluminum fluoride is placed in tanks lined with carbon which acts as the cathode, while suspended carbon cylinders act as the anode. The cryolite melts and readily dissolves the alumina which is added. The current decomposes the latter with the separation of metallic aluminum which collects in the bottom of the tank. About 4 tons of bauxite yield 1 ton of metallic aluminum. The amount of primary metallic aluminum produced in the United States is about 1,700,000 short tons annually.

Metallic aluminum finds extensive use on account of its high heat and electrical conductivity, low density, toughness, durability, and resistance

Fig. 726. Bauxite mining operations at Bauxite, Saline County, Arkansas. (*Courtesy Aluminum Company of America.*)

to corrosion—as in building products, tubing, transportation, cooking utensils, furniture, power transmission, machinery, and flexible wrapping material. Paints in which aluminum powder is used reflect approximately 70 per cent of the light. Many alloys of aluminum have been prepared. The most important are those with copper, zinc, tin, nickel, magnesium, manganese, silicon, and cadmium. *Duralumin*, an important alloy of aluminum, contains 4 per cent copper, 0.5 per cent magnesium, 0.6 per cent manganese, and small amounts of iron and silicon. When this alloy is heated to 500°C. and quenched, after 4 days it has a strength of about 60,000 pounds per square inch. *Aluminum bronze* contains 10 per cent aluminum and 90 per cent copper. *Thermite*, used in welding, is a mixture of aluminum and iron oxide, while the explosive *ammonal* consists of aluminum dust and ammonium nitrate. Alum and aluminum sulfate and chloride are the chief chemical salts and are employed in water purification, dyeing, and tanning. Bauxite bricks containing about 77 per cent of alumina are used in the construction of copper, iron, and lead furnaces and of cement kilns.

A typical bauxite contains 55 to 65 per cent Al_2O_3, 2 to 5 per cent SiO_2, 1 to 25 per cent Fe_2O_3, 1 to 3 per cent TiO_2, and 10 to 30 per cent combined water. The production of bauxite in the United States amounts to about 1,800,000 long tons, of which over 95 per cent is obtained from Arkansas (Fig. 726); the balance, from Georgia, Virginia, and Alabama. About 17,000 short tons of alum and over 800,00 short tons of total aluminum salts are produced annually. The quantity of cryolite imported from Greenland is approximately 18,000 long tons. Synthetic (manufactured) cryolite is replacing natural Na_3AlF_6 in the production of aluminum. The world's production of bauxite is about 17,500,000 long tons. The United States imports about 5,300,000 long tons.

ANTIMONY

STIBNITE, 284	Sb_2S_3	Orthorhombic
Pyrargyrite, 289	Ag_3SbS_3	Hexagonal
TETRAHEDRITE, 290	$M_{12}R_4S_{13}$	Cubic
Bournonite, 291	$PbCuSbS_3$	Orthorhombic

Of the above-named antimony minerals, stibnite is the most important. Considerable antimony is also recovered from antimonial lead ores carrying 12 to 20 per cent of antimony. Except for a small amount of antimony in the form of a fine powder (*antimony black*) used for bronzing metals and plaster casts, antimony metal is used chiefly in the manufacture of alloys. These alloys include *type metal* (lead, antimony, tin, and copper); *babbitt*, *antifriction*, or *bearing metal* (usually antimony, tin, and copper); *britannia* or *white metal* (tin, antimony, copper, with some zinc); and so forth. Antimony imparts hardness to lead and prevents it from contracting when solidifying from a molten condition. At the present time, antimonial lead finds extensive employment in the manufacture of storage batteries. Antimony oxide is used in making opaque white enamel and other sanitary ware. The white oxide has been employed in the making of paint which is sold under the name of *Timonox*. Salts of antimony are used in medicine and as a mordant in dyeing, while the sulfide of antimony is employed for vulcanizing and coloring rubber, in paint pigments, safety matches, and fireworks.

Under normal conditions, the United States is not a large producer of antimony ores, importing practically its entire supply from China, Bolivia, and Mexico. The domestic production is about 600 short tons of metallic antimony, while the world's production is about 54,000 tons. Considerable antimony is recovered from old alloys, scrap, and dross.

ARSENIC

Native Arsenic, 263	As	Hexagonal
Niccolite, 281	$NiAs$	Hexagonal
REALGAR, 283	AsS	Monoclinic
ORPIMENT, 283	As_2S_3	Monoclinic
Cobaltite, 286	$CoAsS$	Cubic
ARSENOPYRITE, 287	$FeAsS$	Monoclinic
Smaltite, 289	$(Co,Ni)As_{3-x}$	Cubic
Proustite, 290	Ag_3AsS_3	Hexagonal
TETRAHEDRITE, 290	$M_{12}R_4S_{13}$	Cubic
Enargite, 291	Cu_3AsS_4	Orthorhombic

Arsenopyrite is the most important arsenical mineral. The commercial uses of arsenic are very limited. Shot metal is an alloy of arsenic and lead. Arsenious oxide is used in the manufacture of insecticides and fungicides, such as paris green and the arsenates of calcium, lead, magnesium, and manganese. It is also used to counteract the iron coloration in the manufacture of glass. Arsenic compounds are also used in the preservation of wood. Organic insecticides, such as DDT and benzene hexachloride, are replacing arsenates as pesticides. A new arsenical drug, p-arseno-sophenylbutyric acid, has been developed for the treatment of African sleeping sickness. The production of arsenic is recorded in the terms of *white arsenic*, arsenic trioxide (As_2O_3), very little of which is obtained directly from arsenic minerals. Large quantities are, however, available as a by-product in the smelting of copper, cobalt, gold, silver, and lead ores. The domestic production of As_2O_3 amounts to about 10,000 short tons annually.

BARIUM

WITHERITE, 335	$BaCO_3$	Orthorhombic
BARITE, 340	$BaSO_4$	Orthorhombic

Barite (barytes) is the more important of the above minerals, commercially. The largest single use of barite is in oil-well drilling. When added to rotary drilling mud in high gas-pressure areas it prevents blowouts. This purpose consumes 90 per cent of the barite. About 2 per cent is used in the manufacture of paints. *Lithopone*, one of the chief constituents of sanitary flat wall paints, is an intimate mixture of 70 per cent barium sulfate, 25 to 29 per cent zinc sulfide, and 1 to 5 per cent zinc oxide. *Blanc fixe*, or permanent white, is artificially prepared barium sulfate. Ground barite is used as an inert filler in the manufacture of rubber goods, linoleum, oilcloth, artificial ivory, and heavy glazed paper, such as playing cards, and bristol board. Barite bricks are opaque to X rays and are used in X-ray laboratories. The barium salts have a wide variety of uses: barium dioxide (BaO_2) in the preparation of hydrogen peroxide, barium chloride as a water softener, the carbonate and chloride to prevent efflorescence on bricks and as insecticides, and the carbonate, sulfate, or nitrate in the manufacture of optical glass. By the addition of a small amount of metallic barium to the electrodes of spark plugs their efficiency is increased. Vaporized metallic barium is also used in electronic tubes to absorb residual gases. Barium forms alloys with aluminum, magnesium, nickel, and copper.

Barite is obtained mainly from Arkansas, Missouri, Georgia, Tennessee, and Nevada. The annual production amounts to about 1,200,000 short tons. Germany is also a large producer of barite.

BERYLLIUM

Chrysoberyl, 308	$BeAl_2O_4$	Orthorhombic
BERYL, 379	$Be_3Al_2Si_6O_{18}$	Hexagonal

Aside from the use of transparent beryllium minerals as gems, the application of the pure metal, beryllium alloys, and compounds in industry is increasing in importance. A major commercial use of pure beryllium metal is as X-ray disk or windows because of its high permeability to X rays; also in mechanisms for guided missiles and for structural purposes. Beryllium-copper alloys provide an important outlet for the metal. By the addition of 1.5 to 2.5 per cent beryllium, followed by heat-treatment, the tensile strength of copper is raised from 33,000 to nearly 200,000 pounds per square inch. These alloys possess increased hardness and high fatigue resistance and are used for electrical springs, contact clips, thermostat controls, and telegraph relay parts. Beryllium also forms alloys with nickel and iron. Ferroberyllium is used in wrought stainless alloys. Beryllium-aluminum alloys have been suggested for pistons and in airplane construction. A beryllium alloy is used in the manufacture of nonsparking safety tools.

Alkaline beryllium borate glasses (4.4 per cent BeO) may replace quartz lenses for transmitting ultraviolet light. They can be sealed like ordinary glass. Beryllium oxide is used to a certain extent as a refractory because of its high melting point (2570°C.) and resistance to thermal shock; also in fluorescent lamps as a phosphor (material capable of absorbing ultraviolet light and emitting it as visible light).

A limited amount of beryl is obtained from the pegmatites of the Black Hills, South Dakota, New Mexico, and Colorado. The domestic production is about 750 short tons. Importation of beryl amounts to about 11,500 short tons from Union of South Africa, Rhodesia, Brazil, and India.

BISMUTH

Native Bismuth, 263	Bi	Hexagonal
Bismuthinite, 284	Bi_2S_3	Orthorhombic

Bismuth is extensively used in alloys with lead, tin, copper, antimony, and cadmium. The melting point of some of these alloys is as low as 64°C., and they are therefore employed as safety fuses for electrical apparatus, safety plugs for boilers, and automatic sprinklers. Bismuth salts are used in dressing wounds. The nitrate and carbonate are sometimes given internally before producing a roentgenograph, as bismuth salts are opaque to X rays; also in pharmacology. The salts are also used in calico printing and in the manufacture of high-refractive glass. No native bismuth is mined in the United States. The entire domestic production is obtained as a by-product in the electrolytic refining of lead and copper, the bismuth being recovered from the anode slime. The domestic consumption is about 1,500,000 pounds of the metal annually. Bismuth pharmaceuticals consume about 28 per cent and metallurgical uses about 72 per cent. About 800,000 pounds are imported annually from United Kingdom, Peru, Mexico, and Canada.

BORON

Colemanite, 337	$Ca_2B_6O_{11}.5H_2O$	Monoclinic
Kernite, 338	$Na_2B_4O_7.4H_2O$	Monoclinic
Datolite, 373	$CaB(OH)SiO_4$	Monoclinic
TOURMALINE, 381	$M_7Al_6(OH,F)_4(BO_3)_3Si_6O_{18}$	Hexagonal

Commercially, the most important boron compound is borax ($Na_2B_4O_7.10H_2O$), which prior to 1927 was obtained by treating colemanite with sodium carbonate or sulfate. In 1927 large deposits of kernite (rasorite) were found in Kern County, California, and the supply of borax is now largely obtained from this mineral by solution and recrystallization. Borax is also recovered from the brines of Searles Lake, San Bernardino County, and Owens Lake, Inyo County, California. About one-half of the boron compounds sold are consumed by the ceramics industry. Borohydrides are easily oxidized with large energy liberation and are used as a constituent of jet and rocket fuels. Boron is an important constituent of many alloys. Borax is used in assaying, soldering, welding of metals, and in the manufacture of flint and heat-resistant glass; also in making the enameled coating for cast iron used in plumbing and kitchen utensils, and as a fertilizer for specific crops. Because of its antiseptic and cleansing properties, it is also used in the manufacture of soap, washing powders, and ointments. Chromium borate is a green pigment employed in calico printing, and the borate of manganese is sometimes used as a drier in paints and oils. Boron carbide is extremely hard and is used as an abrasive, while ferroboron and manganese-boron are finding increased employment as a hardening and deoxidizing agent. Borides of titanium, zirconium, tantalum, and tungsten are being investigated.

Practically the entire output of crude borates in the United States is obtained from southern California and amounts to nearly 1,000,000 short tons.

CADMIUM

Greenockite, 280	CdS	Hexagonal

All the cadmium used in industry is obtained as a by-product in the treatment of zinc and lead ores. It is recovered from flue dusts from blast and roasting furnaces and from the sludges precipitated from zinc solutions in the electrolytic recovery of zinc. The principal use of the metal cadmium is as a protective coating for steel and copper and in the preparation of bearings, solders, copper alloys, and low-melting alloys used for fire-detector systems and valve seats for high-pressure gas containers. Cadmium-base bearings are of two types, the cadmium-nickel composed of 98.65 per cent of cadmium and 1.35 of nickel, and the cadmium-silver bearing with 0.2 to 2.25 per cent of silver and 0.25 to 2 per cent of copper in place of nickel. Such bearings are used principally in automotive engines for service under high pressure and at high speeds. An alloy of copper-zirconium-cadmium is used for power-transmission lines. A nickel-cadmium storage battery using an aqueous solution of potassium hydroxide as the electrolyte has been used in Europe for many years. Cadmium sulfide and sulfoselenide are used as yellow and red pigments in paints, ceramics, inks, rubber, and leather. Cadmium oxide, hydrate, and chloride are used in electroplating, and cadmium bromide, chloride, and iodide in preparing special photographic films. The apparent annual consumption of metallic cadmium for all purposes obtained from domestic and foreign ores amounts to about 11,000,000 pounds.

CALCIUM

FLUORITE, 322	CaF_2	Cubic
CALCITE, 326	$CaCO_3$	Hexagonal
DOLOMITE, 329	$CaMg(CO_3)_2$	Hexagonal
ARAGONITE, 333	$CaCO_3$	Orthorhombic
Colemanite, 337	$Ca_2B_6O_{11}.5H_2O$	Monoclinic
ANHYDRITE, 339	$CaSO_4$	Orthorhombic
GYPSUM, 345	$CaSO_4.2H_2O$	Monoclinic
SCHEELITE, 349	$CaWO_4$	Tetragonal
APATITE, 351	$Ca_5F(PO_4)_3$	Hexagonal

Calcium is one of the most abundant metals in nature and is an important constituent of many minerals. Only those of prime importance commercially are listed above. The production and uses of calcite, dolomite, and gypsum will be given here.

Iceland spar variety of calcite, because of its purity and strong double refraction, is utilized in the Nicol prism, an essential part of polarizing microscopes, saccharimeters, dichroscopes, and other instruments making use of polarized light. Polaroid plates consisting of ultramicroscopic crystals of quinine iodosulfate which are strongly diochroic are used in place of Iceland spar in some optical equipment.

Calcite and Dolomite. The value of limestone, massive forms of calcite and dolomite, sold in the United States has at times amounted to about $300,000,000 annually, or 65 per cent of the total value of all stone sold, while the value of marble may be placed at about $12,000,000. The distribution of this production is summarized in Table 42.

TABLE 42

	Building	Monu-mental	Paving, curbing, flagging	Rubble	Riprap	Crushed	Other uses
Limestone.......	$15,000,000		$140,000	$500,000	$6,000,000	$250,000,000	$87,000,000
Marble..........	$ 6,000,000	$3,000,000					

Under other uses, in the case of limestone, are included furnace flux valued at $50,000,000, stone for alkali works and sugar factories valued at $7,000,000, and ground stone for agricultural purposes valued at $30,000,000. Furnace flux, terrazzo, and marble dust are other uses of marble. In addition, large quantities of limestone are employed in the manufacture of cement and lime. It is estimated that these industries use the following quantities of limestone annually:

	Short Tons
Portland cement.........	66,000,000
Lime....................	19,000,000

Dead-burned dolomite is used as refractory lining for metallurgical furnaces. Dolomite is also a source of magnesium oxide applied as a refractory and a source of magnesium metal.

The leading limestone-producing states are Indiana, Pennsylvania, Ohio, New York, Illinois, and Michigan.

Gypsum. This mineral is used in both the uncalcined and calcined conditions. In the former state, its chief uses are (1) as a retarder in portland cement; (2) as a pigment base for paints, especially in making cold-water paints; and (3) as a filler for paper and cloth. The use of gypsum in agriculture for alkaline soils has declined in recent years.

In calcining gypsum the water content is reduced from 20.9 to 5.6 per

Fig. 727. Mining gypsum at Plaster City, California. The deposit varies from 20 to 24 feet in thickness. (*Courtesy United States Gypsum Company.*)

cent ($CaSO_4.\frac{1}{2}H_2O$). This product is called *plaster of paris.* Calcined gypsum is used chiefly in wall plasters, wall and plaster boards, gypsum blocks and tile, molds for pottery and terra cotta, surgical casts, and for many other purposes. Gypsum tile reinforced with metal is frequently used for roof decks of laundries, foundries, and textile mills where condensation of moisture causes considerable trouble. As gypsum has a low heat conductivity, its use largely prevents this condensation or drip.

Keene's cement, which differs from ordinary wall plasters in the time of setting and its greater hardness, is made by burning pure gypsum at a low temperature, then immersing in a solution of alum, aluminum sulfate, or borax, and recalcining at about 500°C. *Soluble anhydrite*, prepared by heating gypsum for 3 hours in an oven at about 460°F., can be used as a drying or desiccating agent.

Gypsum is produced in many states; the more important are Michigan, New York, Texas, Kansas, Iowa, and California (Fig. 727). The production in the United States under normal conditions is over 10,000,000 short tons. The chief uses are as follows:

	Short Tons
Uncalcined:	
Portland cement, paint, agriculture, etc.	2,700,000
Calcined:	
Plaster of paris, wall plasters, lath, etc.	7,200,000
Plate glass, pottery, plastics, and other uses	250,000

The metal calcium is employed as an alloying agent for aluminum and for bearing metals of the lead-calcium or lead-barium-calcium type; also as a reducing agent for beryllium, chromium, thorium, uranium, and zirconium.

CARBON

DIAMOND, 267	C	Cubic
GRAPHITE, 274	C	Hexagonal

Carbon is also an essential constituent of the carbonates (pages 325 to 337) and of such organic substances as petroleum, asphalt, and coal.

Diamond. Africa at the present time supplies over 95 per cent of the world's production of diamonds. Formerly the volcanic pipes (Fig. 728) furnished almost the entire output, but in recent years the production from alluvial deposits in South Africa, South-West Africa, Angola, Ghana, Tanganyika, Sierra Leone, Liberia, Belgian Congo, and British Guiana exceeds the production from the mines. Up to 1942 about 48,000 diamonds have been recovered from Pike County, Arkansas; about 10 per cent were of gem quality. The largest stone found in this region weighed 40.22 carats; it is a flattened, irregular octahedron and is the largest diamond found to date on the North American continent. The value of other scattered finds in the United States rarely exceeds a few thousand dollars annually.

Aside from their use in jewelry, diamonds are extensively employed in industry. Three types are used for industrial purposes, bort, ballas, and carbonado. These varieties are used in rock drills for prospecting operations and the determination of the character of subsurface rock formations; for truing grinding wheels, in order to retain the wheels in cylindrical shape and for restoring the cutting surface when glazed; for wire-drawing dies; for stone-cutting saws; for glass cutting; and as diamond points for drilling holes in gems, watch jewels, and glass lenses. Bearings for balances and large-capacity electric meters are sometimes composed of bort. The efficiency in drilling operations is appreciably improved by proper crystallographic orientation of the diamonds in the drill.

The size of diamond-drill bits varies from 1 to 12 inches, and the rate of penetration averages between 30 to 50 feet a day in granite to 100 to 200 feet in soft formations. In drilling, six to eight relatively large diamonds

Fig. 728. Early view of Premier Diamond Mine, near Pretoria, Transvaal.

were formerly used, but now many small stones, called *drilling bort*, are employed as they distribute the stresses over a large number of points, and they are much cheaper.

Wires drawn through diamond dies are characterized by a high polish and uniformity of size. Wires can be drawn as fine as 0.0003 inch in diameter. From 300 to 400 tons of copper wire can be drawn through a single die without variation in gauge. Practically the entire production of carbonado, 2,000 to 8,000 carats annually, comes from Bahia in Brazil. Total production of diamonds for all industrial purposes is about 16,000,000 carats. Because of their sensitivity to radioactivity, some diamonds are used as counters for alpha, beta, and gamma rays in place of Geiger-Muller counters. The world's production of diamonds is estimated at 21,500,000 metric carats.

Graphite. The trade makes a sharp distinction between crystalline and "amorphous" graphite. By the former is meant *flake graphite* of sufficient size to be visible to the naked eye. The most important use of crystalline graphite is in the manufacture of crucibles used in the steel, brass, and bronze industries. For this purpose a flaky or fibrous graphite is essential, and the Ceylon lump or Madagascar flake is generally preferred, although it is sometimes mixed with American flake graphite. For crucibles, graphitic carbon should exceed 85 per cent and, at the same time, be practically free from mica, pyrite, and iron oxide. Graphite crucibles are superior to clay crucibles because of their infusibility, conductivity of heat, and ability to withstand sudden temperature changes. As graphite has but little binding strength, clay, sand, and kaolin are added in the proportion of about 3 parts of graphite, 2 parts of clay, 1 part of sand, and smaller amounts of kaolin. The increase in the number of electric furnaces, however, is decreasing the demand for crucible steel and also for graphite crucibles.

Most "amorphous" graphite is the result of the metamorphism of coal seams. Except for the manufacture of crucibles, amorphous graphite is suitable for all purposes. For paints and for foundry facings, which consume about 36 per cent of the graphite used, a high degree of purity is not demanded; but for lubricants, pencils, and electrical purposes, high-grade material is essential. In the manufacture of self-lubricating metals, graphite is incorporated in the molten metal, and the resulting mixture contains about 60 per cent by weight or 25 per cent by volume of the metal.

Artificial "amorphous" graphite is manufactured on a large scale in the United States. It is used chiefly for electrodes for electric furnaces and also in many cases in place of the natural product.

Imported crystalline graphite is obtained chiefly from Ceylon and Madagascar, while Montana, Alabama, Pennsylvania, Texas, Nevada, and California are small and intermittent producers. The better grades of "amorphous" graphite are imported from Mexico and Korea. The domestic production ordinarily amounts to about 16,000 short tons, while about 52,000 short tons are imported annually.

CERIUM

Monazite, 350	$(Ce,La)PO_4$	Monoclinic
Allanite, 377	$(Ca,Ce,La)_2(Al,Fe)_3O(OH)SiO_4Si_2O_7$	Monoclinic

When struck or scratched, alloys of cerium readily emit sparks, and this property is utilized in many forms of automatic lighters. The master alloy (*misch metal*), containing about 40 to 52 per cent cerium, 22 to 30 per cent lanthanum, 15 to 17 per cent neodymium, 8 to 10 per cent praseodymium, yttrium, and other rare metals, is diluted with 15 to 40 per cent iron in making ferrocerium for the so-called sparking "flints." Addition of 3 to 5 pounds of misch metal to 1 ton of stainless steel increases the impact strength 33 to 67 per cent. Nearly half of the rare-earth ores are made into rare-earth metal oxides and fluorides for use in carbon-arc electrode cores for motion-picture projectors, floodlights, searchlights, and therapy lamps. Because of the great affinity of cerium for oxygen, it is also used as a reducing agent in the production of metallic zirconium and thorium. Cerium sulfate is employed in the manufacture of aniline black, in photography for the purpose of removing silver from overdeveloped negatives, and as a catalyst in the contact process for the manufacture of sulfuric acid. Cerium is particularly effective in absorbing ultraviolet rays and is employed, either alone or with didymium, in spectacle lenses. The oxide, ceria, is used as a constituent of incandescent-gas mantles in conjunction with thorium oxide. Lanthanum with thorium oxides is used in optical glass for aerial camera lenses. Rare-earth materials are also used in aluminum and zirconium-magnesium alloys, paint driers, textile waterproofing, and activators for fluorescent lighting.

CHROMIUM

CHROMITE, 307	$Fe(Cr,Fe)_2O_4$	Cubic
Crocoite, 346	$PbCrO_4$	Monoclinic

Chromite is the more important of these minerals. Three grades of chromite depending upon major uses are (1) metallurgical (consumption 56 per cent), (2) refractory (about 33 per cent), and (3) chemical (about 11 per cent). Specifications for metallurgical chromite normally require a minimum of 48 per cent Cr_2O_3 with Cr : Fe ratio of 3 : 1. When chromium is added in small amounts (1 to 2 per cent) to steel, it increases its hardness and shock resistance. In larger amounts (18 per cent Cr and 8 per cent Ni), it imparts corrosion resistance and is known as *stainless steel, enduro,* or *Allegheny metal.* Chrome steel is used in the manufacture of armor plate, armor-piercing projectiles, and for high-speed tools. Chromium is also used in plating. The coating is hard and white and somewhat resembles platinum. *Nichrome* (60 per cent Ni, 14 per cent Cr, 15 per cent Fe) is used extensively in electric heating elements. *Stellite* (essentially cobalt, chromium, and tungsten or molybdenum) is used in high-speed tools and instruments of precision. A manganese-chromium-vanadium steel has been developed for automotive forgings. Chromite is an important refractory and is often employed in lining copper and steel furnaces. For this purpose it has certain advantages over magnesite, as it resists corrosion, withstands sudden changes of temperature, and requires less delicate handling. Compounds of chromium are used as pigments (yellow, green, and red colors), as mordants in dyeing and printing cloth, and in tanning leather.

The chief foreign sources of chromite in recent years have been Union of South Africa, Rhodesia, Soviet Union, New Caledonia, Philippine Islands, Turkey, and Cuba. Over 2,000,000 short tons are imported each year. The domestic production at the present time is about 200,000 short tons and comes from California, Montana, Alaska, and Oregon. The average Cr_2O_3 content of the ore shipped was about 43 per cent.

COBALT

Cobaltite, 286	CoAsS	Cubic
Smaltite, 289	$(Co,Ni)As_{3-x}$	Cubic
Erythrite, 354	$Co_3(AsO_4)_2.8H_2O$	Monoclinic

The United States is the largest consumer of cobalt in the world but produces very little. Cobalt is often associated with nickel and silver minerals. It is also obtained as a by-product of ores of lead, copper, and iron. The metal cobalt, usually in conjunction with tungsten, is used in the manufacture of high-speed tool steels and in *stellite*, which is an alloy of cobalt, chromium, and tungsten. Cobalt increases the strength and elasticity of steel but lowers its ductility. Cobalt steel retains its cutting edge at high temperatures. The addition of cobalt to molybdenum high-speed steels also improves their properties. Cobalt has also found extensive use in the preparation of permanent magnets (*Alnico*) and magnet steels. Cobalt oxide is used as a blue pigment in the manufacture of glass and pottery. Cobalt salts are also used as driers in paints and in electroplating. Cobalt 60 emits gamma rays accompanied by beta radiation and is used for radiographic and therapeutic purposes.

The Belgian Congo is the chief source, with other importations from Northern Rhodesia, French Morocco, and Canada. The world's production is about 16,000 metric tons of cobalt.

COLUMBIUM (NIOBIUM)

COLUMBITE, 312	$(Fe,Mn)(Cb,Ta)_2O_6$	Orthorhombic
TANTALITE, 312	$(Fe,Mn)(Ta,Cb)_2O_6$	Orthorhombic
Microlite, 318	$(Ca,Na)_2Ta_2O_6(O,OH,F)$	Cubic

To the above, pyrochlore, $(Na,Ca)_2Cb_2O_6F$, cubic, should be added.

The chemists prefer the name niobium instead of columbium. Columbium (niobium) is used as a "getter" in vacuum tubes and, as ferrocolumbium, finds employment in the manufacture of stainless steel, high-temperature alloys, and is considered vital to the jet-engine and gas-turbine programs. The carbides of columbium (and tantalum) are used in ultrahard cutting tools and fine-wire-drawing dies. Tantalum, which is nearly always present in columbium minerals, is characterized by high melting point and resistance to corrosion and chemical attack. It is used in the manufacture of drills, stainless steels, pen points, watch springs, electric-lamp filaments (now largely replaced by tungsten), electronics, and chemical laboratory equipment. Tantalum potassium fluoride is used as a catalyst for the manufacture of synthetic rubber. Many of the commercial applications of tantalum are due to its remarkable resistance to the corrosive action of all chemicals except strong alkalies and mixtures containing hydrofluoric or fuming sulfuric acid. Tantalum can be easily fabricated into bars, thin sheets, and fine wires. When heated above 350°C., it absorbs gases and therefore is used in the construction of radio and radar tubes. Tantalum, used as an electrode in electrolytic solutions, acts as an electrolytic valve, passing the current in one direction only, thus automatically rectifying an alternating current. Tantalum becomes incandescent at 1700°C., more than 400° lower than the incandescent point of tungsten. A tantalum lamp is, therefore, 20 per cent cooler than a tungsten lamp. Tantalum filaments are made by pressing a mixture of the oxide and paraffin into threads which are then reduced to the metal by the passage of an electric current in a vacuum. The use of tantalum and columbium in special steels and in complex nonferrous alloys is increasing. Tantalum plates and wire are used in surgery and the oxide in optical glass of high refractive index.

About 99 per cent of the United States supply of columbium and tantalum is imported. Imports of columbite are principally from Nigeria, Belgian Congo, and the Federation of Malaya, and those of tantalite chiefly from the Belgian Congo, Brazil, Portugal, Western Australia, and Southern Rhodesia.

COPPER

Mineral	Formula	System
NATIVE COPPER, 259	Cu	Cubic
CHALCOCITE, 276	Cu_2S	Orthorhombic
BORNITE, 277	Cu_5FeS_4	Cubic
CHALCOPYRITE, 280	$CuFeS_2$	Tetragonal
TETRAHEDRITE, 290	$M_{12}R_4S_{13}$	Cubic
Enargite, 291	Cu_3AsS_4	Orthorhombic
Bournonite, 291	$PbCuSbS_3$	Orthorhombic
CUPRITE, 298	Cu_2O	Cubic
MALACHITE, 336	$Cu_2(OH)_2CO_3$	Monoclinic
AZURITE, 337	$Cu_3(OH)_2(CO_3)_2$	Monoclinic
Brochantite, 342	$Cu_4(OH)_6SO_4$	Monoclinic
Chalcanthite, 343	$CuSO_4.5H_2O$	Triclinic
CHRYSOCOLLA, 383	$CuSiO_3.nH_2O$	Amorphous

The United States produces about 30 per cent of the world's copper. Copper is used most extensively for the transmission of electricity and in castings and alloys. *Brass* consists of copper and zinc; *German silver* of copper, zinc, and nickel; *bronze* and *bell metal* of copper, tin, and zinc. Other bronzes contain small amounts of nickel, manganese, silicon, or lead. A typical manganese bronze for propeller blades, valve stems, and parts requiring toughness, strength, and resistance to corrosive action of salt water contains 57 per cent Cu, 40.5 Zn, 0.75 Sn, 1 Fe, 0.5 Al, and 0.25 Mn. *Alcumite* is an alloy of copper, aluminum, and iron. The hydrous copper sulfate, or blue vitriol, is used in calico printing, in galvanic cells, and as a crop nutrient.

In recent years, about 14 states and territories produced copper, with Arizona, Montana, Utah (Fig. 729), New Mexico, Nevada, and Michigan

Fig. 729. Mine of the Utah Copper Division of the Kennecott Copper Corporation at Bingham Canyon, Utah.

as the leading producers. These six states contribute about 97 per cent of the total output. Table 43 shows the approximate production, in normal times, percentage of total production, copper content of the crude ore mined, and the value of gold and silver per ton recovered as by-products in the six leading copper-producing states.

The average copper content of all ores mined in the United States is slightly under 1 per cent. The total output of this country is about 1,100,000 short tons. Approximately 475,000 short tons of secondary copper are recovered annually. The world's production is about 3,750,000 short tons.

Table 43

Copper-producing state	Approximate production, pounds	Per cent of total production	Approximate per cent in ore	Approximate value in gold and silver per ton
Arizona	800,000,000	42	0.82	$0.13
Utah	500,000,000	30	0.85	0.62
Montana	155,000,000	8	1.71	0.50
New Mexico	145,000,000	8	0.74	0.02
Nevada	125,000,000	7	0.79	0.30
Michigan	50,000,000	2	0.57	*

* Recent figures not available.

FLUORINE

FLUORITE, 322	CaF_2	Cubic
CRYOLITE, 323	Na_3AlF_6	Monoclinic
APATITE, 351	$Ca_5F(PO_4)_3$	Hexagonal
TOPAZ, 372	$Al_2(F,OH)_2SiO_4$	Orthorhombic

Fluorite is the most important commercial mineral containing fluorine. About 50 per cent of the domestic fluorite is consumed in the manufacture of basic open-hearth steel, as it gives fluidity to the slag and aids in the removal of phosphorus and sulfur. For every ton of steel produced by the open-hearth process 6 pounds of fluorspar are required. For this purpose, the fluorite should contain at least 80 per cent calcium fluoride, less than 6 per cent silica, and 0.3 per cent sulfur. Other uses are as flux in blast furnaces, iron foundries, silver, copper, and lead smelters, and in the manufacture of glass and enamelware and of hydrofluoric acid; also in the preparation of organic fluorinated compounds for insect sprays and in making Freon 12 (used extensively as a refrigerant). Because of its low refractive and dispersive powers, fluorite is in demand for apochromatic lenses, used in telescopes and spectroscopes. Material suitable for this work must be glass clear and free from clouds, gas bubbles, strains, and fractures. When fluorite is fused with bauxite and soda ash, an artificial cryolite is produced. Every ton of aluminum requires 120 pounds of fluorite.

The production, which amounts to about 350,000 short tons, is obtained principally from Illinois, Kentucky, Nevada, Colorado, Utah, and New Mexico, the first two states furnishing about 70 per cent of the total output.

GOLD

NATIVE GOLD, 256	Au	Cubic
Calaverite, 288	$AuTe_2$	Monoclinic

The purity of gold is given in carats, 24 carats being the pure metal. Gold used in jewelry is alloyed with copper and silver to harden it. Most gold used is 14 carats fine, 14 parts gold and 10 parts other metals. The standard gold coin in the United States is 9 parts gold and 1 part copper.

Approximately 60 per cent of the total domestic production of gold is obtained from placers (20 per cent) and dry or siliceous ores (40 per cent). The remaining 40 per cent is recovered from the refining of copper bullion and from copper, lead, and zinc ores. The seven leading states, which produce about 90 per cent of the total output, are California, South Dakota, Alaska, Colorado, Utah, Arizona, and Nevada. The total production in the United States is about 2,000,000 fine ounces, valued at about $70,000,000 based on the price of $35 per ounce. White gold is obtained by fusing gold with a special alloy containing nickel, silver, palladium, and zinc—14 parts of gold and 10 parts of the alloy. Cadmium gives green gold; iron, blue gold; aluminum, purple gold. The largest gold-producing region in the world is the Witwatersrand district of Transvaal, South Africa. The United States is the fourth largest producer. Other important gold-producing countries are Soviet Russia, Canada, Australasia, and Mexico. The world's production amounts to about 28,600,000 fine ounces.

IRON

BORNITE, 277	Cu_5FeS_4	Cubic
CHALCOPYRITE, 280	$CuFeS_2$	Tetragonal
PYRRHOTITE, 281	FeS	Hexagonal
PYRITE, 285	FeS_2	Cubic
MARCASITE, 286	FeS_2	Orthorhombic
ARSENOPYRITE, 287	$FeAsS$	Monoclinic
HEMATITE, 301	Fe_2O_3	Hexagonal
ILMENITE, 303	$FeTiO_3$	Hexagonal
MAGNETITE, 305	$FeFe_2O_4$	Cubic
FRANKLINITE, 306	$(Zn,Mn)Fe_2O_4$	Cubic
CHROMITE, 307	$Fe(Cr,Fe)_2O_4$	Cubic
GOETHITE-LIMONITE, 315	$HFeO_2$	Orthorhombic
SIDERITE, 332	$FeCO_3$	Hexagonal
Melanterite, 344	$FeSO_4.7H_2O$	Monoclinic
Ferberite, 347	$FeWO_4$	Monoclinic
WOLFRAMITE, 347	$(Fe,Mn)WO_4$	Monoclinic

Next to aluminum, iron is the most abundant metal in nature. While there are numerous minerals containing iron, only a few can be regarded as iron ores, namely, hematite, goethite-limonite (brown ore), magnetite, and siderite, with hematite by far the most important, furnishing annually about 80 per cent of all the iron ore mined. A small amount, about 600,-000 tons, of cinder and sinter from the roasting of pyrite in the manufacture of sulfuric acid is shipped as iron ore to steel and blast furnaces.

Fig. 730. Western portion of the Hull-Rust-Mahoning Mine, Hibbing, Minnesota. (*Courtesy United States Steel Corporation.*)

Fig. 731. Iron-ore ship loading at dock at Marquette, Michigan. (*Courtesy Inland Steel Company.*)

The uniformity in iron content in the merchantable ore produced (about 50 per cent) over a long period of years is maintained by mixing ores from different deposits. Most of the iron ore mined is from certain well-defined regions, such as the Lake Superior, the Birmingham, and the Adirondack and Western districts. The Lake Superior district alone produces about 80 per cent of the total output. The mine production of the various districts follows:

Approximate Production in Long Tons (2,240 Pounds)

District	Long tons
Lake Superior (Minnesota, Michigan, and Wisconsin)	95,000,000
Western (Utah, California, Nevada, and Montana)	9,000,000
Birmingham (Alabama), Chattanooga (Tennessee), Georgia, and North Carolina	8,000,000
Adirondack (New York), Cornwall (Pennsylvania), and northern New Jersey	6,000,000

The Mesabi Range in Minnesota is the largest producer in the Lake Superior district, supplying about 70 per cent of the ore of that region (Fig. 730).

Fig. 732. Iron-ore ship unloading at Indiana Harbor, East Chicago, Indiana. (*Courtesy Inland Steel Company.*)

The total production in the United States amounts to about 118,000,000 long tons in normal times. In addition, large amounts of iron are recovered annually from scrap iron.

Copperas (green vitriol) ($FeSO_4.7H_2O$) is the most important iron salt and is used in dyeing, in making inks, and as a disinfectant. Rouge (Fe_2O_3) is used as a polishing powder and as red paint.

LEAD

GALENA, 277	PbS	Cubic
Bournonite, 291	$PbCuSbS_3$	Orthorhombic
CERUSSITE, 335	$PbCO_3$	Orthorhombic
ANGLESITE, 341	$PbSO_4$	Orthorhombic
Crocoite, 346	$PbCrO_4$	Monoclinic
Wulfenite, 349	$PbMoO_4$	Tetragonal
Pyromorphite, 353	$Pb_5Cl(PO_4)_3$	Hexagonal
Vanadinite, 353	$Pb_5Cl(VO_4)_3$	Hexagonal

Galena is the most important source of lead and is frequently associated with zinc and silver ores. Large quantities of metallic lead, alloys of lead, and lead pigments are consumed annually in the trade. *Solder* consists of lead and tin; *type metal*, of lead and antimony; and low fusing alloys, of lead, bismuth, and tin. *Frary metal* is an alloy of lead with small amounts of barium and calcium, and is equal in hardness to the common lead alloy with 15 per cent of antimony. Some of the pigments obtained from lead, such as sublimed white lead (lead sulfate, 75 per cent; lead oxide, 20 per cent; and zinc oxide, 5 per cent) and sublimed blue lead (lead sulfate, 45 to 53 per cent; lead oxide, 38 to 41 per cent; with small amounts of lead sulfide, lead sulfite, and zinc oxide), are smelted directly from the ore. Pigments chemically prepared from pig lead include white lead (basic carbonate), red lead, and litharge. Large amounts of lead oxides are used in storage batteries. Other uses include atomic shielding and preparation of tetraethyl lead.

The lead ores from the Mississippi Valley and southeastern Missouri contain little or no silver, and the lead produced from them is designated as "soft" lead, in distinction from the "hard" lead obtained from many western desilverized lead-antimony ores. Antimonial lead, or hard lead, is used in the manufacture of storage batteries, bearing metals, corrosion-resistant alloys, and type metal. A distribution of the total lead consumed by uses indicates 42 per cent for metallic products, 30 per cent storage batteries, 11 per cent pigments, 14 per cent chemical products, and 3 per cent miscellaneous. The refined primary lead produced from domestic ores is approximately 350,000 short tons each year, obtained principally from Missouri, Idaho, Utah, Colorado, Montana, and Arizona. In addition, about 150,000 short tons of refined lead are obtained annually from foreign ores and 500,000 short tons are recovered as secondary lead mainly from scrap and lead alloys.

LITHIUM

Amblygonite, 351	$LiAl(F,OH)PO_4$	Triclinic
TOURMALINE, 381	$M_7Al_6(OH,F)_4(BO_3)_3Si_6O_{18}$	Hexagonal
SPODUMENE, 387	$LiAlSi_2O_6$	Monoclinic
Lepidolite, 400	$K_2Li_3Al_3(F,OH)_4(AlSi_3O_{10})_2$	Monoclinic

Spodumene and lepidolite have been used in the glass and ceramic industries. Lithium metal was one of the first elements fissioned to produce alpha particles under the impact of highly accelerated protons. Minute quantities of metallic lithium impart valuable properties to certain metals (aluminum, lead, magnesium, zinc) and alloys, increasing the hardness, toughness, and tensile strength. In alloys of iron, nickel, and copper, lithium acts as a degasifier, deoxidizer, and purifying agent. The lithium is introduced as a calcium-lithium alloy. Lithium salts are used to a limited extent in pharmaceutical and other chemical products.

Fig. 733. Gigantic crystals of spodumene, Etta Mine, near Keystone, South Dakota. (*Photograph by South Dakota School of Mines.*)

The bromide and iodide are used in photography and the chloride in fireworks and for dehumidifying air for air conditioning and industrial drying. Several new uses for lithium compounds include lithium peroxide, lithium borohydride, and lithium diborane for generating oxygen and hydrogen, and lithium-aluminum hydride, which reduces organic compounds at room temperature in ether solutions. Other uses for lithium include lubricants, brazing fluxes, for nuclear shielding, in catalytic processes and in alkaline storage and dry-cell batteries.

The production of lithium minerals in the United States is increasing, amounting to about 27,000 short tons, obtained from North Carolina, South Dakota (Fig. 733), California, and New Mexico. The brines of Searles Lake, near Trona, California, are the most important sources of lithium compounds, especially lithium sodium phosphate.

MAGNESIUM

SPINEL, 304	$MgAl_2O_4$	Cubic
Brucite, 318	$Mg(OH)_2$	Hexagonal
DOLOMITE, 329	$CaMg(CO_3)_2$	Hexagonal
MAGNESITE, 330	$MgCO_3$	Hexagonal
Espomite, 344	$MgSO_4.7H_2O$	Orthorhombic
OLIVINE, 363	$(Mg,Fe)_2SiO_4$	Orthorhombic
TALC, 395	$Mg_3(OH)_2Si_4O_{10}$	Monoclinic
SERPENTINE, 402	$Mg_6(OH)_8Si_4O_{10}$	Monoclinic
Garnierite, 404	$(Ni,Mg)_6(OH)_8Si_4O_{10}$	Monoclinic
Sepiolite, 405	$Mg_4(OH)_2Si_6O_{15}.6H_2O$	Monoclinic

Magnesium and its compounds serve industry in five principal ways: (1) as a refractory oxide, (2) as heat-resisting materials in the form of basic magnesium carbonate, (3) as magnesite cement, (4) as magnesium salts, chiefly the chloride and sulfate, and (5) as metallic magnesium. The uses and production of magnesite, dolomite, and talc only will be discussed.

Magnesite. Nearly all magnesite is used in the calcined condition. Depending upon the temperature of burning, the product is either "caustic" calcined or "dead-burned" magnesite. The *caustic* magnesia results from a moderate heat-treatment (700 to 1200°C.) and retains 3 to 8 per cent carbon dioxide. This product is chemically active, combining readily with magnesium chloride forming an oxychloride, or Sorel cement. This cement solidifies into an extremely hard and strong mass and is the basis of many of the sanitary flooring and stucco preparations placed upon the market under various trade names. Fillers in this cement may be cork, talc, asbestos, clay, crushed marble, sand, etc. Magnesite cement floors may be laid in large areas without cracking. They take color easily and are susceptible to polish. It is claimed that the surface does not pulverize or dust.

Dead-burned magnesite is the result of heating to incipient fusion (1450 to 1500°C.). The product is chemically inert. This material is employed for refractory purposes, such as brick and linings in open-hearth steel and electric furnaces and in copper converters. As a refractory substance, magnesia must not only resist corrosion but, in addition, must possess sufficient bonding to retain its form in the furnace. If iron oxide is present, it acts as a binder; if absent in the crude ore, it is added in the calcining process.

Magnesite, raw or calcined, is also used in the manufacture of magnesium sulfate, employed in medicine and in the textile industries; magnesium chloride, for making Sorel cement; and magnesium bisulfite, for disintegrating wood and dissolving the noncellulose matter in the manufacture of wood-pulp paper. The basic carbonate known as *magnesia alba* is used in fire-retarding paint and as a nonconductor of heat in coverings for steam pipes. Natural brines and bitterns also furnish considerable chloride and sulfate of magnesium.

Magnesium-thorium alloys have high strength and are used in jet-engine castings, supersonic air-frame construction, and satellite rockets. The production of metallic magnesium which reached an all-time high of about 180,000 tons during the Second World War (1943)—largely for the production of aircraft, incendiaries, and other military uses—and aluminum alloys is about 70,000 tons. New uses are being constantly developed in the general fields of portable equipment and reciprocating- and rotating-machine parts. The metal makes good castings, machines well, and is about one-third lighter than aluminum and two to four times as strong. Alloys of magnesium with lithium, beryllium, thorium, zinc, and aluminum can readily be prepared. The latter is known as *magnalium*. Metallic magnesium is also used as scavenging alloys (removing oxygen and nitrogen), as a reducing agent in preparing titanium and zirconium, and for military illumination in the form of shrapnel trailers, star bombs, and flare lights. *Dow metal* is an alloy of magnesium (90 to 98 per cent), aluminum (0 to 10 per cent), and small amounts of manganese (0.3 to 1.5 per cent). New alloys, notably with cerium and zirconium, are being investigated.

Much of the domestic consumption of primary magnesium has been supplied since 1927 by the Dow Chemical Company, by electrolysis of fused magnesium chloride derived from brines and sea water.

The domestic production of magnesite is obtained mainly from Washington, Nevada, Texas, and California and amounts to about 500,000 short tons.

Dolomite. The less expensive dolomite may be substituted for many of the uses given for magnesite above. This is true especially in the preparation of basic magnesium carbonate used in sheets and as pipe covering, and magnesium bisulfite used in paper manufacture. Likewise the quantity of dead-burned dolomite, used for refractory materials, exceeds the quantity of dead-burned magnesite. Dolomite is also an important source of carbon dioxide. About 2,300,000 short tons of crude dolomite are sold for these purposes annually.

Talc and Soapstone. Talc and soapstone are, as a rule, not found together. New York, North Carolina, California, and Vermont are the leading talc-producing states, furnishing about 76 per cent of the total domestic output, which amounts to about 760,000 short tons annually. Five industries—paint, rubber, roofing, ceramics, and insecticides—consume about 78 per cent of the domestic production of talc. It has been shown that 15 to 20 per cent of talc imparts to ceramic products improved physical properties and greater resistance to thermal shock. Accordingly, it is an important ingredient of electric-stove plates, gas-stove back walls, radiants, and saggers. Talc when used in the manufacture of wall tile and semivitreous bodies reduces crazing and warping. Talc is also used as a filler in the manufacture of paper, linoleum, oil cloth, textile fabrics, and rubber, for foundry facing, in crayons, lubricants, toilet powders, and as a waterproofing agent in concrete. Almost the entire supply of soapstone in the United States is obtained from Nelson and Albemarle counties, Virginia. This material is largely employed in the manufacture of laundry tubs, laboratory table tops, sinks, chemical hoods, firebrick, griddles, acid tanks, switchboards, insulators, furnace linings, and so forth. Pyrophyllite, an aluminum silicate possessing many of the same physical properties of talc, has frequently been substituted for talc.

MANGANESE

FRANKLINITE, 306	$(Zn,Mn)Fe_2O_4$	Cubic
Hausmannite, 308	$MnMn_2O_4$	Tetragonal
PYROLUSITE, 311	MnO_2	Tetragonal
MANGANITE, 315	$MnO(OH)$	Orthorhombic
Psilomelane group, 318		
RHODOCHROSITE, 331	$MnCO_3$	Hexagonal
WOLFRAMITE, 347	$(Fe,Mn)WO_4$	Monoclinic
Huebnerite, 348	$MnWO_4$	Monoclinic
RHODONITE, 388	$MnSiO_3$	Triclinic

Only the oxides and carbonate are the important ores of manganese. The economic demand for manganese is due largely to the importance of its alloys, especially *ferromanganese*, *spiegeleisen*, and *silicomanganese*. About 95 per cent of the manganese produced is used in the manufacture of steel. It is estimated that 13 pounds of manganese, in the form of an alloy, are added to every ton of steel produced. Ferromanganese contains about 50 per cent manganese and is used in making open-hearth steel, while spiegeleisen consists of 5 to 20 per cent manganese and finds employment in the Bessemer process. The role of manganese is to improve the rolling and forging qualities, to produce a harder steel, and to act at the same time as a deoxidizing and desulfurizing agent. Manganese is also used in special bronzes and in nearly all commercial alloys of aluminum and magnesium.

The oxide MnO_2 finds employment in the manufacture of chlorine and bromine. It is also used as a drier in paints and varnishes, to color glass and pottery, and in making flint glass and dry batteries. For dry batteries, the ore should contain at least 80 per cent MnO_2, less than 1 per cent iron, and under 0.05 per cent copper, nickel, or cobalt.

Manganese sulfate is used as a fertilizer in limestone soils. Other useful chemical salts of manganese include barium manganate (green pigment), manganese arsenate (insecticide), and manganese phosphate (protective coating for steel).

The chief sources of manganese are (1) manganese ores, which should contain not less than 35 per cent manganese and less than 8 per cent silica, 6 per cent iron, and 0.15 per cent phosphorus; (2) manganiferous iron ores, which contain 5 to 35 per cent manganese; (3) manganiferous silver ores, which are used largely as a flux in smelting precious and semiprecious metals; and (4) manganiferous zinc residues.

The domestic production of manganese ores (about 225,000 short tons) is by no means equal to the demand, and importations from Soviet Russia, Brazil, India, Cuba, Union of South Africa, Mexico, and from Ghana of West Africa are absolutely necessary. Normally, the United States uses about 2,400,000 long tons of manganese ore, or about one-fourth of the world's consumption, and depends upon foreign sources for about 90 per cent of this amount.

MERCURY

CINNABAR, 282	HgS	Hexagonal

Cinnabar is the chief source of mercury. Mercury and its compounds are used in pharmaceutical products, as catalysts in chemical warfare, fulminate for detonating high explosives, antifouling paint for ship bottoms, dental amalgams, electrical apparatus, thermometers, barometers, gauges and other scientific instruments, amalgamation of gold ores, and in boilers for generating power. Mercuric oxide is used in a new dry-cell battery, the chloride (calomel) in medicine, and the sulfide (vermilion) and the red oxide as pigments. Antifouling paints contain the oxide which the chlorides in the sea water convert into mercuric chloride, which serves as an effective poison.

The average content of mercury recovered from the domestic ores is lower than that obtained from ores of Italy and Spain. The domestic production of mercury amounts to about 24,000 flasks of 76 pounds each, while the consumption is about 50,000 flasks. California is an important source in the United States, as well as Nevada, Oregon, Idaho, and Alaska. Italy and Spain furnish about 60 per cent of the world's supply.

MOLYBDENUM

MOLYBDENITE, 288	MoS_2	Hexagonal
Wulfenite, 349	$PbMoO_4$	Tetragonal

By far the chief use of molybdenum is in the manufacture of special steels to increase their hardness and strength. A typical steel contains 6 per cent Mo, 6 per cent W, 4 per cent Cr, and 3 per cent V. Molybdenum and tungsten can be substituted for each other. It is added in the form of molybdenum oxide, calcium molybdate, or as a ferro- or manganese-molybdenum alloy (50 to 75 per cent molybdenum). A nickel molybdenum alloy is used in wire drawing. A chrome-molybdenum steel has been used rather extensively in automobile construction. "Alloy 548" used for steel-cutting tools contains about 30 per cent Co, 19 W, 3 Mo, 2 V, low C, and the remainder Fe. It is given a high-temperature heat-treatment at 1275°C. Several alloys of molybdenum, titanium, and nickel carbides have been prepared for special cutting tools; and the use of molybdenum boride, carbide, nitride, or silicide in percussion drills has also been proposed. Molybdenum is likewise used for electronic tubes, grids, plates, and reflectors in vacuum and X-ray tubes, and for windings in electric furnaces. The use of molybdenum chemicals is increasing. Sodium and ammonium molybdates are employed to some extent in fireproofing fabrics and in dyeing leather, silk, and wool, and as a fertilizer. As a lubricant, molybdenite is preferable to graphite, especially for high-pressure work.

The United States is the largest producer of molybdenum concentrates in the world (about 90 per cent), the production being equivalent to about 30,000 short tons of metallic molybdenum. The ore mined is of low grade (under 1 per cent MoS_2); the chief deposits are in Colorado, Utah, New Mexico, Arizona, and Nevada. Some molybdenum is also recovered as a by-product from copper and uranium ores.

NICKEL

Niccolite, 281	NiAs	Hexagonal
Millerite, 281	NiS	Hexagonal
Pentlandite, 282	$(Fe,Ni)_9S_8$	Cubic
Garnierite, 404	$(Ni,Mg)_6(OH)_8Si_4O_{10}$	Monoclinic

To the above, nickeliferous pyrrhotite, FeS, should be added; page 281.

The demand for nickel is due largely to the importance of its ferrous alloys. One of the largest outlets for nickel is for chromium-nickel stainless steels. The addition of 2 to 3.50 per cent of nickel to steel increases both its elasticity and tensile strength. Nickel is used, together with chromium, molybdenum, and vanadium, in many types of special steels employed for structural purposes. *Invar*, an alloy of iron containing 36 per cent nickel, is not affected by temperature changes and is used for scientific instruments, pendulums, and steel tapes. Other important alloys are *coinage metal* (75 per cent copper and 25 per cent nickel); *German silver* (55 per cent copper, 27 per cent zinc, and 18 per cent nickel); *nichrome* (nickel and chromium) used as a substitute for platinum in electrical resistance, crucible triangles, and as heating elements in electric appliances; and *permalloy*, used as a medium for rapidly transmitting messages by cable. It contains 80 per cent nickel and 20 per cent iron.

Monel is obtained by smelting the Sudbury ores without separating the metals and consists of 67 per cent nickel, 28 per cent copper, and 5 per cent other metals, mostly iron and manganese. This alloy has a tensile strength equal to that of nickel steel and is very resistive to corrosive agents. It is used for propellers, acid pumps, valves on high-pressure steam lines, valve stems, pickling apparatus for sheet and tin plate, and laundry and kitchen equipment. Nickel also forms alloys with copper, aluminum, and zinc. Nickel is also used for plating metals. Nickel-plated iron serves as a base for chromium plating.

The world's production of new or primary nickel, which amounts to about 225,000 short tons of the metal, is obtained principally from the copper and nickel ores of Sudbury, Ontario, and from northern Manitoba (furnishing about 80 per cent), from Cuban laterite deposits, and from the garnierite ores of New Caledonia. No nickel ores are mined in the United States, although an equivalent of about 600 short tons of nickel is obtained annually as a by-product in the electrolytic refining of copper and about 8,000 tons from scrap. The imports each year are mainly for Canada, chiefly in the form of ore, matte, alloys, and nickel oxide, and total about 140,000 short tons.

NIOBIUM (See Columbium)

NITROGEN

SODA NITER, 325	$NaNO_3$	Hexagonal
Niter, 325	KNO_3	Orthorhombic

While small quantities of sodium nitrate have been found in caves and disseminated through clays in several of the Western states, no deposits that can be depended upon to produce considerable amounts have been discovered in this country. Sodium nitrate is obtained almost entirely from the arid regions of northern Chile (Fig. 734). The crude ore (caliche), containing about 25 per cent $NaNO_3$, yields after leaching with hot water a product of 95 per cent purity. Synthetic nitrogen compounds involving atmospheric nitrogen are replacing the use of the naturally occurring soda niter.

In normal times about 600,000 short tons of niter or Chile saltpeter are imported annually. This is used principally as a fertilizer to promote stalk growth in plants, for munitions, and also in the manufacture of nitric and sulfuric acids.

Niter (saltpeter) occurs in very limited quantities in nature, hence is of minor importance commercially.

The synthetic cubic boron nitride (*borazon*), recently prepared by the General Electric Company, has the same general range of hardness as the diamond and is a very effective abrasive.

Fig. 734. Plant for the refining of crude sodium nitrate, Maria Elena, Chile. (*Courtesy Anglo-Chilean Nitrate Corporation.*)

PHOSPHORUS

Monazite, 350	$(Ce,La)PO_4$	Monoclinic
Triphylite, 351	$Li(Fe,Mn)PO_4$	Orthorhombic
Amblygonite, 351	$LiAl(F,OH)PO_4$	Triclinic
APATITE, 351	$Ca_5F(PO_4)_3$	Hexagonal
Pyromorphite, 353	$Pb_5Cl(PO_4)_3$	Hexagonal
Vivianite, 354	$Fe_3(PO_4)_2.8H_2O$	Monoclinic
Wavellite, 355	$Al_3(OH)_3(PO_4)_2.5H_2O$	Orthorhombic
Turquois, 355	$CuAl_6(OH)_8(PO_4)_4.4H_2O$	Triclinic

Plant life requires soluble phosphates, and an impure massive calcium carbonate-phosphate (collophane), known as *phosphate rock,* a variety of apatite, furnishes the raw material to supply this need. By treating the raw ground rock with approximately an equal weight of sulfuric acid, a superphosphate is formed which is readily assimilated by plants. About 85 per cent of the phosphate rock produced is used in the manufacture of superphosphates. When briquets composed of phosphate rock and pulverized coal are smelted with coke and silica gravel in a blast or electric furnace, ferrophosphorus, elemental phosphorus, anhydrous phosphorus pentoxide, and liquid phosphoric acid are produced. Trisodium phosphate is made from the ferrophosphorus. Phosphate chemicals are used in the silk industry, baking powders, beverages, water softeners, manufacture of glass and ceramic products, and in sugar refining.

Under normal conditions, the United States produces annually about 15,800,000 long tons of phosphate rock. Of this amount Florida furnishes about 75 per cent. Tennessee is also a large producer. Enormous deposits of phosphate rock have been located in the Western states, particularly in Idaho, Utah, Wyoming, and Montana, but the production thus far from these western localities is moderate (about 14 per cent). Aside from the United States, other important producers of phosphate rock include French Morocco, Tunisia, Soviet Russia, Algeria, and the Pacific Islands (Nauru, Oceania, Christmas).

PLATINUM

NATIVE PLATINUM, 262	Pt	Cubic
Sperrylite, 286	$PtAs_2$	Cubic

Of the various members of the platinum group, platinum, palladium, and iridium are the chief ones of commercial importance at present.

Some of the important uses of platinum are as a catalytic agent in the manufacture of sulfuric, acetic, and nitric acids, and for producing high-octane gasoline. Because of its high fusibility and resistance to acids, platinum is in great demand in the manufacture of chemical, physical, and electrical apparatus. It is also employed in certain parts of the ignition systems of internal-combustion engines. Platinum is also used for electric-furnace windings for temperatures up to 2600°F. and as pins in dental work. The jewelry trade likewise consumes considerable amounts, estimated at about 15 per cent of the total platinum used in this country. As iridium imparts hardness to platinum, the so-called platinum used in electrical work and by jewelers is an alloy of platinum, iridium (10 to 15 per cent), tantalum, and palladium. Palladium finds employment in electronic tubes and in dental alloys to replace gold; as palladium leaf is silver white in color, but nontarnishable, it is used in jewelry and for decorative effects. *Palau* (80 per cent gold and 20 per cent palladium) is marketed as a substitute for platinum in chemical ware. Platinum with 10 per cent rhodium is used for thermocouples. The high price of platinum has greatly stimulated research for suitable substitutes, and alloys of palladium with gold and silver, tungsten, and molybdenum have, in certain instances, replaced the more expensive metal.

The disintegration of basic magnesium rocks, such as peridotite, dunite, hornblendite, and pyroxenite, containing disseminated platinum, has frequently resulted in the concentration of the metal in platinum placers. The world's production of platinum comes largely from Canada (from the nickel ore of the Sudbury district), Soviet Russia, Colombia, and the Union of South Africa.

The United States produces a very small amount of the platinum consumed. About 24,000 troy ounces of platinum are recovered annually, mainly from the placers in Alaska, California, and Oregon. In addition, about 5,000 troy ounces of refined metals of the platinum group are obtained as by-products in the refining of domestic copper matte and gold bullion. A considerable amount of secondary platinum (65,000 troy ounces) is also recovered from the refining of scrap and sweeps. The imports of platinum in the United States are about 600,000 troy ounces yearly. It is estimated that the world's known workable deposits of platinum could supply an annual production of about 950,000 troy ounces of new platinum and allied metals with the Union of South Africa, Canada, and U.S.S.R. supplying about 95 per cent.

POTASSIUM

Sylvite, 321	KCl	Cubic
Polyhalite, 321	$K_2Ca_2Mg(SO_4)_4.2H_2O$	Triclinic
Kainite, 321	$KMgClSO_4.3H_2O$	Monoclinic
Alunite, 342	$KAl_3(OH)_6(SO_4)_2$	Hexagonal
Langbeinite, 468	$K_2Mg_2(SO_4)_3$	Cubic

Potassium chloride and sulfate are used in large quantities as fertilizers Other potassium salts are also essential in certain industries. Thus caustic potash is used in the manufacture of the better grades of soap; the hydrated carbonate in cut glass, optical glass, and incandescent-light bulbs; the chlorate in matches; the nitrate in black powders; the bichromate in dyeing and tanning; the cyanide as a solvent in extracting gold from ores; the ferricyanide in photography. Medicinal and other chemical uses demand varying amounts of potassium salts.

The present production in the United States, which amounts to the equivalent of about 2,500,000 short tons of K_2O, is about equal to the consumption. Minor domestic sources are from natural brines in California, Utah, Michigan, and from flue dust of cement kilns. Core drillings in western Texas and southeastern New Mexico have revealed at depths from 800 to 2,000 feet beds of potash minerals—polyhalite, sylvite, langbeinite, kainite. These deposits are at present the most important sources of potash. Recently, enormous deposits of potassium salts, mainly sylvite, have been discovered in Saskatchewan, Canada.

SILICON

QUARTZ, 293	SiO_2	Hexagonal
OPAL, 313	$SiO_2.nH_2O$	Amorphous

Silicon is also an essential constituent of all silicates.

The greatest demand for quartz comes from the building trade. The value of sandstone (including quartzite), for all purposes, sold in the United States in normal years is about $28,000,000, which represents about 6 per cent of the total value of all stone sold each year. The three leading states which contribute nearly 75 per cent of the total value of sandstone are Ohio, Pennsylvania, and Tennessee.

Quartz crystals are used in ornaments and in making lenses and prisms for certain optical instruments. Other uses include quartz oscillator plates for wave-frequency control in electric circuits, especially in telephonic and radio communications. Quartz for this purpose has come largely from Brazil. Crystals of quartz of excellent quality can be produced by laboratory methods.

The best-known application of the element silicon is in rectifiers and transistors; also in the preparation of various silicides and silicones.

SILVER

NATIVE SILVER, 258	Ag	Cubic
Argentite, 276	Ag_2S	Pseudocubic
Pyrargyrite, 289	Ag_3SbS_3	Hexagonal
Proustite, 290	Ag_3AsS_3	Hexagonal
Miagyrite, 291	$AgSbS_2$	Monoclinic
Stephanite, 291	Ag_5SbS_4	Orthorhombic
Pearceite, 291	$(Ag,Cu)_{16}As_2S_{11}$	Monoclinic
Polybasite, 291	$(Ag,Cu)_{16}Sb_2S_{11}$	Monoclinic
Cerargyrite, 322	$AgCl$	Cubic

Practically all the silver is obtained as a by-product from gold, nickel, copper, lead, and zinc ores.

The four most important sources of silver in the United States which furnish annually about 98 per cent of this country's total output are dry or siliceous ores (28 per cent), copper ores (25 per cent), lead ores (5 per cent), and lead-zinc ores (40 per cent).

Siliceous ores are those consisting mainly of quartz with small amounts of gold and silver. Some of the chief deposits of this type are at Tonopah, Nevada; the Tintic district, Utah; San Juan, Leadville, and Aspen, Colorado; Granite, Jefferson, and Silver Bow counties, Montana; and California. The important silver-bearing copper ores are found at Butte, Montana; in the Bingham and Tintic districts, Utah; and at Bisbee and Jerome, Arizona. Deposits of argentiferous galena are mined in the Coeur d'Alene district, Idaho; the Park City and Tintic districts, Utah; and at Aspen and Leadville, Colorado.

Small additions of silver impart hardness to commutator bars. Silver used as coinage contains 90 per cent silver and 10 per cent copper, while *sterling silver* has 92.5 per cent silver and 7.5 per cent copper. Silver is also used in electroplating tableware and other articles that have as a base either nickel, brass, or britannia metal (tin, antimony, copper, and zinc). Silver is likewise employed in alloys for jewelry and dental purposes. *Dental amalgam* consists of an alloy of silver and tin with small amounts of copper and zinc in a powder form. When used, the powder is mixed with mercury. Silver salts find employment in photography and in chemistry.

The normal domestic production is 35 to 40,000,000 troy ounces. The following six states are important producers: Idaho, Utah, Montana, Colorado, Arizona, and Nevada. The world's production of silver is about 225,000,000 ounces.

SODIUM

HALITE, 319	NaCl	Cubic
CRYOLITE, 323	Na_3AlF_6	Monoclinic
SODA NITER, 325	$NaNO_3$	Hexagonal

In addition to the above minerals there are many silicates which contain sodium as a minor constituent.

Fig. 735. Mining rock salt 1,131 feet below the surface, Detroit, Michigan. The salt layer is about 30 feet thick. (*Courtesy International Salt Company.*)

Halite or salt, as produced in this country, is of two types, either rock salt or brine salt. Rock salt often occurs in beds of great thickness (Fig. 735) and is mined by means of shafts. The annual output of rock salt is about 4,500,000 short tons. Brine salt may be made from natural or artificial brines. In the majority of cases, fresh water is forced through drill holes to the salt beds and the artificial brine then pumped to the surface. The salt is obtained by the evaporation of the brine by either solar or vacuum-pan processes. Other chemical products produced from the brine include salt cake, soda ash, caustic soda, sodium bicarbonate, sodium acetate, sodium chlorate, sodium phosphate, Glauber's salt, calcium chloride, bromine, potassium and sodium bromides, ethylene dibromide, iodine, chlorine, and hydrochloric acid.

The United States furnishes practically all the salt consumed in this country, and the supply seems inexhaustible. The domestic production amounts to about 24,000,000 short tons (equivalent to about 172,000,000 barrels of 280 pounds). Although 16 states report a production, the seven leading producers are:

	Short Tons
Michigan	5,125,000
New York	3,300,000
Ohio	3,100,000
Louisiana	3,100,000
Texas	2,850,000
California	1,125,000
Kansas	900,000

STRONTIUM

STRONTIANITE, 334	$SrCO_3$	Orthorhombic
CELESTITE, 339	$SrSO_4$	Orthorhombic

The principal sources of supply are the United Kingdom and Mexico. Strontium chemicals and ore, imported into the United States, total about 28,000 tons annually. The carbonate is the more valuable ore, as it can be easily converted into the various salts, but the sulfate is more abundant. Strontium salts are used in pyrotechnics, for the recovery of sugar in beet-sugar refineries, as a lead replacement in certain enamels, and in medicine. Small quantities of strontium metal and its alloys are used as "getters" for extracting traces of gases from electronic tubes.

SULFUR

NATIVE SULFUR, 264	S	Orthorhombic
PYRITE, 285	FeS_2	Cubic
MARCASITE, 286	FeS_2	Orthorhombic

Sulfur is also an essential constituent of sulfides and sulfates.

Deposits of native sulfur in Culberson, Fort Bend, Wharton, and Brazoria counties, Texas (Fig. 736), and Iberia and Plaquemines parishes, Louisiana, furnish about 99 per cent of the entire output of this country. Occurrences of minor importance are known in Wyoming, Utah, Nevada, California, and Colorado. The annual production of sulfur is about 7,000,000 long tons. At present, the bulk of the sulfur employed in the manufacture of sulfuric acid is obtained from the native element, the balance coming from pyrite and from copper- and zinc-bearing sulfides, which are burned to sulfur dioxide. The domestic production of pyrite is about 900,000 long tons, while about 100,000 tons are imported annually, mainly from Spain and Canada. In the manufacture of paper, it is estimated that $\frac{1}{8}$ ton of sulfur is used for each ton of sulfite pulp produced.

The production of sulfuric acid (100 per cent H_2SO_4) is about 13,000,000 tons annually. The acid is used largely in the manufacture of fertilizers, sulfate of ammonia, and alum, in the steel industry (for pickling purposes), for the purification of petroleum, and in the manufacture of explosives, rayon and textiles, coal-tar products, paints, and pigments.

Fig. 736. Storage vats of sulfur at Newgulf, Texas. Each completed vat is 1,200 feet long, 180 feet wide, and 50 feet high, and contains approximately 500,000 long tons of sulfur. (*Courtesy Texas Gulf Sulphur Company.*)

TANTALUM

See Columbium (Niobium)

COLUMBITE, 312	$(Fe,Mn)(Cb,Ta)_2O_6$	Orthorhombic
Tantalite, 312	$(Fe,Mn)(Ta,Cb)_2O_6$	Orthorhombic
Microlite, 318	$(Ca,Na)_2Ta_2O_6(O,OH,F)$	Cubic

To the above, pyrochlore, $(Na,Ca)_2Cb_2O_6F$, cubic, should be added.

TIN

CASSITERITE, 310	SnO_2	Tetragonal

The United States is the world's leading consumer of tin, owing largely to its canning and automobile industries. While cassiterite, which is the only source of tin, is rather widely distributed, only in a few places are the occurrences of the mineral of commercial importance. The production of cassiterite in the United States is insignificant, although approximately the equivalent of about 28,000 long tons of secondary tin are recovered annually from tin-plate clippings, tin-bearing alloys, and melting-pot drosses. The consumption, on the other hand, in terms of the metal is approximately 80,000 to 85,000 tons annually, nearly 85 per cent of which is used for tin plate, solder, and in babbitt and other bearing metals. Tin plate is made by coating steel sheets with pure tin. One pound of tin, ordinarily, will make 220 square feet of tin plate. *Terneplate* is similar to tin plate, except that an alloy of lead and tin is substituted for pure tin in the coating. *Taggers tin* is extra-thin tin plate. The larger part of the tin plate and taggers tin is used for making food containers. Terneplate is used largely for roofing and for gasoline tanks on automobiles, and some is substituted for tin plate in nonfood-product containers. The artificial oxide of tin is used as a polishing powder.

Tin has the ability to strengthen and harden alloys and improves its castings. Pewter is essentially tin and lead; type metal—tin, antimony, and lead; solder—tin and lead; bronze—copper and tin; babbitt metal—tin 88.9 per cent, antimony 7.4 per cent, and copper 3.7 per cent. Phosphor bronze contains 89 per cent copper, 10 per cent tin, and 1 per cent phosphorus. Deposits have been worked intermittently in Alaska, South Dakota, Texas, North Carolina, South Carolina, and California.

The world's chief sources of tin ore are the Malay States, Bolivia, Netherlands East Indies, China, Thailand, Nigeria, Australia, Union of South Africa, and Cornwall, England. The world's production is not restricted and amounts to about 180,000 tons of metallic tin.

TITANIUM

ILMENITE, 303	$FeTiO_3$	Hexagonal
RUTILE, 309	TiO_2	Tetragonal
SPHENE, 374	$CaTiOSiO_4$	Monoclinic

Ilmenite is the most important source of titanium and its compounds. Rutile and ilmenite are both used in making *ferrotitanium* and *ferrocarbon-titanium*, which, when added to steel, serve as deoxidizing agents. They also increase the tensile strength of the steel. These alloys contain 15 to 25 per cent titanium. Rutile is likewise the source of titanium for *cuprotitanium* used in brass and other copper-bearing alloys. Titanium-aluminum bronze, which is extremely resistant to the action of sea water and chemical liquors, possesses physical properties equaling those of phosphor and manganese bronzes, although it is considerably lighter than either. Titanium also finds employment in welding-rod coatings and as carbide cutting tools. One of the greatest demands for titanium is in the form of the oxide. The oxide of titanium is used as an opacifier in enamelware, also as a white pigment, as it is chemically inert, nontoxic, and possesses high covering power. Titanium tetrachloride is used as a smokescreen.

Paints containing titanium pigments wear down evenly without cracking or peeling. The greater part of the titanium pigment used is a composite pigment of TiO_2 (75 per cent) and $BaSO_4$ (25 per cent), known as *titanox*. Lithopone-titanium pigments are also on the market. Titanium oxide is also used in the manufacture of lacquer enamels and rayon, rubber, glass, and certain types of lightweight paper of high opacity.

The Virginia mines and the beach deposits of Florida produce some rutile and ilmenite concentrates, which partially supply the demand for titanium. The titaniferous magnetite of the Adirondack region in New York is another possible source. Imports of titanium ores and slag are obtained from India, Norway, Brazil, Canada, and Australia. The domestic production of titanium ores amounts to about 685,000 short tons.

TUNGSTEN

Ferberite, 347	$FeWO_4$	Monoclinic
WOLFRAMITE, 347	$(Fe,Mn)WO_4$	Monoclinic
Huebnerite, 348	$MnWO_4$	Monoclinic
SCHEELITE, 349	$CaWO_4$	Tetragonal

While in other countries wolframite is the most important ore of tungsten, in the United States both scheelite and ferberite surpass it in importance. Over 90 per cent of the tungsten mined is converted into ferroalloys and tungsten steels for jet-aircraft construction. American high-speed tool steels used for rapid cutting are capable of holding their temper at a red heat. They contain about 18 per cent tungsten, 4 per cent chromium, and 1 per cent vanadium. In some cases, 3 to 5 per cent of cobalt is also added. These steels are also used for armor plate and for projectiles. Tungsten alloys readily with many metals, and some of these alloys have been proposed as substitutes for platinum, particularly a tungsten-molybdenum alloy for dental work. *Carboloy* is an alloy of tungsten carbide and cobalt and is used for core drilling and high-speed machine tools and for dies for drawing wire.

Metallic tungsten has an exceedingly high melting point (3370°C.) and finds employment as targets in X-ray tubes, filaments in incandescent lights, in radio tubes, and as electrical contact points in automobile-engine timers and voltage regulators. Manufacturers of tungsten lamp filaments usually introduce a small amount of thorium oxide into the metal. This retards crystallization and assists in preventing the filaments from becoming brittle when heated. In radio tubes the presence of some thorium is likewise necessary for the emission of electrons in the proper functioning of the tubes. Sodium tungstate is used in fireproof cloth and calcium tungstate as a luminous screen in X-ray apparatus.

The production of tungsten ores in the United States is equivalent to about 16,000 short tons of concentrates containing 60 per cent WO_3. The domestic production is obtained mainly from Mill City, Nevada, and the Atolia district, California. Other producing localities include Boulder County, Colorado; Idaho; and North Carolina. The world's production of concentrates is about 80,000 short tons, and about one-third of this amount comes from China. Important foreign producers include Burma, Brazil, Bolivia, Portugal, Korea, U.S.S.R., and China.

URANIUM

URANINITE, 312	UO_2	Cubic
Carnotite, 356	$K_2(UO_2)_2(VO_4)_2.3H_2O$	Orthorhombic

To the above, autunite, $Ca(UO_2)_2(PO_4)_2.10\text{-}12H_2O$, orthorhombic, should be added.

Consumption of uranium for nonenergy purposes is extremely small. Alloys of uranium include *ferro-uranium* and *aluminum-uranium. Ferro-uranium* is used to a limited extent in high-speed steel, while *aluminum-uranium* finds employment in nonferrous metals. Uranium compounds are employed to some extent in coloring glass yellow with a green reflex; in photography; in the ceramic industry to impart yellow, brown, gray, and velvety tints; and as a mordant for silk and wool. Radium is frequently recovered from uranium minerals. The amount present, however, is extremely small, about ⅓ mg. of radium in 1 kg. (2.2046 pounds) of uranium. The chief uses of radium are in therapeutics (treatment of cancer and other diseases) and as an illuminant. When used as an illuminant, the radium salt is usually mixed with artificial zinc sulfide and some cementing material, such as amyl acetate. The alpha rays given off by the radium salt strike the particles of zinc sulfide and cause them to glow. Radium is also used for the detection of flaws in steel. By placing a tube containing radium on one side of the metal and a photographic plate on the opposite side, flaws are revealed on the developed plate by differences in exposure. Most of the uranium produced currently is being used in producing the artificial element plutonium in nuclear reactor systems for atomic weapons and as a source for industrial power. Radioactive isotopes are also being used in radiation therapy.

Carnotite from southwestern Colorado, southeastern Utah, Globe district, Arizona, and from Wyoming, and ores from northwest New Mexico are domestic sources of uranium minerals. Rich deposits of pitchblende (uraninite) and of the numerous uranium minerals formed from its decomposition are found in Katanga, Belgian Congo. Likewise, important uranium deposits are being worked in the Great Bear Lake region, Mackenzie district, Goldfields district, Saskatchewan, and Blind River district, Ontario, Canada; and in Australia. Thorium when combined with uranium becomes fissionable. Uranium is also recovered as a by-product from the Florida phosphate deposits and from the Rand gold deposits in South Africa. The domestic production of U_3O_8 concentrates amounts to about 8,000 tons.

VANADIUM

Vanadinite, 353	$Pb_5Cl(VO_4)_3$	Hexagonal
Carnotite, 356	$K_2(UO_2)_2(VO_4)_2.3H_2O$	Orthorhombic
Roscoelite, 398	$K(V,Al)_2(OH)_2AlSi_3O_{10}$	Monoclinic

The most important use of vanadium (about 90 per cent) is in the manufacture of special steels, because it removes the objectionable elements oxygen and nitrogen. The small amount of vanadium remaining in the steel increases its toughness, tensile strength, and resistance to shock. In structural steel it is usually employed in combination with chromium, nickel, manganese, boron, and tungsten. Vanadium steel is extensively used for locomotive and automobile cylinders, pistons, and bushings, and also for high-speed tools (see Tungsten), die blocks, and so forth. One of the current uses of vanadium is as a target metal in X-ray applications. Because of their strength and toughness, vanadium bronzes are suitable for trolley wheels and bronze gears. Vanadium compounds are employed in ceramics to produce a golden glaze, in the preparation of indelible ink, and for fixing aniline black on silk. V_2O_5 is replacing platinum to a large extent in the manufacture of sulfuric acid by the contact process.

Formerly the world's chief supply of vanadium was the sulfide *patronite*, which occurred only at Minasragra, Peru. The patronite has now all been mined, and the present vanadium ore is largely a mixture of hydrous calcium vanadates and the hydrous sulfate. One important domestic source of the metal and its compounds is the vanadium mica, *roscoelite*. Roscoelite occurs in the vicinity of Rifle, Placerville, and Vanadium, Colorado, also in Utah, where it occurs in small bands in, and disseminated throughout, a greenish sandstone. Substantial amounts of vanadium can be obtained from carnotite and vanadinite and from the by-product recovery of vanadium pentoxide from phosphate rock mined in Idaho and Montana.

The United States produces about 90 per cent of the world's supply of vanadium ores and concentrates.

ZINC

SPHALERITE, 278	ZnS	Cubic
Zincite, 299	ZnO	Hexagonal
FRANKLINITE, 306	$(Zn,Mn)Fe_2O_4$	Cubic
SMITHSONITE, 331	$ZnCO_3$	Hexagonal
Willemite, 362	Zn_2SiO_4	Hexagonal
HEMIMORPHITE, 375	$Zn_4(OH)_2Si_2O_7.H_2O$	Orthorhombic

The United States produces about 25 per cent of all the zinc used in the world. In normal times, about 42 per cent of the spelter (zinc) output is used for galvanizing, 18 per cent in making brass, 6 per cent is rolled into sheet zinc, 30 per cent is used for die castings, and 4 per cent for all other purposes. It is estimated that the average automobile contains 25 to 30 pounds of zinc in the form of die castings and rolled zinc. Zinc dust is used for precipitating gold from cyanide solutions, and some of the zinc compounds are employed as pigments. The four white pigments involving the use of zinc are zinc oxide (zinc white), leaded zinc oxide, zinc-lead oxide, and lithopone. Lithopone is a mixture obtained by chemical precipitation of zinc sulfide (28 to 30 per cent) and barium sulfate. Zinc oxide is also used in the manufacture of a number of rubber products, such as gutta-percha, inner tubes, rubber footwear, fire hose, and conveyer belting. Zinc chloride is used as a wood preservative.

Zinc mining is centered largely in seven areas: the Tri-State area of southeastern Kansas, southwestern Missouri, and northeastern Oklahoma; Tennessee-Virginia; Sussex County, New Jersey; St. Lawrence County, New York; northern Illinois and Wisconsin; southern Illinois and Kentucky; and the Western states (Idaho, Arizona, Colorado, New Mexico, Utah, Nevada, Washington, and Montana). The Western states contribute about 56 per cent, the Tri-State area about 12 per cent, and the Eastern states (east of the Mississippi) about 32 per cent of the zinc.

The domestic production of zinc is about 600,000 short tons annually.

ZIRCONIUM

ZIRCON, 366 $ZrSiO_4$ Tetragonal

The uses of zirconium and its compounds are increasing rapidly. By the addition of small amounts of zirconium to steels, brass, and copper, it is claimed sound castings are secured and their strength and resistance to acids increased. *Cooperite* is an alloy of zirconium and nickel and is very resistant to acids and alkalies. It is also recommended for use in the manufacture of machine and cast tools. As its heat conductivity is higher than for other high-speed metals, the cutting efficiency is increased. Cooperite is claimed to be self-hardening, and no tempering is necessary. The pure metal is used in vacuum tubes, flash bulbs, and pyrotechnics. The oxide *zirconia* glows intensely when heated and, therefore, has been used for coating the lime and magnesia pencils used in the Drummond or "lime" light. The filaments of the Nernst lamp consisted mainly of zirconia with variable amounts of yttria, erbia, thoria, and ceria. The oxide is used as an opacifier in enamelware, as a permanent white pigment not affected by acids or alkalies, in electrical and chemical porcelains, pottery glazes, as a polishing powder, and for refractory purposes.

Foreign sources are the oxide *baddeleyite* found in Minas Gerais, Brazil, and the zircon imported from Australia, and India. The zircon in the sands along the east coast of Florida is concentrated by Wilfley tables and magnetic separators. Zircon sand has also been separated from Oregon beach sands. Florida zircon contains 1 to 1.5 per cent hafnium which must be removed from zircon used in nuclear reactors. Uranium-zircon and other zirconium alloys are being employed for nuclear power reactors and as jet-engine parts in the aircraft industry. Zirconium-ferrosilicon is used in the manufacture of steel and zirconium boride for cutting tools. Other uses include surgical equipment, high-intensity electric arc lamps, and as a "getter" in radio tubes; zirconium hydroxide and lactate in medicine, and other compounds in tanning and in the manufacture of textiles. Oil bonded zircon sands are used as core material for foundry applications involving difficult casting conditions. Zircon consumption in the United States is estimated as 45,000 short tons, while the production of zirconium ores and concentrates is estimated at about 44,000 short tons.

Glossary

This glossary contains all the important terms used in the descriptive and determinative portions of the book. See the Index for page references to other terms.

Acicular—needle-like.
Acute—sharply pointed.
Adamantine luster—like that of the diamond.
Aggregate—mass, cluster, group.
Alkaline taste—like that of soda.
Allochromatic—having a color which is not an inherent property of the mineral, but due to pigments, inclusions, or other impurities, hence, variable.
Alluvial—relating to deposits made by flowing water.
Amorphous—devoid of crystallinity.
Amygdaloid—igneous rock containing small cavities, which are filled entirely, or in part, with minerals of secondary origin.
Arborescent—branching, tree-like.
Argillaceous—clay-like odor.
Asterism—star-like effect seen in either transmitted or reflected light.
Astringent taste—causing contraction or puckering.
Basal—parallel to the basal pinacoid.
Basalt—basic igneous rock, dark and compact.
Bipyramid—two pyramids placed base to base.
Bisphenoid—four-sided form of the tetragonal system, each face being an isosceles triangle.
Bituminous odor—due to the presence of bitumen or other organic matter.
Bladed—elongated and flattened, like a knife blade.
Botryoidal—closely united spherical masses, resembling a bunch of grapes.
Brachypinacoid—form with two faces in the orthorhombic or triclinic systems, parallel to the brachy (a) and vertical axes.
Brittle—crumbles under knife or hammer, cannot be cut into slices.
Capillary—hair- or thread-like.
Carbonatization—formation of carbonates; also termed *carbonation.*
Cellular—porous, like a sponge.
Chatoyant—having a changeable, undulating, or wavy color or luster.
Clastic—made up of fragments.
Clay—fine, soft, aluminous sediments that are plastic when wet.
Cleavable—capable of splitting in definite crystallographic directions.

Cleavage—property of many crystalline substances of breaking or splitting in definite directions, yielding more or less smooth surfaces.

Clinopinacoid—form with two faces in the monoclinic system, parallel to the clino (a) and vertical axes.

Columnar—long thick fibers, often parallelly grouped.

Compact—closely or firmly united.

Complex crystals—highly modified, having many crystal forms or faces.

Concentric—spherical layers about a common center, similar to layers of an onion.

Conchoidal—curved, shell-like.

Concretion—rounded mass formed by accumulation about a center.

Concretionary—formed as a concretion.

Conglomerate—sedimentary rock, composed of rounded fragments, coarse or fine,

Contact mineral—formed under the influence of an igneous intrusion.

Crested—tabular crystals arranged in ridges.

Cruciform—in the form of a cross, cross shaped.

Cryptocrystalline—finely crystalline, revealed only under the microscope.

Crystal—substance bounded, entirely or partially, by natural plane surfaces.

Crystalline—having crystal structure, with or without definite geometrical form.

Crystallization—process of solidification in the form of well-developed crystals, or in crystalline masses.

Crystallography—study of crystal forms and properties.

Cyclic—repeated twinning, yielding circular forms.

Decrepitate—to snap and break into fine powder when heated.

Dendritic—branching, fern-like.

Dichroism—property of exhibiting different colors by transmitted light when viewed in two perpendicular directions.

Dike—an igneous intrusion filling a fissure.

Disseminated—scattered through a substance.

Dodecahedral—pertaining to the rhombic dodecahedron, a form with 12 faces in the cubic system.

Domatic—relating to a dome, a horizontal prism.

Drusy—rough surface due to a large number of small, closely crowded crystals.

Ductile—capable of being drawn into wire. Ductile substances are also malleable.

Dull luster—not bright or shiny.

Earthy—without luster, dull.

Efflorescence—thin crust or coating, often powdery.

Elastic—resumes original position after bending.

Enantiomorphous—forms related to one another as is the right hand to the left; hence, not superimposable.

Eruptive rock—formed by the solidification of a surface flow of molten rock. Often used as a synonym of igneous.

Etched—corroded.

Felted—fibers closely matted.

Ferruginous—containing iron.

Fetid—emitting an offensive odor.

Fibrous—consisting of slender fibers or filaments.

Fissure—crack or crevice.

Flexible—capable of bending without breaking, and does not resume original position when the force is removed.

Fluorescence—property of emitting light during exposure to ultraviolet light and other radiations, or while being heated. Best observed in the dark.

Folia—having the form of thin plates or leaves.
Foliated—in plates or leaves which separate easily.
Fracture—refers to surface obtained when breaking in a direction other than parallel to cleavage or parting.
Friable—easily crumbled or reduced to powder.
Furrowed—deeply striated, grooved.
Gangue—associates of more valuable minerals or ores.
Garlic—odor observed when arsenic minerals are heated.
Geode—cavity lined or completely filled with minerals, often well crystallized.
Globular—spherical or nearly so.
Gneiss—laminated or foliated metamorphic rock consisting usually of quartz, feldspar, and mica.
Granite—coarsely crystalline igneous rock, consisting usually of quartz, potash feldspar, and mica or hornblende.
Granodiorite—coarsely crystalline igneous rock, intermediate in composition between granite and quartz diorite.
Granular—consisting of closely packed grains, either coarse or fine.
Guano—excrement of sea fowl.
Habit—development or form of crystals.
Hackly—rough surface, covered with sharp points.
Hardness—resistance offered to abrasion or scratching.
Hemimorphic—having different planes about the two ends of a crystallographic axis.
Hexoctahedron—form of the cubic system having 48 faces.
Hopper shaped—cavernous and tapering, square funnel shaped.
Hydration—combining chemically with water.
Hygroscopic—property of absorbing moisture from the atmosphere.
Idiochromatic—minerals with a constant color, an inherent property.
Igneous rock—one formed by the solidification of a molten mass from within the earth.
Impregnated—finely disseminated in rock.
Impressed—marked by pressure, indented.
Inclusion—foreign material enclosed within a mineral.
Incrustation—crust or coating on another substance.
Inelastic—not elastic.
Interlaced, **Interwoven**—intertwined, confused.
Iridescence—showing play of colors, usually due to thin film or coating.
Isochromatic—lines or sections possessing the same color.
Kimberlite—altered, very basic igneous rock, consisting essentially of serpentine, olivine, augite, pyrope; sometimes diamond bearing.
Lamellae, **Laminae**—small, thin plates or layers, curved or straight.
Lamellar—consisting of lamellae or laminae.
Lava—molten rock, especially surface flows; also applied to the solidified product.
Lenticular—lens shaped.
Limestone—rock composed essentially of calcium carbonate, calcite.
Luster—manner in which the surface reflects light.
Macropinacoid—form with two faces in the orthorhombic or triclinic systems, parallel to the macro (*b*) and vertical axes.
Macroscopic—visible to the unaided eye, opposed to microscopic.
Malleable—capable of being flattened by hammering.
Mammillary—rounded mass, larger than that of a grape.

Marble—recrystallized limestone or dolomite; may also include other limestones susceptible to a polish, and serpentine.
Massive—without definite crystal form; either crystalline or amorphous.
Meager—rough touch.
Metallic luster—simulating a metal and exhibited by minerals which are opaque, or nearly so.
Metalloidal—having the appearance of a metal.
Metamorphic rock—one that has been altered by heat, pressure, liquids, or gases, so as to render its texture either crystalline or schistose.
Meteorite—mass of stone or iron which has fallen to the earth from outer space.
Micaceous—composed of very thin plates or scales, like those of mica.
Mimicry—imitation of forms of a higher symmetry by those of lower grade of symmetry, usually the result of twinning.
Modified, highly—consisting of a large number of crystal forms or faces.
Monochromatic—homogeneous light of a definite wave length.
Mottled—spotted.
Multicolored—having many colors.
Neolithic—later Stone Age, that of smooth or polished stone implements.
Nodular, **Nodule**—rounded mass of irregular shape.
Nugget—rounded, irregular lump, especially of a metal.
Ocherous—earthy, and usually red, yellow, or brown in color.
Octahedral—pertaining to the octahedron, eight-sided form of the cubic system.
Oölitic—rounded particles the size of fish eggs.
Opalescent—with milky or pearly reflections.
Opaque—will not transmit light even through thin layers or edges.
Ore—a mineral deposit of economic importance.
Orthopinacoid—form with two faces in the monoclinic system, parallel to the ortho (*b*) and vertical axes.
Oxidation—combining chemically with oxygen, or increase in valence of an element.
Paleolithic—earlier Stone Age, that of rough stone implements.
Parameters—linear intercepts of a crystal face on the crystallographic axes.
Parting—false cleavage, usually the result of twinning.
Pearly—similar to the luster of mother of pearl.
Peat—dark-brown to black substance, formed by the partial decomposition of vegetable tissue in marshes.
Pegmatite—very coarse-grained acid igneous rock, consisting essentially of quartz, microcline, and mica.
Peridotite—very basic igneous rock, composed largely of olivine and augite or hornblende.
Phanerocrystalline—crystals or coarsely crystalline.
Phonolite—compact extrusive rock, consisting essentially of orthoclase, nepheline, and pyroxene.
Phosphorescence—property of emitting light after exposure to ultraviolet light and other radiations or after being heated. Best observed in the dark.
Pinacoidal—relating to forms with two planes, parallel to two or more crystallographic axes.
Pisolitic—composed of small, rounded masses, the size of peas.
Plastic—capable of being molded or shaped.
Plates—broad, relatively thin masses.
Plumose—feathery.

Pocket—cavity in a rock, often filled with minerals.
Polar—a dissimilar arrangement of forms about the ends of a crystallographic axis.
Polysynthetic—consisting of thin lamellae due to repeated twinning.
Prismatic—elongated parallel to one of the crystallographic axes, usually the vertical axis.
Pseudo—false.
Pseudomorph, **Pseudomorphous**—possessing the geometrical form of another mineral.
Pungent—sharp, biting.
Pyramidal—pertaining to the pyramid, a form which usually intersects three crystallographic axes.
Pyritohedron—form of the cubic system with 12 five-sided faces.
Rectangular—intersecting at 90°.
Reduction—loss of oxygen chemically, or decrease in valance of an element.
Refraction, double—yielding two refracted rays.
Reniform—large, rounded masses, kidney shaped.
Resinous—luster of resin.
Reticulated—fibers crossing like a net.
Rhombic—diamond shaped.
Rhombohedral—relating to the rhombohedron, a form of the hexagonal system, with six faces intersecting at angles other than 90°.
Rosette—simulating a rose.
Saline—salty.
Sandstone—sedimentary rock consisting of consolidated sand.
Scalenohedral—relating to the scalenohedron, a 12-sided form of the hexagonal system, each face being a scalene triangle.
Scaly—consisting of scales.
Schiller—peculiar bronze-like luster.
Schist—metamorphic rock with foliated or parallel structure, splitting easily along certain planes.
Seam—narrow vein.
Sectile—capable of having slices cut off.
Semiopaque—between opaque and transparent.
Shale—laminated sedimentary rock, consisting of hardened muds, silts, or clays.
Sheaf-like—resembling a sheaf of wheat.
Silky—luster of silk, due to fibrous structure.
Skeletal—pertaining to crystals with incomplete development of their faces, often with cavernous appearance.
Slate—dense, fine-grained metamorphic rock, which splits easily into broad, thin layers or sheets.
Splendent—very bright in reflected light.
Splintery—breaking into splinters.
Stalactitic—cylindrical or conical masses resembling icicles.
Stalky—consisting of long, stout fibers.
Stellate—radiating from a center producing star-like forms.
Streak—color of fine powder, usually obtained by rubbing the mineral on unglazed porcelain.
Subadamantine—imperfectly adamantine.
Subconchoidal—imperfectly conchoidal.
Sublimation—direct solidification from a vapor.
Submetallic—imperfectly metallic.

Syenite—granular igneous rock, commonly consisting of potash feldspar and hornblende or biotite.

Tabular—flat, tablet-like.

Tarnish—thin film formed on the surface when exposed to air and different in color from that of the fresh fracture.

Terminations—faces on the end of a crystal.

Tetragonal trisoctahedron—form of the cubic system with 24 trapezohedral faces.

Tetrahedral—pertaining to the tetrahedron, a four-sided form of the cubic system.

Tetrahexahedron—form of the cubic system with 24 triangular faces.

Tough—not easily broken.

Translucent—when light passes through, but objects cannot be seen distinctly.

Transparency—refers to the amount of light passing through a substance.

Transparent—when sufficient light passes through the substance so that objects may be distinctly seen.

Trap—dark, basic fine-grained igneous rock.

Trichroism—property of exhibiting different colors by transmitted light when viewed in three perpendicular directions.

Trillings—intergrowth of three crystals in a symmetrical manner.

Twinned—crystals consisting of more than one individual, arranged in a definite manner.

Twins—symmetrical intergrowth of two crystals.

Variegated—with different colors.

Vein—crack or fissure, partially or completely filled with mineral matter.

Vitreous luster—like that of glass.

Vug—a term sometimes used for geode.

Warty—small, rounded masses resembling warts.

Waxy—luster of wax.

Zonal—in zones or layers.

Tabular Classification Showing Elements of Symmetry and the Simple Forms of the 32 Classes of Crystals

The use of the elements of symmetry in the classification of crystals is discussed on pages 17 to 20.

(Pages 486 to 492)

Tabular Classification Showing the Elements of Symmetry and the Simple Forms of the Thirty-two Classes of Crystals

1. Cubic System

Class and symbol	Symmetry						Forms							Representative
	Planes		Axes											
	Axial	Diagonal	■	▲	●	Center	$a:a:a$ {111}	$a:a:\infty a$ {110}	$a:\infty a:\infty a$ {100}	$a:a:ma$ {*hhl*}	$a:ma:ma$ {*hll*}	$a:ma:\infty a$ {*hk*0}	$a:na:ma$ {*hkl*}	
1. **Hexoctahedral** (*holohedrism*)* $\frac{4}{m}\bar{3}\frac{2}{m}$	3	6	3	4	6	1	Octahedron (8)†	Rhombic dodecahedron (12)	Hexahedron (6)	Trigonal trisoctahedrons (24)	Tetragonal trisoctahedrons (24)	Tetrahexahedrons (24)	Hexoctahedrons (48)	Galena (PbS)
2. **Pentagonal icositetrahedral** (*plagihedral hemihedrism*) 432	—	—	3	4	6	—	Octahedron (8)	Rhombic dodecahedron (12)	Hexahedron (6)	Trigonal trisoctahedrons (24)	Tetragonal trisoctahedrons (24)	Tetrahexahedrons (24)	(*r*, *l*) Pentagonal Icositetrahedrons (24)	Sal ammoniac (NH_4Cl)
3. **Hextetrahedral** (*tetrahedral hemihedrism*) $\bar{4}3m$	—	6	—	4 (*Polar*)	3	—	(±) Tetrahedrons (4)	Rhombic dodecahedron (12)	Hexahedron (6)	± Tetragonal tristetrahedrons (12)	(±) Trigonal tristetrahedrons (12)	Tetrahexahedrons (24)	(±) Hextetrahedrons (24)	Tetrahedrite ($M_{12}R_4S_{13}$)
4. **Dyakisdodecahedral** (*pyritohedral hemihedrism*) $\frac{2}{m}\bar{3}$	3	—	—	4	3	1	Octahedron (8)	Rhombic dodecahedron (12)	Hexahedron (6)	Trigonal trisoctahedrons (24)	Tetragonal trisocathedrons (24)	(±) Pyritohedrons (12)	(±) Dyakis-dodecahedrons (24)	Pyrite (FeS_2)
5. **Tetrahedral pentagonal dodecahedral** (*tetartohedrism*) 23	—	—	—	4 (*Polar*)	3	—	(±) Tetrahedrons (4)	Rhombic dodecahedron (12)	Hexahedron (6)	(±) Tetragonal tristetrahedrons (12)	(±) Trigonal tristetrahedrons (12)	(±) Pyritohedrons (12)	(± *r*, ± *l*) Tetrahedral pentagonal dodecahedrons (12)	Sodium bromate ($NaBrO_3$)

* Although the older ideas of holohedrism and hemihedrism have not been used in the development of crystallographic forms (pages 9 to 88), for the sake of completeness, however, these older terms are also given in this classification of the 32 classes of symmetry.

† The figures below the names of the forms indicate the number of faces they possess.

Class and symbols	Symmetry: Planes, Horizontal, Axial	Planes, Vertical, Axial	Planes, Vertical, Intermediate	Axes, Vertical, ⬢	Axes, Vertical, ▲	Axes, Horizontal, ⬬	Center	Forms: $a:\infty a:a:mc$ $\{h0\bar{h}l\}$	$2a:2a:a:mc$ $\{hh\bar{2h}l\}$	$na:pa:a:mc$ $\{hk\bar{i}l\}$	$a:\infty a:a:\infty c$ $\{10\bar{1}0\}$	$2a:2a:a:\infty c$ $\{11\bar{2}0\}$	$na:pa:a:\infty c$ $\{hk\bar{i}0\}$	$\infty a:\infty a:\infty a:c$ $\{0001\}$	Representative
6. Dihexagonal bipyramidal (*holohedrism*) $\frac{6}{m}\frac{2}{m}\frac{2}{m}$	1	3	3	1	—	3 + 3	1	Hexagonal bipyramids, first order (12)	Hexagonal bipyramids, second order (12)	Dihexagonal bipyramids (24)	Hexagonal prism, first order (6)	Hexagonal prism, second order (6)	Dihexagonal prisms (12)	Basal pinacoid (2)	Beryl ($Be_3Al_2Si_6O_{18}$)
7. Hexagonal trapezohedral [*trapezohedral hemihedrism*] 622	—	—	—	1		3 + 3	—	Hexagonal bipyramids, first order (12)	Hexagonal bipyramids, second order (12)	(*r*, *l*) Hexagonal trapezohedrons (12)	Hexagonal prism, first order (6)	Hexagonal prism, second order (6)	Dihexagonal prisms (12)	Basal pinacoid (2)	β Quartz (SiO_2)
8. Dihexagonal pyramidal [*holohedrism with hemimorphism*] 6*mm*	—	3	3	1 (*Polar*)	—	—	—	(*u*, *l*) Hexagonal pyramids, first order (6)	(*u*, *l*) Hexagonal pyramids, second order (6)	(*u*, *l*) Dihexagonal pyramids (12)	Hexagonal prism, first order (6)	Hexagonal prism, second order (6)	Dihexagonal prisms (12)	(*u*, *l*) Basal pinacoids (1)	Zincite (ZnO)
9. Ditrigonal bipyramidal [*trigonal hemihedrism*] $\bar{6}m2$	1	—	3	—	1	3 (*Polar*)	—	(±) Trigonal bipyramids, first order (6)	Hexagonal bipyramids, second order (12)	(±) Ditrigonal bipyramids (12)	(±) Trigonal prisms, first order (3)	Hexagonal prism, second order (6)	(±) Ditrigonal prisms (6)	Basal pinacoid (2)	Benitoite ($BaTiSi_3O_9$)
10. Hexagonal bipyramidal [*pyramidal hemihedrism*] $\frac{6}{m}$	1	—	—	1	—	—	1	Hexagonal bipyramids, first order (12)	Hexagonal bipyramids, second order (12)	(±) Hexagonal bipyramids, third order (12)	Hexagonal prism, first order (6)	Hexagonal prism, second order (6)	(±) Hexagonal prisms, third order (6)	Basal pinacoid (2)	Apatite ($Ca_5F(PO_4)_3$)
11. Hexagonal pyramidal [*pyramidal hemihedrism with hemimorphism*] 6	—	—	—	1 (*Polar*)	—	—	—	(*u*, *l*) Hexagonal pyramids, first order (6)	(*u*, *l*) Hexagonal pyramids, second order (6)	(±*u*, ±*l*) Hexagonal pyramids, third order (6)	Hexagonal prism, first order (6)	Hexagonal prism, second order (6)	(±) Hexagonal prisms, third order (6)	(*u*, *l*) Basal pinacoids (1)	Nepheline ($NaAlSiO_4$)

2. Hexagonal System (*Continued*)

Class and symbol	Symmetry: Planes: Horizontal: Axial	Planes: Vertical: Axial	Planes: Vertical: Intermediate	Axes: Vertical: ⬢	Axes: Vertical: ▲	Axes: Horizontal: ⬬	Center	Forms: $a:\infty a:a:mc$ $\{h0\bar{h}l\}$	Forms: $2a:2a:a:mc$ $\{hh\overline{2h}l\}$	Forms: $na:pa:a:mc$ $\{hkil\}$	Forms: $a:\infty a:a:\infty c$ $\{10\bar{1}0\}$	Forms: $2a:2a:a:\infty c$ $\{11\bar{2}0\}$	Forms: $na:pa:a:\infty c$ $\{hki0\}$	Forms: $\infty a:\infty a:\infty a:c$ $\{0001\}$	Representative
12. Trigonal bipyramidal [*trigonal tetartohedrism*] $\bar{6}$	1	—	—	—	1	—	—	(±) Trigonal bipyramids, first order (6)	(±) Trigonal bipyramids, second order (6)	(±r, ±l) Trigonal bipyramids, third order (6)	(±) Trigonal prisms, first order (3)	(±) Trigonal prisms, second order (3)	(±r, ±l) Trigonal prisms, third order (3)	Basal pinacoid (2)	Disilverorthophosphate (Ag_2HPO_4)
13. Ditrigonal scalenohedral (*rhombohedral hemihedrism*) $\bar{3}\frac{2}{m}$	—	—	3	—	1	3	1	(±) Rhombohedrons, first order (6)	Hexagonal bipyramids, second order (12)	(±) Scalenohedrons (12)	Hexagonal prism, first order (6)	Hexagonal prism, second order (6)	Dihexagonal prisms (12)	Basal pinacoid (2)	Calcite ($CaCO_3$)
14. Trigonal trapezohedral [*trapezohedral tetartohedrism*] 32	—	—	—	—	1	3 (*Polar*)	—	(±) Rhombohedrons, first order (6)	(±) Trigonal bipyramids, second order (6)	(±r, ±l) Trigonal trapezohedrons (6)	Hexagonal prism, first order (6)	(±) Trigonal prism, second order (3)	(±) Ditrigonal prisms (6)	Basal pinacoid (2)	α Quartz (SiO_2)
15. Ditrigonal pyramidal [*trigonal hemihedrism with hemimorphism*] 3m	—	—	3	—	1 (*Polar*)	—	—	(±u, ±l) Trigonal pyramids, first order (3)	(u, l) Hexagonal pyramids, second order (6)	(±u, ±l) Ditrigonal pyramids (6)	(±) Trigonal prisms, first order (3)	Hexagonal prism, second order (6)	(±) Ditrigonal prisms (6)	(u, l) Basal pinacoids (1)	Tourmaline ($M_7Al_6(OH,F)_4(BO_3)_3Si_6O_{18}$)
16. Trigonal rhombohedral [*rhombohedral tetartohedrism*] $\bar{3}$	—	—	—	—	1	—	1	(±) Rhombohedrons, first order (6)	(±) Rhombohedrons, second order (6)	(±r, ±l) Rhombohedrons, third order (6)	Hexagonal prism, first order (6)	Hexagonal prism, second order (6)	(±) Hexagonal prisms, third order (6)	Basal pinacoid (2)	Dioptase ($Cu_3Si_3O_9.3H_2O$)
17. Trigonal pyramidal (*ogdohedrism*) 3	—	—	—	—	1 (*Polar*)	—	—	(±u, ±l) Trigonal pyramids, first order (3)	(±u, ±l) Trigonal pyramids, second order (3)	[±r, u; ±r, l; ±l, u; ±l, l] Trigonal pyramids, third order (3)	(±) Trigonal prisms, first order (3)	(±) Trigonal prisms, second order (3)	(±r, ±l) Trigonal prisms, third order (3)	(u, l) Basal pinacoids (1)	Sodium periodate ($NaIO_4.3H_2O$)

3. Tetragonal System

Class and symbol	Symmetry						Forms							Representative
	Planes			Axes										
	Horizontal	Vertical												
	Axial	Axial	Intermediate	■	●	Center	$a:a:mc$ {hhl}	$a:\infty a:mc$ {h0l}	$a:na:mc$ {hkl}	$a:a:\infty c$ {110}	$a:\infty a:\infty c$ {100}	$a:na:\infty c$ {hk0}	$\infty a:\infty a:c$ {001}	
18. **Ditetragonal bipyramidal** (*holohedrism*) $\frac{4}{m}\frac{2}{m}\frac{2}{m}$	1	2	2	1	2+2	1	Tetragonal bipyramids, first order (8)	Tetragonal bipyramids, second order (8)	Ditetragonal bipyramids (16)	Tetragonal prism, first order (4)	Tetragonal prism, second order (4)	Ditetragonal prisms (8)	Basal pinacoid (2)	Cassiterite (SnO_2)
19. **Tetragonal trapezohedral** [*trapezohedral hemihedrism*] 422	—	—	—	1	2+2	—	Tetragonal bipyramids, first order (8)	Tetragonal bipyramids, second order (8)	(*r*, *l*) Tetragonal trapezohedrons (8)	Tetragonal prism, first order (4)	Tetragonal prism, second order (4)	Ditetragonal prisms (8)	Basal pinacoid (2)	Nickel Sulfate ($NiSO_4.6H_2O$)
20. **Ditetragonal pyramidal** [*holohedrism with hemimorphism*] 4*mm*	—	2	2	1 (*Polar*)	—	—	(*u*, *l*) Tetragonal pyramids, first order (4)	(*u*, *l*) Tetragonal pyramids, second order (4)	(*u*, *l*) Ditetragonal pyramids (8)	Tetragonal prism, first order (4)	Tetragonal prism, second order (4)	Ditetragonal prisms (8)	(*u*, *l*) Basal pinacoids (1)	Diaboleite ($Pb_2CuCl_2(OH)_4$)
21. **Tetragonal scalenohedral** [*sphenoidal hemihedrism*] $\bar{4}2m$	—	—	2	—	1+2	—	(±) Tetragonal bisphenoids, first order (4)	Tetragonal bipyramids, second order (8)	(±) Tetragonal scalenohedrons (8)	Tetragonal prism, first order (4)	Tetragonal prism, second order (4)	Ditetragonal prisms (8)	Basal pinacoid (2)	Chalcopyrite ($CuFeS_2$)
22. **Tetragonal bipyramidal** [*pyramidal hemihedrism*] $\frac{4}{m}$	1	—	—	1	—	1	Tetragonal bipyramids, first order (8)	Tetragonal bipyramids, second order (8)	(±) Tetragonal bipyramids, third order (8)	Tetragonal prism, first order (4)	Tetragonal prism, second order (4)	(±) Tetragonal prisms, third order (4)	Basal pinacoid (2)	Scheelite ($CaWO_4$)
23. **Tetragonal pyramidal** [*pyramidal hemihedrism with hemimorphism*] 4	—			1 (*Polar*)		—	(*u*, *l*) Tetragonal pyramids, first order (4)	(*u*, *l*) Tetragonal pyramids, second order (4)	(±*u*, ±*l*) Tetragonal pyramids, third order (4)	Tetragonal prism, first order (4)	Tetragonal prism, second order (4)	(±) Tetragonal prism, third order (4)	(*u*, *l*) Basal pinacoids (1)	Wulfenite ($PbMoO_4$)
24. **Tetragonal bisphenoidal** (*tetartohedrism*) $\bar{4}$	—	—	—	1*		—	(±) Tetragonal bisphenoids, first order (4)	(±) Tetragonal bisphenoids, second order (4)	(±*r*, ±*l*) Tetragonal bisphenoids, third order (4)	Tetragonal prism, first order (4)	Tetragonal prism, second order (4)	(±) Tetragonal prisms, third order (4)	Basal pinacoid (2)	Cahnite ($4CaO.B_2O_3.$-$As_2O_5.4H_2O$)

* Axis of rotary inversion.

4. Orthorhombic System

Class and symbol	Symmetry			Forms							Representative
	Planes	Axes									
	Axial	⬬	Center	$n\breve{a}:\bar{b}:m\grave{c}$ {hkl}	$n\breve{a}:\bar{b}:\infty\grave{c}$ {hk0}	$\infty\breve{a}:\bar{b}:m\grave{c}$ }0kl}	$\breve{a}:\infty\bar{b}:m\grave{c}$ {h0l}	$\infty\breve{a}:\bar{b}:\infty\grave{c}$ {010}	$\breve{a}:\infty\bar{b}:\infty\grave{c}$ {100}	$\infty\breve{a}:\infty\bar{b}:\grave{c}$ {001}	
25. **Orthorhombic bipyramidal** (*holohedrism*) $\frac{2}{m}\frac{2}{m}\frac{2}{m}$	1 + 1 + 1	1 + 1 + 1	1	Bipyramids (8)	Prisms (4)	Brachydomes (4)	Macrodomes (4)	Brachy-pinacoid (2)	Macro-pinacoid (2)	Basal pinacoid (2)	Barite ($BaSO_4$)
26. **Orthorhombic bisphenoidal** (*hemihedrism*) 222	—	1 + 1 + 1	—	(*r*, *l*) Bisphenoids (4)	Prisms (4)	Brachydomes (4)	Macrodomes (4)	Brachy-pinacoid (2)	Macro-pinacoid (2)	Basal pinacoid (2)	**Epsomite** (**$MgSO_4.7H_2O$**)
27. **Orthorhombic pyramidal** [*holohedrism with hemimorphism*] *mm*2	1 + 1	1 (*Polar*)	—	(*u*, *l*) Pyramids (4)	Prisms (4)	(*u*, *l*) Brachydomes (2)	(*u*, *l*) Macrodomes (2)	Brachy-pinacoid (2)	Macro-pinacoid (2)	(*u*, *l*) Basal pinacoids (1)	Hemimorphite ($Zn_4(OH)_2$-$Si_2O_7.H_2O$)

5. Monoclinic System

Class and symbol	Symmetry			Forms							Representative
	Plane	Axis	Center	$n\acute{a}:\bar{b}:m\grave{c}$ {hkl}	$n\acute{a}:\bar{b}\infty\grave{c}$ {hk0}	$\infty\acute{a}:\bar{b}:m\grave{c}$ {0kl}	$\acute{a}:\infty\bar{b}:m\grave{c}$ {h0l}	$\infty\acute{a}:\bar{b}:\infty\grave{c}$ {010}	$\acute{a}:\infty\bar{b}:\infty\grave{c}$ {100}	$\infty\acute{a}:\infty\bar{b}:\grave{c}$ {001}	
28. Prismatic (*holohedrism*) $\frac{2}{m}$	1	1	1	(±) Hemibipyramids (4)	Prisms (4)	Clinodomes (4)	(±) Hemi-orthodomes (2)	Clinopinacoid (2)	Orthopinacoid (2)	Basal pinacoid (2)	Gypsum ($CaSO_4.2H_2O$)
29. Sphenoidal (*hemimorphism*) 2	—	1 (*Polar*)	—	(±*r*, ±*l*) Tetarto-bipyramids (*sphenoids*) (2)	(*r*, *l*) Hemiprisms (2)	(*r*, *l*) Hemi-clinodomes (2)	(±) Hemi-orthodomes (2)	(*r*, *l*) Clinopinacoids (1)	Orthopinacoid (2)	Basal pinacoid (2)	Tartaric acid ($C_4H_6O_6$)
30. Domatic (*hemihedrism*) *m*	1	—	—	(±*u*, ±*l*) Tetarto-bipyramids (2)	(*f*, *r*) Hemiprisms (2)	(*u*, *l*) Hemi-clinodomes (2)	(±*u*, ±*l*) Tetarto-orthodomes (1)	Clinopinacoid (2)	(*f*, *r*) Orthopinacoids (1)	(*u*, *l*) Basal pinacoids (1)	Tetrathionate of potassium ($K_2S_4O_6$)

6. Triclinic System

Class and symbol	Symmetry			Forms							Representative
	Plane	Axis	Center	$n\breve{a}:\bar{b}:m\grave{c}$ {hkl}	$n\breve{a}:\bar{b}:\infty\grave{c}$ {$hk0$}	$\infty\breve{a}:\bar{b}:m\grave{c}$ {$0kl$}	$\breve{a}:\infty\bar{b}:m\grave{c}$ {$h0l$}	$\infty\breve{a}:\bar{b}:\infty\grave{c}$ {010}	$\breve{a}:\infty\bar{b}:\infty\grave{c}$ {100}	$\infty\breve{a}:\infty\bar{b}:\grave{c}$ {001}	
31. **Pinacoidal** (*holohedrism*) $\bar{1}$	—	—	1	$\left(\frac{u}{l}r, \frac{u}{l}l\right)$ Tetarto-bipyramids (2)	(r, l) Hemiprisms (2)	(r, l) Hemi-brachydomes (2)	(u, l) Hemi-macrodomes (2)	Brachy-pinacoid (2)	Macro-pinacoid (2)	Basal Pinacoid (2)	Albite ($NaAlSi_3O_8$)
32. **Asymmetric** (*hemihedrism*) 1	—	—	—	$\left\{\begin{matrix} \frac{u}{l}r, f \\ \frac{u}{l}l, f \\ \frac{u}{l}r, r \\ \frac{u}{l}l, r \end{matrix}\right\}$ Ogdo-bipyramids (1)	$\left(\frac{r}{l}f, \frac{r}{l}r\right)$ Tetarto-prisms (1)	$\left(\frac{u}{l}r, \frac{u}{l}l\right)$ Tetarto-brachydomes (1)	$\left(\frac{u}{l}f, \frac{u}{l}r\right)$ Tetarto-macrodomes (1)	(l, r) Brachy-pinacoids (1)	(f, r) Macro-pinacoids (1)	(u, l) Basal Pinacoids (1)	Strontium bitartrate ($Sr(C_4H_4O_6H)_2 \cdot 4H_2O$)

Tables for the Determination of Minerals by Means of Their Physical Properties, Occurrences, and Associates

(Pages **494** to **661**)

DIRECTIONS FOR USING THE TABLES

These tables for the determination of minerals depend largely upon the use of those physical properties that are easily, rapidly, and accurately recognizable at sight. As luster and color can be determined at first glance, they are made the basis of the tables. Thus, the minerals are divided into two large groups depending upon whether they possess a metallic or nonmetallic luster. Minerals with metalloidal or submetallic lusters are listed in both divisions. Each of these groups is then subdivided according to color, the other property readily recognized at first glance. There are also further subgroupings according to streak, and then according to increasing hardness. Within each of the latter smaller subdivisions the minerals are listed with reference to increasing specific gravity.

To illustrate the use of the tables let us assume that we have a specimen of magnetite. As the luster is metallic and the color black, the mineral falls into group 1, page 494. The streak is then determined and is found to be black. Consequently it is placed in the second subdivision under streak. The hardness is next tested and found to be 6. Accordingly, reference should be made to page 512, where the minerals with metallic luster, black color and streak, and hardness over 3 are listed with concise descriptions. The hardness column is now followed until values of 6 or thereabouts are encountered. At this point it becomes necessary to determine the various other properties, such as crystallization, structure, transparency, cleavage, fracture, tenacity, and specific gravity, as well as the general characteristics and associates. A comparison of these observations with the descriptions of the various minerals with a hardness of approximately 6 should lead readily to an accurate determination.

A. MINERALS WITH METALLIC LUSTER

Color of mineral	Streak	Hardness	Page
1. **Dark gray or black**	White, gray, green, red, brown, or yellow	1 to 3	**496**
		3 to 6	**498**
		Over 6	**506**
	Black	1 to 3	**510**
		Over 3	**512**
2. **Metallic white or light metallic gray**	Metallic white or steel gray	1 to 6	**516**
	Black	1 to 3	**518**
		Over 3	**520**
3. **Yellow**	Brown or yellow	1 to 6	**520**
	Black	Over 3	**522**
4. **Brass, bronze, or copper red**	Gray, red, or yellow	1 to 3	**522**
	Black	Over 3	**524**
5. **Red, brown, or blue**	White, gray, green, red, brown, or yellow	1 to 3	**526**
		3 to 6	**528**
		Over 6	**532**
	Black	1 to 6	**534**

B. MINERALS WITH NONMETALLIC LUSTER

Color of mineral	Streak	Hardness	Page
1. Dark gray or black	Green, red, brown, yellow, or black	1 to 6	536
		Over 6	540
	Uncolored, white, or light gray	1 to 3	542
		3 to 6	544
		Over 6	548
2. Pink, red, red-brown, or red-violet	Red, brown, or yellow	1 to 3	552
		Over 3	554
	Uncolored, white, or light gray	1 to 3	558
		3 to 6	560
		Over 6	568
3. Green, blue, or blue-violet	Blue, green, brown, or yellow	1 to 3	574
		Over 3	574
	Uncolored, white, or light gray	1 to 3	578
		3 to 6	582
		Over 6	592
4. Yellow or brown	Red, brown, or yellow	1 to 3	600
		Over 3	602
	Uncolored, white, or light gray	1 to 3	606
		3 to 6	612
		Over 6	622
5. Colorless, white, or light gray	Uncolored, white, or light gray	1 to 3	630
		3 to 6	638
		Over 6	654

Streak—White, gray, green, red, brown, or yellow			
Name, Composition, and Reference	Crystallization Structure Crystals = C Massive = M	Luster Transparency	Color
CHLORITE (Prochlorite, clinochlorite) $Mg_5Al(OH)_8AlSi_3O_{10}$ **401**	Monoclinic **C**—Tabular, six-sided, often bent and twisted **M**—Foliated, scaly, granular, earthy	Dull Submetallic Translucent to opaque	Black Greenish black
HEMATITE, variety *Specular iron ore* Fe_2O_3 **301**	Hexagonal **C**—Thin tabular, often in parallel position **M**—Scaly, micaceous, platy, foliated	Metallic Splendent Opaque to translucent	Iron black Dark steel gray
BIOTITE (Black mica) $K(Mg,Fe)_3(OH,F)_2AlSi_3O_{10}$ **399**	Monoclinic **C**—Tabular, with hexagonal or rhombic outline **M**—Plates, disseminated scales	Submetallic Pearly Opaque to transparent	Black Brownish black Greenish black
Pyrargyrite Ag_3SbS_3 **259**	Hexagonal **C**—Small, complex, hemimorphic, rare **M**—Compact, disseminated, bands, crusts	Metallic Adamantine Opaque to transparent	Dark lead gray
SILVER **Ag** **258**	Cubic **C**—Small, often distorted **M**—Grains, scales, plates, twisted hair- or wire-like forms	Metallic Opaque	Dark gray to black after exposure, otherwise silver white

[1] Page reference for description of mineral.

Hardness 1 to 3

Hardness	Streak	Cleavage = C Fracture = F Tenacity	Specific Gravity	Characteristics and Associates
1. **2.5**	Pale green	**C**—Basal, perfect; when foliated, conspicuous **F**—Scaly, earthy Tough to brittle	2.6 3.	Laminae are flexible but inelastic, with slightly soapy feel. Common in schists and serpentine. With magnetite, garnet, diopside, magnesite. Often as a scaly or dusty coating on other minerals. Pseudomorphous after garnet
2. **3.**	Cherry red Reddish brown	**C**—None, but distinct parting **F**—Uneven Brittle to elastic	4.9 5.3	Bright, shiny scales, often loosely compact; foliated or micaceous masses. In metamorphic rocks or as sublimation product around volcanoes
2.5 **3.**	White Grayish	**C**—Basal, perfect, conspicuous Tough, laminae of fresh biotite very elastic	2.7 3.2	Easily recognized by structure, highly perfect cleavage, and elasticity. Important constituent of many igneous and metamorphic rocks—granite, syenite, gneiss
2.5 **3.**	Cherry red Purplish red	**C**—Imperfect **F**—Conchoidal Brittle	5.8	Frequently as gray or dark red bands, known as *dark ruby silver ore*. With proustite; in veins with other silver minerals and galena
2.5 **3.**	Silver white Light lead gray	**C**—None **F**—Hackly Malleable, ductile	10.5 12.	Color and streak darken on exposure. With silver, lead, arsenic, cobalt, and nickel minerals—argentite, pyrargyrite, proustite, galena, smaltite; also fluorite, calcite, barite

Streak—White, gray, green, red, brown, or yellow			
Name, Composition, and Reference	Crystallization Structure Crystals = C Massive = M	Luster Transparency	Color
TETRAHEDRITE $M_{12}R_4S_{13}$ M = Usually Cu R = Sb, As **290**	Cubic **C**—Tetrahedral, often highly modified **M**—Granular, compact	Metallic Opaque	Dark steel gray Iron black
URANINITE (Pitchblende) UO_2 **312**	Cubic **C**—Octahedral, rare **M**—Botryoidal, columnar, curved lamellar; granular, compact; apparently amorphous	Pitch-like Submetallic Dull Opaque	Pitch black Brownish black Greenish black
SIDERITE $FeCO_3$ **332**	Hexagonal **C**—Rhombohedral, curved or saddleshaped, common **M**—Cleavable, granular, compact, botryoidal, rarely fibrous	Submetallic Dull Opaque to translucent	Brownish black Black
Alabandite MnS **278**	Cubic **C**—Rare **M**—Granular, compact	Submetallic Dull Opaque	Iron black
SPHALERITE (Blackjack) ZnS **278**	Cubic **C**—Tetrahedral, common, often very complex **M**—Compact, cleavable, fine or coarse granular	Submetallic Resinous Opaque to translucent	Black Yellowish black Brownish black

Hardness 3 to 6

Hardness	Streak	Cleavage = C Fracture = F Tenacity	Specific Gravity	Characteristics and Associates
3. **4.5**	Reddish brown	**C**—Indistinct **F**—Uneven Brittle	4.6 5.1	Crystals have characteristic tetrahedral habit. Sometimes coated with chalcopyrite. With sphalerite, galena, bournonite, chalcopyrite, siderite
3. **6.**	Dark brown Olive green	**F**—Conchoidal, uneven Brittle	4.8 9.7	Pitch-like appearance and fracture important. Fresh material is hard and heavy. With ores of lead, silver, and bismuth; also allanite
3.5 **4.**	Yellowish brown	**C**—Rhombohedral, perfect, conspicuous **F**—Conchoidal Brittle	3.7 3.9	Distinguished from sphalerite by curved crystals and rhombohedral cleavage. In ore deposits; beds and concretions in limestones and shales. With pyrite, chalcopyrite, galena, tetrahedrite, cryolite
3.5 **4.**	Olive green Dirty green	**C**—Cubical, not conspicuous **F**—Uneven Brittle	3.9 4.	Color may tarnish brownish black. Streak characteristic. With rhodochrosite, galena, pyrite, argentite, sphalerite
3.5 **4.**	Dark brown Yellowish brown Grayish	**C**—Dodecahedral, perfect, usually conspicuous **F**—Conchoidal Brittle	3.9 4.2	Color and streak vary with impurities. Extensively in limestone. With galena, chalcopyrite, pyrite, barite, fluorite, siderite, rhodochrosite

Streak—White, gray, green, red, brown, or yellow

Name, Composition, and Reference	Crystallization Structure Crystals = C Massive = M	Luster Transparency	Color
MANGANITE MnO(OH) **315**	Monoclinic **C**—Columnar, prismatic, vertically striated; often in groups or bundles **M**—Columnar, granular, stalactitic	Metallic Submetallic Opaque	Iron black Dark steel gray
SPHENE (Titanite) $CaTiOSiO_4$ **374**	Monoclinic **C**—Wedge- or envelope-shaped when disseminated, tabular or prismatic when attached **M**—Compact, lamellar	Submetallic Vitreous Opaque to translucent	Black Brownish black
GOETHITE-LIMONITE $HFeO_2$ **315**	Orthorhombic **C**—Rare; pseudomorphs, commonly after pyrite, marcasite, siderite **M**—Compact, stalactitic, botryoidal, reniform; often with internal, radial fibrous structure	Metallic Dull Opaque	Black Brownish black
Hausmannite $MnMn_2O_4$ **308**	Tetragonal **C**—Acute pyramidal, cyclic twins not uncommon **M**—Granular, compact	Metallic Greasy Opaque	Black Brownish black
Huebnerite $MnWO_4$ **348**	Monoclinic **C**—Long fibrous, bladed, stalky; often divergent, without good terminations **M**—Compact, lamellar, granular	Submetallic Resinous Translucent to opaque	Brownish black Black

Hardness 3 to 6				
Hard-ness	Streak	Cleavage = C Fracture = F Tenacity	Specific Gravity	Characteristics and Associates
3.5 **4.**	Reddish brown Blackish brown	C—Brachypina-coidal, perfect F—Uneven Brittle	4.2 4.4	Alters easily to pyrolusite, hence, surface may give black streak. With other manganiferous minerals; also barite, calcite, siderite
5. **5.5**	White Gray	C—Prismatic F—Conchoidal Brittle	3.4 3.6	Generally in crystals. With feldspars, pyroxenes, amphiboles, chlorite, scapolite, zircon, apatite
5. **5.5**	Yellowish brown	F—Conchoidal, splintery Brittle	3.6 4.	Often with black varnish-like surface, passing into the soft, yellow earthy or ocherous variety. With pyrite, hematite, magnetite, siderite. Pseudomorphs after pyrite very common
5. **5.5**	Chestnut brown	C—Basal, perfect F—Uneven Brittle	4.7 4.8	Steep, horizontally striated, octahedral-like bipyramids; complex twins. With manganese minerals—pyrolusite, psilomelane, braunite; magnetite, barite, hematite
5. **5.5**	Yellowish brown Greenish gray	C—Clinopinacoidal, perfect, conspicuous Brittle	6.7 7.3	Structure, cleavage, and specific gravity important. Compare wolframite. In quartz veins, with fluorite, pyrite, scheelite, galena, tetrahedrite

Streak—White, gray, green, red, brown, or yellow			
Name, Composition, and Reference	Crystallization Structure Crystals = C Massive = M	Luster Transparency	Color
WOLFRAMITE (Fe,Mn)WO_4 **347**	Monoclinic **C**—Thick tabular, short columnar, often large **M**—Bladed, curved lamellar, granular	Submetallic Metallic Opaque	Dark gray Brownish black Iron black
Ferberite $FeWO_4$ **347**	Monoclinic **C**—Wedge shaped, short prismatic, tabular **M**—Fan-shaped aggregates, bladed, granular, compact	Submetallic Splendent Opaque	Iron black Brownish black
HORNBLENDE (Amphibole) Silicate of Ca, Mg, Fe, Al, etc. **392**	Monoclinic **C**—Long prismatic, prism angle 124°; often with rhombohedral-like terminations **M**—Bladed, fibrous, granular, compact	Submetallic Vitreous Opaque to translucent	Pitch black Greenish black Brownish black
AUGITE (Pyroxene) Silicate of Ca, Mg, Fe, Al, etc. **386**	Monoclinic **C**—Short prismatic, thick columnar, prism angle 87° **M**—Compact, granular, disseminated	Submetallic Vitreous Opaque to translucent	Pitch black Greenish black Brownish black
Psilomelane A group of manganese oxide minerals **319**	**M**—Botryoidal, reniform, stalactitic; smooth surfaces	Metallic Dull Opaque	Iron black Bluish black Dark gray

Hardness 3 to 6

Hardness	Streak	Cleavage = C Fracture = F Tenacity	Specific Gravity	Characteristics and Associates
5. **5.5**	Dark red-brown	**C**—Clinopinacoidal, perfect, conspicuous **F**—Uneven Brittle	7.1 7.5	Distinguished from huebnerite by streak. Powder may be slightly magnetic. With cassiterite, quartz, mica, fluorite, apatite, scheelite, molybdenite, huebnerite, chalcopyrite
5. **5.5**	Dark brown	**C**—Clinopinacoidal, perfect **F**—Uneven Brittle	7.5	In granites and pegmatites. With quartz, chalcopyrite, galena, scheelite
5. **6.**	Gray Grayish green Grayish brown Yellow	**C**—Prismatic, perfect, conspicuous—124° Brittle	2.9 3.3	Simple, pseudohexagonal crystals and cleavages at 56 and 124° important. Very common and in nearly all types of rocks. With calcite, feldspars, quartz, pyroxenes, chlorite
5. **6.**	Grayish green Gray	**C**—Prismatic, perfect, conspicuous—87° Brittle	3.2 3.6	Crystals usually eight-sided, more rarely four-sided. Pseudotetragonal, with prism angles of 87 and 93°. Cleavage less distinct than on horn blende. Common in basic eruptive rocks and crystalline limestones
5. **6.**	Dark brown Blackish brown	**F**—Conchoidal, uneven Brittle	4.3 5.5	Often with fine sooty coating of pyrolusite. With other manganese minerals; limonite, barite

Streak—White, gray, green, red, brown, or yellow			
Name, Composition, and Reference	Crystallization Structure Crystals = C Massive = M	Luster Transparency	Color
ILMENITE (Menaccanite) $FeTiO_3$ **303**	Hexagonal **C**—Thick tabular, rhombohedral **M**—Thin plates, granular, compact; disseminated grains; pebbles or sand	Metallic Submetallic Opaque	Iron black Brownish black
CHROMITE $Fe(Cr,Fe)_2O_4$ **307**	Cubic **C**—Octahedral, rare **M**—Compact, granular, disseminated	Submetallic Pitchy Opaque	Iron black Brownish black
Allanite (Orthite) $(Ca,Ce,La)_2(Al,Fe)_3O(OH)\text{-}SiO_4Si_2O_7$ **377**	Monoclinic **C**—Tabular, rare **M**—Compact, granular, bladed, disseminated grains	Submetallic Greasy Opaque to translucent	Black Pitch black Brownish black
HEMATITE, varieties *Specular iron ore* Fe_2O_3 *Compact* *Martite* *Argillaceous* **301**	Hexagonal **C**—Pyramidal, tabular, rhombohedral **M**—Compact, granular, micaceous, columnar, radiated reniform or botryoidal	Metallic Dull Opaque	Iron black Reddish black Dark steel gray
FRANKLINITE $(Zn,Mn)Fe_2O_4$ **306**	Cubic **C**—Octahedrons, alone or with dodecahedron; often with rounded edges **M**—Compact, granular, rounded grains	Metallic Dull Opaque	Iron black

Hardness 3 to 6

Hardness	Streak	Cleavage = C Fracture = F Tenacity	Specific Gravity	Characteristics and Associates
5. 6.	Dark brown Reddish brown	**C**—None, partings may be noted **F**—Conchoidal Brittle	4.3 5.5	Often slightly magnetic. With hematite, magnetite, apatite, serpentine, sphene, rutile. Common in black sands
5.5	Dark brown Grayish brown	**C**—Octahedral, indistinct **F**—Uneven, conchoidal Brittle	4.2 4.8	May be slightly magnetic. Pitch-like appearance. With serpentine, talc, chrome garnet; also in black sands and platinum placers
5.5 6.	Grayish Brownish gray Pale brown	**C**—Pinacoidal, indistinct **F**—Uneven, conchoidal Brittle	3.5 4.2	Often coated with yellowish or brownish alteration product. Disseminated in the more acid igneous rocks; also in limestones. With magnetite, epidote, quartz, feldspars
5.5 6.	Cherry red Reddish brown	**C**—None, parting sometimes noted **F**—Uneven Brittle	4.9 5.3	*Specular iron ore*, crystals or sparkling scales and grains, often with iridescent tarnish; *compact hematite*, fibrous, columnar, reniform; *martite*, octahedral forms, pseudomorphous after magnetite; *argillaceous hematite*, impure from sand, clay, jasper
5.5 6.	Reddish brown Dark brown	**C**—Octahedral, indistinct **F**—Conchoidal Brittle	5. 5.2	Powder frequently slightly magnetic. Distinguished by associates—willemite (yellow to green), zincite (red), rhodonite (flesh red), calcite (white)

Streak—White, gray, green, red, brown, or yellow

Name, Composition, and Reference	Crystallization Structure Crystals = C Massive = M	Luster Transparency	Color
Aegirite (Acmite, pyroxene) $NaFeSi_2O_6$ **387**	Monoclinic **C**—Prismatic **M**—Fibrous, acicular; often in tufts	Vitreous Submetallic Translucent to opaque	Greenish black Brownish black
HEMATITE, varieties *Specular iron ore* Fe_2O_3 *Compact* *Martite* *Argillaceous* **301**	Hexagonal **C**—Pyramidal, tabular, rhombohedral **M**—Compact, granular, micaceous, columnar, radiated reniform or botryoidal	Metallic Dull Opaque	Iron black Reddish black Dark steel gray
FRANKLINITE $(Zn,Mn)Fe_2O_4$ **306**	Cubic **C**—Octahedrons, alone or with dodecahedron; often with rounded edges **M**—Compact, granular, rounded grains	Metallic Dull Opaque	Iron black
COLUMBITE (Tantalite) $(Fe,Mn)(Cb,Ta)_2O_6$ **312**	Orthorhombic **C**—Short prismatic, tabular **M**—Compact, disseminated	Submetallic Greasy Dull Opaque	Iron black Brownish black
RUTILE TiO_2 **309**	Tetragonal **C**—Prismatic, vertically striated; twinned, yielding knee-shaped or rosette forms **M**—Compact, disseminated	Metallic Adamantine Opaque to translucent	Iron black Brownish black Reddish black

Hardness over 6

Hardness	Streak	Cleavage = C Fracture = F Tenacity	Specific Gravity	Characteristics and Associates
6. **6.5**	Grayish	C—Prismatic, perfect F—Uneven Brittle	3.4 3.5	In pegmatites and igneous rocks. With leucite, nepheline, feldspars. With blunt end faces, *aegirite*. With acute, *acmite*
6. **6.5**	Cherry red Reddish brown	C—None, parting sometimes noted F—Uneven Brittle	4.9 5.3	*Specular iron ore*, crystals or sparkling scales and grains, often with iridescent tarnish; *compact hematite*, fibrous, columnar, reniform; *martite*, octahedral forms, pseudomorphous after magnetite; *argillaceous hematite*, impure from sand, clay, jasper
6. **6.5**	Reddish brown Dark brown	C—Octahedral, indistinct F—Conchoidal Brittle	5. 5.2	Powder frequently slightly magnetic. Distinguished by associates—willemite (yellow to green), zincite (red), rhodonite (flesh red), calcite (white)
6. **6.5**	Reddish brown Blackish brown	C—Pinacoidal, not conspicuous F—Conchoidal, uneven Brittle	5.4 7.8	Fracture surface sometimes iridescent. With beryl, tourmaline, spodumene, cryolite. Tantalum predominates in *tantalite* and has a higher specific gravity
6. **7.**	Pale yellowish brown Gray	C—Prismatic, pyramidal, not conspicuous F—Uneven Brittle	4.2 4.3	Not as heavy as cassiterite. Sometimes in fine hair-like inclusions. Widely distributed. With quartz, feldspar, hematite, ilmenite, chlorite, apatite

Streak—White, gray, green, red, brown, or yellow

Name, Composition, and Reference	Crystallization Structure Crystals = C Massive = M	Luster Transparency	Color
CASSITERITE, varieties *Ordinary* *Stream tin* SnO_2 **310**	Tetragonal **C**—Thick prismatic, knee-shaped twins, common **M**—Compact, reniform, botryoidal, rounded pebbles	Submetallic Dull Translucent to opaque	Black Brownish black
GARNET, varieties *Andradite* *Almandite* $M''_3M'''_2(SiO_4)_3$ M'' = Ca, Fe, Mg M''' = Al, Fe **363**	Cubic **C**—Dodecahedrons, tetragonal trisoctahedrons, alone or in combination, common **M**—Granular, compact, lamellar, disseminated, sand	Submetallic Translucent to opaque	Velvet black Brownish black
TOURMALINE, variety *Schorl* $M_7Al_6(OH,F)_4(BO_3)_3Si_6O_{18}$ **381**	Hexagonal **C**—Prismatic, vertically striated, terminated with broken or rhombohedral-like surfaces **M**—Compact, divergent columnar, disseminated	Submetallic Pitchy Opaque	Pitch black Brownish black Bluish black
CORUNDUM, variety *Emery* Al_2O_3 with $FeFe_2O_4$, Fe_2O_3, SiO_2 **299**	Hexagonal **M**—Fine to coarse granular	Metallic Dull Opaque	Dark gray Black

Hardness over 6				
Hard-ness	Streak	Cleavage = C Fracture = F Tenacity	Specific Gravity	Characteristics and Associates
6. **7.**	Pale brown Pale yellow White	**C**—Prismatic, imperfect **F**—Uneven Brittle	6.8 7.	Distinguished by high specific gravity and hardness. In veins cutting granite, gneiss; also in alluvial deposits, as *stream tin.* With quartz, wolframite, scheelite, arsenopyrite, molybdenite, tourmaline, fluorite, apatite, mica
6.5 **7.5**	White	**C**—Dodecahedral, indistinct **F**—Conchoidal, uneven Brittle	3.7 4.2	*Andradite,* commonly with magnetite, epidote, feldspars, nepheline, leucite; *almandite,* with mica, staurolite, andalusite, kyanite, tourmaline
7. **7.5**	White Gray	**C**—None **F**—Conchoidal, uneven Brittle	2.9 3.2	Spherical triangular cross-section and hemimorphic development important. In pegmatites; metamorphic rocks; alluvial deposits. With quartz, feldspar, cassiterite, beryl, topaz, fluorite
7. **9.**	Yellowish brown Blackish brown	**C**—Indistinct **F**—Uneven Brittle to tough	3.7 4.3	Corundum mixed with magnetite, hematite, quartz. Resembles iron ore, powder may be magnetic. Properties vary with composition. With mica, amphiboles, chlorite, spinel; in crystalline limestones, schists, peridotite

Name, Composition, and Reference	Crystallization Structure Crystals = C Massive = M	Luster Transparency	Color
Streak—White, gray, green, red, brown, or yellow			
SPINEL, varieties *Pleonaste* $M''M'''_2O_4$ *Hercynite* $M'' = Mg, Fe, Zn, Mn$ *Gahnite* *Picotite* $M''' = Al, Fe$ **304**	Cubic **C**—Octahedral, well developed, common **M**—Compact, granular, disseminated grains; sand	Submetallic Dull Nearly opaque	Black Brownish black Greenish black
Streak—Black			
MOLYBDENITE MoS_2 **288**	Hexagonal **C**—Tabular, rare **M**—Scales, foliated, disseminated grains	Metallic Opaque	Bluish lead gray
GRAPHITE (Plumbago, black lead) C **274**	Hexagonal **C**—Tabular, rare **M**—Foliated, scaly, granular, earthy	Metallic Dull Opaque	Dark steel gray Iron black
PYROLUSITE MnO_2 **311**	Tetragonal **C**—Often pseudomorphous after manganite **M**—Fibrous, acicular, often divergent columnar; dendritic; powdery	Metallic Dull Opaque	Iron black Dark steel gray
STIBNITE Sb_2S_3 **284**	Orthorhombic **C**—Prismatic, bent, twisted, common **M**—Bladed, fibrous, columnar, granular	Metallic Opaque	Dark lead gray Black

Hardness	Streak	Cleavage = C Fracture = F Tenacity	Specific Gravity	Characteristics and Associates
Hardness over 6				
7.5 **8.**	Grayish Grayish green Pale brown White	**C**—Octahedral, indistinct **F**—Conchoidal Brittle	3.6 4.4	Common contact mineral in granular limestones; in igneous rocks, especially the basic olivine-bearing types; rounded grains in placers. With calcite, chondrodite, serpentine, brucite, olivine, corundum, graphite, pyroxenes
Hardness 1 to 3				
1. **1.5**	Dark lead gray; greenish on glazed porcelain (graphite, shiny black)	**C**—Basal, perfect Sectile, lamellae are flexible	4.7 4.8	Marks paper. Soft and greasy like graphite, but heavier and lighter colored. In granite with cassiterite, wolframite; also in quartz veins
1. **2.**	Black, shiny Dark silver gray	**C**—Basal, perfect Sectile, lamellae are flexible	1.9 2.3	Greasy feel; marks paper; darker than molybdenite and not as heavy. In crystalline limestone with garnet, spinel, pyroxenes, amphiboles; also in shale, gneiss, and mica schist
1. **2.5**	Black Bluish black	**C**—Indistinct Brittle	4.7 4.8	Often soils fingers. Darker than stibnite. With psilomelane, manganite, hematite, limonite, barite
2. **2.5**	Dark lead gray Black	**C**—Brachypinacoidal, perfect, conspicuous, yielding long, shiny faces Slightly sectile	4.6 4.7	Tarnishes black, sometimes iridescent. In veins with quartz, sphalerite, galena, cinnabar, barite, gold

Streak—Black

Name, Composition, and Reference	Crystallization Structure Crystals = C Massive = M	Luster Transparency	Color
Argentite (Silver glance) Ag_2S **276**	Pseudocubic **C**—Octahedral, cubical, often distorted **M**—Compact, arborescent; coatings	Metallic Opaque	Dark lead gray Black
GALENA (Galenite) PbS **277**	Cubic **C**—Cubes alone, or with octahedron, well developed, common **M**—Cleavable granular, aggregates, compact	Metallic Opaque	Dark lead gray
CHALCOCITE Cu_2S **276**	Orthorhombic **C**—Tabular, pseudohexagonal, deeply striated **M**—Granular, compact, disseminated	Metallic Opaque	Dark lead gray, often tarnished dull black, blue, or green
Bournonite (Cogwheel ore) $PbCuSbS_3$ **291**	Orthorhombic **C**—Thick tabular; cogwheel twins **M**—Compact, granular	Metallic Opaque	Dark steel gray Iron black
Enargite Cu_3AsS_4 **291**	Orthorhombic **C**—Prismatic, small, rare **M**—Compact, granular, columnar	Metallic Submetallic Opaque	Grayish black Iron black

Streak—Black

Name, Composition, and Reference	Crystallization Structure Crystals = C Massive = M	Luster Transparency	Color
TETRAHEDRITE $M_{12}R_4S_{13}$ M = Usually Cu R = Sb, As **290**	Cubic **C**—Tetrahedral, often highly modified **M**—Granular, compact	Metallic Opaque	Dark steel gray Iron black

Hardness 1 to 3

Hardness	Streak	Cleavage = C Fracture = F Tenacity	Specific Gravity	Characteristics and Associates
2. 2.5	Dark lead gray, shiny	**C**—Indistinct **F**—Hackly Perfectly sectile	7.2 7.4	Cuts and takes impression like lead, hence easily distinguished from other soft, black minerals. With silver, cobalt, nickel ores—proustite, pyrargyrite, smaltite, niccolite
2.5	Grayish black Dark lead gray	**C**—Cubic, perfect, very conspicuous Brittle	7.3 7.6	Characterized by cleavage and high specific gravity. Changes to cerussite or anglesite. With sphalerite, pyrite, chalcopyrite, calcite, fluorite, barite
2.5 3.	Dark gray, shiny Black, shiny	**C**—Indistinct **F**—Conchoidal Rather brittle	5.5 5.8	More brittle than argentite. Often coated with malachite (green), azurite (blue). With chalcopyrite, bornite, tetrahedrite, galena
2.5 3.	Dark gray Black	**C**—Imperfect **F**—Uneven Brittle	5.7 5.9	Easily recognized by cross or cogwheel appearance. With galena, sphalerite, tetrahedrite, siderite, stibnite, chalcocite
3.	Grayish black	**C**—Prismatic, perfect, often conspicuous **F**—Uneven Brittle	4.4	In artificial light usually resembles sphalerite. In veins with other copper minerals—chalcopyrite, bornite, chalcocite

Hardness over 3

Hardness	Streak	Cleavage = C Fracture = F Tenacity	Specific Gravity	Characteristics and Associates
3. 4.5	Dark gray Black	**C**—Indistinct **F**—Uneven Brittle	4.6 5.1	Characteristic crystals, sometimes coated with chalcopyrite. With sphalerite, galena, bournonite, siderite, malachite

Streak—Black			
Name, Composition, and Reference	Crystallization Structure Crystals = C Massive = M	Luster Transparency	Color
Arsenic As 263	Hexagonal **C**—Rare **M**—Compact, scaly, fine granular, with reniform or botryoidal structure	Metallic Opaque	Dark gray to black on exposure, tin white on fresh fracture
URANINITE (Pitchblende) UO_2 312	Cubic **C**—Octahedral, rare **M**—Botryoidal, columnar, curved lamellar, granular, compact, apparently amorphous	Pitch-like Submetallic Dull Opaque	Pitch black Brownish black Greenish black
Ferberite $FeWO_4$ 347	Monoclinic **C**—Wedge-shaped, short prismatic, tabular **M**—Fan-shaped aggregates, bladed, granular, compact	Submetallic Splendent Opaque	Iron black Brownish black
WOLFRAMITE $(Fe,Mn)WO_4$ 347	Monoclinic **C**—Thick, tabular, short columnar, often large **M**—Bladed, curved lamellar, granular, compact	Submetallic Metallic Opaque	Dark gray Brownish black Iron black
Psilomelane (A group of manganese oxide minerals) 319	**M**—Botryoidal, reniform, stalactitic; smooth surface	Metallic Dull Opaque	Iron black Bluish black Dark gray
ILMENITE (Menaccanite) $FeTiO_3$ 303	Hexagonal **C**—Thick tabular, rhombohedral **M**—Thin plates, granular, compact, disseminated grains, pebbles, sand	Metallic Submetallic Opaque	Iron black Brownish black

Hardness over 3

Hardness	Streak	Cleavage = C Fracture = F Tenacity	Specific Gravity	Characteristics and Associates
3. **4.**	Dark gray Black	**C**—Basal, not conspicuous **F**—Uneven, granular Brittle	5.6 5.8	Often breaks in concentric or onion-like layers. Color and streak darken on exposure. With silver, cobalt, nickel ores—prousite, smaltite
3. **5.5**	Brownish black Grayish black	**F**—Conchoidal, uneven Brittle	4.8 9.7	Pitch-like appearance and fracture important. Fresh material is hard and heavy. With ores of lead, silver, bismuth; pyrite, allanite
5. **5.5**	Brownish black	**C**—Clinopinacoidal, perfect **F**—Uneven Brittle	7.1 7.5	In granites and pegmatites. With quartz, chalcopyrite, galena, scheelite
5. **5.5**	Brownish black Black	**C**—Clinopinacoidal, perfect, conspicuous **F**—Uneven Brittle	7.1 7.5	Structure, cleavage, and specific gravity important. Powder may be slightly magnetic. With cassiterite, quartz, mica, fluorite, apatite, scheelite, molybdenite, huebnerite
5. **6.**	Black Brownish black	**F**—Conchoidal, uneven Brittle	4.3 5.5	Often with fine, sooty coating of pyrolusite. With other manganese minerals; limonite, barite
5. **6.**	Black Brownish black	**C**—None, partings may be noted **F**—Conchoidal Brittle	4.5 5.5	Sometimes slightly magnetic but not as strongly as magnetite. With hematite, magnetite, apatite, serpentine, sphene, rutile. Common in black sands

Streak—Black

Name, Composition, and Reference	Crystallization Structure Crystals = C Massive = M	Luster Transparency	Color
MAGNETITE $FeFe_2O_4$ **305**	Cubic **C**—Octahedrons, dodecahedrons, common **M**—Compact, granular, lamellar, disseminated, sand	Metallic Submetallic Dull Opaque	Iron black
FRANKLINITE $(Zn,Mn)Fe_2O_4$ **306**	Cubic **C**—Octahedrons, alone or with dodecahedron; edges often rounded **M**—Compact, granular, rounded grains	Metallic Dull Opaque	Iron black
COLUMBITE (Tantalite) $(Fe,Mn)(Cb,Ta)_2O_6$ **312**	Orthorhombic **C**—Short prismatic, tabular **M**—Compact, disseminated	Submetallic Greasy Dull Opaque	Iron black Brownish black
CORUNDUM, variety *Emery* Al_2O_3, with $FeFe_2O_4$, Fe_2O_3, SiO_2 **299**	Hexagonal **M**—Always massive, fine to coarse granular	Metallic Dull Opaque	Dark gray Black

A. MINERALS WITH METALLIC LUSTER

Streak—Metallic white or steel gray

Name, Composition, and Reference	Crystallization Structure Crystals = C Massive = M	Luster Transparency	Color
Bismuth Bi **263**	Hexagonal **C**—Rare **M**—Reticulated, arborescent, platy	Metallic Opaque	Silver white, with reddish tinge

Hardness over 3

Hard-ness	Streak	Cleavage = C Fracture = F Tenacity	Specific Gravity	Characteristics and Associates
5.5 **6.5**	Black	**C**—Indistinct, octahedral parting **F**—Conchoidal, uneven Brittle	4.9 5.2	Very strongly magnetic. Crystals usually perfect and with bright surfaces. Independent deposits; disseminated; black sands. With chlorite, hornblende, pyroxene, feldspar, quartz, pyrite, chalcopyrite, epidote
5.5 **6.5**	Black Brownish black	**C**—Octahedral, indistinct **F**—Conchoidal Brittle	5. 5.2	Powder frequently slightly magnetic. Distinguished by associates—willemite (yellow or green), zincite (red), rhodonite (flesh red), calcite (white)
6. **6.5**	Black Brownish black Grayish black	**C**—Pinacoidal, not conspicuous **F**—Conchoidal, uneven Brittle	5.4 7.8	Fracture surface sometimes iridescent. With beryl, tourmaline, spodumene, cryolite. Tantalum predominates in *tantalite* and has a higher specific gravity
7. **9.**	Black Brownish black	**C**—Indistinct **F**—Uneven Brittle to tough	3.7 4.3	Corundum mixed with iron ore. May be magnetic. With mica, amphiboles, chlorite, spinel; in crystalline limestone, schist peridotite

2. METALLIC WHITE OR LIGHT METALLIC GRAY IN COLOR

Hardness 1 to 6

Hard-ness	Streak	Cleavage = C Fracture = F Tenacity	Specific Gravity	Characteristics and Associates
2. **2.5**	Lead gray, shiny	**C**—Basal, perfect, usually conspicuous Sectile	9.7 9.8	Often shows brassy tarnish colors. With silver, cobalt, nickel, tin ores—smaltite, niccolite, cassiterite; wolframite

Name, Composition, and Reference	Crystallization Structure Crystals = C Massive = M	Luster Transparency	Color
Streak—Metallic white or steel gray			
SILVER Ag **258**	Cubic **C**—Small, often distorted **M**—Grains, scales, plates, twisted hair- or wire-like forms, lumps	Metallic Opaque	Silver white tarnishing yellow, brown, or black
PLATINUM Pt **262**	Cubic **C**—Small, rare **M**—Scales, grains, nuggets	Metallic Opaque	Tin white Steel gray
Streak—Black			
MOLYBDENITE MoS_2 **288**	Hexagonal **C**—Tabular, rare **M**—Scales, foliated, disseminated grains	Metallic Opaque	Bluish lead gray
STIBNITE Sb_2S_3 **284**	Orthorhombic **C**—Prismatic, bent, twisted, common **M**—Bladed, fibrous, columnar, granular, compact	Metallic Opaque	Light lead gray
GALENA (Galenite) PbS **277**	Cubic **C**—Cubes, alone or with octahedron, common, well developed **M**—Cleavable, granular aggregates	Metallic Opaque	Lead gray

Hardness	Streak	Cleavage = C Fracture = F Tenacity	Specific Gravity	Characteristics and Associates
Hardness 1 to 6				
2.5 **3.**	Silver white, shiny Light lead gray, shiny	**C**—None **F**—Hackly Malleable, ductile	10.5 12.	Color and streak darken on exposure. With silver, lead, arsenic, cobalt, nickel ores—argentite, pyrargyrite, proustite, galena, smaltite; fluorite, calcite, barite
4. **5.**	Light steel gray, shiny	**C**—None **F**—Hackly Malleable, ductile	14. 19.	Heavier than silver and does not tarnish. May be magnetic if much iron be present. With chromite, magnetite, gold
Hardness 1 to 3				
1. **1.5**	Dark lead gray, greenish on glazed porcelain (graphite, shiny black)	**C**—Basal, perfect Sectile, lamellae flexible	4.7 4.8	Marks paper. Soft and greasy like graphite but heavier and lighter colored. In granite with cassiterite, wolframite; in quartz veins
2. **2.5**	Dark lead gray Black	**C**—Brachypinacoidal, perfect, conspicuous, yielding long shiny faces Slightly sectile	4.6 4.7	Differs from galena in cleavage and specific gravity. Tarnishes black, sometimes iridescent. In veins with quartz, sphalerite, galena, cinnabar, barite, gold
2.5	Dark lead gray Grayish black	**C**—Cubic, perfect, very conspicuous Brittle	7.3 7.6	Characterized by cleavage and high specific gravity. Changes to cerussite, pyromorphite, or anglesite. With sphalerite, pyrite, chalcopyrite, calcite, fluorite, barite

Streak—Black

Name, Composition, and Reference	Crystallization Structure Crystals = C Massive = M	Luster Transparency	Color
Arsenic As **263**	Hexagonal **C**—Rare **M**—Compact, scaly, fine grained, reniform, botryoidal	Metallic Opaque	Tin white, on fresh fracture
Cobaltite CoAsS **286**	Cubic **C**—Cubes, pyritohedrons, small, well developed **M**—Granular, compact	Metallic Opaque	Silver white Steel gray, at times with reddish tinge
ARSENOPYRITE FeAsS **287**	Monoclinic, pseudo-orthorhombic **C**—Prismatic, common **M**—Compact, granular columnar, radial	Metallic Opaque	Tin white Light steel gray, tarnishes yellow
Smaltite $(Co,Ni)As_{3-x}$ **289**	Cubic **C**—Rare **M**—Granular, compact	Metallic Opaque	Tin white Light steel gray
MARCASITE (White iron pyrites) FeS_2 **286**	Orthorhombic **C**—Tabular, often twinned, resembling cock's combs **M**—Compact, stalactitic, globular, radiated	Metallic Opaque	Steel gray Pale brass yellow, more brassy on exposure

A. MINERALS WITH METALLIC LUSTER

Streak—Brown or yellow

GOETHITE-LIMONITE, varieties *Yellow ocher* *Bog iron ore* $HFeO_2$ **315**	**M**—Earthy, porous, clay-like	Earthy Dull Opaque	Yellow Brownish yellow

Hardness over 3

Hard-ness	Streak	Cleavage = C Fracture = F Tenacity	Specific Gravity	Characteristics and Associates
3. **4.**	Lead gray Grayish black	**C**—Basal, not conspicuous **F**—Uneven, granular Brittle	5.6 5.8	Often breaks in concentric or onion-like layers. Color and streak darken on exposure. With silver, cobalt, nickel ores—proustite, smaltite
5.5	Dark grayish black	**C**—Cubic, not conspicuous **F**—Uneven Brittle	6. 6.4	May show red tarnish. Often with pink coating of erythrite (cobalt bloom). With native silver, smaltite, niccolite, pyrrhotite, chalcopyrite
5.5 **6.**	Dark grayish black	**C**—Prismatic, not conspicuous **F**—Uneven Brittle	5.9 6.2	Whiter than marcasite. More common than smaltite. With chalcopyrite, pyrite, sphalerite, cassiterite, smaltite, native gold and silver, serpentine
5.5 **6.**	Grayish black	**C**—Indistinct **F**—Uneven Brittle	6.4 6.6	May have dull tarnish and pink coating of erythrite. With niccolite, cobaltite, native bismuth and silver, proustite, barite, fluorite, calcite
6. **6.5**	Dark greenish black	**C**—Indistinct **F**—Uneven Brittle	4.6 4.8	Alters to limonite, melanterite. With other sulfides—galena, sphalerite, chalcopyrite, pyrite; calcite, dolomite

3. YELLOW IN COLOR

Hardness 1 to 6

Hard-ness	Streak	Cleavage = C Fracture = F Tenacity	Specific Gravity	Characteristics and Associates
1. **4.**	Yellowish brown	**C**—None **F**—Earthy Brittle	3.4 4.	*Yellow ocher*, earthy, may have greasy feel, when impure gritty; *bog iron ore*, porous

Name, Composition, and Reference	Crystallization Structure Crystals = C Massive = M	Luster Transparency	Color
Streak—Brown or yellow			
GOLD Au **256**	Cubic **C**—Small, often distorted **M**—Grains, scales, nuggets, dust	Metallic Opaque	Golden yellow Brassy yellow Light yellow
Streak—Black			
CHALCOPYRITE $CuFeS_2$ **280**	Tetragonal **C**—Bisphenoids, resembling tetrahedrons, common **M**—Compact	Metallic Opaque	Brass yellow Golden yellow
MARCASITE (White iron pyrites) FeS_2 **286**	Orthorhombic **C**—Tabular, often twinned, resembling cock's combs **M**—Compact, stalactitic, globular, radiated	Metallic Opaque	Pale brass yellow, more brassy on exposure
PYRITE (Iron pyrites, fool's gold) FeS_2 **285**	Cubic **C**—Cubes, octahedrons, pyritohedrons, common, often striated **M**—Compact, fine granular; botryoidal, stalactitic	Metallic Opaque	Brass yellow Golden yellow with variegated tarnish

A. MINERALS WITH METALLIC LUSTER

Name, Composition, and Reference	Crystallization Structure Crystals = C Massive = M	Luster Transparency	Color
Streak—Gray, red, or yellow			
Bismuth Bi **263**	Hexagonal **C**—Rare **M**—Reticulated, arborescent, platy	Metallic Opaque	Light copper red

Hardness 1 to 6

Hardness	Streak	Cleavage = C Fracture = F Tenacity	Specific Gravity	Characteristics and Associates
2.5 **3.**	Golden yellow	**C**—None **F**—Hackly Malleable, ductile	15.6 19.3	Does not tarnish. Characterized by streak, specific gravity, and tenacity. Frequently in quartz veins; placers. Commonly with pyrite, and other sulfides

Hardness over 3

Hardness	Streak	Cleavage = C Fracture = F Tenacity	Specific Gravity	Characteristics and Associates
3.5 **4.**	Greenish black	**C**—Indistinct **F**—Uneven Brittle	4.1 4.3	Softer, and deeper yellow than pyrite. Frequently with iridescent tarnish. With pyrite, bornite, galena, sphalerite, tetrahedrite, chalcocite
6. **6.5**	Dark greenish black Brownish black	**C**—Indistinct **F**—Uneven Brittle	4.8 4.9	Distinguished from pyrite by crystallization and lighter color on fresh fracture. Alters more readily than pyrite, forming limonite, melanterite. Occurrence same as pyrite, less abundant
6. **6.5**	Greenish black Brownish black	**C**—Indistinct **F**—Uneven Brittle	5. 5.2	Harder than chalcopyrite. Alters to limonite. Widely distributed in all types of rocks. With other sulfides—galena, sphalerite, chalcopyrite; quartz

4. BRASS, BRONZE, OR COPPER RED IN COLOR

Hardness 1 to 3

Hardness	Streak	Cleavage = C Fracture = F Tenacity	Specific Gravity	Characteristics and Associates
2. **2.5**	Lead gray, shiny	**C**—Basal, perfect, usually conspicuous Sectile	9.7 9.8	Often shows brassy tarnish. Frequently with silver, cobalt, nickel, tin ores; smaltite, niccolite, cassiterite, wolframite

Name, Composition, and Reference	Crystallization Structure Crystals = C Massive = M	Luster Transparency	Color
Streak—Gray, red, or yellow			
COPPER Cu **259**	Cubic **C**—Cubes, octahedrons, tetrahexahedrons **M**—Scales, plates, lumps, arborescent aggregates	Metallic Opaque	Copper red, tarnishing readily red, blue, green, black
GOLD **Au** **256**	Cubic **C**—Small, distorted, rare **M**—Grains, scales, dust, nuggets	Metallic Opaque	Golden yellow Brassy yellow Light yellow
Streak—Black			
BORNITE Cu_5FeS_4 **277**	Cubic **C**—Rare **M**—Compact, granular	Metallic Opaque	Bronze Copper red, on fresh fracture
CHALCOPYRITE $CuFeS_2$ **280**	Tetragonal **C**—Bisphenoids, resembling tetrahedrons, common **M**—Compact, granular	Metallic Opaque	Brass yellow Golden yellow
PYRRHOTITE (Magnetic pyrites) FeS **281**	Hexagonal **C**—Tabular, rare **M**—Compact, granular	Metallic Opaque	Bronze yellow Bronze brown

Hardness	Streak	Cleavage = C Fracture = F Tenacity	Specific Gravity	Characteristics and Associates
Hardness 1 to 3				
2.5 **3.**	Copper red, shiny	C—None F—Hackly Ductile, malleable	8.5 9.	Cementing material in conglomerate or filling cavities in trap rocks. With cuprite, malachite, azurite, native silver, melaconite, epidote, datolite, zeolites
2.5 **3.**	Golden yellow	C—None F—Hackly Malleable, ductile	15.6 19.3	Does not tarnish. Characterized by streak, specific gravity, and tenacity. Frequently in quartz veins; placers. Commonly with pyrite and other sulfides
Hardness over 3				
3. **3.5**	Grayish black	C—Indistinct F—Uneven Brittle	4.9 5.2	Usually with peacock tarnish colors (purple copper ore). With chalcopyrite, chalcocite, malachite, cassiterite, siderite
3.5 **4.**	Greenish black	C—Indistinct F—Uneven Brittle	4.1 4.3	Softer, and deeper yellow in color than pyrite. Frequently with iridescent tarnish. With pyrite, bornite, galena, sphalerite, tetrahedrite, chalcocite
3.5 **4.5**	Dark grayish black	C—Basal, not conspicuous F—Uneven Brittle	4.5 4.6	May be slightly magnetic. Subject to dark-brown tarnish. In basic igneous rocks. With chalcopyrite, galena

Streak—Black			
Name, Composition, and Reference	Crystallization Structure Crystals = C Massive = M	Luster Transparency	Color
Niccolite NiAs **281**	Hexagonal **C**—Rare **M**—Compact, disseminated	Metallic Opaque	Light copper red
MARCASITE (White iron pyrites) FeS_2 **286**	Orthorhombic **C**—Tabular, often twinned resembling cocks' combs **M**—Compact, stalactitic, globular, radiated	Metallic Opaque	Steel gray Pale brass yellow, more brassy on exposure
PYRITE (Iron pyrites, fool's gold) FeS_2 **285**	Cubic **C**—Cubes, octahedrons, pyritohedrons, very common, often striated **M**—Compact, fine granular; botryoidal, stalactitic	Metallic Opaque	Brass yellow Golden yellow, with variegated tarnish

A. MINERALS WITH METALLIC LUSTER

Streak—White, gray, green, red, brown, or yellow			
GOETHITE-LIMONITE, varieties *Brown ocher* $HFeO_2$ *Bog iron ore* *Brown clay ironstone* **315**	Orthorhombic **M**—Compact, earthy, porous, pisolitic, oölitic	Dull Earthy Opaque	Yellowish brown Dark brown
HEMATITE, varieties *Red ocher* Fe_2O_3 *Oölitic* *Fossiliferous* **301**	Hexagonal **M**—Fine granular, earthy, scaly, oölitic, fossiliferous	Dull Earthy Opaque	Brownish Cherry red

Hardness over 3				
Hard-ness	Streak	Cleavage = C Fracture = F Tenacity	Specific Gravity	Characteristics and Associates
5. **5.5**	Dark brownish black	C—Indistinct F—Uneven Brittle	7.3 7.7	Often with green coating of annabergite (nickel bloom). With cobalt, nickel, silver minerals—smaltite, proustite, native silver; native bismuth and arsenic; calcite
6. **6.5**	Dark greenish black	C—Indistinct F—Uneven Brittle	4.8 4.9	Distinguished from pyrite by crystallization and lighter color on fresh fracture. Alters more readily than pyrite, forming limonite, melanterite. Occurrence same as for pyrite, but not as abundant
6. **6.5**	Greenish black Brownish black	C—Indistinct F—Uneven Brittle	5. 5.2	Alters to limonite. Widely distributed in all types of rocks. With other sulfides—galena, sphalerite, chalcopyrite; quartz

5. RED, BROWN, OR BLUE IN COLOR

Hardness 1 to 3				
1. **3.**	Yellowish brown	C—None F—Earthy Brittle	3.4 4.	*Brown ocher*, earthy, may soil fingers; *bog iron ore*, porous; *brown clay ironstone*, massive or concretionary, impure from clay, sand
1. **3.**	Cherry red Reddish brown	C—None F—Earthy Brittle	4.9 5.3	*Red ocher*, earthy; *oölitic*, fish-egg structure; *fossiliferous*, replacement of shells

Streak—White, gray, green, red, brown, or yellow

Name, Composition, and Reference	Crystallization Structure Crystals = C Massive = M	Luster Transparency	Color
CINNABAR HgS **282**	Hexagonal **C**—Rhombohedral, thick tabular, small, rare **M**—Fine granular, fibrous, disseminated, earthy coating	Adamantine Dull Transparent to opaque	Scarlet red Brownish red
Proustite Ag_3AsS_3 **290**	Hexagonal **C**—Small, complex, rare **M**—Disseminated, crusts, bands	Adamantine Dull Transparent to translucent	Scarlet Vermilion
Pyrargyrite Ag_3SbS_3 **289**	Hexagonal **C**—Small, complex, rare **M**—Disseminated, crusts, bands	Adamantine Metallic Transparent to opaque	Dark red
COPPER Cu **259**	Cubic **C**—Cubes, octahedrons, tetrahexahedrons **M**—Scales, plates, lumps, arborescent aggregates	Metallic Opaque	Copper red, tarnishing readily to red, blue green, black

Streak—White, gray, green, red, brown, or yellow

Name, Composition, and Reference	Crystallization Structure Crystals = C Massive = M	Luster Transparency	Color
GOETHITE-LIMONITE, varieties *Compact* *Bog iron ore* *Brown clay ironstone* $HFeO_2$ **315**	Orthorhombic **C**—Rare; pseudomorphs, commonly after pyrite, marcasite, siderite **M**—Compact, stalactitic, botryoidal, nodular; often with internal radial fibrous structure; porous	Metallic Dull Opaque	Yellowish brown Dark brown

Hardness 1 to 3

Hardness	Streak	Cleavage = C Fracture = F Tenacity	Specific Gravity	Characteristics and Associates
2. **2.5**	Scarlet Reddish brown	**C**—Prismatic, not conspicuous **F**—Uneven Brittle to sectile	8. 8.2	Color, streak, high specific gravity important; the latter often reduced by gangue. Disseminated in siliceous rocks, with native mercury, pyrite, marcasite, realgar, stibnite
2.5	Scarlet Aurora red	**C**—Indistinct **F**—Conchoidal Brittle	5.5 5.6	Termed light ruby silver ore. Distinguished from cinnabar by associates. With pyrargyrite, in veins with other silver minerals and galena
2.5 **3.**	Cherry red Purplish red	**C**—Indistinct **F**—Conchoidal Brittle	5.8	Frequently as gray or dark-red bands, dark ruby silver ore. With proustite, in veins with other silver minerals and galena
2.5 **3.**	Copper red, shiny	**C**—None **F**—Hackly Ductile, malleable	8.5 9.	Cementing material in conglomerate, or filling cavities in trap rocks. With cuprite, malachite, azurite, native silver, melaconite, epidote, datolite, zeolites, quartz, calcite
		Hardness 3 to 6		
3. **5.5**	Yellowish brown	**F**—Conchoidal, uneven, splintery, earthy Brittle	3.4 4.	Often with black, varnish-like surface, passing into soft, yellow ocherous variety. *Compact limonite,* massive, with fibrous structure, rather pure; *brown clay ironstone* massive or concretionary, impure from clay, sand; *bog iron ore,* porous

Streak—White, gray, green, red, brown, or yellow			
Name, Composition, and Reference	Crystallization Structure Crystals = C Massive = M	Luster Transparency	Color
URANINITE (Pitchblende) UO_2 **312**	Cubic **C**—Octahedral, rare **M**—Botryoidal, columnar, curved lamellar, granular, compact; apparently amorphous	Submetallic Dull Opaque	Brown Blackish brown
HEMATITE, varieties *Argillaceous* *Compact* Fe_2O_3 **301**	Hexagonal **M**—Compact, granular, columnar, splintery, radiated, reniform and botryoidal	Submetallic Dull Opaque	Brownish red Dark red Blackish red
SIDERITE $FeCO_3$ **332**	Hexagonal **C**—Rhombohedral, curved or saddle-shaped, common **M**—Cleavable, granular, compact, botryoidal	Submetallic Dull Vitreous Translucent to opaque	Dark brown Reddish brown
SPHALERITE ZnS **278**	Cubic **C**—Tetrahedral, common **M**—Cleavable, fine and coarse-grained aggregates, compact	Submetallic Resinous Opaque to translucent	Brown Yellowish brown Reddish brown
Cuprite Cu_2O **298**	Cubic **C**—Octahedrons, dodecahedrons, alone or in combination; slender crystal aggregates (*chalcotrichite*) **M**—Compact, granular, earthy	Submetallic Adamantine Dull Translucent to opaque	Cochineal red Brick red Dark red

Hardness 3 to 6

Hardness	Streak	Cleavage = C Fracture = F Tenacity	Specific Gravity	Characteristics and Associates
3. **5.5**	Dark brown Olive green Grayish	**F**—Conchoidal, uneven Brittle	4.8 9.7	Structure and fracture important. Fresh material is hard and heavy. With ores of lead, silver, bismuth; also allanite
3. **6.**	Cherry red Reddish brown	**C**—None, parting sometimes noted **F**—Uneven, splintery Brittle	4.9 5.3	*Argillaceous hematite,* impure from clay, sand, jasper; *compact hematite,* usually quite pure
3.5 **4.**	Yellowish brown Pale yellow	**C**—Rhombohedral, perfect, conspicuous **F**—Conchoidal Brittle	3.7 3.9	Curved crystals, cleavage, and rather high specific gravity characteristic. In ore deposits; beds and concretions in limestone and shale. With pyrite, chalcopyrite, galena, tetrahedrite, cryolite
3.5 **4.**	Light brown Pale yellow	**C**—Dodecahedral, perfect, conspicuous **F**—Conchoidal Brittle	3.9 4.2	Color and streak vary with impurities. Extensively in limestone. With galena, chalcopyrite, pyrite, barite, fluorite, siderite, rhodochrosite
3.5 **4.**	Brownish red Dirty brown	**C**—Indistinct **F**—Uneven Brittle	5.8 6.2	Characterized by associates, copper minerals—malachite (green), azurite (blue), chalcocite and melaconite (black), chalcopyrite (yellow), native copper

Name, Composition, and Reference	Crystallization Structure Crystals = C Massive = M	Luster Transparency	Color
	Streak—White, gray, green, red, brown, or yellow		
Zincite ZnO **299**	Hexagonal **C**—Hemimorphic, rare **M**—Compact, granular, foliated	Subadamantine Vitreous Translucent to opaque	Dark red Blood red
Huebnerite $MnWO_4$ **348**	Monoclinic **C**—Long, fibrous, bladed, stalky, often divergent, without good terminations **M**—Compact, lamellar, granular	Submetallic Resinous Opaque to translucent	Reddish brown Brown
WOLFRAMITE $(Fe,Mn)WO_4$ **347**	Monoclinic **C**—Thick, tabular, short columnar, often large **M**—Bladed, curved lamellar, granular, compact	Submetallic Opaque	Reddish brown Dark brown
Ferberite $FeWO_4$ **347**	Monoclinic **C**—Wedge-shaped, short prismatic, tabular **M**—Fan-shaped aggregates, bladed, granular, compact	Submetallic Opaque	Brown Blackish brown
	Streak—White, gray, green, red, brown, or yellow		
RUTILE TiO_2 **309**	Tetragonal **C**—Prismatic, vertically striated; twinned, yielding knee-shaped or rosette forms **M**—Compact, disseminated	Metallic Adamantine Opaque to transparent	Reddish brown Dark red

Hardness	Streak	Cleavage = C Fracture = F Tenacity	Specific Gravity	Characteristics and Associates
Hardness 3 to 6				
4. **4.5**	Reddish yellow Orange yellow	C—Basal, perfect, may be conspicuous F—Uneven Brittle	5.7	Distinguished by associates—calcite, franklinite (black), willemite (yellow to green), rhodonite (flesh red). On exposure becomes coated with the white carbonate
5. **5.5**	Yellowish brown Greenish gray	C—Clinopinacoidal, perfect, conspicuous Brittle	6.7 7.3	Structure, cleavage, specific gravity important. In quartz veins. With fluorite, pyrite, scheelite, wolframite, galena, tetrahedrite
5. **5.5**	Dark red-brown	C—Clinopinacoidal, perfect, conspicuous F—Uneven Brittle	7.1 7.5	Distinguished from huebnerite by streak. Powder may be slightly magnetic. With cassiterite, quartz, mica, fluorite, apatite, scheelite, molybdenite, huebnerite
5. **5.5**	Brown Dark brown	C—Clinopinacoidal, perfect F—Uneven Brittle	7.5	In granites and pegmatites. With quartz, chalcopyrite, galena, scheelite
Hardness over 6				
6. **7.**	Pale yellowish brown Gray	C—Prismatic, pyramidal, not conspicuous F—Uneven Brittle	4.2 4.3	Not as heavy as cassiterite. Often in fine, hair-like inclusions. Widely distributed. With quartz, feldspar, ilmenite, chlorite, apatite

Name, Composition, and Reference	Crystallization Structure Crystals = C Massive = M	Luster Transparency	Color
Streak—White, gray, green, red, brown, or yellow			
CASSITERITE, varieties *Ordinary* *Wood tin* *Stream tin* SnO_2 **310**	Tetragonal **C**—Thick prismatic, knee-shaped twins, common **M**—Compact; reniform, botryoidal, rounded pebbles, often with internal, radial fibrous structure, *wood tin*	Adamantine Resinous Dull Translucent to opaque	Reddish brown Yellowish brown Dark brown
Streak—Black			
BORNITE (Purple copper ore) Cu_5FeS_4 **277**	Cubic **C**—Rare **M**—Compact, granular	Metallic Opaque	Bronze Copper red tarnishes readily
URANINITE (Pitchblende) UO_2 **312**	Cubic **C**—Octahedral, rare **M**—Botryoidal, columnar, curved lamellar, granular compact, apparently amorphous	Submetallic Dull Opaque	Brown Blackish brown
PYRRHOTITE (Magnetic pyrites) FeS **281**	Hexagonal **C**—Tabular, rare **M**—Compact, granular	Metallic Opaque	Bronze brown Bronze yellow
Niccolite NiAs **281**	Hexagonal **C**—Rare **M**—Compact, disseminated	Metallic Opaque	Light copper red
WOLFRAMITE $(Fe,Mn)WO_4$ **347**	Monoclinic **C**—Thick tabular, short columnar, often large **M**—Bladed, curved lamellar, granular	Submetallic Opaque	Grayish brown Dark brown

Hardness over 6

Hardness	Streak	Cleavage = C Fracture = F Tenacity	Specific Gravity	Characteristics and Associates
6. **7.**	Pale yellow Pale brown White	**C**—Indistinct **F**—Uneven Brittle	6.8 7.	Distinguished by high specific gravity. In veins cutting granite, gneiss; in alluvial deposits, as *stream tin.* With quartz, mica, wolframite, scheelite, arsenopyrite, molybdenite. tourmaline, fluorite, apatite, chlorite

Hardness 1 to 6

Hardness	Streak	Cleavage = C Fracture = F Tenacity	Specific Gravity	Characteristics and Associates
3.	Grayish black	**C**—Indistinct **F**—Uneven Brittle	4.9 5.2	Usually with peacock tarnish colors—purple copper ore. With chalcopyrite. chalcocite, malachite, cassiterite, siderite
3. **6.**	Brownish black Grayish black	**F**—Conchoidal, uneven Brittle	4.8 9.7	Structure and fracture important. Fresh material is hard and heavy. With ores of lead, silver, bismuth; also pyrite, allanite
3.5 **4.5**	Dark grayish black	**C**—Basal, not conspicuous **F**—Uneven Brittle	4.5 4.6	May be slightly magnetic. Subject to dark-brown tarnish. In basic igneous rocks. With chalcopyrite, pyrite, galena
5. **5.5**	Dark brownish black	**C**—Indistinct **F**—Uneven Brittle	7.3 7.7	Often with green crust of annabergite (nickel bloom). With cobalt, nickel, silver minerals—smaltite, proustite, pyrargyrite; native bismuth and arsenic, calcite
5.5	Black Brownish black	**C**—Clinopinacoidal, perfect, conspicuous **F**—Uneven Brittle	7.1 7.5	Structure, cleavage, specific gravity important. Powder may be slightly magnetic. With cassiterite, quartz, mica, fluorite, apatite, scheelite, molybdenite, huebnerite

Streak—Green, red, brown, yellow, or black			
Name, Composition, and Reference	Crystallization Structure Crystals = C Massive = M	Luster Transparency	Color
GRAPHITE (Plumbago, black lead) C **274**	Hexagonal **C**—Tabular, rare **M**—Scaly, foliated, granular, earthy, sooty	Dull Opaque	Dark gray Iron black
CHLORITE (Prochlorite, clinochlorite) $Mg_5Al(OH)_8AlSi_3O_{10}$ **401**	Monoclinic **C**—Tabular, six-sided, often bent, twisted **M**—Foliated, scaly, granular, earthy	Dull Submetallic Translucent to opaque	Black Greenish black
URANINITE (Pitchblende) UO_2 **312**	Cubic **C**—Octahedral, rare **M**—Botryoidal, columnar, curved lamellar, granular, compact, apparently amorphous	Pitch-like Submetallic Dull Opaque	Pitch black Brownish black Greenish black
SIDERITE $FeCO_3$ **332**	Hexagonal **C**—Rhombohedral, curved or saddle-shaped, common **M**—Cleavable, granular, compact, botryoidal	Vitreous Dull Translucent to opaque	Brownish black Black
SPHALERITE (Black Jack) ZnS **278**	Cubic **C**—Tetrahedral, common **M**—Cleavable, fine- and coarse-grained, compact	Submetallic Resinous Opaque to translucent	Black Yellowish black Brownish black

Hardness 1 to 6				
Hard-ness	Streak	Cleavage = C Fracture = F Tenacity	Specific Gravity	Characteristics and Associates
1. **2.**	Dark gray Iron black	**C**—Basal, perfect (scales) Scales flexible	1.9 2.3	Greasy feel. Marks paper. Often impure. In crystalline limestone with garnet, spinel, pyroxenes, amphiboles; also in shale, gneiss, mica schist
1. **2.5**	Pale green	**C**—Basal, conspicuous, when foliated **F**—Scaly, earthy Tough to brittle	2.6 3.	Laminae flexible but inelastic, with slightly soapy feel. Common in schists and serpentine. With magnetite, magnesite, garnet, diopside. Often as scaly or dusty coating on other minerals. Pseudomorphous after garnet
3. **6.**	Olive green Dark brown Brownish black Grayish black	**F**—Conchoidal, uneven Brittle	4.8 9.7	Pitch-like appearance and fracture characteristic. Fresh material is hard and heavy. With lead, silver, bismuth minerals; also pyrite, allanite
3.5 **4.**	Yellowish brown	**C**—Rhombohedral, perfect, conspicuous **F**—Conchoidal Brittle	3.7 3.9	Curved crystals, cleavage, and rather high specific gravity characteristic. In ore deposits; beds and concretions in limestone and shale. With pyrite, chalcopyrite, galena, tetrahedrite, cryolite
3.5 **4.**	Dark brown Yellowish brown Gray	**C**—Dodecahedral, perfect, usually conspicuous **F**—Conchoidal Brittle	3.9 4.2	Color and streak vary with impurities. When massive distinguished from siderite by cleavage. Extensively in limestone. With galena, chalcopyrite, pyrite, barite, fluorite, siderite, rhodochrosite

Streak—Green, red, brown, yellow, or black			
Name, Composition, and Reference	Crystallization Structure Crystals = C Massive = M	Luster Transparency	Color
Huebnerite $MnWO_4$ **348**	Monoclinic **C**—Long fibrous, bladed, stalky; often divergent, without good terminations **M**—Compact, lamellar, granular	Resinous Submetallic Translucent to opaque	Brownish black Black
WOLFRAMITE $(Fe,Mn)WO_4$ **347**	Monoclinic **C**—Thick tabular, short columnar, often large **M**—Bladed, curved lamellar, granular	Submetallic Opaque	Dark gray Brownish black Iron black
Ferberite $FeWO_4$ **347**	Monoclinic **C**—Wedge-shaped, short prismatic, tabular **M**—Fan-shaped aggregates, bladed, granular, compact	Submetallic Splendent Opaque	Iron black Brownish black
HORNBLENDE (Amphibole) Silicate of Ca, Mg, Fe, Al, etc. **392**	Monoclinic **C**—Long prismatic, prism angle 124°; often with rhombohedral-like terminations **M**—Bladed, fibrous granular, compact	Vitreous Silky Translucent to opaque	Pitch black Greenish black Brownish black
AUGITE (Pyroxene) Silicate of Ca, Mg, Fe, Al, etc. **386**	Monoclinic **C**—Short prismatic; thick columnar, prism angle 87° **M**—Compact, granular, disseminated	Vitreous Submetallic Translucent to opaque	Pitch black Greenish black Brownish black

Hardness 1 to 6

Hardness	Streak	Cleavage = C Fracture = F Tenacity	Specific Gravity	Characteristics and Associates
5. **5.5**	Yellowish brown	**C**—Clinopinacoidal, perfect, conspicuous Brittle	6.7 7.3	Structure, cleavage, and high specific gravity characteristic. In quartz veins. With wolframite, fluorite, pyrite, scheelite, galena, tetrahedrite
5. **5.5**	Dark reddish brown Black	**C**—Clinopinacoidal, perfect, conspicuous **F**—Uneven Brittle	7.1 7.5	Distinguished from huebnerite by streak. Powder may be slightly magnetic. With cassiterite, quartz, mica, fluorite, apatite, scheelite, molybdenite, huebnerite
5. **5.5**	Dark brown Brownish black	**C**—Clinopinacoidal, perfect **F**—Uneven Brittle	7.5	In granites and pegmatites. With quartz, chalcopyrite, galena, scheelite
5. **6.**	Grayish green Grayish brown Yellow	**C**—Prismatic, perfect, often conspicuous—124° Brittle	2.9 3.3	Simple, pseudohexagonal crystals, and cleavage at 124° important. Very common; in nearly all types of rocks. With calcite, quartz, feldspar, pyroxene, chlorite
5. **6.**	Pale green Grayish green	**C**—Prismatic, perfect, conspicuous—87° Brittle	3.2 3.6	Crystals usually eight-sided, more rarely four-sided; pseudotetragonal with prism angles of 87 and 93°. Cleavage less distinct than on hornblende. Common in basic eruptive rocks and crystalline limestones

Streak—Green, red, brown, yellow, or black

Name, Composition, and Reference	Crystallization Structure Crystals = C Massive = M	Luster Transparency	Color
GOETHITE-LIMONITE $HFeO_2$ **315**	Orthorhombic **C**—Rare; pseudomorphs, after pyrite, marcasite, siderite **M**—Compact, stalactitic, botryoidal, reniform; fibrous structure	Submetallic Dull Opaque	Black Brownish black
Psilomelane A group of manganese oxide minerals **319**	**M**—Botryoidal, reniform, stalactitic; smooth surfaces	Submetallic Dull Opaque	Iron black Bluish black Dark gray
CHROMITE $Fe(Cr,Fe)_2O_4$ **307**	Cubic **C**—Octahedral, rare **M**—Compact, granular, disseminated grains	Submetallic Pitchy Opaque	Iron black Brownish black
Allanite (Orthite) $(Ca,Ce,La)_2(Al,Fe)_3O(OH)SiO_4Si_2O_7$ **377**	Monoclinic **C**—Tabular, rare **M**—Compact, granular, bladed, disseminated grains	Submetallic Greasy Translucent to opaque	Black Pitch black Brownish black

Streak—Green, red, brown, yellow, or black

Name, Composition, and Reference	Crystallization Structure Crystals = C Massive = M	Luster Transparency	Color
RUTILE TiO_2 **309**	Tetragonal **C**—Prismatic, vertically striated; twinned, yielding knee-shaped or rosette forms **M**—Compact	Adamantine Submetallic Opaque to transparent	Iron black Brownish black Reddish black
CASSITERITE SnO_2 **310**	Tetragonal **C**—Prismatic; knee-shaped twins common **M**—Compact, reniform, botryoidal, pebbles, with radial fibrous structure	Submetallic Dull Translucent to opaque	Black Brownish black

Hardness 1 to 6				
Hard-ness	Streak	Cleavage = C Fracture = F Tenacity	Specific Gravity	Characteristics and Associates
5. 6.	Yellowish brown	F—Conchoidal, splintery Brittle	3.6 4.	Often with black varnish-like surface, passing into the soft, yellow earthy or ocherous variety. With pyrite, hematite, magnetite, siderite
5. 6.	Black Brownish black	F—Conchoidal, uneven Brittle	4.3 5.5	Often with fine sooty coating of pyrolusite. With manganese minerals; also limonite, barite
5.5	Dark brown Grayish brown	C—Indistinct F—Uneven, conchoidal Brittle	4.2 4.8	May be slightly magnetic. Pitch-like appearance. With serpentine, talc, chrome garnet; also in black sands, platinum placers
5.5 6.	Pale brown Grayish brown	C—Pinacoidal, indistinct F—Uneven, conchoidal Brittle	3.5 4.2	Often with yellowish or brownish coating. Disseminated through acid igneous rocks; also in limestones. With magnetite, epidote, quartz, feldspar
Hardness over 6				
6. 7.	Pale yellow Pale brown	C—Prismatic, pyramidal, not conspicuous F—Uneven Brittle	4.2 4.3	Not as heavy as cassiterite. Often as hair-like inclusions. Disseminated. Widely distributed. With quartz, feldspar, hematite ilmenite, chlorite
6. 7.	Pale brown Pale yellow	C—Indistinct F—Uneven Brittle	6.8 7.	Distinguished by high specific gravity. In veins cutting granite; in alluvial deposits as *stream tin*. With wolframite, scheelite, molybdenite, tourmaline, fluorite, apatite, mica

Streak—Green, red, brown, yellow or black

Name, Composition, and Reference	Crystallization Structure Crystals = C Massive = M	Luster Transparency	Color
CORUNDUM, variety *Emery* Al_2O_3, with $FeFe_2O_4$, Fe_2O_3, SiO_2 **299**	Hexagonal **M**—Fine to coarse granular	Dull Submetallic Opaque	Dark gray Black
SPINEL, varieties *Hercynite* *Picotite* $M''M'''_2O_4$ M'' = Mg, Fe, Zn, Mn M''' = Al, Fe **304**	Cubic **C**—Octahedral, small **M**—Compact, granular, disseminated grains	Vitreous Dull Nearly opaque	Black Brownish black

Streak—Uncolored, white, or light gray

Name, Composition, and Reference	Crystallization Structure Crystals = C Massive = M	Luster Transparency	Color
APATITE, variety *Phosphate rock* Mainly calcium carbonate -phosphate (collophane) **351**	**C**—Hexagonal **M**—Compact, nodular, reniform, earthy	Dull Opaque	Black
BIOTITE (Black mica) $K(Mg,Fe)_3(OH,F)_2AlSi_3O_{10}$ **399**	Monoclinic **C**—Tabular, with hexagonal or rhombic outline **M**—Plates, disseminated scales	Pearly Submetallic Transparent to opaque	Black Brownish black Greenish black
CALCITE, varieties *Limestone* *Marble* *Stalactites*, etc. *Calcareous tufa* *Travertine* $CaCO_3$ **326**	Hexagonal **M**—Cleavable, granular, fibrous, banded, stalactitic, oölitic, porous, compact, crusts, shells	Vitreous Dull Translucent to opaque	Dark gray Brownish black Black

Hardness over 6

Hardness	Streak	Cleavage = C Fracture = F Tenacity	Specific Gravity	Characteristics and Associates
7. **9.**	Yellowish brown Black	**C**—Indistinct **F**—Uneven Brittle to tough	3.7 4.3	Corundum mixed with iron ore. Powder may be magnetic. With mica, amphibole, chlorite, spinel; in crystalline limestones, schists, peridotites
7.5 **8.**	Grayish green Pale brown	**C**—Octahedral, indistinct **F**—Conchoidal Brittle	3.9 4.1	Commonly in basic igneous rocks, especially the olivine-bearing types. With olivine, serpentine, corundum, magnetite, hornblende, garnet

Hardness 1 to 3

Hardness	Streak	Cleavage = C Fracture = F Tenacity	Specific Gravity	Characteristics and Associates
2. **3.**	White	**F**—Conchoidal, uneven Brittle	3.1 3.2	More or less impure masses, frequently resembling compact bituminous limestone. Independent beds, nodules, or concretions
2.5 **3.**	White Grayish	**C**—Basal, perfect, conspicuous Tough, lamellae of fresh biotite very elastic	2.7 3.2	Easily recognized by structure, highly perfect cleavage, and elasticity. Important constituent of many igneous and metamorphic rocks—granite, syenite, gneiss
3.	White Gray	**C**—Rhombohedral, perfect **F**—Conchoidal Brittle	2.7	Rhombohedral cleavage may be observed. Cleavages often striated. Yields bituminous odor when struck with hammer. To distinguish varieties, see page reference

Streak—Uncolored, white, or light gray			
Name, Composition, and Reference	Crystallization Structure Crystals = C Massive = M	Luster Transparency	Color
ANHYDRITE $CaSO_4$ **339**	Orthorhombic **C**—Thick tabular, prismatic, rare **M**—Granular, compact, fibrous, lamellar, cleavable	Vitreous Pearly Translucent to opaque	Dark gray Blackish
SERPENTINE $Mg_6(OH)_8Si_4O_{10}$ **402**	Monoclinic **C**—Unknown **M**—Compact, columnar, fibrous, lamellar, granular	Greasy Waxy Translucent to opaque	Greenish black Brownish black
APATITE, variety *Phosphate rock* Mainly calcium carbonate-phosphate (collophane) **351**	**C**—Hexagonal **M**—Compact, nodular, reniform, earthy	Dull Opaque	Black
SPHALERITE (Blackjack) ZnS **278**	Cubic **C**—Tetrahedral, common **M**—Cleavable, fine- or coarse-grained, compact	Submetallic Opaque to translucent	Black Brownish black Yellowish black
SPHENE (Titanite) $CaTiOSiO_4$ **374**	Monoclinic **C**—Wedge- or envelope-shaped when disseminated; tabular or prismatic when attached **M**—Compact, lamellar	Vitreous Submetallic Translucent to opaque	Black Brownish black

Hardness 3 to 6

Hardness	Streak	Cleavage = C Fracture = F Tenacity	Specific Gravity	Characteristics and Associates
3. **3.5**	White	C—Pinacoidal, perfect, 3 directions at 90° F—Conchoidal Brittle	2.8 3.	Color due to organic matter. Pseudocubical cleavage sometimes noted. Granular varieties resemble marble. In limestones, shales. With halite, gypsum
3. **4.**	White	F—Conchoidal, splintery Brittle	2.5 2.8	Smooth and greasy feel. Often spotted, clouded, multicolored. Sometimes crossed by seams of asbestos (chrysotile). With magnesite, calcite, chromite, garnierite, pyrope, platinum
3. **5.**	White	F—Conchoidal, uneven Brittle	3.1 3.2	More or less impure masses frequently resembling compact, bituminous limestone. Independent beds, nodules, or concretions
3.5 **4.**	Grayish	C—Dodecahedral perfect, usually conspicuous F—Conchoidal Brittle	3.9 4.2	Color and streak vary with impurities. Extensively in limestones with galena, chalcopyrite, pyrite, barite, fluorite, siderite, rhodochrosite
5. **5.5**	White Gray	C—Prismatic, conspicuous partings often noted F—Conchoidal Brittle	3.4 3.6	With feldspars, pyroxenes, amphiboles, chlorite, scapolite, zircon

Streak—Uncolored, white, or light gray			
Name, Composition, and Reference	Crystallization Structure Crystals = C Massive = M	Luster Transparency	Color
Huebnerite $MnWO_4$ **348**	Monoclinic **C**—Long fibrous, bladed, stalky often divergent, without good terminations **M**—Compact, lamellar, granular	Resinous Submetallic Translucent to opaque	Brownish black Black
HORNBLENDE (Amphibole) Silicate of Ca, Mg, Fe, Al, etc. **392**	Monoclinic **C**—Long prismatic, prism angle 124°, often with rhombohedral-like terminations **M**—Bladed, fibrous, granular, compact	Vitreous Silky Translucent to opaque	Pitch black Greenish black Brownish black
AUGITE (Pyroxene) Silicate of Ca, Mg, Fe, Al, etc. **386**	Monoclinic **C**—Short prismatic, thick columnar, prism angle 87° **M**—Compact, granular, disseminated	Vitreous Submetallic Translucent to opaque	Pitch black Greenish black Brownish black
Allanite (Orthite) $(Ca,Ce,La)_2(Al,Fe)_3$-$O(OH)SiO_4Si_2O_7$ **377**	Monoclinic **C**—Tabular, rare **M**—Compact, granular, bladed, disseminated grains	Submetallic Greasy Translucent to opaque	Black Pitch black Brownish black
LABRADORITE (Feldspar) Silicate of Na,Ca,Al **412**	Triclinic **C**—Thin tabular, often with rhombic cross-section **M**—Compact, cleavable, granular	Vitreous Pearly Translucent to nearly opaque	Dark gray Greenish gray

Streak—Uncolored, white, or light gray			
Aegirite (*Acmite*, Pyroxene) $NaFeSi_2O_6$ **387**	Monoclinic **C**—Prismatic **M**—Fibrous, acicular; often in tufts	Submetallic Vitreous Opaque to translucent	Greenish black Brownish black

Hardness 3 to 6

Hardness	Streak	Cleavage = C Fracture = F Tenacity	Specific Gravity	Characteristics and Associates
5. **5.5**	Greenish gray	**C**—Clinopinacoidal, perfect, conspicuous Brittle	6.7 7.3	Structure, cleavage, and specific gravity characteristic. In quartz veins. With wolframite, fluorite, pyrite, scheelite, galena, tetrahedrite
5. **6.**	Gray Greenish gray Brownish gray	**C**—Prismatic, perfect, often conspicuous—124° Brittle	2.9 3.3	Simple, pseudohexagonal crystals, and cleavage (124°) important. Very common. In nearly all types of rocks. With feldspars, quartz, pyroxenes, chlorite, calcite
5. **6.**	White Gray Greenish gray	**C**—Prismatic, perfect, conspicuous—87°, less distinct than on hornblende Brittle	3.2 3.6	Crystals usually eight-sided, more rarely four-sided; pseudotetragonal with prism angles of 87 and 93°. In basic rocks and limestones
5.5 **6.**	Gray Greenish gray Brownish gray	**C**—Pinacoidal, indistinct **F**—Uneven, conchoidal Brittle	3.5 4.2	Often covered with yellowish or brownish crust. Disseminated in the more acid igneous rocks; limestones. With magnetite, epidote, quartz, feldspars
6.	White	**C**—Basal, brachypinacoidal, perfect, conspicuous—86° **F**—Uneven, conchoidal Brittle	2.7	Often with play of colors—yellow, green, blue, red. Inclined cleavages are striated. In basic igneous rocks. With pyroxenes, amphiboles

Hardness over 6

Hardness	Streak	Cleavage = C Fracture = F Tenacity	Specific Gravity	Characteristics and Associates
6. **6.5**	Grayish	**C**—Prismatic, perfect **F**—Uneven Brittle	3.4 3.5	In pegmatites and igneous rocks. With leucite, nepheline, feldspars. With blunt end faces, *aegirite;* with acute, *acmite*

Streak—Uncolored, white, or light gray

Name, Composition, and Reference	Crystallization Structure Crystals = C Massive = M	Luster Transparency	Color
EPIDOTE $Ca_2(Al,Fe)_3O(OH)SiO_4$-Si_2O_7 **376**	Monoclinic **C**—Prismatic, elongated and deeply striated parallel to *b* axis; generally terminated on one end only **M**—Columnar, fibrous, parallel and divergent, granular	Vitreous Translucent to opaque	Greenish black
RUTILE TiO_2 **309**	Tetragonal **C**—Prismatic, vertically striated; twinned, yielding knee-shaped or rosette forms **M**—Compact, disseminated	Submetallic Adamantine Opaque to translucent	Iron black Brownish black Reddish black
CASSITERITE SnO_2 **310**	Tetragonal **C**—Thick prismatic, knee-shaped twins, quite common **M**—Compact, reniform, botryoidal, rounded pebbles, often with internal, radial fibrous structure	Submetallic Dull Translucent to opaque	Black Brownish black
GARNET, varieties *Andradite* $M''_3M'''_2(SiO_4)_3$ *Almandite* M'' = Ca, Fe, Mg M''' = Al, Fe **365**	Cubic **C**—Dodecahedrons, tetragonal trisoctahedrons, alone or in combination **M**—Granular, compact, lamellar, disseminated, sand	Vitreous Translucent to opaque	Velvety black Brownish black

Hardness over 6

Hardness	Streak	Cleavage = C Fracture = F Tenacity	Specific Gravity	Characteristics and Associates
6. **7.**	White Grayish	**C**—Basal, perfect **F**—Uneven Brittle	3.3 3.5	Crystals are often dark green or blackish green, massive aggregates lighter colored. Widely distributed. With quartz, feldspar, garnet, hornblende, pyroxene, magnetite, native copper
6. **7.**	Gray Yellowish white Brownish white	**C**—Prismatic, pyramidal, not conspicuous **F**—Uneven Brittle	4.2 4.3	Not as heavy as cassiterite. Often in hair-like inclusions. Widely distributed. With quartz, feldspar, hematite, ilmenite, chlorite
6. **7.**	White Yellowish white Brownish white	**C**—Indistinct **F**—Uneven Brittle	6.8 7.	Distinguished by high specific gravity. In veins cutting granite, gneiss; in alluvial deposits as *stream tin.* With quartz, wolframite, scheelite, molybdenite, tourmaline, fluorite, mica, chlorite
6.5 **7.5**	White	**C**—Dodecahedral, usually indistinct **F**—Conchoidal, uneven Brittle	3.7 4.2	*Andradite,* commonly with magnetite, epidote, feldspars, nepheline, leucite; *almandite,* with mica, staurolite, andalusite, kyanite, tourmaline

Streak—Uncolored, white, or light gray

Name, Composition, and Reference	Crystallization Structure Crystals = C Massive = M	Luster Transparency	Color
QUARTZ, Crystalline variety SiO_2 *Smoky quartz* **295**	Hexagonal **C**—Prismatic, horizontally striated **M**—Compact, granular	Vitreous Transparent to translucent	Grayish black Brownish black
Cryptocrystalline varieties *Chalcedony* *Onyx* *Flint* **296**	Hexagonal Fine crystalline masses, banded, nodular, botryoidal, stalactitic	Waxy Vitreous Translucent to opaque	Grayish black Brownish black Velvet black
TOURMALINE, variety *Schorl* $M_7Al_6(OH,F)_4(BO_3)_3Si_6O_{18}$ **381**	Hexagonal **C**—Prismatic, vertically striated; terminated with broken or rhombohedral-like surfaces; well-developed crystals are hemimorphic **M**—Compact, divergent columnar	Pitchy Vitreous Translucent to opaque	Pitch black Brownish black Bluish black
STAUROLITE $Fe(OH)_2.2Al_2OSiO_4$ **371**	Orthorhombic **C**—Prismatic; twins plus- (+) or X-shaped, well developed, often large	Vitreous Dull Translucent to opaque	Brownish black Dark gray
SPINEL, varieties *Pleonaste* *Gahnite* $M''M'''_2O_4$ M'' = Mg, Fe, Zn, Mn M''' = Al, Fe **304**	Cubic **C**—Octahedral, well developed, common **M**—Compact, granular, disseminated grains	Vitreous Dull Nearly opaque	Brownish black Grayish black Greenish black

Hardness over 6

Hardness	Streak	Cleavage = C Fracture = F Tenacity	Specific Gravity	Characteristics and Associates
7.	White	**C**—Indistinct **F**—Conchoidal, conspicuous Brittle	2.6	Characteristic conchoidal fracture and glassy luster. Common in granitic rocks
7.	White	**C**—Indistinct **F**—Conchoidal, conspicuous Brittle to tough	2.6	Conchoidal fracture characteristic. *Chalcedony*, waxy luster; *onyx*, banded; *flint*, generally with white coating; *basanite*, velvet black
7. **7.5**	White Gray	**C**—None **F**—Conchoidal, uneven Brittle	2.9 3.2	Spherical triangular cross section, coal-black color, and lack of cleavage important. In pegmatites, metamorphic rocks; alluvial deposits. With quartz, feldspar, cassiterite, beryl, topaz, fluorite
7. **7.5**	White Gray	**C**—Brachypinacoidal **F**—Conchoidal, uneven Brittle	3.4 3.8	Fresh crystals usually possess bright and smooth faces; when altered, dull, rough, softer, and with colored streak. In metamorphic rocks—gneiss, mica schist, slate. With kyanite, garnet, tourmaline, sillimanite
7.5 **8.**	White Grayish	**C**—Octahedral, indistinct **F**—Conchoidal	3.6 4.4	Commonly as contact mineral in granular limestones; in more basic igneous rocks; rounded grains in placers. With calcite, chondrodite, serpentine, corundum, graphite, pyroxene, phlogopite

Streak—Uncolored, white, or light gray

Name, Composition, and Reference	Crystallization Structure Crystals = C Massive = M	Luster Transparency	Color
CORUNDUM, varieties *Common* Al_2O_3 **299**	Hexagonal **C**—Prismatic, tabular, pyramidal, rhombohedral; rounded barrel-shaped **M**—Compact, lamellar	Vitreous Translucent to transparent	Dark gray Black
DIAMOND, varieties *Diamond proper*, *Bort*, *Carbonado* C **267**	Cubic **C**—Octahedrons, hexoctahedrons, usually with curved surfaces **M**—Rounded or irregular grains or pebbles, often with radial structure	Adamantine Vitreous Translucent to opaque	Black Dark gray

B. MINERALS WITH NONMETALLIC LUSTER

Streak—Red, brown, or yellow

Name, Composition, and Reference	Crystallization Structure Crystals = C Massive = M	Luster Transparency	Color
BAUXITE A mixture of aluminum oxide minerals **317**	Never in crystals **M**—Pisolitic, oölitic, rounded disseminated grains, clay-like, earthy	Dull Earthy Opaque	Red Reddish brown
HEMATITE, varieties *Red ocher*, *Oölitic*, *Fossiliferous* Fe_2O_3 **301**	Hexagonal **M**—Fine granular, earthy, oölitic, replacement of shells	Dull Opaque	Brownish red Cherry red
REALGAR AsS **283**	Monoclinic **C**—Short prismatic, rare **M**—Granular, compact, incrustations	Resinous Transparent to translucent	Aurora red Orange yellow
Proustite Ag_3AsS_3 **290**	Hexagonal **C**—Small, complex, rare **M**—Compact, disseminated, crusts, bands	Adamantine Dull Translucent to transparent	Scarlet Vermilion

Hardness over 6

Hardness	Streak	Cleavage = C Fracture = F Tenacity	Specific Gravity	Characteristics and Associates
9.	White	**C**—None; basal and nearly rectangular rhombohedral partings, conspicuous; striated **F**—Conchoidal Brittle to tough	3.9 4.1	In limestone, granite, syenite, alluvial deposits. With magnetite, nepheline, mica, spinel, chlorite
10.	Ash gray	**C**—Octahedral, perfect (diamond proper) **F**—Conchoidal Brittle	3.1 3.5	*Diamond proper*, crystals and cleavage fragments; *bort*, translucent, radial structure; *carbonado*, granular to compact, opaque. In kimberlite—called *blue ground*, in placers. With pyrope, magnetite, chromite, zircon

2. PINK, RED, RED-BROWN, OR RED-VIOLET IN COLOR

Hardness 1 to 3

Hardness	Streak	Cleavage = C Fracture = F Tenacity	Specific Gravity	Characteristics and Associates
1. **3.**	Reddish Yellowish	**F**—Earthy Brittle	2.5 2.6	Color and streak variable. Clay odor. With clay or kaolinite in nodules or irregular deposits in limestone or dolomite. Considered a rock
1. **3.**	Cherry red Reddish brown	**C**—None **F**—Earthy Brittle	4.9 5.3	*Red ocher*, red earthy variety; *oölitic hematite*, fish-egg structure; *fossiliferous hematite*, replacement of shells
1.5 **2.**	Orange yellow	**C**—Clinopinacoidal, basal **F**—Conchoidal Slightly sectile	3.4 3.6	Frequently disseminated in clay or dolomite. With orpiment, stibnite, arsenic, pyrite, barite, calcite
2. **2.5**	Scarlet Aurora red	**C**—Imperfect **F**—Conchoidal Brittle	5.5 5.6	*Light ruby silver ore.* Distinguished from cinnabar by associates. With pyrargyrite, in veins with other silver minerals and galena. Compare pyrargyrite

Streak—Red, brown, or yellow			
Name, Composition, and Reference	Crystallization Structure Crystals = C Massive = M	Luster Transparency	Color
CINNABAR HgS **282**	Hexagonal **C**—Rhombohedral, thick tabular, small **M**—Fine granular, fibrous, earthy coatings	Adamantine Dull Transparent to opaque	Scarlet red Brownish red
Crocoite $PbCrO_4$ **346**	Monoclinic **C**—Prismatic, acicular **M**—Columnar, granular, crusts	Adamantine Greasy Translucent	Hyacinth red Aurora red
Pyrargyrite Ag_3SbS_3 **289**	Hexagonal **C**—Small, complex, rare **M**—Compact, disseminated, crusts, bands	Adamantine Submetallic Transparent to opaque	Dark red
Wulfenite $PbMoO_4$ **349**	Tetragonal **C**—Square, thin tabular, more rarely pyramidal **M**—Coarse, fine granular	Resinous Adamantine Transparent to translucent	Orange-red Bright red
Vanadinite $Pb_5Cl(VO_4)_3$ **353**	Hexagonal C—Prismatic, small, at times skeletal **M**—Compact, globular, fibrous, crusts	Resinous Translucent to opaque	Ruby red Brownish red Orange-red

Streak—Red, brown, or yellow			
HEMATITE, varieties *Argillaceous* *Compact* Fe_2O_3 **301**	Hexagonal **M**—Compact, granular, columnar, splintery, radiated reniform or botryoidal	Submetallic Dull Opaque	Brownish red Dark red

Hardness 1 to 3

Hardness	Streak	Cleavage = C Fracture = F Tenacity	Specific Gravity	Characteristics and Associates
2. **2.5**	Scarlet Red-brown	**C**—Prismatic, not conspicuous **F**—Uneven Brittle to sectile	8. 8.2	Characterized by color, streak, and high specific gravity. In siliceous rocks. With native mercury, pyrite, marcasite, realgar, stibnite
2.5	Orange-yellow	**C**—Basal, prismatic **F**—Conchoidal, uneven Sectile	5.9 6.1	Resembles potassium bichromate in color. Alteration product of galena. With galena, quartz, pyrite, vanadinite, wulfenite
2.5 **3.**	Cherry red Purplish red	**C**—Indistinct **F**—Conchoidal Brittle	5.8	Frequently as gray or dark red bands. Darker than proustite—*dark ruby silver ore.* With proustite, in veins with other silver minerals and galena
3.	Lemon yellow Pale yellow	**C**—Pyramidal, indistinct **F**—Conchoidal, uneven Brittle	6.3 7.	Square plates, sometimes with forms of the third order. With lead minerals—galena, pyromorphite, vanadinite
3.	Pale yellow Yellow	**C**—None **F**—Conchoidal, uneven Brittle	6.7 7.2	Crystal faces smooth with sharp edges. With lead minerals but never in large quantities

Hardness over 3

Hardness	Streak	Cleavage = C Fracture = F Tenacity	Specific Gravity	Characteristics and Associates
3. **6.**	Cherry red Reddish brown	**C**—None **F**—Uneven, splintery Brittle	4.9 5.3	*Argillaceous hematite,* impure from clay, sand, jasper; *compact hematite,* usually quite pure

Streak—Red, brown, or yellow			
Name, Composition, and Reference	Crystallization Structure Crystals = C Massive = M	Luster Transparency	Color
SPHALERITE ZnS **278**	Cubic **C**—Tetrahedral, common **M**—Cleavable, fine to coarse granular, compact	Resinous Submetallic Translucent to opaque	Brownish red Yellowish red
Cuprite Cu_2O **298**	Cubic **C**—Octahedrons, dodecahedrons, alone or in combination **M**—Compact, granular, earthy; slender crystal aggregates (*chalcotrichite*)	Adamantine Dull Translucent to opaque	Cochineal red Brick red Dark red
Zincite ZnO **299**	Hexagonal **C**—Hemimorphic, rare **M**—Compact, granular, foliated	Adamantine Vitreous Translucent to opaque	Dark red Blood red
Huebnerite $MnWO_4$ **348**	Monoclinic **C**—Long, fibrous, bladed, stalky; often divergent, without good terminations **M**—Compact, lamellar, granular	Greasy Submetallic Translucent to opaque	Brownish red
WOLFRAMITE $(Fe,Mn)WO_4$ **347**	Monoclinic **C**—Thick tabular, short columnar, often large **M**—Bladed, curved lamellar, granular, compact	Submetallic Opaque	Brownish red

Hardness over 3

Hardness	Streak	Cleavage = C Fracture = F Tenacity	Specific Gravity	Characteristics and Associates
3.5 **4.**	Pale yellow Brownish yellow	C—Dodecahedral, perfect, usually conspicuous F—Conchoidal Brittle	3.9 4.2	Color and streak vary with impurities. Extensively in limestone. With galena, chalcopyrite, pyrite, barite, fluorite, siderite, rhodochrosite
3.5 **4.**	Brownish red Dirty brown	C—Indistinct F—Uneven Brittle	5.8 6.2	Characterized by associates, usually with copper minerals—malachite (green), azurite (blue), chalcocite and melaconite (black), chalcopyrite (yellow), native copper
4. **4.5**	Orange-yellow Reddish yellow	C—Basal, sometimes conspicuous F—Uneven Brittle	5.7	Associates important—calcite, franklinite (black), willemite (yellow to green), rhodonite (flesh red). On exposure becomes coated with the white carbonate
5. **5.5**	Yellowish brown	C—Clinopinacoidal, perfect, conspicuous Brittle	6.7 7.3	Structure, cleavage, and specific gravity characteristic. In quartz veins. With wolframite, fluorite, scheelite, galena, tetrahedrite
5. **5.5**	Dark reddish brown	C—Clinopinacoidal, perfect, conspicuous F—Uneven Brittle	7.1 7.5	Distinguished from huebnerite by streak. Powder may be slightly magnetic. With cassiterite, quartz, mica, scheelite, molybdenite, huebnerite

Name, Composition, and Reference	Crystallization Structure Crystals = C Massive = M	Luster Transparency	Color
Streak—Red, brown, or yellow			
RUTILE TiO_2 **309**	Tetragonal **C**—Prismatic, vertically striated; twinned, yielding knee-shaped or rosette forms **M**—Compact, disseminated	Adamantine Submetallic Translucent to opaque	Dark red Brownish red
CASSITERITE SnO_2 **310**	Tetragonal **C**—Thick prismatic; knee-shaped twins quite common **M**—Compact, reniform, botryoidal, rounded pebbles, often with radial fibrous structure (*wood tin*)	Adamantine Dull Translucent to opaque	Brownish red Yellowish red
Streak—Uncolored, white, or light gray			
GYPSUM $CaSO_4.2H_2O$ **345**	Monoclinic **C**—Rare **M**—Coarse, fine granular, fibrous, cleavable, sand	Vitreous Silky Dull Transparent to opaque	Flesh red Brick red
HALITE (Rock salt) NaCl **319**	Cubic **C**—Cubes, often skeletal or hopper-shaped, rare **M**—Compact, cleavable, granular, fibrous, crusts, stalactitic	Vitreous Transparent to translucent	Red Reddish Purplish
Lepidolite (Lithium mica) $K_2Li_3Al_3(F,OH)_4(AlSi_3O_{10})_2$ **400**	Monoclinic **C**—Short prismatic **M**—Granular, coarse or fine; scales, cleavable plates	Pearly Translucent	Pink Rose red Red-violet

Hardness over 3

Hardness	Streak	Cleavage = C Fracture = F Tenacity	Specific Gravity	Characteristics and Associates
6. **7.**	Yellowish Brownish	C—Prismatic, pyramidal, not conspicuous F—Uneven Brittle	4.2 4.3	Not as heavy as cassiterite. Often in fine, hair-like inclusions. Widely distributed. With quartz, feldspars, hematite, ilmenite, chlorite
6. **7.**	Pale yellow Pale brown	C—Indistinct F—Uneven Brittle	6.8 7.	Recognized by high specific gravity. In veins cutting granite, gneiss; in alluvial deposits as *stream tin.* With quartz, wolframite, scheelite, arsenopyrite, tourmaline, fluorite, apatite, chlorite, mica

Hardness 1 to 3

Hardness	Streak	Cleavage = C Fracture = F Tenacity	Specific Gravity	Characteristics and Associates
2.	White	C—Clinopinacoidal, perfect conspicuous; pyramidal, orthopinacoidal (crystals) F—Conchoidal Brittle, laminae flexible	2.2 2.4	Ferruginous gypsum. In limestones, shales. With halite, celestite, sulfur, aragonite, anhydrite, ore deposits
2. **2.5**	White	C—Cubic, perfect, conspicuous F—Conchoidal Brittle	2.1 2.3	Characteristic cubical cleavage and saline taste. Color due to impurities. May absorb moisture and become damp. With shale, gypsum, anhydrite
2. **3.**	White	C—Basal, perfect F—Scaly, granular Tough	2.8 2.9	When massive may resemble granular limestone. In pegmatites, granites, gneisses. With red tourmaline (rubellite), amblygonite, spodumene, topaz

Streak—Uncolored, white, or light gray			
Name, Composition, and Reference	Crystallization Structure Crystals = C Massive = M	Luster Transparency	Color
PHLOGOPITE (Bronze mica) $KMg_3(F,OH)_2AlSi_3O_{10}$ **399**	Monoclinic **C**—Tabular, prismatic, hexagonal or rhombic outline, often large and coarse **M**—Plates, disseminated scales	Pearly Submetallic Transparent to translucent	Copper red Bronze red Brownish red
CALCITE $CaCO_3$ **326**	Hexagonal **C**—Scalenohedral, rhombohedral, prismatic, tabular, often highly modified, twinned **M**—Cleavable, granular, fibrous, compact	Vitreous Dull Transparent to nearly opaque	Pink Red Violet Amethystine
Wulfenite $PbMoO_4$ **349**	Tetragonal **C**—Square, thin tabular, more rarely pyramidal **M**—Coarse to fine granular	Greasy Adamantine Transparent to translucent	Orange-red Bright red
Vanadinite $Pb_5Cl(VO_4)_3$ **353**	Hexagonal **C**—Prismatic, small, at times skeletal **M**—Compact, globular, fibrous, crusts	Greasy Translucent to opaque	Ruby red Orange-red Brownish red
Streak—Uncolored, white, or light gray			
STILBITE (Zeolite) $(Ca,Na_2)Al_2Si_7O_{18}.7H_2O$ **420**	Monoclinic **C**—Twinned in sheaflike, radial, or globular aggregates	Vitreous Pearly Transparent to translucent	Pale red Brick red
Lepidolite (Lithium mica) $K_2Li_3Al_3(F,OH)_4(AlSi_3O_{10})_2$ **400**	Monoclinic **C**—Short prismatic **M**—Granular, coarse or fine; scales, cleavable plates	Pearly Translucent	Pink Rose red Red-violet

Hardness 1 to 3

Hardness	Streak	Cleavage = C Fracture = F Tenacity	Specific Gravity	Characteristics and Associates
2.5 **3.**	White	C—Basal, perfect, conspicuous Tough, laminae very elastic	2.8 3.	When cleavage laminae are held close to the eye in viewing a source of light, a star-like form is sometimes observed. Characteristic of crystalline limestones, dolomites, schists. With pyroxenes, amphiboles, serpentine
3.	White	C—Rhombohedral, perfect, very conspicuous F—Conchoidal Brittle	2.7	Rhombohedral cleavage characteristic, especially on crystals. Cleavages often show striations. Very strong double refraction observed when transparent
3.	White Yellowish white	C—Pyramidal, indistinct F—Conchoidal, uneven Brittle	6.3 7.	Square plates, sometimes with forms of the third order. With lead minerals—galena, pyromorphite, vanadinite
3.	White Yellowish white	C—None F—Conchoidal, uneven Brittle	6.7 7.2	Crystal faces smooth with sharp edges. With lead minerals but never in large quantities

Hardness 3 to 6

Hardness	Streak	Cleavage = C Fracture = F Tenacity	Specific Gravity	Characteristics and Associates
3. **4.**	White	C—Pinacoidal F—Uneven Brittle	2.1 2.2	Radial and sheaf-like structure important. In basic igneous rocks, ore deposits. With chabazite, apophyllite, datolite, calcite
3. **4.**	White	C—Basal, perfect F—Scaly, granular Tough	2.8 2.9	When massive often like granular limestone. In pegmatites, granites, gneisses. With red tourmaline (rubellite), amblygonite, spodumene, topaz

Streak—Uncolored, white, or light gray			
Name, Composition, and Reference	Crystallization Structure Crystals = C Massive = M	Luster Transparency	Color
ALUNITE (Alum stone) $KAl_3(OH)_6(SO_4)_2$ **342**	Hexagonal **C**—Rhombohedrons, resembling cubes, tabular, rare **M**—Compact, granular, fibrous, earthy	Vitreous Pearly Transparent to translucent	Pink Reddish white
DOLOMITE $CaMg(CO_3)_2$ **329**	Hexagonal **C**—Rhombohedral, with curved surfaces **M**—Coarsely crystalline, compact, granular, friable	Vitreous Transparent to translucent	Light pink Pink Reddish
SPHALERITE ZnS **278**	Cubic **C**—Tetrahedral, common **M**—Cleavable, fine or coarse granular, compact	Resinous Submetallic Translucent to opaque	Brownish red Yellowish red
RHODOCHROSITE $MnCO_3$ **331**	Hexagonal **C**—Rhombohedral, rare **M**—Cleavable, granular, compact, botryoidal, crusts	Vitreous Translucent	Rose red Brownish red Pink
FLUORITE (Fluor spar) CaF_2 **322**	Cubic **C**—Cubes, alone or modified, well developed, common; penetration twins **M**—Cleavable, granular, fibrous	Vitreous Transparent to nearly opaque	Red-violet Pink Rose red
CHABAZITE (Zeolite) $CaAl_2Si_4O_{12}.6H_2O$ **421**	Hexagonal **C**—Rhombohedral, cube-like, lenticular **M**—Compact	Vitreous Translucent to transparent	Flesh red Red

Hardness 3 to 6

Hardness	Streak	Cleavage = C Fracture = F Tenacity	Specific Gravity	Characteristics and Associates
3.5 **4.**	White	C—Basal F—Splintery, conchoidal, earthy Brittle	2.6 2.8	Hardness often greater due to admixture of quartz, feldspar, then tough. Deposits and veins in feldspathic rocks. With kaolin, pyrite, opal
3.5 **4.**	White Gray	C—Rhombohedral, perfect F—Conchoidal Brittle	2.9	Crystals generally curved or saddle-shaped. *Marble* includes some compact varieties. In fissures and cavities; with ore deposits
3.5 **4.**	Gray Yellowish white	C—Dodecahedral, perfect, usually conspicuous F—Conchoidal Brittle	3.9 4.2	Color and streak vary with impurities. Extensively in limestones. With galena, chalcopyrite, pyrite, barite, fluorite, rhodochrosite
3.5 **4.5**	White	C—Rhombohedral, perfect, conspicuous F—Uneven Brittle	3.3 3.6	When weathered may be brown to black due to MnO_2. With galena, sphalerite, pyrite, rhodonite, psilomelane, silver minerals
4.	White	C—Octahedral, perfect, conspicuous Brittle	3. 3.2	Easily recognized by crystal form, cleavage, and hardness. Common gangue mineral of metallic ores. With galena, sphalerite, cassiterite, calcite, quartz, barite
4. **5.**	White	C—Rhombohedral, not conspicuous F—Uneven Brittle	2.1 2.2	Generally in cube-like crystals. Inferior cleavage distinguishes it from fluorite and calcite. In basic igneous rocks. With analcite, stilbite

Streak—Uncolored, white, or light gray			
Name, Composition, and Reference	Crystallization Structure Crystals = C Massive = M	Luster Transparency	Color
APOPHYLLITE $KCa_4F(Si_4O_{10})_2.8H_2O$ **394**	Tetragonal **C**—Prismatic, pyramidal, pseudocubical, tabular **M**—Lamellar, granular, compact	Vitreous Pearly Transparent to nearly opaque	Pale red Flesh red Rose red
APATITE $Ca_5F(PO_4)_3$ **351**	Hexagonal **C**—Prismatic, thick tabular, common; may be vertically striated and have fused appearance **M**—Granular, compact, fibrous, nodular	Greasy Vitreous Translucent to opaque	Violet-red Brownish red Red
ANALCIME (Zeolite) $NaAlSi_2O_6.H_2O$ **419**	Cubic **C**—Tetragonal trisoctahedrons, cubes **M**—Granular, compact	Vitreous Translucent to opaque	Reddish Brick red
Datolite $CaB(OH)SiO_4$ **373**	Monoclinic **M**—Compact, fibrous, granular, botryoidal	Vitreous Greasy Dull Translucent to opaque	Pink Red Red-violet
SPHENE (Titanite) $CaTiOSiO_4$ **374**	Monoclinic **C**—Wedge- or envelope-shaped when disseminated; tabular or prismatic when attached **M**—Compact, lamellar	Vitreous Greasy Transparent to opaque	Brownish red Red
Monazite $(Ce,La)PO_4$ **350**	Monoclinic **C**—Thick tabular, square prismatic **M**—Angular, rolled grains	Resinous Vitreous Translucent to opaque	Hyacinth red Brownish red

Hardness 3 to 6

Hardness	Streak	Cleavage = C Fracture = F Tenacity	Specific Gravity	Characteristics and Associates
4.5 5.	White	C—Basal, perfect, conspicuous F—Uneven Brittle	2.3 2.4	Prism faces vertically striated. In fissures and cavities in basic igneous rocks. With natrolite, analcite, datolite, pectolite, native copper, calcite
5.	White Reddish white	C—Basal, imperfect F—Conchoidal, uneven Brittle	3.1 3.2	Color often unevenly distributed,—mottled brown and green. In crystalline limestones, metalliferous ore deposits, igneous rocks. With quartz, cassiterite, fluorite, wolframite, magnetite
5. 5.5	White Reddish white	C—None F—Uneven, conchoidal Brittle	2.2 2.3	Good crystals common. In basic igneous rocks with apophyllite, chabazite, natrolite, datolite, native copper, epidote
5. 5.5	White	C—None F—Conchoidal, uneven Brittle	2.9 3.	Compact masses resemble unglazed porcelain. Often spotted. In basic igneous rocks with calcite, epidote, native copper, zeolites
5. 5.5	White Gray	C—Prismatic, conspicuous parting often noted F—Conchoidal Brittle	3.4 3.6	With feldspars, pyroxenes, amphiboles, chlorite, scapolite, zircon
5. 5.5	White	C—Basal F—Conchoidal, uneven Brittle	4.9 5.3	Crystals commonly small, highly modified, or as rolled grains in sand. With magnetite, zircon, garnet, gold, chromite, diamond

Streak—Uncolored, white, or light gray

Name, Composition, and Reference	Crystallization Structure Crystals = C Massive = M	Luster Transparency	Color
Huebnerite $MnWO_4$ **348**	Monoclinic **C**—Long fibrous, bladed, stalky; poorly terminated **M**—Compact, lamellar, granular	Resinous Submetallic Translucent to opaque	Brownish red
SCAPOLITE (Wernerite) $nNa_4Cl(AlSi_3O_8)_3 + mCa_4CO_3(Al_2Si_2O_8)_3$ **417**	Tetragonal **C**—Prismatic **M**—Compact, granular, fibrous, columnar	Vitreous Greasy Translucent	Pink Red-violet Brick red
RHODONITE $MnSiO_3$ **388**	Triclinic **C**—Tabular, prismatic, rounded edges, often large **M**—Compact, cleavable, granular, disseminated grains	Vitreous Dull Transparent to opaque	Brownish red Flesh red Rose red
OPAL, varieties *Fire opal* *Opal jasper* $SiO_2.nH_2O$ **314**	Amorphous **M**—Reniform, botryoidal, stalactitic, compact	Vitreous Greasy Transparent to opaque	Red Brownish red
FELDSPARS: **ORTHOCLASE** $KAlSi_3O_8$ **406**	Monoclinic **C**—Prismatic, thick tabular, twins; often large **M**—Cleavable, granular, disseminated	Vitreous Pearly Translucent to opaque	Flesh red Brick red
FELDSPARS: **MICROCLINE** $KAlSi_3O_8$ **408**	Triclinic **C**—Prismatic, thick tabular; twins **M**—Cleavable, granular, compact, disseminated	Vitreous Pearly Translucent to transparent	Red Reddish

Hardness 3 to 6

Hardness	Streak	Cleavage = C Fracture = F Tenacity	Specific Gravity	Characteristics and Associates
5. **5.5**	Greenish gray	C—Clinopinacoidal, perfect, conspicuous Brittle	6.7 7.3	Structure, cleavage, and specific gravity characteristic. In quartz veins. With wolframite, fluorite, pyrite, scheelite, galena, tetrahedrite
5. **6.**	White	C—Prismatic, not conspicuous F—Conchoidal Brittle	2.6 2.8	Often resembles pink fluorite in color, but cleavage less distinct, and harder. In metamorphic rocks, especially granular limestones. With pyroxenes, apatite, garnet, sphene, biotite, amphiboles
5. **6.**	White Reddish white	C—Prismatic, basal F—Conchoidal, uneven Tough, when massive; crystals brittle	3.4 3.7	May be stained brown to black on exposure. *Fowlerite*, variety containing zinc. With franklinite, zincite, willemite, calcite, tetrahedrite
5.5 **6.**	White	F—Conchoidal, conspicuous Brittle	1.9 2.3	Structure and fracture characteristic. *Fire opal*, transparent to translucent and red; *opal jasper*, greasy and opaque, resembling jasper. In veins, cavities, and masses of irregular outline
6.	White	C—Basal, clinopinacoidal, perfect, conspicuous—90° F—Conchoidal, uneven Brittle	2.5 2.6	Characterized by rectangular cleavage and absence of twinning striations. In granitic rocks. With quartz, other feldspars, mica, hornblende, zircon
6.	White	C—Basal, brachypinacoidal, conspicuous, 90°30′ Brittle	2.5 2.6	Slightly inclined cleavages; may show gridiron structure on basal pinacoid. With quartz, other feldspars, mica, hornblende, topaz

Streak—Uncolored, white, or light gray			
Name, Composition, and Reference	Crystallization Structure Crystals = C Massive = M	Luster Transparency	Color
Chondrodite $Mg(F,OH)_2.2Mg_2SiO_4$ **373**	Monoclinic **C**—Small, highly modified, rare **M**—Rounded, disseminated grains; compact	Vitreous Greasy Translucent to opaque	Brownish red Dark red
RUTILE TiO_2 **309**	Tetragonal **C**—Prismatic, vertically striated; twinned, yielding knee-shaped or rosette forms **M**—Compact, disseminated	Adamantine Submetallic Translucent to opaque	Dark red Brownish red
CASSITERITE SnO_2 **310**	Tetragonal **C**—Thick prismatic; knee-shaped twins quite common **M**—Compact, reniform, botryoidal, rounded pebbles, often with internal, radial fibrous structure, *wood tin*	Adamantine Resinous Dull Translucent to opaque	Brownish red Yellowish red
ANDALUSITE Al_2OSiO_4 **368**	Orthorhombic **C**—Prismatic, rough, nearly square, often large and without terminations **M**—Columnar, fibrous, granular, disseminated	Vitreous Dull Translucent opaque	Pink Rose red Red-violet

Hardness over 6

Hard-ness	Streak	Cleavage = C Fracture = F Tenacity	Specific Gravity	Characteristics and Associates
6. **6.5**	White	C—Basal F—Conchoidal, uneven Brittle	3.1 3.3	Associates important. Chiefly in crystalline limestones and dolomites. With spinel, vesuvianite, pyroxenes, magnetite, mica
6. **7.**	Gray Yellowish white Brownish white	C—Prismatic, pyramidal, not conspicuous F—Uneven Brittle	4.2 4.3	Not as heavy as cassiterite. Often as fine hair-like inclusions. Widely distributed. With quartz, feldspar, hematite, ilmenite, chlorite
6. **7.**	White Yellowish white Brownish white	C—Indistinct F—Uneven Brittle	6.8 7.	Distinguished by high specific gravity. In veins cutting granite, gneiss; in alluvial deposits as *stream tin.* With quartz, wolframite, scheelite, arsenopyrite, tourmaline, fluorite, mica, chlorite
6. **7.5**	White	C—Prismatic F—Uneven Brittle	3.1 3.2	Due to alteration, surface may be covered with scales of mica and, hence, is softer. In metamorphic rocks often as rounded or knotty projections. With kyanite, sillimanite, garnet, tourmaline

Streak—Uncolored, white, or light gray

Name, Composition, and Reference	Crystallization Structure Crystals = C Massive = M	Luster Transparency	Color
GARNET, varieties *Grossularite* $M''_3M'''_2(SiO_4)_3$ *Pyrope* *Spessartite* M'' = Ca, Fe, Mg, Mn *Almandite* M''' = Al, Fe *Andradite* **365**	Cubic **C**—Dodecahedrons, tetragonal trisoctahedrons, alone or in combination **M**—Granular, compact, lamellar, disseminated, sand	Vitreous Transparent to opaque	Rose red Ruby red Brownish red Dark red
QUARTZ, Crystalline varieties SiO_2 *Amethyst* *Rose quartz* *Aventurine* *Ferruginous* **295**	Hexagonal **C**—Prismatic, horizontally striated, common **M**—Compact, granular	Vitreous Greasy Transparent to opaque	Red-violet Rose red Brick red Brownish red
Cryptocrystalline varieties *Carnelian* *Agate* *Sard* *Jasper* *Heliotrope* **296**	Hexagonal **C**—Never in crystals **M**—Banded, spotted, compact	Waxy Vitreous Translucent to opaque	Bright red Dark red Brownish red
Clastic varieties *Sand* *Sandstone* *Quartzite* **297**	Hexagonal **M**—Loose or strongly consolidated grains or fragments	Vitreous Dull Translucent to opaque	Red Brownish red Purplish red

Hardness over 6

Hardness	Streak	Cleavage = C Fracture = F Tenacity	Specific Gravity	Characteristics and Associates
6.5 **7.5**	White Gray	C—Dodecahedral, indistinct F—Conchoidal, uneven Brittle	3.5 4.3	*Grossularite*, in crystalline limestones and dolomites, with wollastonite, vesuvianite, diopside, scapolite; *pyrope*, rounded grains, in serpentine; *spessartite*, in granitic rocks, with topaz, tourmaline, quartz, orthoclase; *almandite*, with mica, staurolite, andalusite, kyanite; *andradite*, with magnetite, epidote, feldspar, nepheline, leucite
7.	White Reddish white	C—Indistinct F—Conchoidal, conspicuous Brittle	2.6	Characteristic conchoidal fracture and glassy luster. *Amethyst*, usually in crystals, purple or blue-violet; *rose quartz*, usually massive, pink to rose red; *aventurine*, massive and glistening, due to included scales; *ferruginous quartz*, colored by iron oxide
7.	White Reddish white	C—Indistinct F—Conchoidal, conspicuous Brittle to tough	2.6	Not so glassy as crystalline varieties. *Carnelian, jasper*, uniform in color; *agate, sard*, banded; *heliotrope*, spotted. To distinguish, see reference
7.	White Reddish white	C—Indistinct F—Uneven Brittle to tough	2.6	Pigment is usually ferruginous matter. *Sand*, loose, unconsolidated grains; *sandstone*, consolidated sand; *quartzite*, metamorphosed sand stone

Streak—Uncolored, white, or light gray

Name, Composition, and Reference	Crystallization Structure Crystals = C Massive = M	Luster Transparency	Color
TOURMALINE, variety *Rubellite* $M_7Al_6(OH,F)_4$-$(BO_3)_3Si_6O_{18}$ **382**	Hexagonal **C**—Prismatic, often vertically striated, rarely with good terminations **M**—Divergent, columnar, compact	Vitreous Transparent to translucent	Pink Rose red Ruby red
ZIRCON $ZrSiO_4$ **366**	Tetragonal **C**—Prismatic, pyramidal, small, well developed **M**—Irregular lumps, grains	Adamantine Vitreous Resinous Transparent to opaque	Brownish red Dark red
SPINEL, varieties $M''M'''_2O_4$ *Ruby* M'' = Mg, Fe, Mn *Balas ruby* *Rubicelle* M''' = Al, Fe *Almandine* **304**	Cubic **C**—Octahedral, twins, small **M**—Rounded grains, small pebbles	Vitreous Splendent Transparent to translucent	Deep red Rose red Orange-red Bluish red
CORUNDUM, varieties *Ruby* Al_2O_3 *Oriental amethyst* *Common* **299**	Hexagonal **C**—Prismatic, tabular, pyramidal, rhombohedral, rough or rounded barrel-shaped **M**—Compact, granular, lamellar	Vitreous Transparent to translucent	Pink Red Red-violet

Hardness over 6

Hardness	Streak	Cleavage = C Fracture = F Tenacity	Specific Gravity	Characteristics and Associates
7. **7.5**	White	C—None F—Conchoidal, uneven Brittle	2.9 3.2	Spherical triangular cross-section. Often with zonal distribution of color—red, green, colorless. Frequently as long, divergent, columnar masses imbedded in lepidolite
7.5	White	C—Indistinct F—Uneven Brittle	4.6 4.7	Often in the more acid igneous rocks—granites, syenites; alluvial deposits, with gold, spinel, corundum, garnet. *Hyacinth,* clear and transparent
8.	White	C—Octahedral, indistinct F—Conchoidal Brittle	3.5 4.1	*Balas ruby,* rose red; *ruby spinel,* deep red; *rubicelle,* yellow to orange-red; *almandine,* bluish red. Usually in precious stone placers, with zircon, garnet, magnetite; more rarely as contact mineral in crystalline limestones
9.	White	C—None; basal and nearly rectangular rhombohedral partings, conspicuous; often striated F—Conchoidal Brittle to tough	3.9 4.1	When massive often multicolored—blue, green, gray. *Ruby,* transparent red; *oriental amethyst,* violet. In limestones, granites; schists, peridotites, alluvial deposits. With magnetite, hematite, nepheline, mica, spinel

Streak—Blue, green, brown, or yellow			
Name, Composition, and Reference	Crystallization Structure Crystals = C Massive = M	Luster Transparency	Color
CHLORITE (Prochlorite, clinochlorite) $Mg_5Al(OH)_8AlSi_3O_{10}$ **401**	Monoclinic **C**—Tabular, six-sided, often bent and twisted. Pseudomorphs after garnet, common **M**—Foliated, scaly, granular, earthy	Pearly Vitreous Dull Translucent to opaque	Grass green Brownish green Blackish green
CHRYSOCOLLA $CuSiO_3.nH_2O$ **383**	Amorphous? **M**—Compact, reniform, incrustations, seams, stains, earthy	Vitreous Greasy Dull Translucent to opaque	Green Greenish blue Blue
Garnierite $(Ni,Mg)_6(OH)_8Si_4O_{10}$ **404**	Monoclinic **M**—Compact, reniform, earthy	Dull Greasy Opaque	Pale green Apple green Emerald green
Chalcanthite (Blue vitriol) $CuSO_4.5H_2O$ **343**	Triclinic **C**—Tabular, small, rare **M**—Crusts, reniform, stalactitic, powdery	Vitreous Dull Translucent	Deep blue Sky blue Greenish blue

Streak—Blue, green, brown, or yellow			
Brochantite $Cu_4(OH)_6SO_4$ **342**	Monoclinic **C**—Prismatic, acicular, vertically striated **M**—Reniform, fibrous, drusy crusts	Vitreous Pearly Transparent to translucent	Emerald green Blackish green

Hardness 1 to 3

Hardness	Streak	Cleavage = C Fracture = F Tenacity	Specific Gravity	Characteristics and Associates
1. **2.5**	Pale green	C—Basal, perfect; when foliated, conspicuous F—Scaly, earthy Tough to brittle	2.6 3.	Laminae are flexible but inelastic, with slightly soapy feel. Common in schists and serpentine. With magnetite, garnet, diopside, magnesite. Often as a scaly or dusty coating on other minerals. Pseudomorphous after garnet
2. **4.**	Pale green Pale blue	F—Conchoidal Brittle	2. 2.2	Usually recognized by enamel-like appearance, conchoidal fracture, and nonfibrous structure. When impure brownish or blackish. With copper minerals—malachite, azurite, chalcopyrite
2. **3.**	Pale green	C—None F—Conchoidal, earthy Brittle	2.3 2.8	Often as rounded, pea-shaped masses with varnish-like surfaces and earthy interior. Frequently adheres to tongue. With olivine, serpentine, chromite, talc
2.5	Light blue	C—Indistinct F—Conchoidal Brittle	2.1 2.3	Disagreeable metallic taste. Oxidation product of copper sulfide minerals. With chalcopyrite, bornite, melanterite, pyrite

Hardness over 3

Hardness	Streak	Cleavage = C Fracture = F Tenacity	Specific Gravity	Characteristics and Associates
3.5	Light green	C—Orthopinacoidal F—Uneven Brittle	3.8 3.9	Not as common as malachite. Secondary copper mineral. With malachite, azurite, cuprite, chalcopyrite, limonite

Streak—Blue, green, brown, or yellow

Name, Composition, and Reference	Crystallization Structure Crystals = C Massive = M	Luster Transparency	Color
AZURITE $Cu_3(OH)_2(CO_3)_2$ **337**	Monoclinic **C**—Short prismatic, tabular, often in spherical aggregates **M**—Fibrous; botryoidal, with velvety or radial structure; earthy, crusts	Vitreous Dull Translucent to opaque	Azure blue Dark blue
MALACHITE $Cu_2(OH)_2CO_3$ **336**	Monoclinic **C**—Acicular, often in groups or tufts **M**—Fibrous; stalactitic, botryoidal with smooth surface and internal banded or radial fibrous structure; velvety crusts, earthy	Silky Adamantine Dull Translucent to opaque	Emerald green Grass green Dark green
Pyromorphite $Pb_5Cl(PO_4)_3$ **353**	Hexagonal **C**—Prismatic, thick tabular, rounded and barrel-shaped **M**—Globular, reniform, disseminated, crusts	Greasy Adamantine Translucent to opaque	Dark green Emerald green Yellowish green
Lazurite (Lapis lazuli) $Na_5S(AlSiO_4)_3$ **416**	Cubic **C**—Dodecahedrons, rare **M**—Compact, irregular grains	Vitreous Translucent to opaque	Azure blue Violet-blue Greenish blue
HORNBLENDE (Amphibole) Silicate of Ca, Mg, Fe, Al, etc. **392**	Monoclinic **C**—Long prismatic, prism angle 124°; often with rhombohedral-like terminations **M**—Bladed, fibrous, granular, compact	Vitreous Silky Translucent to opaque	Blackish green Dark green

Hardness over 3

Hardness	Streak	Cleavage = C Fracture = F Tenacity	Specific Gravity	Characteristics and Associates
3.5 **4.**	Blue	C—Domatic F—Conchoidal Brittle	3.7 3.8	Common alteration product of copper minerals. With malachite, cuprite, native copper, chalcocite, chalcopyrite, bornite. Pseudomorphous after cuprite, tetrahedrite. Alters to malachite
3.5 **4.**	Light green	C—Basal, pinacoidal F—Conchoidal, splintery Brittle	3.9 4.1	Very common alteration product of copper minerals. With azurite, cuprite, native copper, chalcocite, chalcopyrite, bornite. Pseudomorphous after cuprite, azurite, native copper. Surface may be almost black, due to the oxide, melaconite
3.5 **4.**	Yellow Greenish yellow	C—None F—Conchoidal, uneven Brittle	6.7 7.1	Alteration product of lead minerals. With galena, cerussite, barite, limonite
5. **5.5**	Pale blue	C—Dodecahedral, distinct F—Uneven Brittle	2.4 2.5	Always blue and contains disseminated pyrite. Occurs as contact mineral in crystalline limestone
5. **6.**	Grayish green Grayish brown Yellowish	C—Prismatic, perfect, often conspicuous—124° Brittle	2.9 3.3	Simple, pseudohexagonal crystals, and cleavage—124°—important. In nearly all types of igneous rocks. With quartz, feldspar, pyroxene, chlorite, calcite

Name, Composition, and Reference	Crystallization Structure Crystals = C Massive = M	Luster Transparency	Color
Streak—Blue, green, brown, or yellow			
AUGITE (Pyroxene) Silicate of Ca, Mg, Fe, Al, etc, **386**	Monoclinic **C**—Short, prismatic, thick columnar; prism angle 87° **M**—Compact, granular, disseminated	Vitreous Submetallic Translucent to opaque	Blackish green Leek green
Turquois $CuAl_6(OH)_8(PO_4)_4.4H_2O$ **355**	Triclinic **C**—Small, rare **M**—Reniform, stalactitic, disseminated, rounded pebbles	Waxy Dull Opaque to translucent	Sky blue Bluish green Apple green
Glaucophane (Amphibole) $Na_2Mg_3Al_2(OH)_2Si_8O_{22}$ **394**	Monoclinic **C**—Prismatic, indistinct **M**—Fibrous, columnar, granular	Vitreous Pearly Translucent	Azure blue Lavender blue Grayish blue Bluish black
Streak—Uncolored, white, or light gray			
Asbestos, variety *Chrysotile* $Mg_6(OH)_8Si_4O_{10}$ **403**	Monoclinic **M**—Fibrous, fine; felted	Silky Silky metallic Opaque	Light green Olive green
variety *Amphibole* Silicate of Ca, Mg, Fe, Al, etc. **391**	Monoclinic **M**—Fibrous, coarse or fine; felted	Silky Opaque	Greenish
TALC, varieties *Foliated* *Soapstone* or *steatite* $Mg_3(OH)_2Si_4O_{10}$ **395**	Monoclinic **C**—Thin tabular, indistinct **M**—Foliated, globular, granular, compact, fibrous	Pearly Greasy Opaque to transparent	Pale green Apple green Dark green

Hardness over 3

Hard-ness	Streak	Cleavage = C Fracture = F Tenacity	Specific Gravity	Characteristics and Associates
5. **6.**	Pale green Grayish green	C—Prismatic, perfect, conspicuous—87° Brittle	3.2 3.6	Crystals, usually eight-sided, more rarely four-sided; pseudotetragonal with prism angles of 87 and 93°. Cleavage less distinct than on hornblende. Common in basic eruptive rocks and crystalline limestones
6.	Pale green	F—Conchoidal Brittle	2.6 2.8	Secondary mineral, common in thin veins, crusts, or coatings. With limonite, quartz, feldspar, kaolin
6. **6.5**	Grayish blue	C—Prismatic F—Uneven, conchoidal Brittle	3. 3.1	In metamorphic rocks. With mica, amphibole, pyroxene, garnet, epidote, rutile

Hardness 1 to 3

Hard-ness	Streak	Cleavage = C Fracture = F Tenacity	Specific Gravity	Characteristics and Associates
1. **2.5**	White	F—Fibrous Flexible	2.2	Delicate, fine, parallel-flexible fibers perpendicular to walls, easily separable, called *short-fibered asbestos;* compare below. In veins or seams in compact serpentine
1. **2.5**	White	F—Fibrous Flexible	3.	*Long-fibered asbestos,* parallel, flexible fibers. Fibers parallel to walls. Compare above
1. **2.5**	White	C—Basal, conspicuous on foliated masses F—Uneven Sectile, laminae flexible	2.6 2.8	Greasy or soapy feel. *Foliated,* easily separable, inelastic folia or plates, H = 1; *soapstone* or *steatite,* coarse to fine granular, more or less impure, H = 1.5 – 2.5. With serpentine, dolomite, magnesite, actinolite

Streak—Uncolored, white, or light gray

Name, Composition, and Reference	Crystallization Structure Crystals = C Massive = M	Luster Transparency	Color
CHLORITE (Prochlorite, clinochlorite) $Mg_5Al(OH)_8AlSi_3O_{10}$ **401**	Monoclinic **C**—Tabular, six-sided, often bent, twisted. Pseudomorphs after garnet, common **M**—Foliated, scaly, granular, earthy	Pearly Vitreous Dull Translucent to opaque	Grass green Brownish green Blackish green
Melanterite (Copperas) $FeSO_4.7H_2O$ **344**	Monoclinic **C**—Rare **M**—Capillary, fibrous, stalactitic, concretionary, powdery	Vitreous Dull Transparent to translucent	Green Yellowish green
CHRYSOCOLLA $CuSiO_3.nH_2O$ **383**	Amorphous? **M**—Compact, reniform, incrustations, seams, stains, earthy	Vitreous Greasy Dull Translucent to opaque	Green Greenish blue Blue
Garnierite $(Ni,Mg)_6(OH)_8Si_4O_{10}$ **404**	Monoclinic **M**—Compact, reniform, earthy	Dull Greasy Opaque	Pale green Apple green Emerald green
Actinolite (Amphibole) $Ca_2(Mg,Fe)_5(OH)_2Si_8O_{22}$ **392**	Monoclinic **C**—Fine, acicular **M**—Interwoven fibrous aggregates, radiating masses	Vitreous Silky Translucent to opaque	Grass green Grayish green

Hardness 1 to 3

Hardness	Streak	Cleavage = C Fracture = F Tenacity	Specific Gravity	Characteristics and Associates
1. 2.5	White Greenish white	C—Basal, conspicuous, when foliated F—Scaly, earthy Tough to brittle	2.6 3.	Laminae flexible but inelastic, with slightly soapy feel. Common in schists and serpentine. With magnetite, magnesite, garnet, diopside. Often as scaly or dusty coating on other minerals. Pseudomorphous after garnet
2.	White	C—Basal, not conspicuous F—Conchoidal, earthy Brittle	1.8 1.9	On exposure loses water and crumbles to powder. Sweet, astringent taste, somewhat metallic. Oxidation product of iron sulfide minerals—marcasite, pyrite, chalcopyrite, pyrrhotite
2. 3.	White Greenish white Bluish white	F—Conchoidal Brittle	2. 2.2	Usually recognized by enamel-like appearance, conchoidal fracture, and nonfibrous structure. When impure brownish or blackish. With copper minerals—malachite, azurite, chalcopyrite; also limonite
2. 3.	White Greenish white	C—None F—Conchoidal, earthy Brittle	2.3 2.8	Often as rounded, pea-shaped masses, with varnish-like surfaces and earthy interior. May adhere to tongue. With olivine, serpentine, chromite, talc
2. 3.	White Greenish white	C—Fibrous Brittle	2.9 3.2	Masses of delicate, interwoven fibers—*actinolite schist*. A pale grayish green, highly ferruginous variety (*grünerite*, $MgFe_6(OH)_2Si_8O_{22}$) associated with quartz and magnetite is termed *magnetite-grünerite schist*

Streak—Uncolored, white, or light gray			
Name, Composition, and Reference	Crystallization Structure Crystals = C Massive = M	Luster Transparency	Color
Chalcanthite (Blue vitriol) $CuSO_4.5H_2O$ **343**	Triclinic **C**—Tabular, small, rare **M**—Crusts, reniform, stalactitic, fibrous, powdery	Vitreous Dull Translucent	Deep blue Sky blue Greenish blue
BIOTITE (Mica) $K(Mg,Fe)_3(OH,F)_2$-$AlSi_3O_{10}$ **399**	Monoclinic **C**—Tabular, hexagonal or rhombic outline **M**—Plates, disseminated scales	Pearly Submetallic Transparent to opaque	Brownish green Blackish green
CALCITE $CaCO_3$ **326**	Hexagonal **M**—Cleavable, granular, fibrous, compact	Vitreous Dull Transparent to nearly opaque	Sky blue Deep blue Greenish

Streak—Uncolored, white, or light gray			
ANHYDRITE $CaSO_4$ **339**	Orthorhombic **C**—Thick tabular, prismatic, rare **M**—Granular, compact, fibrous, lamellar, cleavable, reniform	Vitreous Pearly Translucent to opaque	Bluish Grayish blue Blue
CELESTITE $SrSO_4$ **339**	Orthorhombic **C**—Tabular, prismatic, common; pyramidal **M**—Compact, cleavable, fibrous, granular, reniform	Vitreous Pearly Transparent to translucent	Sky blue Blue Greenish

Hardness 1 to 3

Hardness	Streak	Cleavage = C Fracture = F Tenacity	Specific Gravity	Characteristics and Associates
2.5	White Bluish white	C—Indistinct F—Conchoidal, earthy Brittle	2.1 2.3	Disagreeable metallic taste. Oxidation product of copper sulfide minerals. With chalcopyrite, bornite, melanterite, pyrite
2.5 **3.**	White Grayish	C—Basal, perfect, conspicuous Tough, laminae of fresh biotite very elastic	2.7 3.2	Easily recognized by structure, highly perfect cleavage, and elasticity. Important constituent of many igneous and metamorphic rocks—granite, syenite, gneiss
3.	White	C—Rhombohedral perfect, conspicuous F—Conchoidal Brittle	2.7	Rhombohedral cleavage generally characteristic. Cleavages often show striations

Hardness 3 to 6

Hardness	Streak	Cleavage = C Fracture = F Tenacity	Specific Gravity	Characteristics and Associates
3. **3.5**	White	C—Pinacoidal, perfect, 3 directions at 90° F—Conchoidal Brittle	2.8 3.	Pseudocubical cleavage, sometimes noted. Granular varieties resemble marble. Not so heavy as celestite or barite. In limestone, shale. With halite, gypsum
3. **3.5**	White	C—Basal, prismatic, conspicuous F—Uneven Brittle	3.9 4.	Heavier than calcite, anhydrite; lighter than barite. In limestones, dolomites, shales. With sulfur, gypsum, aragonite, halite, galena, sphalerite

Streak—Uncolored, white, or light gray

Name, Composition, and Reference	Crystallization Structure Crystals = C Massive = M	Luster Transparency	Color
BARITE (Heavy spar) $BaSO_4$ **340**	Orthorhombic **C**—Tabular, prismatic, crested divergent groups, common **M**—Compact, lamellar, fibrous, cleavable, reniform	Vitreous Pearly Transparent to translucent	Bluish Greenish
CHRYSOCOLLA $CuSiO_3.nH_2O$ **383**	Amorphous? **M**—Compact, reniform, incrustations, seams, stains, earthy	Vitreous Greasy Dull Translucent to opaque	Blue Bluish green Green
SERPENTINE *Antigorite* *Chrysotile* $Mg_6(OH)_8Si_4O_{10}$ **403**	Monoclinic **C**—Unknown **M**—Compact, columnar, fibrous, lamellar, granular	Greasy Waxy Translucent to opaque	Light green Olive green Yellowish green Blackish green
Wavellite $Al_3(OH)_3(PO_4)_2.5H_2O$ **355**	Orthorhombic **C**—Capillary, small **M**—Crusts, globular or hemispherical, with radial fibrous structure	Vitreous Translucent	Green Bluish green Blue

Hardness 3 to 6

Hardness	Streak	Cleavage = C Fracture = F Tenacity	Specific Gravity	Characteristics and Associates
3. **3.5**	White	C—Basal, prismatic, conspicuous F—Uneven Brittle	4.3 4.7	Characterized by rather high specific gravity and cleavages. In metalliferous veins; pockets, lenticular masses in limestone. With galena, sphalerite, chalcopyrite, manganese and iron minerals
3. **4.**	White Greenish white Bluish white	F—Conchoidal Brittle	2. 2.2	Usually recognized by enamel-like appearance, conchoidal fracture, and nonfibrous structure. When impure brownish or blackish. With copper minerals—malachite, azurite, chalcopyrite; also limonite
3. **4.**	White	F—Conchoidal, splintery Brittle	2.5 2.8	Smooth and greasy feel. Often spotted, clouded, and multicolored. Sometimes crossed by seams of asbestos (chrysotile). *Verd antique,* massive, green and mixed with calcite, dolomite, or magnesite; takes an excellent polish. With magnesite, chromite, garnierite, pyrope, platinum
3.5 **4.**	White	C—Pinacoidal, domatic F—Conchoidal, uneven, fibrous Brittle	2.3 2.5	Secondary mineral occurring on surfaces of rocks or minerals, as crystalline crusts with pronounced radial fibrous structure

Streak—Uncolored, white, or light gray			
Name, Composition, and Reference	Crystallization Structure Crystals = C Massive = M	Luster Transparency	Color
Pyromorphite $Pb_5Cl(PO_4)_3$ **353**	Hexagonal **C**—Prismatic, thick, tabular, rounded and barrel-shaped; acicular **M**—Globular, reniform, disseminated, crusts	Greasy Adamantine Translucent to opaque	Dark green Emerald green Yellowish green
FLUORITE (Fluor spar) CaF_2 **322**	Cubic **C**—Cubes, alone or modified, well developed, common; penetration twins **M**—Cleavable, granular, fibrous	Vitreous Transparent to nearly opaque	Greenish Bluish green Blue-violet
KYANITE (Disthene, cyanite) Al_2OSiO_4 **369**	Triclinic **C**—Long bladed, without good terminations; sometimes curved and radially grouped **M**—Coarsely bladed, columnar, fibrous	Vitreous Translucent to transparent	Sky blue Greenish blue Bluish white
APATITE $Ca_5F(PO_4)_3$ **351**	Hexagonal **C**—Prismatic, thick, tabular, common, sometimes large with rounded edges **M**—Granular, compact, fibrous, nodular, reniform	Greasy Vitreous Translucent to opaque	Grass green Brownish green Bluish green Blue-violet
SMITHSONITE $ZnCO_3$ **331**	Hexagonal **C**—Small, usually as druses or crusts **M**—Botryoidal, stalactitic, granular, fibrous, compact	Vitreous Dull Translucent	Green Grayish green Greenish blue Blue

Hardness 3 to 6

Hardness	Streak	Cleavage = C Fracture = F Tenacity	Specific Gravity	Characteristics and Associates
3.5 **4.**	White Yellowish white	C—None F—Conchoidal, uneven Brittle	6.5 7.1	Common alteration product of lead minerals. With galena, cerussite, barite, limonite
4.	White	C—Octahedral, perfect, conspicuous Brittle	3. 3.2	May show fluorescence. Easily recognized by crystal form, octahedral cleavage, and hardness. Common gangue of metallic ores—galena, sphalerite, cassiterite; also with calcite, barite
4. **5.**	White	C—Pinacoidal, perfect, conspicuous Brittle	3.5 3.7	Color irregularly distributed, frequently with lighter longitudinal margins. Hardness varies with direction, 4–5 parallel to long direction, 6–7 at right angles thereto. In gneiss, mica schist. With staurolite, garnet, corundum
5.	White	C—Basal, imperfect F—Conchoidal, uneven Brittle	3.1 3.2	Crystals may be vertically striated and have fused appearance. Color often unevenly distributed—brownish spots. In crystalline limestones; metalliferous ore deposits; igneous rocks. With quartz, cassiterite, fluorite, wolframite
5.	White Gray	C—Rhombohedral, not often observed F—Uneven, splintery Brittle	4.1 4.5	With zinc minerals, especially sphalerite, hemimorphite

Streak—Uncolored, white, or light gray

Name, Composition, and Reference	Crystallization Structure Crystals = C Massive = M	Luster Transparency	Color
Lazurite (Lapis lazuli) $Na_5S(AlSiO_4)_3$ **416**	Cubic **C**—Dodecahedrons, rare **M**—Compact, irregular grains	Vitreous Translucent to opaque	Azure blue Violet blue Greenish blue
Datolite $CaB(OH)SiO_4$ **373**	Monoclinic **C**—Prismatic, pyramidal, tabular, highly modified **M**—Compact, fibrous, granular, botryoidal	Vitreous Greasy Dull Transparent to opaque	Pale green Olive green
SPHENE (Titanite) $CaTiOSiO_4$ **374**	Monoclinic **C**—Wedge- or envelope-shaped when disseminated; tabular or prismatic when attached **M**—Compact, lamellar	Vitreous Greasy Transparent to translucent	Green Yellowish green
Sodalite $Na_4Cl(AlSiO_4)_3$ **415**	Cubic **C**—Dodecahedrons **M**—Compact, disseminated grains, nodular	Vitreous Greasy Transparent to translucent	Lavender blue Sky blue Dark blue Greenish
NEPHELINE (Nephelite, elaeolite) $Na(AlSiO_4)$ **414**	Hexagonal **C**—Short prismatic, tabular **M**—Compact, disseminated grains	Greasy Vitreous Transparent to opaque	Grayish green Brownish green Grayish blue
SCAPOLITE (Wernerite) $nNa_4Cl(AlSi_3O_8)_3 + mCa_4CO_3(Al_2Si_2O_8)_3$ **417**	Tetragonal **C**—Thick prismatic, coarse, often large **M**—Compact, granular, fibrous, columnar	Vitreous Greasy Translucent to opaque	Grayish green Bluish

Hardness 3 to 6

Hardness	Streak	Cleavage = C Fracture = F Tenacity	Specific Gravity	Characteristics and Associates
5. 5.5	White Bluish white	C—Dodecahedral, imperfect F—Uneven Brittle	2.4 2.5	Always blue and contains disseminated pyrite. Occurs as contact mineral in crystalline limestone
5. 5.5	White	C—None F—Conchoidal, uneven Brittle	2.9 3.	Crystals glassy and usually well developed. Compact masses resemble unglazed porcelain. Often spotted. In cracks and cavities in basic igneous rocks. With calcite, native copper, magnetite, zeolites
5. 5.5	White Grayish	C—Prismatic, conspicuous parting often noted F—Conchoidal Brittle	3.4 3.6	With feldspars, pyroxenes, amphiboles, chlorite, scapolite, zircon
5. 6.	White	C—Dodecahedral F—Conchoidal, uneven Brittle	2.2 2.4	Commonly massive and blue in color. Recognized by associates—nepheline, cancrinite, leucite, feldspar, zircon; not with quartz
5. 6.	White	C—Indistinct F—Conchoidal, uneven Brittle	2.6	Greasy luster and associates important. With feldspar, cancrinite, biotite, sodalite, zircon, leucite; not with quartz
5. 6.	White	C—Prismatic F—Conchoidal Brittle	2.6 2.8	Crystals may appear as though fused. Typical contact mineral. In metamorphic rocks, especially granular limestones. With pyroxenes, garnet, mica, amphiboles, wollastonite

	Streak—Uncolored, white, or light gray			
	Name, Composition, and Reference	Crystallization Structure Crystals = C Massive = M	Luster Transparency	Color
AMPHIBOLES	**Actinolite** $Ca_2(Mg,Fe)_5(OH)_2Si_8O_{22}$ **392**	Monoclinic C—Bladed, without terminations M—Columnar, fibrous, often divergent; granular, compact	Vitreous Silky Transparent to opaque	Light green Grayish green Dark green
AMPHIBOLES	**HORNBLENDE** Silicate of Ca, Mg, Fe, Al, etc. **392**	Monoclinic C—Long prismatic, prism angle 124°; often with rhombohedral-like terminations M—Bladed, fibrous, granular, compact	Vitreous Silky Translucent to opaque	Blackish green Dark green
PYROXENES	**ENSTATITE** (Bronzite) $(Mg,Fe)_2Si_2O_6$ **384**	Orthorhombic C—Prismatic, rare M—Fibrous, lamellar, compact	Bronzy Silky Translucent to opaque	Grayish green Brownish green Olive green
PYROXENES	**DIOPSIDE** $CaMgSi_2O_6$ **385**	Monoclinic C—Prismatic, thick columnar, prism angle 87° M—Compact, granular, columnar, lamellar	Vitreous Dull Transparent to opaque	Pale green Bright green Dark green
PYROXENES	**AUGITE** Silicate of Ca, Mg, Fe, Al, etc. **386**	Monoclinic C—Short prismatic, thick columnar, prism angle 87° M—Compact, granular, disseminated	Vitreous Submetallic Translucent to opaque	Blackish green Leek green

Hardness 3 to 6

Hardness	Streak	Cleavage = C Fracture = F Tenacity	Specific Gravity	Characteristics and Associates
5. **6.**	White Greenish white	C—Prismatic, often conspicuous, 124° Brittle	2.9 3.2	Often as radiating masses. In talc and chlorite schists. With serpentine, epidote, calcite. The compact massive variety *nephrite* is called *jade*. See also *jadeite*, page 388
5. **6.**	Gray Greenish gray Brownish gray	C—Prismatic, often conspicuous, 124° Brittle	2.9 3.3	Simple pseudohexagonal crystals, and cleavage—124°—important. Common in many types of rocks. With quartz, feldspar, pyroxene, chlorite, calcite
5. **6.**	White Grayish	C—Prismatic, pinacoidal, often conspicuous F—Uneven Brittle	3.2 3.5	Cleavage surfaces often fibrous or lamellar, irregular or wavy, may have distinct bronzy luster. In basic igneous rocks
5. **6.**	White Gray	C—Prismatic; conspicuous basal parting F—Uneven Brittle	3.2 3.3	Crystals prismatic and pseudotetragonal with distinct basal parting. May have colorless and dark-green zones. In crystalline limestones and schists. With vesuvianite, garnet, scapolite, spinel, apatite
5. **6.**	White Gray Greenish gray	C—Prismatic, perfect, conspicuous—87°, (less distinct than on hornblende) Brittle	3.2 3.6	Crystals usually eight-sided, more rarely four-sided; pseudotetragonal with prism angles of 87 and 93°. In basic rocks and limestones

Streak—Uncolored, white, or light gray

Name, Composition, and Reference	Crystallization Structure Crystals = C Massive = M	Luster Transparency	Color
Willemite Zn_2SiO_4 **362**	Hexagonal **C**—Prismatic **M**—Compact, granular, disseminated grains	Vitreous Greasy Translucent to opaque	Apple green Yellowish green
OPAL $SiO_2.nH_2O$ **313**	Amorphous **M**—Reniform, botryoidal, compact	Vitreous Greasy Translucent to opaque	Green Bluish green Blue
Turquois $CuAl_6(OH)_8(PO_4)_4.4H_2O$ **355**	Triclinic **C**—Small, rare **M**—Reniform, stalactitic, disseminated, pebbles	Waxy Dull Opaque to translucent	Sky blue Bluish green Apple green
FELDSPARS: **MICROCLINE,** variety *Amazon stone* $KAlSi_3O_8$ **408**	Triclinic **C**—Prismatic, thick tabular, twins **M**—Cleavable, granular, compact, disseminated	Vitreous Pearly Translucent to transparent	Bright green Bluish green
FELDSPARS: **LABRADORITE** Silicate of Ca, Na, Al **412**	Triclinic **C**—Thin tabular, often with rhombic cross-section **M**—Compact, cleavable, granular	Vitreous Pearly Translucent to nearly opaque	Grayish green Greenish
Amblygonite $LiAl(F,OH)PO_4$ **351**	Triclinic **C**—Large, poorly developed **M**—Cleavable, columnar, compact	Pearly Vitreous Translucent	Greenish Bluish

Streak—Uncolored, white, or light gray

Name, Composition, and Reference	Crystallization Structure Crystals = C Massive = M	Luster Transparency	Color
Prehnite $Ca_2Al_2(OH)_2Si_3O_{10}$ **379**	Orthorhombic **C**—Tabular, prismatic; curved, sheaf-like groups **M**—Globular, reniform, radial fibrous	Vitreous Pearly on basal pinacoid Transparent to translucent	Light green Apple green Yellowish green

Hardness 3 to 6

Hardness	Streak	Cleavage = C Fracture = F Tenacity	Specific Gravity	Characteristics and Associates
5. 6.	White	C—Basal F—Uneven Brittle	3.9 4.3	Characterized by associates—franklinite (black), zincite (red), rhodonite (flesh red), calcite
5.5 6.	White	F—Conchoidal, conspicuous	1.9 2.3	Structure and fracture characteristic. *Precious opal,* play of colors. In veins, cavities, and masses of irregular outline
6.	White Greenish white	F—Conchoidal, Brittle	2.6 2.8	Secondary mineral, in thin veins, crusts, or coatings. With quartz, feldspar, kaolin, limonite
6.	White	C—Basal, brachypinacoidal, conspicuous, 90° 30′ F—Uneven Brittle	2.5 2.6	Slightly inclined cleavages; may show gridiron structure on basal pinacoid. With quartz, other feldspars, mica, hornblende, topaz
6.	White	C—Basal, brachypinacoidal, conspicuous, 86° F—Uneven, conchoidal Brittle	2.7	Often with play of colors—yellow, green, blue, red. Inclined cleavages are striated. In basic igneous rocks. With pyroxenes, amphiboles
6.	White	C—Basal, perfect, conspicuous; macropinacoidal, domatic F—Conchoidal, uneven Brittle	3. 3.1	Usually in cleavable masses with perfect cleavage in one direction. With lepidolite, spodumene, tourmaline, quartz, apatite

Hardness over 6

Hardness	Streak	Cleavage = C Fracture = F Tenacity	Specific Gravity	Characteristics and Associates
6. 6.5	White	C—Basal F—Uneven Brittle	2.8 3.	Massive varieties usually have rough crystalline surfaces and internal, radial structure. Color fades on exposure. In veins and cavities in basic igneous rocks. With pectolite, datolite, epidote, native copper, zeolites

Streak—Uncolored, white, or light gray			
Name, Composition, and Reference	Crystallization Structure Crystals = C Massive = M	Luster Transparency	Color
Glaucophane (Amphibole) $Na_2Mg_3Al_2(OH)_2Si_8O_{22}$ **394**	Monoclinic **C**—Prismatic, indistinct **M**—Fibrous, columnar, granular	Vitreous Pearly Translucent	Azure blue Lavender blue Grayish blue Bluish black
EPIDOTE $Ca_2(Al,Fe)_3O(OH)SiO_4$-Si_2O_7 **376**	Monoclinic **C**—Prismatic, elongated and deeply striated parallel to *b* axis; usually terminated on one end only **M**—Columnar, fibrous, parallel and divergent; granular	Vitreous Transparent to opaque	Blackish green Yellowish green Brownish green Pea green
KYANITE (Disthene, cyanite) Al_2OSiO_4 **369**	Triclinic **C**—Long bladed, without good terminations; sometimes curved and radially grouped **M**—Coarsely bladed, columnar, fibrous	Vitreous Translucent to transparent	Sky blue Greenish blue Bluish white
VESUVIANITE $Ca_{10}Al_4(Mg,Fe)_2(OH)_4$-$(SiO_4)_5(Si_2O_7)_2$ **378**	Tetragonal **C**—Short prismatic **M**—Compact, granular, aggregates with parallel or divergent striations	Vitreous Greasy Translucent to opaque	Green Brownish green Bluish
OLIVINE (Chrysolite, peridot) $(Mg,Fe)_2SiO_4$ **363**	Orthorhombic **C**—Prismatic, thick tabular **M**—Rounded, disseminated glassy grains; granular aggregates	Vitreous Transparent to translucent	Grass green Olive green Yellowish green
GARNET, varieties *Grossularite* *Uvarovite* *Andradite* $M'''_2M''_3(SiO_4)_3$ $M'' = Ca,Fe,Mg$ $M''' = Al,Fe,Cr$ **363**	Cubic **C**—Dodecahedrons, tetragonal trisoctahedrons, alone or in combination **M**—Granular, compact, lamellar, disseminated grains, sand	Vitreous Transparent to opaque	Pale green Grass green Emerald green

Hardness over 6

Hardness	Streak	Cleavage = C Fracture = F Tenacity	Specific Gravity	Characteristics and Associates
6. **6.5**	Bluish gray	**C**—Prismatic **F**—Uneven, conchoidal Brittle	3. 3.1	In metamorphic rocks. With mica, amphibole, pyroxene, garnet, epidote, rutile
6. **7.**	White Grayish	**C**—Basal **F**—Uneven Brittle	3.3 3.5	Crystals are often dark or blackish green, massive aggregates lighter colored. With quartz, feldspar, garnet, hornblende, pyroxene, magnetite, native copper, zeolites
6. **7.**	White	**C**—Pinacoidal, perfect, conspicuous Brittle	3.5 3.7	Color irregularly distributed, frequently with lighter longitudinal margins. Hardness varies with direction, 4–5 parallel to long direction, 6–7 at right angles thereto. In gneiss, mica schist. With staurolite, corundum
6.5	White	**C**—Basal, prismatic, indistinct **F**—Uneven Brittle	3.3 3.5	In crystalline limestone, gneiss, schists. With garnet, tourmaline, chondrodite, wollastonite, epidote, pyroxene
6.5 **7.**	White Yellowish white	**C**—Pinacoidal **F**—Conchoidal Brittle	3.2 3.6	In basic rocks—basalts, traps; crystalline, limestones. With augite, magnetite, spinel, plagioclase, chromite, pyrope
6.5 **7.5**	White	**C**—Dodecahedral, usually indistinct **F**—Conchoidal, uneven Brittle	3.5 4.3	*Grossularite*, in crystalline limestones and dolomites, with wollastonite, vesuvianite, diopside, scapolite; *uvarovite*, in serpentine, with chromite, or in crystalline limestones; *andradite*, with feldspar, nepheline, leucite, epidote, magnetite

Streak—Uncolored, white, or light gray			
Name, Composition, and Reference	Crystallization Structure Crystals = C Massive = M	Luster Transparency	Color
QUARTZ, Crystalline varieties SiO_2 *Cat's eye* *Amethyst* **295**	Hexagonal **C**—Prismatic, horizontally striated **M**—Compact, granular	Vitreous Greasy Transparent to opaque	Green Greenish blue Blue Blue-violet
Cryptocrystalline varieties *Chalcedony* *Chrysoprase* *Heliotrope* **296**	Hexagonal **C**—Never in crystals **M**—Nodular, spotted, concretionary, stalactitic, compact	Waxy Vitreous Translucent to opaque	Light green Dark green Grayish blue Greenish blue
Cordierite (Iolite, dichroite) $Mg_2Al_3(AlSi_5O_{18})$ **380**	Orthorhombic **C**—Short prismatic, pseudohexagonal **M**—Compact, disseminated, granular	Vitreous Greasy Transparent to translucent	Light blue Smoky blue Dark blue Violet
TOURMALINE $M_7Al_6(OH,F)_4$-$(BO_3)_3Si_6O_{18}$ **381**	Hexagonal **C**—Prismatic, vertically striated; terminated with broken or rhombohedral-like surfaces **M**—Compact, columnar	Vitreous Transparent to translucent	Green Blue
BERYL, varieties *Emerald* $Be_3Al_2Si_6O_{18}$ *Aquamarine* *Common* **380**	Hexagonal **C**—Long prismatic, often vertically striated, large **M**—Columnar, granular, compact, rounded pebbles	Vitreous Transparent to translucent	Pale green Emerald green Bluish green Sky blue

Hardness over 6				
Hard-ness	Streak	Cleavage = C Fracture = F Tenacity	Specific Gravity	Characteristics and Associates
7.	White	C—Indistinct F—Conchoidal, conspicuous Brittle	2.6	Characteristic conchoidal fracture and glassy luster. *Chloritic quartz,* green from included chlorite; *cat's-eye,* opalescent, due to included fibers of asbestos; *amethyst,* purple or blue-violet, usually in crystals
7.	White	C—Indistinct F—Conchoidal, conspicuous Brittle to tough	2.6	Not as glassy as crystalline varieties. *Chalcedony, chrysoprase, prase, plasma,* uniform in color; *heliotrope,* spotted. To distinguish, see reference
7. **7.5**	White	C—Pinacoidal, sometimes conspicuous F—Uneven Brittle	2.6 2.7	When fresh glassy and hard, resembling blue quartz; often altered, then dull and softer. Transparent varieties may show dichroism macroscopically. With quartz, feldspar, hornblende, sillimanite, andalusite
7. **7.5**	White	C—None F—Conchoidal, uneven Brittle	2.9 3.2	Spherical triangular cross-section. With zonal distribution of color—green red, colorless. In igneous and metamorphic rocks. With lepidolite, feldspar, quartz, biotite
7.5 **8.**	White	C—Indistinct F—Conchoidal, uneven Brittle	2.6 2.8	Crystals usually prism and base. *Emerald,* transparent, emerald green; *aquamarine,* transparent, bluish to sea green, yellowish green. In granitic rocks, mica schists, clay slates, placers. With quartz, feldspar, mica, topaz, tourmaline, cassiterite, chrysoberyl, garnet

Streak—Uncolored, white, or light gray

Name, Composition, and Reference	Crystallization Structure Crystals = C Massive = M	Luster Transparency	Color
ZIRCON $ZrSiO_4$ **366**	Tetragonal **C**—Prismatic, pyramidal, small, well developed **M**—Irregular lumps, grains	Adamantine Vitreous Resinous Transparent to opaque	Light blue Dark blue
SPINEL, varieties *Pleonaste*, *Gahnite*, *Blue spinel* $M''M'''_2O_4$ $M'' = $ Mg, Fe Zn, Mn $M''' = $ Al, Fe **304**	Cubic **C**—Octahedral, usually well developed **M**—Compact, granular, disseminated grains	Vitreous Dull Translucent to opaque	Grass green Dark green Grayish green Light blue
Chrysoberyl, varieties *Ordinary*, *Alexandrite*, *Cat's-eye* $BeAl_2O_4$ **308**	Orthorhombic **C**—Tabular; heart-shaped, pseudohexagonal twins **M**—Compact; loose, rounded grains	Vitreous Greasy Transparent to translucent	Light green Yellowish green Emerald green
CORUNDUM, varieties *Sapphire*, *Oriental emerald*, *Oriental amethyst*, *Common* Al_2O_3 **299**	Hexagonal **C**—Prismatic, tabular, pyramidal, rhombohedral; rough or rounded barrel-shaped **M**—Compact, granular, lamellar	Vitreous Transparent to opaque	Green Blue Blue-violet

Hardness over 6

Hardness	Streak	Cleavage = C Fracture = F Tenacity	Specific Gravity	Characteristics and Associates
7.5	White	C—Indistinct F—Uneven Brittle	4.6 4.7	In alluvial deposits near Bangkok, Thailand. When clear and transparent used as a gem
7.5 8.	White Grayish	C—Octahedral, indistinct F—Conchoidal Brittle	3.5 4.4	Contact mineral in granular limestones; in basic igneous rocks; grains in placers. With calcite, chondrodite, serpentine, corundum, graphite, pyroxenes
8.5	White	C—Brachypinacoidal F—Uneven, conchoidal Brittle	3.6 3.8	Crystals disseminated plates with feather-like or radial striations. *Alexandrite*, red in transmitted light; *cat's eye*, opalescent. In mica schist, gneiss; granite; in placers. With beryl, garnet, tourmaline, sillimanite
9.	White	C—None; basal and nearly rectangular rhombohedral partings, conspicuous; often striated F—Conchoidal Brittle to tough	3.9 4.1	When massive, often multicolored. *Sapphire*, transparent, blue; *oriental emerald*, green, transparent; *oriental amethyst*, violet. In limestone, granite, syenite, schist, peridotite; placers. With magnetite, nepheline, mica, chlorite, spinel

Streak—Red, brown, or yellow			
Name, Composition, and Reference	Crystallization Structure Crystals = C Massive = M	Luster Transparency	Color
Carnotite $K_2(UO_2)_2(VO_4)_3.3H_2O$ **356**	Orthorhombic C—Tabular, small rhombic plates M—Scaly aggregates, incrustations, crystalline powder	Resinous Vitreous Dull Transparent to translucent	Canary yellow Greenish yellow
BAUXITE A mixture of aluminum oxide minerals **317**	Never in crystals M—Pisolitic, oölitic, round disseminated grains, clay-like, earthy	Dull Earthy Opaque	Yellow Yellowish brown Brown
GOETHITE-LIMONITE, varieties $HFeO_2$ *Yellow ocher* *Brown ocher* *Bog iron ore* *Brown clay ironstone* **315**	Orthorhombic M—Earthy, porous, clay-like, oölitic, pisolitic	Earthy Dull Opaque	Yellow Yellowish brown Dark brown
ORPIMENT As_2S_3 **283**	Monoclinic C—Rare M—Foliated, granular, reniform, fibrous, crusts	Greasy Pearly Translucent	Lemon yellow
REALGAR AsS **283**	Monoclinic C—Short prismatic, rare M—Compact, granular, incrustations	Resinous Transparent to translucent	Reddish yellow Orange-yellow
SULFUR S **264**	Orthorhombic C—Pyramidal, tabular M—Granular, fibrous, earthy, crusts, compact	Greasy Adamantine Translucent	Straw yellow Honey yellow Brownish yellow Reddish yellow

Hardness 1 to 3

Hardness	Streak	Cleavage = C Fracture = F Tenacity	Specific Gravity	Characteristics and Associates
1. **2.**	Yellow	C—Basal, perfect F—Earthy Brittle		Occurs as a powder or in loosely cohering masses, intimately mixed with sand and sandstones. With malachite, azurite, biotite, magnetite
1. **3.**	Yellow Brown	F—Earthy Brittle	2.5 2.6	Color and streak variable. Clay odor. Commonly with pisolitic or oölitic structure. With clay or kaolinite, in nodules, grains, or irregular masses in limestone or dolomite. Considered a rock
1. **3.**	Yellowish brown Dark brown	F—Earthy	3.4 4.	*Yellow ocher*, earthy, and yellow, when impure gritty; *brown ocher*, earthy and brown; *bog iron ore*, porous; *brown clay ironstone*, massive or concretionary, impure from clay, sand. Ocherous varieties may soil fingers
1.5 **2.**	Lemon yellow	C—Clinopinacoidal, usually conspicuous Slightly sectile, laminae flexible	3.4 3.5	Characteristic lemon yellow color. Frequently disseminated in clay or dolomite. With realgar, stibnite, barite, calcite
1.5 **2.**	Orange-yellow	C—Clinopinacoidal, basal, not conspicuous F—Conchoidal Slightly sectile	3.4 3.6	Redder in color than orpiment. Disseminated in clay or dolomite. With orpiment, stibnite, native arsenic, pyrite, barite, calcite
1.5 **2.5**	Pale yellow	C—Indistinct C—Conchoidal Brittle	1.9 2.1	Independent beds in gypsum, limestone; in lava, result of volcanic exhalations. With celestite, anhydrite, aragonite, clay, metallic sulfides

Streak—Red, brown, or yellow

Name, Composition, and Reference	Crystallization Structure Crystals = C Massive = M	Luster Transparency	Color
Wulfenite $PbMoO_4$ **349**	Tetragonal **C**—Square, thin tabular; more rarely pyramidal **M**—Coarse, fine-grained	Greasy Adamantine Transparent to translucent	Wax yellow Orange-yellow Brown
Vanadinite $Pb_5Cl(VO_4)_3$ **353**	Hexagonal **C**—Prismatic, small, at times skeletal **M**—Compact, globular, fibrous, crusts	Greasy Translucent to opaque	Straw yellow Brownish yellow Reddish brown
Streak—Red, brown, or yellow			
GOETHITE-LIMONITE, varieties $HFeO_2$ *Compact* *Bog iron ore* *Brown clay ironstone* **315**	Orthorhombic **C**—Rare; pseudomorphs, commonly after pyrite, marcasite, siderite **M**—Compact, stalactitic, botryoidal, nodular; often with internal, radial fibrous structure; porous, pisolitic, oölitic	Submetallic Dull Opaque	Yellowish brown Dark brown
SIDERITE $FeCO_3$ **332**	Hexagonal **C**—Rhombohedral, curved or saddle-shaped **M**—Cleavable, granular, compact, botryoidal, rarely fibrous	Vitreous Pearly Dull Translucent to nearly opaque	Light brown Reddish brown Dark brown
SPHALERITE ZnS **278**	Cubic **C**—Tetrahedral, common **M**—Cleavable, fine- or coarse-grained, compact	Resinous Submetallic Transparent to opaque	Honey yellow Yellowish brown Reddish brown

Hardness 1 to 3

Hardness	Streak	Cleavage = C Fracture = F Tenacity	Specific Gravity	Characteristics and Associates
3.	Lemon yellow Pale yellow	C—Indistinct F—Conchoidal, uneven Brittle	6.3 7.	Square plates, sometimes with forms of the third order. With lead minerals—galena, pyromorphite, vanadinite
3.	Pale yellow Yellow	C—None F—Conchoidal, uneven Brittle	6.7 7.2	Crystal faces smooth with sharp edges. With lead minerals, but never in large quantities

Hardness over 3

Hardness	Streak	Cleavage = C Fracture = F Tenacity	Specific Gravity	Characteristics and Associates
3. **5.5**	Yellowish brown	F—Conchoidal, splintery, earthy Brittle	3.4 4.	Often with black varnish-like surface and passing into soft, yellow ocherous variety. *Compact limonite,* massive with fibrous structure, rather pure; *bog iron ore,* porous; *brown clay ironstone,* massive or concretionary, impure from clay, sand
3.5 **4.**	Pale yellow Yellowish brown	C—Rhombohedral, conspicuous F—Conchoidal Brittle	3.7 3.9	Curved crystals and rhombohedral cleavage characteristic. In ore deposits; beds and concretions in limestones and shales. With pyrite, chalcopyrite, galena, tetrahedrite, cryolite
3.5 **4.**	Pale yellow Light brown	C—Dodecahedral, usually conspicuous F—Conchoidal Brittle	3.9 4.2	Distinguished from siderite by crystallization, resinous luster, and cleavage. Color and streak vary with impurities. Extensively in limestones. With galena, chalcopyrite, pyrite, rhodochrosite, barite, fluorite

Streak—Red, brown, or yellow

Name, Composition, and Reference	Crystallization Structure Crystals = C Massive = M	Luster Transparency	Color
Pyromorphite $Pb_5Cl(PO_4)_3$ **353**	Hexagonal **C**—Prismatic, thick tabular, rounded and barrel-shaped; acicular **M**—Globular, reniform, disseminated, crusts	Greasy Adamantine Translucent to opaque	Wax yellow Green-yellow Yellowish brown
Zincite ZnO **299**	Hexagonal **C**—Small, rare **M**—Compact, granular, foliated	Adamantine Vitreous Translucent to opaque	Orange-yellow Reddish yellow
Huebnerite $MnWO_4$ **348**	Monoclinic **C**—Long fibrous, bladed, stalky; often divergent, without good terminations **M**—Compact, lamellar, granular	Greasy Submetallic Translucent to opaque	Reddish brown Hair brown Pale yellow
WOLFRAMITE $(Fe,Mn)WO_4$ **347**	Monoclinic **C**—Thick tabular, short columnar, often large **M**—Bladed, curved lamellar, granular, compact	Submetallic Opaque	Reddish brown Dark brown
Ferberite $FeWO_4$ **347**	Monoclinic **C**—Wedge shaped, short prismatic, tabular **M**—Fan-shaped aggregates, bladed, granular, compact	Submetallic Opaque	Brown Blackish brown
RUTILE TiO_2 **309**	Tetragonal **C**—Prismatic, vertically striated; twinned yielding knee-shaped or rosette forms **M**—Compact, disseminated	Adamantine Submetallic Translucent to opaque	Reddish brown Yellowish brown Dark brown

Hardness over 3

Hardness	Streak	Cleavage = C Fracture = F Tenacity	Specific Gravity	Characteristics and Associates
3.5 4.	Yellow Greenish yellow	C—None F—Conchoidal, uneven Brittle	6.5 7.1	Common alteration product of lead minerals. With galena, cerussite, barite, limonite
4. 4.5	Orange-yellow Reddish yellow	C—Basal, sometimes conspicuous F—Uneven Brittle	5.7	Recognized by associates. With calcite, franklinite (black), willemite (yellow to green), rhodonite (flesh red). On exposure becomes coated with the white carbonate
5. 5.5	Yellowish brown	C—Clinopinacoidal, conspicuous Brittle	6.7 7.3	Structure, cleavage, and high specific gravity characteristic. In quartz veins. With wolframite, fluorite, pyrite, scheelite, galena, tetrahedrite
5. 5.5	Reddish brown Dark brown	C—Clinopinacoidal, conspicuous F—Uneven Brittle	7.1 7.5	Distinguished from huebnerite by streak. Powder may be slightly magnetic. With cassiterite, quartz, mica, apatite, scheelite, molybdenite, huebnerite.
5. 5.5	Brown Dark brown	C—Clinopinacoidal, perfect F—Uneven Brittle	7.5	In granites and pegmatites. With quartz, chalcopyrite, galena, scheelite
6. 7.	Pale yellow Pale brown	C—Prismatic, pyramidal, not conspicuous F—Uneven Brittle	4.2 4.3	Not as heavy as cassiterite. Often in fine hair-like inclusions. With quartz, feldspar, hematite, ilmenite, chlorite, brookite

Streak—Red, brown, or yellow

Name, Composition, and Reference	Crystallization Structure Crystals = C Massive = M	Luster Transparency	Color
CASSITERITE SnO_2 **310**	Tetragonal **C**—Thick prismatic; knee-shaped twins quite common **M**—Compact, reniform, botryoidal, rounded pebbles, often with internal, radial fibrous structure—*wood tin*	Adamantine Greasy Dull Translucent to opaque	Reddish Yellowish brown Dark brown
SPINEL, variety *Picotite* $(Mg,Fe)_2(Al,Cr)_2O_4$ **304**	Cubic **C**—Octahedral, small **M**—Compact, granular, disseminated grains	Dull Nearly opaque	Yellowish brown Greenish brown Brown

Streak—Uncolored, white, or light gray

Name, Composition, and Reference	Crystallization Structure Crystals = C Massive = M	Luster Transparency	Color
Cerargyrite (Horn silver) AgCl **322**	Cubic **C**—Rare **M**—Wax-like crusts and coatings; stalactitic, dendritic	Waxy Greasy Transparent to translucent	Yellowish Brownish
TRIPOLITE (Opal) $SiO_2.nH_2O$ **314**	Amorphous **M**—Porous, earthy, chalk-like	Dull Translucent to opaque	Yellow Yellowish brown Brown
KAOLINITE (Kaolin) $Al_4(OH)_8Si_4O_{10}$ **401**	Monoclinic **C**—Scaly, hexagonal or orthorhombic outline, rare **M**—Compact, friable, mealy, clay-like	Dull Pearly Earthy Opaque to translucent	Yellowish Brownish

Hardness	Streak	Cleavage = C Fracture = F Tenacity	Specific Gravity	Characteristics and Associates
Hardness over 3				
6. **7.**	Pale brown Pale yellow	C—Indistinct F—Uneven Brittle	6.8 7.2	Recognized by high specific gravity. In veins cutting granite, gneiss; in alluvial deposits as *stream tin.* With quartz, mica, wolframite, arsenopyrite, molybdenite, tourmaline, fluorite, chlorite
7.5 **8.**	Pale brown	C—Indistinct F—Conchoidal Brittle	4.1	Commonly in basic igneous rocks, especially olivine-bearing types. With serpentine, olivine, corundum, magnetite, garnet
Hardness 1 to 3				
1. **1.5**	White, shiny Gray, shiny	C—None F—Conchoidal Highly sectile	5.5 5.6	Cuts like wax, yielding shiny surfaces; on exposure turns violet, brown, or black. With silver minerals, especially argentite, native silver; also limonite, calcite, barite
1. **2.5**	White Gray	F—Earthy Friable	1.9 2.3	Apparently very soft. Resembles kaolinite, but is gritty and not plastic. Due to impurities may have clay odor
1. **2.5**	White Yellowish white	C—Basal, scales F—Earthy Brittle	2.2 2.6	Not gritty like tripolite. Very strong clay odor when breathed upon. Usually adheres to tongue and becomes plastic when moistened. Greasy feel. With quartz, feldspar, corundum, topaz

Streak—Uncolored, white, or light gray			
Name, Composition, and Reference	Crystallization Structure Crystals = C Massive = M	Luster Transparency	Color
TALC, variety *Soapstone* or *steatite* $Mg_3(OH)_2Si_4O_{10}$ **395**	Monoclinic M—Compact, globular, granular	Greasy Pearly Translucent to opaque	Yellowish Yellowish brown Brownish
Asbestos, variety *Chrysotile* $Mg_6(OH)_8Si_4O_{10}$ **403**	Monoclinic M—Fibrous, fine; felted	Silky Greasy Opaque	Yellowish Brownish
variety *Amphibole* Silicate of Ca, Mg, Fe, Al, etc. **391**	Monoclinic M—Fibrous, coarse or fine; felted; compact, leather- or cork-like	Silky Dull Opaque	Yellowish Brownish
SODA NITER (Chile saltpeter) $NaNO_3$ **325**	Hexagonal C—Rare M—Granular, crusts, efflorescences	Vitreous Transparent	Yellowish Lemon yellow Reddish brown
SULFUR S **264**	Orthorhombic C—Pyramidal, tabular M—Compact, granular, fibrous, earthy, crusts	Adamantine Greasy Translucent	Straw yellow Brownish yellow Reddish yellow
GYPSUM, varieties *Selenite* $CaSO_4.2H_2O$ *Satin spar* *Ordinary* **345**	Monoclinic C—Tabular, prismatic; swallowtail twins M—Cleavable, coarse- and fine-grained, fibrous, foliated, earthy	Pearly Vitreous Silky Dull Transparent to opaque	Yellow Honey yellow Brown

Hardness 1 to 3

Hardness	Streak	Cleavage = C Fracture = F Tenacity	Specific Gravity	Characteristics and Associates
1. **2.5**	White Yellowish white	F—Uneven, splintery Sectile	2.6 2.8	Greasy or soapy feel important. *Soapstone* or *steatite*, coarse to fine, granular, more or less impure. Hardness varies. With serpentine, chlorite, dolomite, magnesite, actinolite
1. **3.**	White	F—Fibrous Flexible	2.2	Delicate, fine, parallel, flexible fibers, perpendicular to walls, easily separable —*short-fibered asbestos;* compare below. In veins or seams in serpentine
1. **3.**	White	F—Fibrous Flexible, tough	3.	*Long-fibered asbestos*, parallel, flexible fibers, parallel to walls. Compare above. *Mountain leather*, *mountain cork*, *mountain wood*, compact but light and tough
1.5 **2.**	White	C—Rhombohedral F—Conchoidal Brittle	2. 2.3	Cooling and saline taste. Absorbs moisture readily. In deposits with gypsum, sand, clay, guano
1.5 **2.5**	White Yellowish white	C—Indistinct F—Conchoidal Brittle	1.9 2.1	Independent beds in gypsum, limestone; in lava, result of volcanic exhalations. With celestite, anhydrite, aragonite, clay, metallic sulfides
2.	White	C—Clinopinacoidal, conspicuous; pyramidal, orthopinacoidal F—Conchoidal, fibrous Brittle, laminae flexible	2.2 2.4	*Selenite*, crystals and cleavable plates, usually transparent; *satin spar*, fibrous with silky luster; *ordinary*, granular. In limestones and shales. With halite, celestite, sulfur, aragonite, anhydrite; ore deposits

Streak—Uncolored, white, or light gray

	Name, Composition, and Reference	Crystallization Structure Crystals = C Massive = M	Luster Transparency	Color
	HALITE (Rock salt) NaCl **319**	Cubic **C**—Cubes, often skeletal or hopper-shaped **M**—Compact, cleavable, granular, fibrous, stalactitic, crusts	Vitreous Transparent to translucent	Yellow Yellowish brown Brownish
MICAS	**MUSCOVITE** (Isinglass) $KAl_2(OH,F)_2AlSi_3O_{10}$ **397**	Monoclinic **C**—Tabular, pyramidal, with rhombic or hexagonal outline; often large and rough **M**—Scales, plates; foliated and plumose aggregates	Vitreous Pearly Transparent to translucent	Light yellow Yellowish brown Light brown
MICAS	**PHLOGOPITE** $KMg_3(F,OH)_2AlSi_3O_{10}$ **399**	Monoclinic **C**—Prismatic, tabular, with hexagonal or rhombic outline; often large and coarse **M**—Plates, disseminated scales	Pearly Submetallic Transparent to translucent	Yellow Yellowish brown Brown
	APATITE, variety *Phosphate rock* Mainly calcium carbonate -phosphate (collophane) **352**	Hexagonal **M**—Compact, nodular, reniform, earthy, oölitic	Dull Opaque	Brown

Hardness 1 to 3

Hard-ness	Streak	Cleavage = C Fracture = F Tenacity	Specific Gravity	Characteristics and Associates
2. **2.5**	White	C—Cubic, perfect, conspicuous F—Conchoidal Brittle	2.1 2.3	Pigment usually iron oxide. May absorb moisture and become damp. Characteristic cubical cleavage and saline taste. With shale, gypsum, anhydrite
2. **3.**	White	C—Basal, perfect, conspicuous Tough laminae very elastic	2.8 3.1	Lighter colored than phlogopite. Structure, perfect cleavage, and elasticity important. Crystals may show distinct partings perpendicular to cleavage—*ruled mica.* In granitic rocks, schists, crystalline limestones. With feldspar, quartz, tourmaline, beryl, garnet
2. **3.**	White	C—Basal, perfect, conspicuous Tough, laminae very elastic	2.8 3.1	Usually amber brown or bronze in color. When cleavage laminae are held close to the eye in viewing a source of light a star-like form is sometimes observed. Especially characteristic of crystalline limestones, dolomites, schists. With pyroxenes, amphiboles, serpentine
2. **3.**	White	F—Conchoidal, uneven Brittle	3.1 3.2	More or less impure masses, frequently resembling compact limestone. Independent beds, nodules, concretions

Streak—Uncolored, white, or light gray

Name, Composition, and Reference	Crystallization Structure Crystals = C Massive = M	Luster Transparency	Color
CALCITE, varieties $CaCO_3$ *Dog-tooth spar* *Nail-head spar* *Limestone* *Marble* *Calcareous tufa* *Travertine* *Stalactites, etc.* **326**	Hexagonal **C**—Scalenohedral, rhombohedral; prismatic; tabular, acicular; may be highly modified and twinned **M**—Cleavable, granular, fibrous, banded, stalactitic, oölitic, porous, compact, crusts, shells	Vitreous Dull Transparent to nearly opaque	Honey yellow Yellowish brown Dark brown
Wulfenite $PbMoO_4$ **349**	Tetragonal **C**—Square, thin tabular; more rarely pyramidal **M**—Coarse, fine-grained	Greasy Adamantine Transparent to translucent	Wax yellow Orange-yellow Brown
Vanadinite $Pb_5Cl(VO_4)_3$ **353**	Hexagonal **C**—Prismatic, small, at times skeletal **M**—Compact, globular, fibrous, crusts	Greasy Translucent to opaque	Straw yellow Brownish yellow Reddish brown

Streak—Uncolored, white, or light gray

Name, Composition, and Reference	Crystallization Structure Crystals = C Massive = M	Luster Transparency	Color
BARITE (Heavy spar) $BaSO_4$ **340**	Orthorhombic **C**—Tabular, prismatic, very common; crested and divergent groups **M**—Compact, lamellar, fibrous, cleavable, reniform	Vitreous Pearly Transparent to opaque	Yellowish Brownish Dark brown

Hardness 1 to 3

Hardness	Streak	Cleavage = C Fracture = F Tenacity	Specific Gravity	Characteristics and Associates
3.	White	C—Rhombohedral, usually conspicuous F—Conchoidal Brittle	2.7	Often in extensive deposits. Rhombohedral cleavage characteristic especially on crystals. Cleavage surfaces often striated. Very strong double refraction easily observed when transparent. To distinguish varieties, see reference
3.	White Yellowish white	C—Pyramidal, indistinct F—Conchoidal, uneven Brittle	6.3 7.	Square plates sometimes with forms of the third order. With lead minerals—galena, pyromorphite, vanadinite
3.	White Yellowish white	C—None F—Conchoidal, uneven Brittle	6.7 7.2	Crystal faces smooth with sharp edges. With lead minerals, but never in large quantities

Hardness 3 to 6

Hardness	Streak	Cleavage = C Fracture = F Tenacity	Specific Gravity	Characteristics and Associates
3. 3.5	White	C—Basal, prismatic, usually conspicuous F—Uneven Brittle	4.3 4.7	Characterized by rather high specific gravity and cleavages. In metalliferous veins; pockets, lenticular masses in limestone. With galena, sphalerite, fluorite, chalcopyrite; manganese and iron minerals

Streak—Uncolored, white or light gray			
Name, Composition, and Reference	Crystallization Structure Crystals = C Massive = M	Luster Transparency	Color
CERUSSITE $PbCO_3$ **335**	Orthorhombic **C**—Tabular, prismatic, pyramidal; pseudo-hexagonal; clusters and star-shaped groups **M**—Interlaced bundles, granular, stalactitic, compact	Adamantine Greasy Silky Transparent to trans-lucent	Yellow Yellowish brown
STILBITE (Zeolite) $(Ca,Na_2)Al_2Si_7O_{18}.7H_2O$ **420**	Monoclinic **C**—Twinned, sheaf-like, radial, or globular aggregates	Vitreous Pearly Transparent to trans-lucent	Yellowish Yellowish brown Brownish
SERPENTINE *Antigorite* *Chrysotile* $Mg_6(OH)_8Si_4O_{10}$ **403**	Monoclinic **C**—Unknown **M**—Compact, columnar, fibrous, lamellar, granular	Greasy Waxy Translucent to opaque	Greenish brown Greenish yellow Yellowish brown
APATITE, variety *Phosphate rock* Mainly calcium carbonate -phosphate (collophane) **352**	Hexagonal **M**—Compact, nodular, reniform, oölitic	Dull Opaque	Brown
Wavellite $Al_3(OH)_3(PO_4)_2.5H_2O$ **355**	Orthorhombic **C**—Capillary, small **M**—Crusts, globular, hemispherical aggre-gates, with radial fi-brous structure	Vitreous Translucent	Yellow Brown
DOLOMITE $CaMg(CO_3)_2$ **329**	Hexagonal **C**—Rhombohedral, with curved surfaces **M**—Coarsely crystalline, compact, granular, friable	Vitreous Transparent to trans-lucent	Yellowish brown Grayish brown Dark brown

Hardness 3 to 6

Hardness	Streak	Cleavage = C Fracture = F Tenacity	Specific Gravity	Characteristics and Associates
3. **3.5**	White Gray	C—Indistinct F—Conchoidal Brittle	6.4 6.6	Twinning, structure, luster, and specific gravity characteristic. With lead minerals—galena, pyromorphite, anglesite; also malachite, limonite
3. **4.**	White	C—Indistinct F—Uneven Brittle	2.1 2.2	Radial and sheaf-like structure important. In basic igneous rocks and ore deposits. With chabazite, apophyllite, datolite, calcite
3. **4.**	White	F—Conchoidal, splintery Brittle	2.5 2.8	Smooth and greasy feel. Often spotted, clouded, multicolored. Sometimes crossed by seams of asbestos (*chrysotile*). With magnesite, chromite, garnierite, pyrope, platinum, calcite
3. **5.**	White	F—Conchoidal, uneven Brittle	3.1 3.2	More or less impure masses, frequently resembling compact, brown limestone. Independent beds, nodules, concretions
3.5 **4.**	White	C—Pinacoidal, domatic F—Uneven, fibrous Brittle	2.3 2.5	Secondary mineral occurring on surfaces of rocks or minerals, as crystalline crusts with pronounced radial fibrous structure
3.5 **4.**	White Gray	C—Rhombohedral, perfect F—Conchoidal Brittle	2.9	Crystals generally curved or saddle-shaped. *Marble* includes some compact varieties. Independent beds; in fissures and cavities; with ore deposits

Streak—Uncolored, white, or light gray			
Name, Composition, and Reference	Crystallization Structure Crystals = C Massive = M	Luster Transparency	Color
ARAGONITE $CaCO_3$ **333**	Orthorhombic **C**—Chisel- or spear-shaped; pseudohexagonal prisms; radial, columnar, acicular aggregates **M**—Stalactitic, reniform, crusts, oölitic	Vitreous Resinous Transparent to translucent	Wine yellow Yellowish brown
STRONTIANITE $SrCO_3$ **334**	Orthorhombic **C**—Spear-shaped, columnar, acicular; often in divergent groups **M**—Columnar, granular, compact, botryoidal, fibrous	Vitreous Greasy Transparent to translucent	Yellow Yellowish brown Brown
SIDERITE $FeCO_3$ **332**	Hexagonal **C**—Rhombohedral, curved or saddle-shaped, common **M**—Cleavable, granular, compact, botryoidal, rarely fibrous	Vitreous Pearly Dull Translucent to nearly opaque	Light brown Reddish brown Dark brown
SPHALERITE ZnS **278**	Cubic **C**—Tetrahedral, common **M**—Cleavable, fine- and coarse-grained, compact	Resinous Submetallic Translucent to opaque	Honey yellow Yellowish brown Reddish brown
Pyromorphite $Pb_5Cl(PO_4)_3$ **353**	Hexagonal **C**—Prismatic, thick tabular, rounded and barrel-shaped; acicular **M**—Globular, reniform, disseminated, crusts	Greasy Adamantine Translucent to opaque	Wax yellow Greenish yellow Yellowish brown

Hardness 3 to 6

Hard-ness	Streak	Cleavage = C Fracture = F Tenacity	Specific Gravity	Characteristics and Associates
3.5 **4.**	White Gray	C—Pinacoidal, prismatic F—Conchoidal Brittle	2.9 3	Twins common, often pseudohexagonal—prism and striated base. In cracks and cavities; with ore deposits; deposition from hot springs; in shells. With gypsum, celestite, sulfur, siderite, zeolites
3.5 **4.**	White Gray	C—Prismatic, indistinct F—Uneven Brittle	3.6 3.8	Structure similar to aragonite. Divergent columnar masses and higher specific gravity characteristic. In ore deposits; independent beds. With galena, barite, calcite
3.5 **4.**	Gray White	C—Rhombohedral, conspicuous F—Conchoidal Brittle	3.7 3.9	Distinguished from sphalerite by curved crystals and rhombohedral cleavage. In ore deposits; beds and concretions in limestones and shales. With pyrite, chalcopyrite, galena, tetrahedrite, cryolite
3.5 **4.**	White Yellowish white	C—Dodecahedral, usually conspicuous F—Conchoidal Brittle	3.9 4.2	Resinous luster and cleavage important. Color and streak vary with impurities. Extensively in limestones. With galena, chalcopyrite, pyrite, barite, fluorite, rhodochrosite
3.5 **4.**	White Yellowish white	C—None F—Conchoidal, uneven Brittle	6.5 7.1	Common alteration product of lead minerals. With galena, cerussite, barite, limonite

Streak—Uncolored, white, or light gray

Name, Composition, and Reference	Crystallization Structure Crystals = C Massive = M	Luster Transparency	Color
FLUORITE (Fluor spar) CaF_2 **322**	Cubic **C**—Cubes, alone or modified, well developed **M**—Cleavable, granular, fibrous	Vitreous Transparent to nearly opaque	Wine yellow Yellowish brown Brown
SCHEELITE $CaWO_4$ **349**	Tetragonal **C**—Pyramidal, small, more rarely tabular **M**—Drusy crusts, reniform, granular, compact	Greasy Adamantine Transparent to translucent	Pale yellow Yellowish brown Grayish brown
HEMIMORPHITE (Calamine) $Zn_4(OH)_2Si_2O_7.H_2O$ **375**	Orthorhombic **C**—Thin tabular, pyramidal, hemimorphic, highly modified **M**—Compact, globular, granular, stalactitic, cellular, earthy	Vitreous Dull Transparent to translucent	Yellow Yellowish brown Brown
APATITE $Ca_5F(PO_4)_3$ **351**	Hexagonal **C**—Prismatic, thick tabular, sometimes large, with rounded edges **M**—Granular, compact, fibrous, nodular, reniform	Greasy Vitreous Translucent to opaque	Brown Greenish brown Reddish brown Yellow
Huebnerite $MnWO_4$ **348**	Monoclinic **C**—Long fibrous, bladed, stalky; often divergent, without good terminations **M**—Compact, lamellar, granular	Resinous Submetallic Translucent to opaque	Reddish brown Hair brown Pale yellow

Hardness 3 to 6

Hardness	Streak	Cleavage = C Fracture = F Tenacity	Specific Gravity	Characteristics and Associates
4.	White	C—Octahedral, perfect, conspicuous Brittle	3. 3.2	Recognized by crystal form, octahedral cleavage, and hardness. Common gangue of metallic ores, especially galena, sphalerite, cassiterite; also with calcite, barite
4.5	White	C—Pyramidal, not conspicuous F—Conchoidal, uneven Brittle	5.9 6.1	Small octahedral-like crystals, usually on quartz; high specific gravity important. Fluoresces in ultraviolet light. With cassiterite, wolframite, fluorite, apatite, molybdenite
4.5 5.	White	C—Prismatic F—Uneven, conchoidal Brittle	3.4 3.5	Crystals often in sheaf-like groups or druses in cavities. When massive, often porous or cellular. In limestones. With sphalerite, galena, and especially smithsonite
5.	White	C—Basal, imperfect F—Conchoidal, uneven Brittle	3.1 3.2	Crystals may be vertically striated and have fused appearance. Color unevenly distributed, often with greenish spots. In crystalline limestones; metalliferous deposits; igneous rocks. With quartz, cassiterite, fluorite, wolframite
5. 5.5	Greenish gray	C—Clinopinacoidal, conspicuous Brittle	6.7 7.3	Structure, cleavage, and specific gravity characteristic. In quartz veins. With wolframite, fluorite, pyrite, scheelite, galena, tetrahedrite

Streak—Uncolored, white, or light gray			
Name, Composition, and Reference	Crystallization Structure Crystals = C Massive = M	Luster Transparency	Color
SMITHSONITE $ZnCO_3$ **331**	Hexagonal **C**—Small, usually as druses or crusts **M**—Botryoidal, stalactitic, fibrous, compact, cellular, granular	Vitreous Dull Translucent to nearly opaque	Brown Yellowish brown Orange-yellow
Natrolite (Zeolite) $Na_2Al_2Si_3O_{10}.2H_2O$ **418**	Orthorhombic **C**—Slender prismatic, nearly square, radial or interlacing groups **M**—Fibrous, granular, compact	Vitreous Silky Transparent to translucent	Yellowish
SPHENE (Titanite) $CaTiOSiO_4$ **374**	Monoclinic **C**—Wedge- or envelope-shaped when disseminated; tabular or prismatic when attached **M**—Compact, lamellar	Vitreous Greasy Transparent to opaque	Brown Reddish brown Yellow
Monazite $(Ca,La)PO_4$ **350**	Monoclinic **C**—Thick tabular, square prismatic **M**—Angular fragments, rolled grains	Greasy Vitreous Transparent to opaque	Reddish brown Yellowish brown Honey yellow
Cancrinite $Na_3CaCO_3(AlSiO_4)_3.nH_2O$ **415**	Hexagonal **C**—Prismatic, rare **M**—Compact, lamellar, columnar, disseminated	Greasy Vitreous Pearly Translucent to transparent	Yellow Brownish yellow
ENSTATITE (Bronzite, Pyroxene) $(Mg,Fe)_2Si_2O_6$ **384**	Orthorhombic **C**—Prismatic, rare **M**—Fibrous, lamellar, compact	Bronzy Silky Translucent to opaque	Bronze brown Yellowish brown

Hardness 3 to 6				
Hard-ness	Streak	Cleavage = C Fracture = F Tenacity	Specific Gravity	Characteristics and Associates
5.	White Gray	**C**—Rhombohedral, not often observed **F**—Uneven, splintery Brittle	4.1 4.5	Cellular varieties called *dry bone.* Often mixed with sand, clay, limonite, calcite. With zinc minerals, especially sphalerite, hemimorphite. Frequently pseudomorphous after calcite
5. **5.5**	White	**C**—Prismatic, perfect **F**—Uneven Brittle	2.2 2.3	Crystals have nearly square cross section. In basalts and phonolites. With chabazite, analcite, apophyllite, stilbite, datolite
5. **5.5**	White Gray	**C**—Prismatic, conspicuous, parting often noted **F**—Conchoidal Brittle	3.4 3.6	With feldspars, pyroxenes, amphiboles, chlorite, scapolite, zircon
5. **5.5**	White	**C**—Basal **F**—Conchoidal, uneven Brittle	4.9 5.3	Crystals commonly small, highly modified; rounded grains in sand. With quartz, magnetite, zircon, garnet, gold, chromite, diamond
5. **6.**	White	**C**—Prismatic **F**—Uneven Brittle	2.4 2.5	Easily recognized by associates—nepheline, sodalite, biotite, feldspar, sphene
5. **6.**	White Grayish	**C**—Prismatic, pinacoidal, conspicuous **F**—Uneven Brittle	3.2 3.5	Cleavage surfaces usually fibrous or lamellar, irregular or wavy, with distinct bronzy luster. In basic igneous rocks

Streak—Uncolored, white, or light gray			
Name, Composition, and Reference	Crystallization Structure Crystals = C Massive = M	Luster Transparency	Color
RHODONITE $MnSiO_3$ **388**	Triclinic **C**—Tabular, prismatic rounded edges **M**—Cleavable, granular, disseminated grains	Vitreous Dull Translucent to opaque	Yellowish Brownish
Willemite Zn_2SiO_4 **362**	Hexagonal **C**—Prismatic **M**—Compact, granular, disseminated grains	Greasy Vitreous Transparent to opaque	Yellow Greenish yellow Brown
OPAL, varieties *Precious opal* *Wood opal* *Opal jasper* *Siliceous sinter* *Tripolite* $SiO_2.nH_2O$ **314**	Amorphous **M**—Compact, reniform, botryoidal, porous, earthy	Vitreous Greasy Dull Translucent to opaque	Yellow Yellowish brown Brown
FELDSPARS: **ORTHOCLASE** $KAlSi_3O_8$ **406**	Monoclinic **C**—Prismatic, thick tabular; twins; often large **M**—Cleavable, granular, disseminated	Vitreous Pearly Translucent to opaque	Pale yellow Brownish yellow
FELDSPARS: **MICROCLINE** $KAlSi_3O_8$ **408**	Triclinic **C**—Prismatic, thick tabular; twins **M**—Cleavable, granular, compact, disseminated	Vitreous Pearly Translucent to transparent	Cream yellowish Yellowish Yellowish brown
Amblygonite $LiAl(F,OH)PO_4$ **351**	Triclinic **C**—Large, poorly developed **M**—Cleavable, columnar, compact	Pearly Vitreous Translucent	Yellowish Brownish

Streak—Uncolored, white, or light gray			
Chondrodite $Mg(F,OH)_2.2Mg_2SiO_4$ **373**	Monoclinic **C**—Small, highly modified, rare **M**—Disseminated grains; compact	Vitreous Greasy Translucent to opaque	Reddish brown Yellowish brown Honey yellow

Hardness 3 to 6

Hardness	Streak	Cleavage = C Fracture = F Tenacity	Specific Gravity	Characteristics and Associates
5. 6.	White	C—Prismatic, basal F—Conchoidal, uneven Tough, crystals brittle	3.4 3.7	On exposure may be stained brown or black. *Fowlerite*, contains zinc. With franklinite, zincite, willemite, calcite, iron ores
5. 6.	White	C—Basal, prismatic F—Uneven Brittle	3.9 4.3	Crystals of willemite small, of *troostite*, manganiferous variety, often large. Characterized by associates—franklinite, zincite, rhodonite, calcite
5.5 6.	White	F—Conchoidal, conspicuous when compact; earthy Brittle	1.9 2.3	*Precious opal*, play of colors; *wood opal*, woody structure; *opal jasper*, greasy, resembling jasper; *siliceous sinter*, porous; *tripolite*, earthy, gritty
6.	White	C—Basal, clinopinacoidal, conspicuous—90° F—Conchoidal, uneven Brittle	2.5 2.6	Characterized by rectangular cleavages and absence of twinning striations. In granitic rocks. With quartz, other feldspars, mica, hornblende
6.	White	C—Basal, brachypinacoidal, conspicuous—90°30′ F—Uneven Brittle	2.5 2.6	Slightly inclined cleavages; may show gridiron structure on basal pinacoid. With quartz, other feldspars, mica, hornblende, topaz; in pegmatites
6.	White	C—Basal, perfect, conspicuous; macropinacoidal, domatic F—Conchoidal, uneven Brittle	3. 3.1	Usually in cleavable masses with perfect cleavage in one direction. With lepidolite, spodumene, tourmaline, quartz, apatite

Hardness over 6

Hardness	Streak	Cleavage = C Fracture = F Tenacity	Specific Gravity	Characteristics and Associates
6. 6.5	White	C—Basal, indistinct F—Conchoidal, uneven Brittle	3.1 3.3	Associates important. In crystalline limestones and dolomites. With spinel, vesuvianite, pyroxenes, mica

Streak—Uncolored, white, or light gray

Name, Composition, and Reference	Crystallization Structure Crystals = C Massive = M	Luster Transparency	Color
Sillimanite (Fibrolite) Al_2OSiO_4 **370**	Orthorhombic **C**—Long, thin, needle-like **M**—Fibrous, columnar, radiating	Vitreous Silky Transparent to translucent	Hair brown Grayish brown
EPIDOTE $Ca_2(Al,Fe)_3O(OH)SiO_4$-Si_2O_7 **376**	Monoclinic **C**—Prismatic, elongated and deeply striated parallel to *b* axis; usually terminated on one end only **M**—Columnar; fibrous, parallel and divergent; granular	Vitreous Transparent to opaque	Greenish brown Greenish yellow Yellow
RUTILE TiO_2 **309**	Tetragonal **C**—Prismatic, vertically striated; twinned, yielding knee-shaped or rosette forms **M**—Compact, disseminated	Adamantine Submetallic Translucent to opaque	Reddish brown Yellowish brown Dark brown
CASSITERITE SnO_2 **310**	Tetragonal **C**—Thick prismatic; knee-shaped twins quite common **M**—Reniform, botryoidal, compact, rounded pebbles, often with internal radial, fibrous structure, *wood tin*	Adamantine Greasy Dull Translucent to opaque	Reddish brown Yellowish brown Dark brown
VESUVIANITE $Ca_{10}Al_4(Mg,Fe)_2(OH)_4$-$(SiO_4)_5(Si_2O_7)_2$ **378**	Tetragonal **C**—Short prismatic **M**—Compact, granular; aggregates with parallel or divergent striations or furrows	Vitreous Greasy Translucent to opaque	Brown Greenish brown Sulfur yellow

Hardness over 6

Hard-ness	Streak	Cleavage = C Fracture = F Tenacity	Specific Gravity	Characteristics and Associates
6. **7.**	White	**C**—Macropina-coidal **F**—Uneven Brittle	3.2 3.3	Crystals often slender, bent, striated, with rounded edges, without good terminations, and interlaced. In metamorphic rocks—mica, schist, gneiss. With andalusite, garnet
6. **7.**	White Grayish	**C**—Basal **F**—Uneven Brittle	3.3 3.5	Crystals often darker than when massive. With quartz, feldspar, vesuvianite, hornblende, pyroxenes, magnetite, native copper
6. **7.**	Gray Yellowish white Brownish white	**C**—Prismatic, pyramidal, not conspicuous **F**—Uneven Brittle	4.2 4.3	Not as heavy as cassiterite. Often in fine hair-like inclusions. With quartz, feldspar, hematite, ilmenite, chlorite
6. **7.**	White Yellowish white Brownish white	**C**—Indistinct **F**—Uneven Brittle	6.8 7.	Distinguished by high specific gravity. In veins cutting granite, gneiss; in alluvial deposits as *stream tin.* With quartz, wolframite, scheelite, molybdenite, tourmaline, fluorite, mica, chlorite
6.5	White	**C**—Indistinct **F**—Uneven Brittle	3.3 3.5	In crystalline limestone, gneiss, schist. With garnet, tourmaline chondrodite, wollastonite, epidote, pyroxenes

Streak—Uncolored, white, or light gray

Name, Composition, and Reference	Crystallization Structure Crystals = C Massive = M	Luster Transparency	Color
GARNET, varieties *Grossularite* *Spessartite* *Almandite* *Andradite* $M''_3M'''_2$-$(SiO_4)_3$ M'' = Ca, Fe, Mg, Mn M''' = Al, Fe **365**	Cubic **C**—Dodecahedrons, tetragonal trisoctahedrons, alone or in combination **M**—Granular, compact, lamellar, disseminated grains, sand	Vitreous Transparent to opaque	Yellow Cinnamon brown Reddish brown
QUARTZ, Crystalline varieties *Smoky quartz* *Citrine* *Aventurine* *Ferruginous* *Cat's-eye* SiO_2 **295**	Hexagonal **C**—Prismatic, horizontally striated **M**—Compact, granular	Vitreous Greasy Transparent to opaque	Yellow Yellowish brown Smoky brown Reddish brown
Cryptocrystalline varieties *Chalcedony* *Agate* *Jasper* *Flint* **296**	Hexagonal **C**—Never in crystals **M**—Nodular, botryoidal, banded, concretionary, stalactitic, compact	Waxy Vitreous Translucent to opaque	Yellow Brown Blackish brown
Clastic varieties *Sand* *Sandstone* *Quartzite* **297**	Hexagonal **M**—Grains, fragments, either loose or strongly consolidated	Vitreous Dull Translucent to opaque	Yellow Yellowish brown Brown
TOURMALINE $M_7Al_6(OH,F)_4(BO_3)_3$-Si_6O_{18} **381**	Hexagonal **C**—Prismatic, vertically striated; terminated with broken or rhombohedral-like surfaces **M**—Compact, granular	Vitreous Translucent to opaque	Brown Yellowish brown Yellow

Hardness over 6

Hardness	Streak	Cleavage = C Fracture = F Tenacity	Specific Gravity	Characteristics and Associates
6.5 **7.5**	White	**C**—Dodecahedral, usually indistinct **F**—Conchoidal, uneven Brittle	3.5 4.3	*Grossularite*, in crystalline limestone, dolomite, with wollastonite, vesuvianite, diopside, scapolite; *spessartite*, in granitic rocks, with quartz, tourmaline, orthoclase; *almandite*, with mica, staurolite, andalusite, kyanite; *andradite*, with epidote, feldspar, nepheline, leucite
7.	White Yellowish white Brownish white	**C**—Indistinct **F**—Conchoidal, conspicuous Brittle	2.6	Characteristic conchoidal fracture and glassy luster. *Smoky quartz*, smoky yellow to brownish black; *citrine*, yellow; *aventurine*, glistening with included scales; *ferruginous*, colored by iron oxide, *cat's-eye*, opalescent, due to inclusions of fibers of asbestos
7.	White Yellowish white Brownish white	**C**—Indistinct **F**—Conchoidal, conspicuous Brittle to tough	2.6	Not as glassy as crystalline varieties. *Chalcedony*, pale to dark brown, waxy luster; *agate*, banded or clouded; *jasper*, commonly yellow and uniform in color; *flint*, smoky or blackish brown, nodular, often with white coating
7.	White Yellowish white Brownish white	**C**—Indistinct **F**—Uneven Brittle to tough	2.6	Pigment is usually ferruginous matter. *Sand*, loose, unconsolidated grains; *sandstone*, consolidated sand; *quartzite*, metamorphosed sandstone
7. **7.5**	White	**C**—None **F**—Conchoidal, uneven Brittle	2.9 3.2	Spherical triangular cross-section. Commonly as contact mineral in granular limestone and dolomite. With tremolite, scapolite, vesuvianite, apatite, garnet, spinel

Streak—Uncolored, white, or light gray			
Name, Composition, and Reference	Crystallization Structure Crystals = C Massive = M	Luster Transparency	Color
STAUROLITE $Fe(OH)_2.2Al_2OSiO_4$ **371**	Orthorhombic **C**—Prismatic; twins plus-(+) or *X*-shaped; well developed	Vitreous Dull Translucent to opaque	Reddish brown Yellowish brown Blackish brown
ZIRCON $ZrSiO_4$ **366**	Tetragonal **C**—Square prisms and bipyramids, small, well developed **M**—Irregular lumps, grains	Adamantine Vitreous Greasy Transparent to opaque	Reddish brown Dark brown Brownish yellow
BERYL $Be_3Al_2Si_6O_{18}$ **379**	Hexagonal **C**—Long prismatic, often vertically striated, large **M**—Columnar, granular, compact	Vitreous Transparent to translucent	Pale yellow Honey yellow Brownish yellow
SPINEL, varieties *Pleonaste* *Gahnite* $M''M'''_2O_4$ $M'' = Mg, Fe, Zn$ $M''' = Al, Fe$ **304**	Cubic **C**—Octahedral, well developed **M**—Compact, granular, disseminated grains	Vitreous Dull Nearly opaque	Yellow Grayish brown Brown
TOPAZ $Al_2(F,OH)_2SiO_4$ **372**	Orthorhombic **C**—Prismatic, vertically striated, highly modified **M**—Compact, granular, rolled fragments	Vitreous Transparent to opaque	Straw yellow Wine yellow Yellowish brown

Hardness over 6

Hardness	Streak	Cleavage = C Fracture = F Tenacity	Specific Gravity	Characteristics and Associates
7. **7.5**	White Grayish	**C**—Brachypinacoidal **F**—Conchoidal, uneven Brittle	3.4 3.8	Fresh crystals usually possess bright, smooth faces; when altered, dull, rough, softer and with colored streak. In metamorphic rocks—gneiss, mica schist, slate. With kyanite, garnet, tourmaline, sillimanite
7.5	White	**C**—Indistinct **F**—Uneven Brittle	4.6 4.7	In the more acid igneous rocks—granite, syenite; alluvial deposits, with gold, spinel, corundum, garnet. *Hyacinth*, clear and transparent
7.5 **8.**	White	**C**—Basal, indistinct **F**—Conchoidal, uneven Brittle	2.6 2.8	Crystals usually simple, prism and base. In granitic rocks, mica schists, clay slates. With quartz, feldspar, mica, chrysoberyl, topaz, cassiterite, garnet
7.5 **8.**	White Grayish	**C**—Indistinct **F**—Conchoidal Brittle	3.6 4.4	Commonly as contact mineral in granular limestone; in more basic igneous rocks; as rounded grains in placers. With calcite, chondrodite, serpentine, brucite, graphite, pyroxenes
8.	White	**C**—Basal, perfect conspicuous **F**—Conchoidal, uneven Brittle	3.4 3.6	Crystals usually developed on one end only. Color may fade on exposure. Massive varieties distinguished from quartz by higher specific gravity and basal cleavage. In veins and cavities in granitic rocks, also in placers. With cassiterite, tourmaline, fluorite, apatite, beryl, wolframite

Streak—Uncolored, white, or light gray			
Name, Composition, and Reference	Crystallization Structure Crystals = C Massive = M	Luster Transparency	Color
Chrysoberyl $BeAl_2O_4$ **308**	Orthorhombic C—Tabular; heart-shaped, pseudohexagonal twins M—Fragments, loose, rounded grains	Vitreous Greasy Transparent to translucent	Yellow Greenish yellow Brown
CORUNDUM, varieties *Oriental topaz* *Common* Al_2O_3 **299**	Hexagonal C—Prismatic, tabular, pyramidal, rhombohedral; rough or rounded barrel-shaped M—Compact, granular, lamellar	Vitreous Translucent to transparent	Yellow Brown

B. MINERALS WITH NONMETALLIC LUSTER

Streak—Uncolored, white, or light gray			
Cerargyrite (Horn silver) AgCl **322**	Cubic C—Rare M—Wax-like crusts, coatings; stalactitic, dendritic	Waxy Greasy Transparent to translucent	Pearl gray Grayish
Asbestos, variety *Chrysotile* $Mg_6(OH)_8Si_4O_{10}$ **403**	Monoclinic M—Fine fibrous, felted	Silky Silky metallic Opaque	White Greenish white Yellowish white
variety *Amphibole* Silicate of Ca, Mg, Fe, Al, etc. **391**	Monoclinic M—Coarse or fine fibrous, felted; compact, leather- or cork-like	Silky Dull Opaque	White Greenish white Yellowish white

Hardness over 6

Hardness	Streak	Cleavage = C Fracture = F Tenacity	Specific Gravity	Characteristics and Associates
8.5	White	**C**—Brachypinacoidal **F**—Uneven, conchoidal Brittle	3.5 3.8	Crystals disseminated as plates, often with featherlike or radial striations. In granite, gneiss, placers. With beryl, garnet, tourmaline, sillimanite
9.	White	**C**—None; basal and nearly rectangular rhombohedral partings, conspicuous; striated **F**—Conchoidal Brittle to tough	3.9 4.1	When massive often multicolored—red, blue, green, gray. *Oriental topaz*, transparent, yellow. In limestone, granite, syenite, alluvial deposits. With magnetite, nepheline, mica, spinel, chlorite

5. COLORLESS, WHITE, OR LIGHT GRAY IN COLOR

Hardness 1 to 3

Hardness	Streak	Cleavage = C Fracture = F Tenacity	Specific Gravity	Characteristics and Associates
1. **1.5**	White, shiny Gray, shiny	**C**—None **F**—Conchoidal Highly sectile	5.5 5.6	Cuts like wax; on exposure turns violet, brown, or black. With silver minerals; also limonite, calcite, barite
1. **2.5**	White	**F**—Fibrous Flexible	2.2	*Short-fibered asbestos*, delicate, fine, parallel, flexible fibers, easily separable, perpendicular to walls. Compare below. In veins or seams in serpentine
1. **2.5**	White	**F**—Fibrous Flexible, tough	3.	*Long-fibered asbestos*, parallel, flexible fibers, parallel to walls. *Mountain leather*, *mountain cork*, *mountain wood*, compact, but light and tough

Streak—Uncolored, white, or light gray			
Name, Composition, and Reference	Crystallization Structure Crystals = C Massive = M	Luster Transparency	Color
TRIPOLITE (Opal) $SiO_2.nH_2O$ **314**	Amorphous **M**—Porous, earthy, chalk-like	Dull Opaque	Gray White Yellowish white
KAOLINITE (Kaolin, china clay) $Al_4(OH)_8Si_4O_{10}$ **401**	Monoclinic **C**—Scaly, rare **M**—Compact, friable, mealy, clay-like	Dull Pearly Opaque to translucent	White Gray Colorless
CALCITE, varieties *Chalk* $CaCO_3$ *Marl* **328**	Hexagonal **M**—Loose or compact, earthy	Earthy Dull Opaque	White Grayish Yellowish white
TALC, varieties *Foliated* *Soapstone or steatite* *French chalk* $Mg_3(OH)_2Si_4O_{10}$ **395**	Monoclinic **C**—Thin tabular, indistinct **M**—Foliated, globular, fibrous, granular, compact	Pearly Greasy Transparent to opaque	White Greenish white Gray
BAUXITE A mixture of aluminum oxide minerals **317**	Never in crystals **M**—Pisolitic, oölitic, rounded disseminated grains; clay-like, earthy	Dull Earthy Opaque	White Grayish

Hardness 1 to 3

Hard-ness	Streak	Cleavage = C Fracture = F Tenacity	Specific Gravity	Characteristics and Associates
1. **2.5**	White	**F**—Earthy Friable	1.9 2.3	Apparently very soft. Resembles chalk and kaolinite, but is gritty, and not plastic when moistened. Due to impurities may have clay odor
1. **2.5**	White	**C**—Basal, scales **F**—Earthy Brittle	2.2 2.6	Not gritty like tripolite. Very strong clay odor when breathed upon. Usually adheres to tongue and becomes plastic when moistened. Greasy feel. With quartz, feldspar, corundum
1. **2.5**	White	**C**—None **F**—Earthy Brittle	2.7	*Chalk*, earthy masses; *marl*, more clay-like and frequently contains organic material—leaves, twigs. In extensive deposits
1. **2.5**	White	**C**—Basal, conspicuous, when foliated **F**—Uneven, splintery Sectile, laminae flexible	2.6 2.8	Greasy or soapy feel important. *Foliated talc*, easily separable, inelastic folia or plates, H = 1; *soapstone* or *steatite*, coarse to fine granular, rather impure, H = 1.5—2.5; *French chalk*, soft, compact, marks cloth distinctly. With serpentine, dolomite, chlorite, magnesite, actinolite
1. **3.**	White	**F**—Earthy Brittle	2.5	Clay odor. Usually distinguished from clay by pisolitic or oölitic structure. With clay or kaolin in nodules, grains, or irregular masses in limestone or dolomite. Considered a rock

Streak—Uncolored, white, or light gray			
Name, Composition, and Reference	Crystallization Structure Crystals = C Massive = M	Luster Transparency	Color
SODA NITER (Chile saltpeter) $NaNO_3$ **325**	Hexagonal **C**—Similar to those of calcite, rare **M**—Granular, crusts, efflorescences	Vitreous Transparent	Colorless White Grayish
Melanterite (Copperas) $FeSO_4.7H_2O$ **344**	Monoclinic **C**—Rare **M**—Capillary, fibrous, stalactitic, concretionary, powdery	Vitreous Dull Transparent to translucent	White Greenish white Yellowish white
GYPSUM, varieties *Selenite*, *Satin spar*, *Alabaster*, *Common* $CaSO_4.2H_2O$ **345**	Monoclinic **C**—Tabular, prismatic; swallow-tailed twins **M**—Cleavable, coarse or fine grained, fibrous, foliated, earthy	Pearly Vitreous Silky Dull Transparent to opaque	Colorless White Gray
Sepiolite (Meerschaum) $Mg_4(OH)_2Si_6O_{15}.6H_2O$ **405**	Monoclinic **M**—Compact, nodular with smooth feel; earthy, clay-like	Dull Opaque	White Grayish white
Epsomite (Epsom salt) $MgSO_4.7H_2O$ **344**	Orthorhombic **C**—Prismatic, nearly square, rare **M**—Granular, fibrous, earthy, crusts	Vitreous Dull Transparent to translucent	White Colorless Gray
HALITE (Rock salt) NaCl **319**	Cubic **C**—Cubes, often skeletal or hopper-shaped **M**—Compact, cleavable, granular, fibrous, stalactitic, crusts	Vitreous Transparent to translucent	Colorless White Grayish

Hardness 1 to 3

Hardness	Streak	Cleavage = C Fracture = F Tenacity	Specific Gravity	Characteristics and Associates
1.5 **2.**	White	**C**—Rhombohedral **F**—Conchoidal Brittle	2. 2.3	Cooling and saline taste. Absorbs moisture readily. In extensive deposits. With gypsum, sand, clay, guano
2.	White	**C**—Basal **F**—Conchoidal, earthy Brittle	1.8 1.9	On exposure loses water and crumbles. Sweet, astringent taste, somewhat metallic. Oxidation product of iron sulfide minerals—marcasite, pyrite, chalcopyrite, pyrrhotite
2.	White	**C**—Clinopinacoidal, conspicuous; pyramidal, orthopinacoidal **F**—Conchoidal, fibrous Brittle, laminae flexible	2.2 2.4	*Selenite*, crystals and cleavage plates, usually transparent; *satin spar*, fibrous with silky luster; *alabaster*, granular. In limestones, shales. With halite, celestite, sulfur, aragonite, dolomite, ore deposits
2. **2.5**	White	**C**—None **F**—Conchoidal, uneven Brittle	1. 2.	Recognized by smooth feel, adherence to tongue, low specific gravity and lack of clay odor when breathed upon. Impressed by fingernail. With serpentine, magnesite, chlorite
2. **2.5**	White	**C**—Brachypinacoidal **F**—Conchoidal Brittle	1.7 1.8	Efflorescent. Bitter, salty taste. In limestone caves. With serpentine, talc, magnesite
2. **2.5**	White	**C**—Cubic, perfect, conspicuous **F**—Conchoidal Brittle	2.1 2.3	May absorb moisture and become damp. Characteristic cubical cleavage and saline taste. With shale, gypsum, anhydrite

Streak—Uncolored, white, or light gray

Name, Composition, and Reference	Crystallization Structure Crystals = C Massive = M	Luster Transparency	Color
MICAS: **Lepidolite** $K_2Li_3Al_3(F,OH)_4$- $(AlSi_3O_{10})_2$ **400**	Monoclinic **C**—Short prismatic **M**—Coarse or fine granular, scales, cleavable plates	Pearly Translucent	White Pinkish white Lavender Gray
MICAS: **MUSCOVITE** (Isinglass) $KAl_2(OH,F)_2AlSi_3O_{10}$ **397**	Monoclinic **C**—Tabular, pyramidal, with rhombic or hexagonal outline; often large and rough **M**—Scales, plates; foliated and plumose aggregates	Vitreous Pearly Transparent to translucent	Colorless Yellowish white Brownish white
APATITE, variety *Phosphate rock* **Mainly calcium carbonate -phosphate** (collophane) **352**	Hexagonal **M**—Compact, nodular, reniform, earthy, oölitic	Dull Opaque	White Gray
Brucite $Mg(OH)_2$ **318**	Hexagonal **C**—Broad tabular **M**—Foliated, scaly, fibrous	Pearly Vitreous Transparent to translucent	Colorless White Greenish white
Kernite (Rasorite) $Na_2B_4O_7.4H_2O$ **338**	Monoclinic **C**—Large, resembling gypsum (*selenite*) **M**—Cleavable, fibrous	Vitreous Pearly Transparent to translucent	Colorless White
CRYOLITE Na_3AlF_6 **323**	Monoclinic **C**—Small, pseudocubical rare **M**—Cleavable, compact, granular	Vitreous Greasy Pearly Transparent to translucent	Snow white Gray Colorless

Hardness 1 to 3

Hardness	Streak	Cleavage = C Fracture = F Tenacity	Specific Gravity	Characteristics and Associates
2. **3.**	White	**C**—Basal, perfect **F**—Scaly granular Tough	2.8 2.9	When massive often resembles granular limestone. In pegmatites, granites, gneisses. With red tourmaline (rubellite), spodumene, cassiterite
2. **3.**	White	**C**—Basal, perfect, conspicuous Tough, laminae very elastic	2.8 3.1	Structure, perfect cleavage, and elasticity important. Large crystals often show distinct partings perpendicular to cleavage, *ruled mica.* In granitic rocks, schists, limestones. With feldspar, quartz, beryl, tourmaline, garnet, spodumene
2. **3.**	White	**F**—Conchoidal, uneven Brittle	3.1 3.2	More or less impure masses, frequently resembling compact limestone. Independent beds, nodules, concretions
2.5	White	**C**—Basal, perfect, conspicuous Thin plates or scales are flexible	2.4	More pearly luster than selenite, slightly harder; less elastic than mica. With serpentine, limestone
2.5 **3.**	White	**C**—Basal, orthopinacoidal, perfect **F**—Uneven Brittle	1.9	Cleavage angle about 70°. Breaks readily into fibers and laths. With other boron minerals—borax, ulexite, colemanite
2.5 **3.**	White	**C**—Basal, prismatic, nearly at 90°; sometimes conspicuous **F**—Uneven Brittle	2.9 3.	Frequently resembles snow ice. Often contains disseminated siderite, chalcopyrite, galena, pyrite, fluorite, columbite

Streak—Uncolored, white, or light gray

Name, Composition, and Reference	Crystallization Structure Crystals = C Massive = M	Luster Transparency	Color
CALCITE, varieties $CaCO_3$ *Dog-tooth spar* *Nail-head spar* *Iceland spar* *Satin spar* *Limestone* *Coquina* *Marble* *Calcareous tufa* *Travertine* *Stalactites, etc.* **326**	Hexagonal **C**—Scalenohedral, rhombohedral, prismatic, tabular, acicular; highly modified; twins **M**—Cleavable, granular, fibrous, banded, stalactitic, oölitic, porous, compact, crusts, shells	Vitreous Dull Transparent to nearly opaque	White Grayish Colorless

Streak—Uncolored, white, or light gray

Name, Composition, and Reference	Crystallization Structure Crystals = C Massive = M	Luster Transparency	Color
ANHYDRITE $CaSO_4$ **339**	Orthorhombic **C**—Thick tabular, prismatic, rare **M**—Granular, compact, fibrous, cleavable, lamellar, reniform	Vitreous Pearly Transparent to translucent	White Bluish white Reddish white Grayish
CELESTITE $SrSO_4$ **339**	Orthorhombic **C**—Tabular, prismatic, common; pyramidal **M**—Compact, cleavable, fibrous, granular, reniform	Vitreous Pearly Transparent to translucent	Colorless White Gray
BARITE (Heavy spar) $BaSO_4$ **340**	Orthorhombic **C**—Tabular, prismatic; crested divergent groups **M**—Compact, cleavable, lamellar, fibrous, reniform	Vitreous Pearly Transparent to translucent	Colorless White Gray

Hardness 1 to 3				
Hard-ness	Streak	Cleavage = C Fracture = F Tenacity	Specific Gravity	Characteristics and Associates
3.	White	**C**—Rhombohedral, perfect, usually conspicuous **F**—Conchoidal Brittle	2.7	Rhombohedral cleavage characteristic, especially on crystals. Cleavage surfaces often striated. Very strong double refraction easily observed when transparent. To distinguish varieties, see reference

Hardness 3 to 6				
3. **3.5**	White	**C**—Pinacoidal, 3 directions at 90°, sometimes conspicuous **F**—Conchoidal Brittle	2.7 3.	Pseudocubical cleavage sometimes noted. Granular varieties resemble marble. Not so heavy as celestite or barite. With halite, gypsum
3. **3.5**	White	**C**—Basal, prismatic, conspicuous **F**—Uneven Brittle	3.9 4.	Usually with faint bluish tinge. Heavier than calcite, anhydrite; lighter than barite. Good cleavages. In limestones, dolomites, shales. With sulfur, gypsum, aragonite, halite, galena, sphalerite
3. **3.5**	White	**C**—Basal, prismatic, conspicuous **F**—Uneven Brittle	4.3 4.7	Characterized by rather high specific gravity and cleavages. In metalliferous veins; pockets and lenticular masses in limestones. With galena, sphalerite, fluorite, chalcopyrite; manganese and iron ores

Streak—Uncolored, white, or light gray			
Name, Composition, and Reference	Crystallization Structure Crystals = C Massive = M	Luster Transparency	Color
ANGLESITE $PbSO_4$ **341**	Orthorhombic **C**—Prismatic, tabular, pyramidal **M**—Compact, granular, nodular	Adamantine Greasy Transparent to translucent	Colorless White Gray
CERUSSITE $PbCO_3$ **335**	Orthorhombic **C**—Tabular, prismatic, pyramidal; pseudohexagonal; clusters and star-shaped groups **M**—Interlaced bundles, granular, stalactitic, compact	Adamantine Greasy Silky Transparent to translucent	Colorless White Gray
STILBITE (Zeolite) $(Ca,Na_2)Al_2Si_7O_{18}.7H_2O$ **420**	Monoclinic **C**—Twinned, sheaf-like, radial, or globular aggregates	Vitreous Pearly Transparent to translucent	White Yellowish white Gray
Lepidolite (Mica) $K_2Li_3Al_3(F,OH)_4$-$(AlSi_3O_{10})_2$ **400**	Monoclinic **C**—Short prismatic **M**—Granular, coarse or fine; scales, cleavable plates	Pearly Translucent	White Pinkish white Lavender Gray
APATITE, variety *Phosphate rock* Mainly calcium carbonate-phosphate (collophane) **352**	Hexagonal **M**—Compact, nodular, reniform, earthy, oölitic	Dull Opaque	White Gray

Hardness 3 to 6

Hardness	Streak	Cleavage = C Fracture = F Tenacity	Specific Gravity	Characteristics and Associates
3. **3.5**	White	C—Basal, prismatic F—Conchoidal Brittle	6.1 6.4	Luster and very high specific gravity important. Distinguished from cerussite by absence of twins. Oxidation product of lead minerals. Usually in cracks and cavities, with galena, cerrusite
3. **3.5**	White	C—Indistinct F—Conchoidal Brittle	6.4 6.6	Twinning, structure, luster, and specific gravity characteristic. With lead minerals—galena, pyromorphite, anglesite; also malachite, limonite
3. **4.**	White	C—Pinacoidal F—Uneven Brittle	2.1 2.2	Radial or sheaf-like structure. In basic igneous rocks; ore deposits. With chabazite, apophyllite, datolite, calcite
3. **4.**	White	C—Basal, perfect F—Scaly, granular Tough	2.8 2.9	When massive often resembles granular limestone. In pegmatites, granites, gneisses. With red tourmaline (rubellite), spodumene, topaz
3. **5.**	White	F—Conchoidal, uneven Brittle	3.1 3.2	More or less impure masses, frequently resembling compact limestone. Independent beds, nodules, concretions

Streak—Uncolored, white, or light gray			
Name, Composition, and Reference	Crystallization Structure Crystals = C Massive = M	Luster Transparency	Color
ANDALUSITE Al_2OSiO_4 **368**	Orthorhombic C—Prismatic, rough, nearly square, often large without terminations M—Columnar, fibrous, granular, disseminated	Vitreous Dull Transparent to opaque	White Pearl gray Reddish gray
Wavellite $Al_3(OH)_3(PO_4)_2.5H_2O$ **355**	Orthorhombic C—Capillary, small M—Crusts, globular or hemispherical, with radial fibrous structure	Vitreous Translucent	White Gray Colorless
ALUNITE (Alum stone) $KAl_3(OH)_6(SO_4)_2$ **342**	Hexagonal C—Rhombohedrons, resembling cubes; tabular, rare M—Compact, granular, fibrous, earthy	Vitreous Pearly Transparent to translucent	Colorless White Gray
DOLOMITE $CaMg(CO_3)_2$ **329**	Hexagonal C—Rhombohedral with curved surfaces (*pearl spar*) M—Coarsely crystalline, compact, granular, friable	Vitreous Pearly Transparent to translucent	White Gray Colorless
ARAGONITE $CaCO_3$ **333**	Orthorhombic C—Chisel- or spear-shaped; pseudohexagonal prisms; radial, columnar, acicular aggregates M—Branching forms (*flos ferri*), stalactitic, reniform, crusts, oölitic	Vitreous Greasy Transparent to translucent	Colorless White Gray

Hardness 3 to 6

Hardness	Streak	Cleavage = C Fracture = F Tenacity	Specific Gravity	Characteristics and Associates
3. **6.**	White	**C**—Prismatic **F**—Uneven Brittle	3.1 3.2	Due to alteration, surface may be covered with scales of mica, hence, soft. *Chiastolite,* regular internal arrangement of dark, organic matter, best seen in cross section. In metamorphic rocks, often as rounded or knotty projections. With kyanite, sillimanite, garnet, tourmaline
3.5 **4.**	White	**C**—Pinacoidal, domatic **F**—Uneven, conchoidal Brittle	2.3 2.5	Secondary mineral, occurring on surfaces of rocks or minerals as crystalline crusts with pronounced radial, fibrous structure
3.5 **4.**	White	**C**—Basal **F**—Splintery, conchoidal, earthy Brittle	2.6 2.8	Hardness often greater due to admixture of quartz, feldspar; then tough. Deposits and veins in feldspathic rocks. With kaolin, pyrite, opal
3.5 **4.**	White Gray	**C**—Rhombohedral, perfect **F**—Conchoidal Brittle	2.9	Crystals generally curved or saddle-shaped with pearly luster. *Marble* includes some compact varieties. Independent beds; in fissures and cavities; with ore deposits
3.5 **4.**	White	**C**—Pinacoidal, prismatic, indistinct **F**—Conchoidal Brittle	2.9 3.	Twins common, often pseudohexagonal—prism and striated base. In cracks and cavities; with ore deposits; deposition from hot springs; in shells. With gypsum, celestite, sulfur, siderite, serpentine

Streak—Uncolored, white, or light gray

Name, Composition, and Reference	Crystallization Structure Crystals = C Massive = M	Luster Transparency	Color
STRONTIANITE $SrCO_3$ **334**	Orthorhombic **C**—Spear-shaped, columnar, acicular, often divergent **M**—Columnar, granular, compact, fibrous, botryoidal	Vitreous Transparent to translucent	Colorless Gray White
WITHERITE $BaCO_3$ **335**	Orthorhombic **C**—Pseudohexagonal bipyramids resembling quartz **M**—Radial fibrous, compact, globular, granular, lamellar	Vitreous Greasy Translucent to transparent	White Grayish Colorless
MAGNESITE $MgCO_3$ **330**	Hexagonal **C**—Rhombohedral, rare **M**—Compact, granular, resembling unglazed porcelain on fresh fracture	Vitreous Dull Translucent to transparent	Snow white Gray Colorless
FLUORITE (Fluor spar) CaF_2 **322**	Cubic **C**—Cubes, alone or modified, well developed **M**—Cleavable, granular, fibrous	Vitreous Transparent to translucent	Colorless White Greenish white
Colemanite $Ca_2B_6O_{11}.5H_2O$ **337**	Monoclinic **C**—Prismatic, highly modified **M**—Granular, cleavable, compact	Vitreous Dull Transparent to opaque	Colorless Milky white Yellowish white

Hardness 3 to 6

Hardness	Streak	Cleavage = C Fracture = F Tenacity	Specific Gravity	Characteristics and Associates
3.5 **4.**	White	**C**—Indistinct **F**—Uneven Brittle	3.6 3.8	Similar to aragonite. Divergent columnar structure and higher specific gravity characteristic. In ore deposits; independent masses. With galena, barite, calcite
3.5 **4.**	White	**C**—Indistinct **F**—Uneven Brittle	4.2 4.3	Crystals, apparently hexagonal bipyramids; massive, often radial fibrous resembling strontianite, but heavier. Usually with galena
3.5 **5.**	White	**C**—Rhombohedral, perfect (crystals) **F**—Conchoidal, conspicuous Tough to brittle	2.9 3.1	Conchoidal fracture generally prominent. Compact varieties are apparently very hard. Disseminated in talcose and chloritic schists, serpentine, gypsum; independent beds
4.	White	**C**—Octahedral, perfect, conspicuous Brittle	3. 3.2	Recognized by crystal form, octahedral cleavage, and hardness. Common gangue of metallic ores, especially galena, sphalerite, cassiterite; also with calcite, barite
4. **4.5**	White	**C**—Pinacoidal, perfect, conspicuous **F**—Uneven, conchoidal Brittle	2.2 2.4	Transparent crystals, resemble those of datolite, but softer; compact masses look like chalk or porcelain. With gypsum, celestite, quartz

Streak—Uncolored, white, or light gray			
Name, Composition, and Reference	Crystallization Structure Crystals = C Massive = M	Luster Transparency	Color
CHABAZITE (Zeolite) $CaAl_2Si_4O_{12}.6H_2O$ **421**	Hexagonal **C**—Rhombohedral, cube-like; lenticular **M**—Compact	Vitreous Translucent to transparent	White Colorless Gray
APOPHYLLITE $KCa_4F(Si_4O_{10})_2.8H_2O'$ **394**	Tetragonal **C**—Prismatic, pyramidal, pseudocubical, tabular **M**—Lamellar, granular, compact	Vitreous Pearly Transparent to nearly opaque	Colorless White Yellowish white
Pectolite $HNaCa_2(SiO_3)_3$ **389**	Triclinic **C**—Acicular, rarely terminated; tabular **M**—Compact radial fibrous aggregates	Vitreous Silky Translucent to opaque	White Grayish
KYANITE (Disthene, cyanite) Al_2OSiO_4 **369**	Triclinic **C**—Long bladed, without good terminations; sometimes curved and radially grouped **M**—Coarsely bladed, columnar, fibrous	Vitreous Translucent to transparent	White Grayish Colorless
SCHEELITE $CaWO_4$ **349**	Tetragonal **C**—Pyramidal, small; more rarely tabular **M**—Drusy crusts, compact, reniform, granular, disseminated	Adamantine Greasy Transparent to translucent	Gray White Yellowish white

Hardness 3 to 6

Hardness	Streak	Cleavage = C Fracture = F Tenacity	Specific Gravity	Characteristics and Associates
4. **5.**	White	**C**—Rhombohedral, not conspicuous **F**—Uneven Brittle	2.1 2.2	Generally in cube-like crystals. Inferior cleavage distinguishes it from fluorite. In basic igneous rocks. With analcite, stilbite
4. **5.**	White	**C**—Basal, perfect, conspicuous **F**—Uneven Brittle	2.3 2.4	Fish-eye opalescence often observed on basal pinacoid. Prism faces vertically striated. In fissures and cavities in basic igneous rocks. With natrolite, analcite, datolite, native copper, calcite
4. **5.**	White Grayish	**C**—Basal, macropinacoidal **F**—Uneven, fibrous Brittle	2.7 2.8	Fibers usually divergent, long, and very sharp. In fissures and cavities in basic igneous and metamorphic rocks. With zeolites, datolite
4. **5.**	White	**C**—Pinacoidal perfect, conspicuous Brittle	3.5 3.7	Often with bluish streaks or spots irregularly distributed. Hardness varies with direction, 4–5 parallel to long direction, 6–7 at right angles thereto. In gneiss, mica schist. With staurolite, garnet, corundum
4.5	White	**C**—Pyramidal, not conspicuous **F**—Conchoidal, uneven Brittle	5.9 6.1	Small octahedral-like crystals, usually on quartz; high specific gravity important. Fluoresces in ultraviolet light. With cassiterite, wolframite, fluorite, apatite, molybdenite

Streak—Uncolored, white, or light gray			
Name, Composition, and Reference	Crystallization Structure Crystals = C Massive = M	Luster Transparency	Color
Wollastonite (Tabular spar) $CaSiO_3$ **389**	Triclinic **C**—Tabular, prismatic **M**—Cleavable, fibrous, granular, compact	Vitreous Silky Transparent to translucent	White Gray Colorless
HEMIMORPHITE (Calamine) $Zn_4(OH)_2Si_2O_7.H_2O$ **375**	Orthorhombic **C**—Thin tabular, pyramidal, hemimorphic, highly modified **M**—Compact, globular, stalactitic, fibrous, granular, cellular, earthy	Vitreous Dull Transparent to opaque	Colorless White Gray
APATITE $Ca_5F(PO_4)_3$ **351**	Hexagonal **C**—Prismatic, thick tabular **M**—Granular, compact, fibrous, nodular, reniform	Vitreous Greasy Transparent to translucent	White Gray Colorless
SMITHSONITE $ZnCO_3$ **331**	Hexagonal **C**—Small, usually as druses or crusts **M**—Botryoidal, stalactitic, granular, cellular, fibrous, compact	Vitreous Pearly Dull Transparent to nearly opaque	White Brownish white Gray Colorless
ANALCIME (Zeolite) $NaAlSi_2O_6.H_2O$ **419**	Cubic **C**—Tetragonal trisoctahedrons, cubes **M**—Granular, compact	Vitreous Transparent to nearly opaque	Colorless White Grayish

Hardness 3 to 6

Hardness	Streak	Cleavage = C Fracture = F Tenacity	Specific Gravity	Characteristics and Associates
4.5 **5.**	White	**C**—Basal, macro-pinacoidal **F**—Uneven Brittle	2.8 2.9	Fibers may be parallel or divergent. Typical contact mineral often in crystalline limestone. With garnet, diopside, vesuvianite, graphite
4.5 **5.**	White	**C**—Prismatic **F**—Uneven, conchoidal Brittle	3.4 3.5	Crystals often in sheaf-like groups or druses in cavities. When massive may be porous. In limestones. With sphalerite, galena, and especially smithsonite
5.	White	**C**—Basal, imperfect **F**—Conchoidal, uneven Brittle	3.1 3.2	Crystals may be vertically striated and highly modified. In crystalline limetone; ore deposits, igneous rocks. With quartz, cassiterite, fluorite, wolframite
5.	White Gray	**C**—Rhombohedral, not often observed **F**—Uneven, splintery Brittle	4.1 4.5	Cellular varieties are called *dry bone.* Often mixed with sand, clay, limonite, calcite. With zinc minerals, especially sphalerite, hemimorphite. Frequently as a pseudomorph after calcite
5. **5.5**	White	**C**—None **F**—Uneven, conchoidal Brittle	2.2 2.3	Good crystals common. In fissures and cavities in basic igneous rocks. With apophyllite, chabazite, natrolite, datolite, native copper, epidote

Streak—Uncolored, white, or light gray			
Name, Composition, and Reference	Crystallization Structure Crystals = C Massive = M	Luster Transparency	**Color**
Natrolite (Zeolite) $Na_2Al_2Si_3O_{10}.2H_2O$ **418**	Orthorhombic **C**—Slender prismatic, nearly square; radial or interlacing groups **M**—Fibrous, granular, compact	Vitreous Silky Transparent to translucent	White Colorless Grayish
Datolite $CaB(OH)SiO_4$ **373**	Monoclinic **C**—Prismatic, pyramidal, tabular, highly modified **M**—Compact fibrous, granular, botryoidal	Vitreous Greasy Dull Transparent to opaque	Colorless Greenish white Gray
NEPHELINE (Nephelite, elaeolite) $Na(AlSiO_4)$ **414**	Hexagonal **C**—Short prismatic, tabular **M**—Compact, disseminated grains	Greasy Vitreous Transparent to opaque	White Bluish gray Greenish gray Colorless
SCAPOLITE (Wernerite) $nNa_4Cl(AlSi_3O_8)_3 + mCa_4CO_3(Al_2Si_2O_8)_3$ **417**	Tetragonal **C**—Thick prismatic, coarse, often large **M**—Compact, fibrous, columnar, granular	Vitreous Greasy Translucent	White Gray Greenish gray
Tremolite (Amphibole) $Ca_2Mg_5(OH)_2Si_8O_{22}$ **391**	Monoclinic **C**—Bladed, without terminations **M**—Compact, columnar, granular	Silky Vitreous Transparent to opaque	White Yellowish white Colorless

Hardness 3 to 6

Hardness	Streak	Cleavage = C Fracture = F Tenacity	Specific Gravity	Characteristics and Associates
5. **5.5**	White	**C**—Prismatic **F**—Uneven Brittle	2.2 2.3	Needle-like crystals have nearly square cross section. With chabazite, analcite, apophyllite, stilbite, datolite
5. **5.5**	White	**C**—None **F**—Conchoidal, uneven Brittle	2.9 3.	Crystals glassy, often with greenish tinge; compact masses resemble wedgewood ware or unglazed porcelain; often with reddish, brownish, or yellowish streaks and spots. In cracks and cavities in basic igneous rocks. With native copper, calcite, zeolites
5. **6.**	White	**C**—Indistinct **F**—Conchoidal, uneven Brittle	2.6	Distinguished from orthoclase by inferior cleavage and more greasy luster. With feldspar, cancrinite, biotite, sodalite, zircon, corundum; not with quartz
5. **6.**	White	**C**—Prismatic **F**—Conchoidal Brittle	2.6 2.8	Crystals may appear as though fused. Typical contact mineral. In metamorphic rocks, especially granular limestones. With pyroxenes, amphiboles, apatite, garnet, biotite
5. **6.**	White	**C**—Prismatic, conspicuous—124° Brittle	2.9 3.1	Silky luster and distinct cleavage (124°) important. Common contact mineral. In limestones, dolomites, schists

Streak—Uncolored, white, or light gray

	Name, Composition, and Reference	Crystallization Structure Crystals = C Massive = M	Luster Transparency	Color
	DIOPSIDE (Pyroxene) $CaMgSi_2O_6$ **385**	Monoclinic **C**—Prismatic, thick columnar, prism angle 87° **M**—Compact, granular, lamellar, columnar	Vitreous Dull Transparent to opaque	Gray Greenish gray Yellowish white Colorless
	OPAL, varieties $SiO_2.nH_2O$ *Precious opal* *Milk opal* *Wood opal* *Hyalite* *Siliceous sinter* *Tripolite* **314**	Amorphous **M**—Reniform, botryoidal, porous, earthy, compact	Vitreous Pearly Dull Transparent to opaque	Colorless Gray Milk white Yellowish white
	LEUCITE $K(AlSi_2O_6)$ **416**	Pseudocubic **C**—Tetragonal trisoctahedrons **M**—Rounded disseminated grains	Vitreous Greasy Translucent to opaque	Gray White Yellowish white
FELDSPARS	**ORTHOCLASE**, varieties $KAlSi_3O_8$ *Adularia* *Sanidine* *Ordinary* **407**	Monoclinic **C**—Prismatic, thick tabular; twins; often large **M**—Cleavable, granular, disseminated	Vitreous Pearly Translucent to transparent	White Gray Colorless
FELDSPARS	**MICROCLINE** $KAlSi_3O_8$ **408**	Triclinic **C**—Prismatic, thick tabular; twins; often large **M**—Cleavable, granular disseminated	Vitreous Pearly Translucent to transparent	Gray White Yellowish white

(Feldspars continued on page 654.)

Hardness 3 to 6

Hard-ness	Streak	Cleavage = C Fracture = F Tenacity	Specific Gravity	Characteristics and Associates
5. **6.**	White Gray	**C**—Prismatic; conspicuous basal parting **F**—Uneven Brittle	3.2 3.3	Prismatic, pseudotetragonal crystals, with distinct basal parting. May show colorless and dark green zones. In crystalline limestones. With vesuvianite, garnet, scapolite, spinel, apatite
5.5 **6.**	White	**F**—Conchoidal, conspicuous when compact; earthy Brittle	1.9 2.3	*Precious opal,* with play of colors; *milk opal,* compact, milk white; *wood opal,* woody structure; *hyalite,* resembles drops of melted glass; *siliceous sinter,* porous or botryoidal; *tripolite,* earthy and gritty
5.5 **6.**	White	**C**—Indistinct **F**—Conchoidal Brittle	2.5	Well-developed crystals or rounded grains, disseminated in eruptive rocks. With sanidine, augite, nepheline, olivine
6.	White	**C**—Basal, clinopinacoidal, conspicuous, 90°; often step-like **F**—Conchoidal, uneven Brittle	2.5 2.6	Distinguished from other feldspars by rectangular cleavage and absence of twinning striations. *Adularia,* opalescent, transparent or slightly cloudy; *sanidine,* glassy, tabular or square crystals. With quartz, other feldspars, mica, hornblende, zircon
6.	White	**C**—Basal, brachypinacoidal, conspicuous, 90°30′ **F**—Uneven Brittle	2.5 2.6	Resembles orthoclase, but with slightly inclined cleavages and may show gridiron structure on basal pinacoid. Occurs chiefly in pegmatites.

Streak—Uncolored, white, or light gray

Name, Composition, and Reference	Crystallization Structure Crystals = C Massive = M	Luster Transparency	Color
FELDSPARS — Plagioclases — **ALBITE** $NaAlSi_3O_8(Ab)$ **411**	Triclinic **C**—Tabular, twins, small **M**—Compact, curved or divergent lamellar, granular	Vitreous Pearly Transparent to translucent	White Gray Colorless
FELDSPARS — Plagioclases — **LABRADORITE** $Ab_{50}An_{50} \ldots Ab_{30}An_{70}$ **412**	Triclinic **C**—Thin tabular, often with rhombic cross section **M**—Compact, cleavable, granular	Vitreous Pearly Translucent to nearly opaque	Gray Greenish gray White
FELDSPARS — Plagioclases — **Anorthite** $CaAl_2Si_2O_8(An)$ **413**	Triclinic **C**—Prismatic, tabular complex **M**—Compact, cleavable, lamellar	Vitreous Pearly Transparent to translucent	Colorless White Gray
Amblygonite $LiAl(F,OH)PO_4$ **351**	Triclinic **C**—Large, poorly developed **M**—Cleavable, columnar, compact	Pearly Vitreous Translucent	White Yellowish white Gray

Streak—Uncolored, white, or light gray

Name, Composition, and Reference	Crystallization Structure Crystals = C Massive = M	Luster Transparency	Color
Prehnite $Ca_2Al_2(OH)_2Si_3O_{10}$ **379**	Orthorhombic **C**—Tabular, prismatic; curved, sheaf-like groups **M**—Globular, reniform, radial fibrous	Vitreous Pearly on basal pinacoid Transparent to translucent	White Grayish white Greenish white

Hardness 3 to 6

Hardness	Streak	Cleavage = C Fracture = F Tenacity	Specific Gravity	Characteristics and Associates
6.	White	**C**—Basal, brachy-pinacoidal, conspicuous, 86°24′ **F**—Uneven Brittle	2.6	Inclined cleavages often show fine, parallel twinning striations. *Moonstone*, opalescent. With quartz, other feldspars, mica, chlorite, beryl, rutile
6.	White	**C**—Basal, brachy-pinacoidal, conspicuous, 86°4′ **F**—Uneven Brittle	2.7	Often with play of colors—yellow, green, blue, red. Inclined cleavages are striated. In basic igneous rocks. With pyroxenes, amphiboles
6.	White	**C**—Basal, brachy-pinacoidal, conspicuous, 85°50′ **F**—Uneven Brittle	2.7 2.8	Commonly in small, glassy, highly modified crystals. In basic igneous rocks; crystalline limestones. With olivine, pyroxenes, pyrrhotite, magnetite
6.	White	**C**—Basal, perfect, conspicuous; macropinacoidal, domatic **F**—Conchoidal, uneven Brittle	3. 3.1	Usually in cleavable masses with perfect cleavage in one direction. With lepidolite, spodumene, tourmaline, quartz, apatite

Hardness over 6

Hardness	Streak	Cleavage = C Fracture = F Tenacity	Specific Gravity	Characteristics and Associates
6. **6.5**	White	**C**—Basal **F**—Uneven Brittle	2.8 3.	Massive varieties usually have rough crystalline surfaces and internal radial, fibrous structure. In veins and cavities in basic igneous rocks. With pectolite, datolite, epidote, native copper, zeolites

Streak—Uncolored, white, or light gray

Name, Composition, and Reference	Crystallization Structure Crystals = C Massive = M	Luster Transparency	Color
SPODUMENE (Pyroxene) $LiAlSi_2O_6$ **387**	Monoclinic **C**—Prismatic, tabular, vertically striated **M**—Cleavable, broad columnar	Vitreous Pearly Transparent to opaque	White Grayish white Greenish white
Sillimanite (Fibrolite) Al_2OSiO_4 **370**	Orthorhombic **C**—Long, thin, needle-like **M**—Fibrous, columnar, radiating	Vitreous Silky Transparent to translucent	Gray Yellowish gray Grayish white
KYANITE (Disthene, cyanite) Al_2OSiO_4 **369**	Triclinic **C**—Long, bladed, without good terminations; sometimes curved and radially grouped **M**—Coarsely bladed, columnar, fibrous	Vitreous Translucent to transparent	White Grayish Colorless
ANDALUSITE Al_2OSiO_4 **368**	Orthorhombic **C**—Prismatic, rough, nearly square, often large, without terminations **M**—Columnar, fibrous, granular, disseminated	Vitreous Dull Translucent to opaque	White Pearl gray Reddish gray
GARNET, variety *Grossularite* $Ca_3Al_2(SiO_4)_3$ **365**	Cubic **C**—Dodecahedrons, tetragonal trisoctahedrons, alone or in combination **M**—Granular, compact, lamellar, disseminated grains	Vitreous Transparent to translucent	Colorless White Greenish white Yellowish white

Hardness over 6

Hardness	Streak	Cleavage = C Fracture = F Tenacity	Specific Gravity	Characteristics and Associates
6. **7.**	White	**C**—Prismatic; pinacoidal parting conspicuous **F**—Uneven, splintery Brittle	3.1 3.2	Commonly in broad plates due to distinct pinacoidal parting. Prism angle 93°. May have irregular brownish stains. In granitic rocks. With tourmaline, lepidolite, beryl
6. **7.**	White	**C**—Macropinacoidal **F**—Uneven Brittle	3.2 3.3	Crystals often large, bent, striated, with rounded edges, without good terminations, and interlaced. In metamorphic rocks—mica schist, gneiss. With andalusite, zircon
6. **7.**	White	**C**—Pinacoidal, perfect, conspicuous Brittle	3.5 3.7	Often with bluish streaks or spots, irregularly distributed. Hardness varies with direction, 4–5 parallel to long direction, 6–7 at right angles thereto. In gneiss, mica schist. With staurolite, corundum, garnet
6. **7.5**	White	**C**—Prismatic **F**—Uneven Brittle	3.1 3.2	Surface may be coated with scales of mica, then softer. *Chiastolite* has regular internal arrangement of organic matter. In metamorphic rocks, often as rounded or knotty projections. With kyanite, sillimanite, garnet
6.5 **7.5**	White	**C**—Dodecahedral, usually indistinct **F**—Conchoidal, uneven Brittle	3.5 3.7	Typical contact mineral, in crystalline limestones and dolomites. With wollastonite, vesuvianite, diopside, scapolite

Streak—Uncolored, white, or light gray			
Name, Composition, and Reference	Crystallization Structure Crystals = C Massive = M	Luster Transparency	Color
QUARTZ, Crystalline varieties SiO_2 *Rock crystal* *Milky quartz* *Ordinary* **295**	Hexagonal **C**—Prismatic, horizontally striated columnar **M**—Compact, granular	Vitreous Greasy Transparent to translucent	Colorless White Gray Milky
Cryptocrystalline varieties *Chalcedony* *Agate* *Onyx* *Hornstone* *Chert* **296**	Hexagonal **C**—Never in crystals **M**—Nodular, botryoidal, banded, clouded, concretionary, stalactitic, compact	Waxy Vitreous Translucent to opaque	White Gray
Clastic varieties SiO_2 *Sand* *Sandstone* *Itacolumite* *Quartzite* **297**	Hexagonal **M**—Grains, fragments, either loose or strongly consolidated	Vitreous Dull Translucent to opaque	Gray White
Cordierite (Iolite, Dichroite) $Mg_2Al_3(AlSi_5O_{18})$ **380**	Orthorhombic **C**—Short prismatic, pseudohexagonal **M**—Compact, disseminated, granular	Vitreous Greasy Transparent to translucent	Gray Bluish gray Colorless
ZIRCON $ZrSiO_4$ **366**	Tetragonal **C**—Square prisms with bipyramids, small, well developed **M**—Irregular lumps, grains	Adamantine Vitreous Pearly Transparent to opaque	Brownish gray Lavender gray Colorless

Hardness over 6

Hardness	Streak	Cleavage = C Fracture = F Tenacity	Specific Gravity	Characteristics and Associates
7.	White	**C**—Indistinct **F**—Conchoidal, conspicuous Brittle	2.6	Characteristic conchoidal fracture, glassy luster. *Rock crystal,* colorless, or nearly so, generally crystallized; *milky quartz,* milk white and nearly opaque
7.	White	**C**—Indistinct **F**—Conchoidal, conspicuous Brittle to tough	2.6	Not so glassy as crystalline varieties. *Chalcedony, hornstone, chert,* uniform in color; *agate, onyx,* clouded or banded. To distinguish, see reference
7.	White	**C**—Indistinct **F**—Uneven Brittle to tough	2.6	*Sand,* loose, unconsolidated grains; *sandstone,* consolidated sand; *itacolumite,* flexible sandstone; *quartzite,* metamorphosed sandstone
7. **7.5**	White	**C**—Pinacoidal, sometimes conspicuous **F**—Uneven Brittle	2.6 2.7	When fresh, glassy and hard, resembling blue quartz; often altered, then dull and softer. With quartz, feldspar, hornblende, sillimanite, andalusite
7.5	White	**C**—Indistinct **F**—Uneven Brittle	4.6 4.7	In acid igneous rocks—granite; syenite; alluvial deposits; with gold, spinel, corundum, garnet. *Jargon,* colorless or smoky

Streak—Uncolored, white, or light gray			
Name, Composition, and Reference	Crystallization Structure Crystals = C Massive = M	Luster Transparency	Color
BERYL $Be_3Al_2Si_6O_{18}$ **379**	Hexagonal **C**—Long prismatic, often vertically striated, large **M**—Columnar, granular, compact	Vitreous Transparent to translucent	White Yellowish white Greenish white Colorless
TOPAZ $Al_2(F,OH)_2SiO_4$ **372**	Orthorhombic **C**—Prismatic, vertically striated, highly modified **M**—Compact, granular, rolled fragments	Vitreous Transparent to opaque	Colorless White Grayish
CORUNDUM Al_2O_3 **299**	Hexagonal **C**—Prismatic, tabular, pyramidal, rhombohedral; rough or rounded barrel-shaped **M**—Compact, granular, lamellar	Vitreous Translucent to transparent	Gray Greenish gray Bluish gray
DIAMOND C **267**	Cubic **C**—Octahedrons, hexoctahedrons, usually with curved surfaces **M**—Rounded or irregular grains or pebbles, often with internal radial structure	Adamantine Greasy Transparent to translucent	Colorless Gray White

Hardness over 6				
Hard-ness	Streak	Cleavage = C Fracture = F Tenacity	Specific Gravity	Characteristics and Associates
7.5 **8**	White	**C**—Indistinct **F**—Conchoidal, uneven Brittle	2.6 2.8	Crystals usually simple—prism and base. In granitic rocks, mica schists, clay slates. With quartz, feldspars, mica, chrysoberyl, garnet, topaz, tourmaline
8.	White	**C**—Basal, perfect, conspicuous **F**—Conchoidal, uneven Brittle	3.4 3.6	Crystals usually developed on one end only. Massive varieties distinguished from quartz by higher specific gravity and basal cleavage. In veins and cavities in granitic rocks; alluvial deposits. With cassiterite, tourmaline, fluorite, beryl, scheelite, wolframite
9.	White	**C**—None, basal and nearly rectangular, rhombohedral partings conspicuous; often striated **F**—Conchoidal Brittle to tough	3.9 4.1	When massive often multicolored—blue, green, red, yellow. In limestones, granites, syenites, schists, alluvial deposits. With magnetite, nepheline, mica, spinel, chlorite
10.	Ash gray	**C**—Octahedral, perfect, usually conspicuous **F**—Conchoidal Brittle	3.5	May be tinged yellow, brown, red, blue. In serpentine rocks—kimberlite, peridotite, called *blue ground;* placers; with pyrope, magnetite, chromite, cassiterite, zircon, gold

Selected Bibliography

Geometrical Crystallography

BUERGER, M. J.: "Elementary Crystallography—An Introduction to the Fundamental Geometrical Features of Crystals," John Wiley & Sons, Inc., New York, 1956.

EVANS, J. W., and G. M. DAVIES: "Elementary Crystallography," Thomas Murby & Company, London, 1940.

KRAUS, E. H.: "Essentials of Crystallography," George Wahr, Ann Arbor, Michigan, 1906.

LEWIS, W. J.: "A Treatise on Crystallography," The University Press, Cambridge, England, 1899.

PHILLIPS, F. C.: "An Introduction to Crystallography," 2d ed., Longmans, Green & Co., Inc., New York, 1956.

TUNELL, GEORGE, and JOSEPH MURDOCH: "Laboratory Manual of Crystallography for Students of Mineralogy and Geology," Wm. C. Brown Company, Dubuque, Iowa, 1957.

TUTTON, A. E. H.: "Crystallography and Practical Crystal Measurement," 2 vols., 2d ed., Macmillan & Co., Ltd., London, 1922.

WOLFE, C. W.: "Manual for Geometrical Crystallography," Edwards Bros., Inc., Ann Arbor, Michigan, 1953.

Crystal Chemistry

BUCKLEY, H. E.: "Crystal Growth," John Wiley & Sons, Inc., New York; Chapman & Hall, Ltd., London, 1951.

EVANS, R. C.: "An Introduction to Crystal Chemistry," The University Press, Cambridge, England, 1939.

STILLWELL, C. W.: "Crystal Chemistry," McGraw-Hill Book Company, Inc., New York, 1939.

Crystal Structure and X-ray Analysis

BRAGG, W. H., and W. L. BRAGG: "X-rays and Crystal Structure," 4th ed., George Bell & Sons, Ltd., London, 1924.

BRAGG, W. L.: "Atomic Structure of Minerals," Cornell University Press, Ithaca, New York, 1937.

BRAGG, W. L.: "The History of X-ray Analysis," Longmans, Green & Co., New York, 1946.

BRAGG, W. L.: "The Crystalline State," Vol. I, The Macmillan Company, New York, 1934.

Buerger, M. J.: "X-ray Crystallography," John Wiley & Sons, Inc., New York, 1942.

Bunn, C. W.: "Chemical Crystallography, an Introduction to Optical and X-ray Methods," The Clarendon Press, Oxford, England, 1946.

Clark, G. L.: "Applied X-rays," McGraw-Hill Book Company, Inc., New York, 1955.

Lonsdale, Kathleen: "Crystals and X-rays," George Bell & Sons, Ltd., London, 1948.

Wyckoff, R. W. G.: "The Structure of Crystals," 2d ed. and Supplement (1935), Reinhold Publishing Company, New York, 1931.

Optical Mineralogy

Groth, Paul, and B. H. Jackson: "The Optical Properties of Crystals," John Wiley & Sons, Inc., New York, 1910.

Hallimond, A. F.: "Manual of the Polarizing Microscope," 2d ed., Cooke, Troughton, and Simms, Ltd., York, England, 1953.

Heinrich, E. W.: "Microscopic Petrography," McGraw-Hill Book Company, Inc., New York, 1956.

Larsen, E. S., and Harry Berman: "The Microscopic Determination of the Non-opaque Minerals," 2d ed., U.S. Geological Survey Bulletin 848, Washington, D.C., 1934.

Rogers, A. F., and P. F. Kerr: "Optical Mineralogy," 2d ed., McGraw-Hill Book Company, Inc., New York, 1942.

Wahlstrom, E. E.: "Optical Crystallography," 2d ed., John Wiley & Sons, Inc., New York, 1951.

Wahlstrom, E. E.: "Petrographic Mineralogy," John Wiley & Sons, Inc., New York, 1955.

Winchell, A. N.: "Elements of Optical Mineralogy," Part I, Principles and Methods, 5th ed., 1937; Part II, Description of Minerals, 4th ed., with Horace Winchell, 1951; Part III, Determinative Tables, 2d ed., 1929, John Wiley & Sons, Inc., New York.

Rocks and Rock Minerals

Barth, T. F. W.: "Theoretical Petrology," John Wiley & Sons, Inc., New York, 1952.

Bateman, A. M.: The Formation of Mineral Deposits," John Wiley & Sons, Inc., New York, 1951.

Bateman, A. M.: "Economic Mineral Deposits," 2d ed., John Wiley & Sons, Inc., New York, 1950.

Bowen, N. L.: "The Evolution of the Igneous Rocks," Dover Publications, Inc., New York, 1956.

Kemp, J. F., and F. F. Grout: "A Handbook of Rocks," 6th ed., D. Van Nostrand Company, Inc., Princeton, N.J., 1940.

Niggli, Paul: "Rocks and Mineral Deposits," translated by R. L. Parker, W. H. Freeman and Company, San Francisco, 1954.

Pearl, R. M.: "How to Know the Minerals and Rocks," McGraw-Hill Book Company, Inc., New York, 1955.

Pirsson, L. V., and Adolph Knopf: "Rocks and Rock Minerals," 3d ed., John Wiley & Sons, Inc., New York, 1946.

Pough, F. H.: "A Field Guide to Rocks and Minerals," Houghton Mifflin Company, Boston, 1953.

Schaffer, R. J.: "The Weathering of Natural Building Stones," His Majesty's Stationery Office, London, 1932.

SHAND, S. J.: "Rocks for Chemists," Pitman Publishing Corporation, New York, 1952.

WAHLSTROM, E. E.: "Introduction to Theoretical Igneous Petrology," John Wiley & Sons, Inc., New York, 1950.

General Mineralogy

CORRENS, C. W.: "Einführung in die Mineralogie (Kristallographie und Petrologie)," Springer-Verlag, Berlin, 1949.

DANA, E. S., and W. E. FORD: "A Textbook of Mineralogy," 4th ed., John Wiley & Sons, Inc., New York, 1932.

DANA, J. D.: "System of Mineralogy," 6th ed., and 3 appendixes by E. S. Dana and W. E. Ford, 1892–1915; 7th ed., Vol. I, 1944, and Vol. II, 1951, by Charles Palache, Harry Berman, and Clifford Frondel, John Wiley & Sons, Inc., New York. Vol. III, Silicates, in preparation.

DOELTER, CORNELIO, and others: "Handbuch der Mineralogie," 4 vols., Theodor Steinkopff, Verlagsbuchhandlung, Dresden, 1911–1931.

ENGLISH, G. L.: "Getting Acquainted with Minerals," rev. by D. E. Jensen, McGraw-Hill Book Company, Inc., New York, 1958.

HINTZE, CARL, and GOTTLOB LINCK: "Handbuch der Mineralogie," 6 vols., Walter De Gruyter & Co., Berlin, 1889–1939.

HURLBUT, C. S., JR.: "Dana's Manual of Mineralogy," 16th ed., John Wiley & Sons, Inc., New York, 1952.

LINCK, GOTTLOB, and HERMANN JUNG: "Grundriss der Mineralogie und Petrographie," Gustav Fischer Verlagsbuchhandlung, Jena, 1935.

MIERS, H. A., and H. L. BOWMAN: "Mineralogy," 2d ed., Macmillan & Co., Ltd., London, 1929.

RAMDOHR, PAUL: "Klockmann's Lehrbuch der Mineralogie," 14th ed., Ferd. Enke Verlag, Stuttgart, 1954.

READ, H. H.: "Rutley's Elements of Mineralogy," 23d ed., Thomas Murby & Company, London, 1936.

ROGERS, A. F.: "Introduction to the Study of Minerals," 3d ed., McGraw-Hill Book Company, Inc., New York, 1937.

SCHMIDT, WALTER, and E. BAIER: "Lehrbuch der Mineralogie," 2d ed., Verlagsbuchhandlung Gebrüder Borntraeger, Berlin, 1955.

SMITH, O. C.: "Identification and Qualitative Chemical Analysis of Minerals," 2d ed., D. Van Nostrand Company, Inc., Princeton, N.J., 1953.

STRUNZ, HUGO: "Mineralogische Tabellen," 3d ed., Akademische Verlagsgesellschaft m.b.H., Leipzig, 1957.

WINCHELL, A. N.: "Elements of Mineralogy," Prentice-Hall, Inc., Englewood Cliffs, N.J., 1942.

Gems and Gem Materials

BALL, S. H.: "A Roman Book on Precious Stones," Gemological Institute of America, Los Angeles, 1950.

BAUER, M. H., and K. SCHLOSSMACHER: "Edelsteinkunde," 2 vols., 3d ed., Tauchnitz Verlag, Stuttgart, 1928–1932.

EPPLER, A., and W. F. EPPLER: "Edelsteine und Schmucksteine," Wilhelm Diebner, Leipzig, 1934.

GRODZINSKI, PAUL: "Diamond Technology—Production Methods for Diamond and Gem Stones," 2d ed., N. A. G. Press, Ltd., London, 1953.

KRAUS, E. H., and C. B. SLAWSON: "Gems and Gem Materials," 5th ed., McGraw-Hill Book Company, Inc., New York, 1947.

Kunz, G. F.: "Gems and Precious Stones of North America," Scientific Publishing Company, New York, 1890.

Liddicoat, R. T., Jr.: "Handbook of Gem Identification," Gemological Institute of America, Los Angeles, 1947.

Pearl, R. M.: "Popular Gemology," John Wiley & Sons, Inc., New York, 1948.

Smith, G. F. Herbert: "Gemstones," 13th ed., rev. by F. C. Phillips, Methuen & Co., Ltd., London, 1958.

Spencer, L. J.: "A Key to Precious Stones," Blackie & Son, Ltd., Glasgow, 1936.

Webster, Robert: "Practical Gemmology," N. A. G. Press, Ltd., London, 1941.

Determinative Table

Brush, G. J., and S. L. Penfield: "A Manual of Determinative Mineralogy, with Introduction of Blowpipe Analysis," 15th ed., John Wiley & Sons, Inc., New York, 1898.

Eakle, A. S., and Adolf Pabst: "Mineral Tables," 3d ed., John Wiley & Sons, Inc., New York, 1938.

Kraus, E. H., and W. F. Hunt: "Tables for the Determination of Minerals," 2d ed., McGraw-Hill Book Company, Inc., New York, 1930.

Lewis, J. V., and A. C. Hawkins: "A Manual of Determinative Mineralogy with Tables," 4th ed., John Wiley & Sons, Inc., New York, 1931.

Philipsborn v., H.: "Tafeln zum Bestimmen der Minerale nach äusseren Kennzeichen," E. Schweizerbart'sche Verlagsbuchhandlung, Stuttgart, 1953.

Miscellaneous

Agricola, Georgius: "De re metallica," translated by H. C. Hoover and L. H. Hoover, Dover Publications, Inc., New York, 1950.

Clarke, F. W.: "The Data of Geochemistry," 5th ed., U.S. Geological Survey Bulletin 770, Washington, D.C., 1924.

DeMille, J. B.: "Strategic Minerals," McGraw-Hill Book Company, Inc., New York, 1947.

Hotchkiss, W. O.: "Minerals of Might," The Jaques Cattell Press, Lancaster, Pa., 1945.

"Industrial Minerals and Rocks," 2d ed., The American Institute of Mining and Metallurgical Engineers, New York, 1949.

Leith, C. K., J. W. Furness, and Cleona Lewis: "World Minerals and World Peace," Brookings Institution, Washington, D.C., 1943.

Mason, Brian: "Principles of Geochemistry," 2d ed., John Wiley & Sons, Inc., New York, 1958.

"Mineral Facts and Problems," U.S. Bureau of Mines Bulletin 556, Washington, D.C., 1956.

"Mineral Resources of the United States," by the staffs of the U.S. Bureau of Mines and Geological Survey, Public Affairs Press, Washington, D.C., 1948.

"Minerals Yearbook," published annually by the U.S. Department of the Interior, Washington, D.C.

Tyler, P. M.: "From the Ground Up, Facts and Figures of the Mineral Industries of the United States," McGraw-Hill Book Company, Inc., New York, 1948.

Voskuil, W. H.: "Minerals in World Industry," McGraw-Hill Book Company, Inc., New York, 1955.

Index

Names of minerals described or referred to in the text are printed in **boldface** type, synonyms and names of varieties in *italic* type. When there is more than one reference, the important one is printed in **boldface** type.